# LINEAR ALGEBRA
## with BUSINESS APPLICATIONS
### THIRD EDITION

Donald R. Sherbert
University of Illinois at Urbana-Champaign

John W. Brown
University of Illinois at Urbana-Champaign

Omar Adawi
Parkland College

Melvin Royer
Parkland College

 **McGraw-Hill Primis
Custom Publishing**

Boston  Burr Ridge, IL  Dubuque, IA  Madison, WI  New York  San Francisco  St. Louis
Bangkok  Bogotá  Caracas  Lisbon  London  Madrid
Mexico City  Milan  New Delhi  Seoul  Singapore  Sydney  Taipei  Toronto

*McGraw-Hill Higher Education* ⟨logo⟩
*A Division of The McGraw-Hill Companies*

## LINEAR ALGEBRA
## with BUSINESS APPLICATIONS

1 2 3 4 5 6 7 8 9 0 QSR QSR 0 9 8 7 6 5 4 3 2 1

ISBN 0-07-250471-4

Sponsoring Editor: Nada Mraovic
Cover Design: Fairfax Hutter
Printer/Binder: Quebecor World

# PREFACE

This book was written for a course in elementary linear algebra for freshmen and sophomore students who are studying business and economics. However, it is an easy matter to construct a course for a more general audience by treating applications lightly and selecting other topics. The book contains all the standard topics for an introductory course in linear algebra, including a new chapter on linear transformations.

The basic concepts and techniques of linear algebra are now essential background to any modern student of business and managerial disciplines. Applications based on linear models and methods have become incredibly diverse and widespread in recent years. Unfortunately, the subject is often put out of reach of beginning students by texts that emphasize the theoretical and abstract aspects of the subject.

In this book we present the fundamental techniques and computational algorithms of linear algebra, and we provide an introduction to the main concepts of linear algebra, but we do not intimidate students with a great deal of formalism. We prefer to discuss and illustrate theorems so that students find them plausible and can use them with some degree of understanding. In many cases, the discussion of a theorem and the accompanying examples contain the basic idea of its proof and the instructor can supply the formal details if he or she desires. We omit proofs of the most difficult theorems and alert the reader of the omissions.

Throughout the book, we include a variety of applications involving production scheduling, revenue, cost, contingency planning, and so on. This keeps student interest alive, illustrates the great utility of the subject, and most importantly, develops skills in setting up and solving verbally described problems (that is, word problems). Most sections contain some type of application, and some sections are devoted entirely to applications when more extensive background is needed. The applications have a unifying thrust of economics and managerial science which gives the presentation a healthy coherence.

## ORGANIZATION OF THE TEXT

The first three chapters of the book deal with the fundamental computational algorithms and methods of linear systems, linear programming, and matrices. In **Chapter 1** some elementary aspects of linear systems and linear programming are discussed in the geometric setting of the plane, and a number of applications are presented. The first two sections can be treated as review or omitted entirely for a well-prepared class. One approach to this chapter is to pose a production problem as motivation and then develop the material of Chapter 1 as needed tools to solve the problem.

**Chapter 2** deals with the fundamental algorithms based on elementary row operations for solving systems of linear equations and the simplex method for linear programming. Much of linear algebra ultimately rests on the precise use of row operations on matrices, and consequently we develop this material very carefully and thoroughly. Because linear algebra is a subject that is largely concerned with algorithms and procedures rather than manipulations with formulas, the methods are quite different in spirit from the training that students receive in high school algebra. Therefore, the step-by-step nature of the algorithms must be stressed. We also include a short section on planes in 3-space so that the geometry of planes and the solution sets of linear systems can be related. This geometry is also helpful later in Chapter 4.

In **Chapter 3** we discuss the algebra of matrices and the evaluation of determinants. The concept of matrix inverse is important and should be treated carefully, but the computation of inverses by determinants in Section 3.5 can be skipped if desired. Applications to Leontief economic models and to Markov analysis are also covered in separate sections.

**Chapter 4** is concerned with the structure of the vector space $R^n$ of $n$-tuples of numbers and its subspaces. We discuss the fundamental ideas of linear combinations of vectors, linear dependence and independence, basis and dimension, and we relate these concepts to geometric notions and to systems of linear equations. To provide concrete applications of these rather abstract notions, we use vectors to represent production schedules, raw materials, revenue data, and so forth, thereby illustrating the concepts and showing that they have genuine utility. In the final section of the chapter, we use vectors and the concept of basis to delve more deeply into linear programming and develop the two-phase method for solving general linear programs.

**Chapter 5** is concerned with the geometry of the inner product and orthogonal projections. The method of least squares approximation is the main application in this chapter. It is treated in Sections 5.3 and 5.4 in the context of orthogonal projections. If time pressure is a problem, it is possible to present a quick introduction to least squares (without the theoretical trappings of projections) by omitting the derivation of Theorem 1 in Section 5.3 and simply using the formulas of that theorem in the subsequent applications.

In **Chapter 6**, we discuss the notions of eigenvalue and eigenvector. After presenting the basic computations of eigenvalues and eigenvectors, we discuss the procedure of diagonalizing a matrix and then apply it to calculating powers of matrices and to Markov analysis.

**Chapter 7** is a brief introduction to the concept of linear transformation. This appears at first to be a rather abstract idea, but we see in Section 7.2 that each linear transformation is represented by a matrix, and thus we have a new way of thinking about matrices. The change of coordinates of a vector relative to different bases is discussed in Section 7.3. In the final section, we apply these ideas to analyze the simplex method of linear programming.

## EXERCISES

The exercises located at the end of sections emphasize and reinforce the problem solving methods that are developed in the sections. These exercises come in odd-even pairs, so that each even-numbered exercise is similar in nature to the odd-numbered exercise that precedes it. Answers to the odd-numbered exercises are given in the back of the book. Answers to the even-numbered exercises are given in the solutions manual.

A collection of supplementary exercises is located at the end of the book. These exercises extend the text material. They are intended to provoke further thinking about the subject and are more challenging than those found at the end of sections. Some involve more complicated calculations and some are more theoretical than the main text exercises. The instructor can select and assign these exercises as suits his or her needs. Solutions to the supplementary exercises are given in the solutions manual for the book.

## ACKNOWLEDGEMENTS

We owe a debt of gratitude to the students who endured the early drafts of this project and to colleagues who provided advice and constructive criticism. We wish especially to thank Richard Bennett of Parkland College for giving us valuable suggestions for improving the exposition. And we want to thank Hilda K. Britt for her valuable keyboard skills.

John W. Brown
Donald R. Sherbert

# CONTENTS

## SUPPLEMENTARY MATERIAL BY OMAR ADAWI AND MELVIN ROYER, S-1

# 1

# Linear Systems in the Plane

The interplay of algebra and geometry can be easily seen in the plane. Therefore we will begin the study of linear algebra by discussing some basic ideas in the context of geometry in the plane. This work will provide some geometric intuition for understanding the more abstract ideas and methods that will be developed in higher dimensions. When we move to $n$-dimensional spaces, we will have to rely on algebraic techniques, but many situations will have analogues in two and three dimensions, so geometric understanding in these special cases can serve as a guide. This chapter thus gives a general preview of some of the methods to be developed later. In addition, a number of applications illustrate the nature of linear models.

Section 1.1 deals with single linear equations in two variables, that is, with lines in the plane. For many readers this will be largely review. In Section 1.2 we will look at systems of equations in two variables and show that solution sets must be one of three types: no solution, a single solution, or infinitely many solutions. This trichotomy is typical for linear systems and will persist for higher-order systems.

Section 1.3 is concerned with linear inequalities in the plane. In Section 1.4 we will introduce some of the basic ideas of linear programming in a geometric setting. Linear programming is a method of solving certain types of optimization problems that has proved to be extremely valuable in analyzing managerial and industrial problems. We will exhibit some areas of application in Section 1.5. In later chapters the ideas will be extended, and the procedure will be made systematic by means of the simplex method.

## 1.1 LINES IN THE PLANE

*Linear Equations, Slope of a Line, The Point-Slope Equation, Applications*

In this section we survey the basic facts concerning lines and their equations. It is assumed that the reader is familiar with the use of rectangular coordinates in the plane and has had some exposure to lines and their equations. Here we want to examine how certain geometric notions concerning lines, such as intercepts and slope, are related to the algebraic aspects of linear equations. We also give a few applications of linear equations at the end of the section.

## LINEAR EQUATIONS

An equation in the variables $x$ and $y$ that has the form

$$Ax + By = C$$

where $A$, $B$, and $C$ are given constants is called a **linear equation** in two variables. It is assumed that at least one of the constants $A$ or $B$ is not zero, since otherwise the equation would be trivial. The term "linear equation" comes from the fact that the graph of an equation of this form is a line in the plane. Sometimes the term "straight line" is used in this connection, but we will not use the adjective "straight" except for emphasis.

The essential aspects of a linear equation in $x$ and $y$ are that each variable occurs only in the first degree and that at most one variable occurs in each term. Thus the equations $2x + 3y = 6$ and $4x = 7$ are linear equations, but the equations $3x^2 + 2y = 1$ and $2xy = 3$ are not.

The graph of a straight line is obtained from its equation by plotting a few points and then drawing the line that passes through the points. It is a familiar fact that "two points determine a line," so that it suffices to locate just two points on a given line.

**EXAMPLE 1** Graph the equation $2x + 3y = 6$.

SOLUTION Points on the graph are obtained from the equation by specifying a particular value for one of the two variables and then solving for the value of the other variable. For example, if we set $x = 6$, then the equation becomes $2 \cdot 6 + 3y = 6$, so that $y = -2$. Thus the point $(6, -2)$ lies on the line. Similarly, if we set $y = 4$, then we get the value $x = -3$, so that the point $(-3, 4)$ lies on the line.

There are two points that are particularly easy to find. Setting $x = 0$, we get $3y = 6$, so that $y = 2$, and thus we have the point $(0, 2)$. Also if $y = 0$, then $2x = 6$, and we get the point $(3, 0)$. If we plot these two points and draw the line through them, we get the graph in Figure 1.1. ▮▮

The two points $(3, 0)$ and $(0, 2)$ that were used to obtain the graph in the preceding example are called the **intercepts** of the line. The point $(3, 0)$ is the **x-intercept**, and the point $(0, 2)$ is the **y-intercept** of the line. In general, the intercepts of a line are the points at which the line intersects the coordinate axes. The intercepts are easy to find, and they are often convenient to use in graphing lines. However, there are certain types of lines that have only one intercept instead of two, namely, those lines that are parallel to the coordinate axes and those lines that pass through the origin.

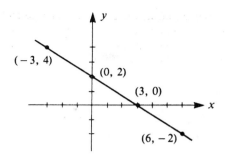

**FIGURE 1.1**                              *The line 2x + 3y = 6*

**EXAMPLE 2**    Graph the equations (a) $x = 2$,   (b) $2y = 5$,   (c) $2y = x$.

SOLUTION    (a) The line given by the equation $x = 2$ consists of all points $(2, y)$ where $y$ is free to be any value. The only intercept is the $x$-intercept $(2, 0)$. See Figure 1.2(a).

(b) Similarly, the equation $2y = 5$ gives us the line consisting of all points $(x, \frac{5}{2})$ where $x$ is unrestricted. The $y$-intercept is $(0, \frac{5}{2})$, and there is no $x$-intercept. See Figure 1.2(b).

(c) The equation $2y = x$ gives us a line whose only intercept is the origin $(0, 0)$. To find a second point on the line, we can set $x = 4$ and get $y = 2$ so that the point $(4, 2)$ lies on the line. We now have two points, and the line is determined. See Figure 1.2(c).  ∎

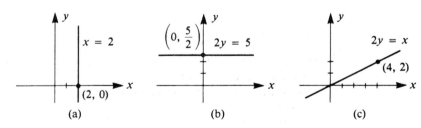

(a)                              (b)                              (c)

**FIGURE 1.2**                    *The lines (a) x = 2, (b) 2y = 5, (c) 2y = x*

## SLOPE OF A LINE

If $B \neq 0$, then we can solve the equation $Ax + By = C$ for $y$ by moving the term $Ax$ and dividing by $B$. In this way we get the equation

$$y = mx + b$$

where $m = -A/B$ and $b = C/B$. For example, the equation $4x + 2y = 10$ can be written in this manner as $y = -2x + 5$.

The equation $y = mx + b$ is called the **slope-intercept** form of the equation of a line. Since the value $y = b$ corresponds to $x = 0$, we see that the point $(0, b)$ is the $y$-intercept of the line. The number $m$ is called the **slope** of the line. The geometric significance of the slope $m$ is revealed by the following calculation.

If we take *any* two distinct points $(x_1, y_1)$ and $(x_2, y_2)$ satisfying the slope-intercept equation, then we have $y_1 = mx_1 + b$ and $y_2 = mx_2 + b$. Subtracting then gives us the equation

$$y_2 - y_1 = (mx_2 + b) - (mx_1 + b) = m(x_2 - x_1)$$

Note that $x_1 \neq x_2$, so we may divide by the nonzero term $x_2 - x_1$ and thereby obtain a formula for the slope:

$$m = \frac{y_2 - y_1}{x_2 - x_1}$$

Note that since $x_1 \neq x_2$ in the formula, slope is not defined for lines that have equations of the form $x = a$, that is, vertical lines.

**EXAMPLE 3**  Find the slope of the line $2x + 3y = 6$.

SOLUTION  There are two ways to find the slope $m$. The simplest way is to rewrite the equation as $y = (-\frac{2}{3})x + 2$. Then we see that the coefficient of $x$ is the slope $m = -\frac{2}{3}$.

An alternative way to find the slope is to find two points on the line and then use the formula. We saw in Example 1 that the points $(6, -2)$ and $(-3, 4)$ are on the line. Taking $x_1 = 6$, $y_1 = -2$, and $x_2 = -3$, $y_2 = 4$, we obtain

$$m = \frac{4 - (-2)}{-3 - 6} = -\frac{6}{9} = -\frac{2}{3}$$

If the two points $(0, 2)$ and $(3, 0)$ were chosen, we would again get $m = \frac{0-2}{3-0} = -\frac{2}{3}$. ∎

The difference $y_2 - y_1$ of the $y$-coordinates can be thought of as the **rise** (or fall) of a line that corresponds to the **run** (or change) $x_2 - x_1$ of the $x$-coordinates. Thus the formula for slope can be interpreted in this way as

$$\text{slope} = \frac{\text{rise}}{\text{run}}$$

See Figure 1.3. We think of a fall as a negative rise.

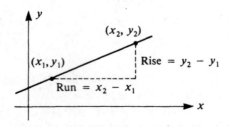

**FIGURE 1.3**

$$\text{Slope } m = \frac{y_2 - y_1}{x_2 - x_1} = \frac{rise}{run}$$

**EXAMPLE 4**   Convert the equation $3x - 2y = -4$ to slope-intercept form and use slope to find the graph.

SOLUTION   First we write the equation in slope-intercept form

$$y = \frac{3}{2}x + 2$$

We see that the $y$-intercept is $(0, 2)$ and the slope is $m = \frac{3}{2}$. Since $m = \frac{3}{2}$, a change of 2 in the value of $x$ results in a change of 3 in the value of $y$. Starting from $(0, 2)$, if we add 2 to $x_1 = 0$ and if we add 3 to $y_1 = 2$, we get another point $(2, 5)$ that must lie on the line. See Figure 1.4.  ▮▮

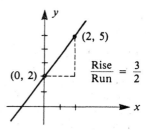

**FIGURE 1.4**                    *The line $3x - 2y = -4$*

To get a geometric feeling for the notion of slope, it is worthwhile to draw a sampling of lines of the form $y = mx$ for different values of $m$. Note that all such lines pass through the origin. See Figure 1.5.

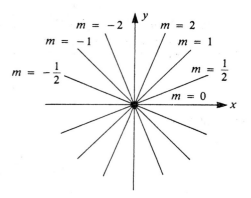

**FIGURE 1.5**                    *Lines $y = mx$*

A word of warning is in order. The graphs in Figure 1.5 are drawn for coordinate axes that have the same unit length. If the coordinate axes have different scales, as occurs in some applications, then the lines will have a different appearance of steepness even though the slopes are not changed.

## THE POINT-SLOPE EQUATION

Up to now, we have been given a linear equation and have used the equation to derive information about the line. However, in many problems the situation is reversed; we are given information about a line, and we wish to determine its equation. One of the most convenient ways to solve a problem of this type is as follows.

A significant feature of the formula for the slope $m$ of a line is that it holds for any pair of points on a nonvertical line. Therefore if $(x_1, y_1)$ is a particular point and $(x, y)$ is *any other* point on a line of slope $m$, then the formula for slope gives us

$$\frac{y - y_1}{x - x_1} = m$$

where $x \neq x_1$. We can then multiply both sides by $x - x_1$ and thus obtain the equation

$$y - y_1 = m(x - x_1)$$

The last equation holds for all points $(x, y)$ on the line, including $x = x_1$, $y = y_1$. It is called the **point-slope** form of the equation of a line.

Thus to derive an equation of a line, it is enough to know a point $(x_1, y_1)$ on the line and the slope of the line. The following example illustrates this idea.

**EXAMPLE 5**   Find an equation of the line (a) that has slope 3 and that contains the point $(-1, 2)$ and (b) that passes through the points $(-4, 3)$ and $(6, 1)$.

**SOLUTION**   (a) We are given $m = 3$ and $x_1 = -1$, $y_1 = 2$. Using the point-slope form, we obtain the equation

$$y - 2 = 3(x + 1)$$

The equation can also be written $y = 3x + 5$ or $3x - y = -5$ if either of these forms of the equation is desired.

(b) The slope is not given, but it is easily found to be $m = \frac{3 - 1}{-4 - 6} = -\frac{1}{5}$. If we use the point-slope form with the point $(6, 1)$, then we get the equation $y - 1 = -\frac{1}{5}(x - 6)$, which can be written in the form $x + 5y = 11$. If the other point $(-4, 3)$ were used, then we would get the equation $y - 3 = -\frac{1}{5}(x + 4)$, which results in the same equation $x + 5y = 11$. Thus the choice of point is immaterial, since each leads to the same equation of the line. ∎

The following theorem relates the slopes of two lines to the geometric properties of parallelism and perpendicularity. The proof will be omitted.

*THEOREM 1*

Suppose that the line $L_1$ has slope $m_1$ and the line $L_2$ has slope $m_2$. Then:

(i) $L_1$ and $L_2$ are parallel if and only if $m_1 = m_2$.

(ii) $L_1$ and $L_2$ are perpendicular if and only if $m_1 m_2 = -1$.

The utility of this theorem is illustrated by the following example.

**EXAMPLE 6**   Find lines through $(1, 1)$ that are (a) parallel to the line $3y = 2x + 7$ and (b) perpendicular to the line $3y = 2x + 7$.

SOLUTION   (a) The slope of the given line is $m_1 = \frac{2}{3}$. Therefore we see that the slope $m_2$ of the desired line must be $m_2 = m_1 = \frac{2}{3}$. Using this value and the point $(1, 1)$, we get the equation $y - 1 = \frac{2}{3}(x - 1)$, which can be written in the form $2x - 3y = -1$.

(b) The given line has slope $m_1 = \frac{2}{3}$. From Theorem 1, the slope $m_2$ of the line sought must satisfy $m_1 m_2 = \frac{2}{3}m_2 = -1$. Thus the slope is $m_2 = -\frac{3}{2}$. The equation of the line is therefore $y - 1 = -\frac{3}{2}(x - 1)$, which can be written $3x + 2y = 5$.   ■■

## APPLICATIONS

Linear equations arise often and naturally in many applications. The following examples indicate a few ways in which linearity can arise.

**EXAMPLE 7**   Find an equation that relates the Fahrenheit and Celsius temperature scales.

SOLUTION   The relationship between the Fahrenheit and Celsius temperature scales is linear. Let $y$ denote Fahrenheit degrees and $x$ denote Celsius degrees. To find an equation relating $x$ and $y$, we shall use the fact that the freezing point of water is $x = 0°C$ and $y = 32°F$ and the boiling point of water is $x = 100°C$ and $y = 212°F$. Thus we have the points $(0, 32)$ and $(100, 212)$ on the line relating Celsius degrees to Fahrenheit degrees. The slope is then $m = \frac{212 - 32}{100} = \frac{9}{5}$. That is, a 5-degree Celsius change corresponds to a 9-degree Fahrenheit change. Using $m = \frac{9}{5}$ and the point $(0, 32)$, we obtain $y - 32 = \frac{9}{5}(x - 0)$, which can be written as

$$y = \frac{9}{5}x + 32$$

or as

$$x = \frac{5}{9}(y - 32)$$

The latter equation expresses Celsius degrees in terms of Fahrenheit.

We may then find, for example, that the normal body temperature of

$y = 98.6°F$ when given on the Celsius scale is $x = \frac{5}{9}(98.6 - 32) = 37°C$. See Figure 1.6. ∎

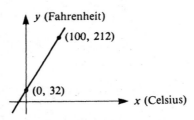

**FIGURE 1.6**

*The Fahrenheit-Celsius equation*
$$y = \frac{9}{5}x + 32$$

An important application of mathematics in business and economics is the construction of models based on past data so that future values can be estimated. A crude approach would be to plot points for such items as costs, sales, profits, and so on from past years and then draw a curve that best fits these points. Extending the curve would be tantamount to predicting the future. The procedure of fitting a curve to data points can be made more exact; but, of course, any prediction of the future based on the past entails the assumption that other conditions will remain unchanged or can be predicted with equal accuracy. The general method of finding the best linear fit for given data points will be discussed in Chapter 5 after the necessary background has been developed. The following elementary example illustrates the idea of using the past to predict the future.

**EXAMPLE 8**   A young company finds that its operating costs increase each month as it grows. In three successive months, operating costs were $5000, $6200, and $7400. Assuming continued growth of the same order, estimate costs six months later.

**SOLUTION**   We let $x$ denote the number of the month, starting with $x = 1$, and we let $y$ denote operating costs in thousands of dollars, starting with $y = 5$. The points $(1, 5)$, $(2, 6.2)$, $(3, 7.4)$ lie on a line with slope $m = 1.2$. We thus obtain the equation $y - 5 = (1.2)(x - 1)$, so that we have

$$y = 1.2x + 3.8$$

Therefore when $x = 9$, we get $y = 14.6$. That is, the estimated cost is $14,600. See Figure 1.7. ∎

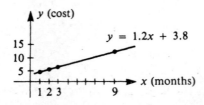

**FIGURE 1.7**

*The cost equation* $y = 1.2x + 3.8$

Another use of mathematical models in business is to estimate the value of assets and equipment over time. Depreciation of durable equipment is often put on a linear scale as illustrated in the next example.

**EXAMPLE 9**   Each piece of equipment that a company purchases will decrease, or depreciate, in value over the years of its use. This depreciation can be used as a business deduction on income tax returns. A common method of calculating the amount of depreciation is known as straight line, or S/L, depreciation. Suppose that a truck has a purchase price of $12,000 and an expected service life of five years. At the end of five years the company plans to sell or trade in the truck for $3000. This amount is called the scrap value and is subtracted from the purchase price to get the net decrease of $9000. The decrease, sometimes called the wear value, is then divided by 5 to get the annual depreciation figure of $1800. We then wish to find an expression relating the value of the truck to the years of service.

SOLUTION   We let $x$ denote the number of years of service, with $x = 0$ being the year of purchase, and let $y$ denote the value of the truck, where 1 unit represents $1000. Then $(0, 12)$ and $(5, 3)$ are two points on the line of depreciation, and the slope $m = -\frac{9}{5}$ (which is the annual depreciation in thousands of dollars) is computed from them. Thus we obtain the equation

$$y = -\frac{9}{5}x + 12$$

The value of the truck after $x = 3$ years is $y = (-\frac{9}{5})3 + 12 = \frac{33}{5}$ or $6600. See Figure 1.8.   ▮▮

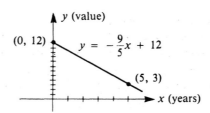

**FIGURE 1.8**            The depreciation line $y = -\dfrac{9}{5}x + 12$

## EXERCISES 1.1

In Exercises 1–2, determine which equations are linear and which are not.

**1.** (a) $3x + 2y = 5$      (b) $4xy - y = -1$      (c) $3 + 4 = 7$
     (d) $(5 + \sqrt{3})x - 4y = 7.6$      (e) $6x^2 - 2y^3 = -5$

**2.** (a) $4x^3 + 2y^2 = 1$      (b) $6 - 2 = 4$      (c) $4x - 7y = 2$
     (d) $6x - (2 - \sqrt{5})y = 3.2$      (e) $x + 5xy = 3$

In Exercises 3–4, determine which of the given points are on the line with the given equation.

**3.** Points (a) $(2, 2)$   (b) $(2, 3)$   (c) $(5, -4)$   (d) $(-1, 7)$
(e) $(1, 3)$   for the equation $2x + y = 6$.

**4.** Points (a) $(-5, 3)$   (b) $(-3, 2)$   (c) $(7, -1)$   (d) $(6, -1)$
(e) $(10, -2)$   for the equation $x + 3y = 4$.

In Exercises 5–8 find the $x$-intercept and $y$-intercept if they exist. Then draw the graph.

**5.** $4x - 2y = 5$   **6.** $3x + 5y = 2$   **7.** $2x = 7$   **8.** $-3y = 10$

In Exercises 9–12, rewrite the linear equation in slope-intercept form. Find the slope and intercept in each case. Graph.

**9.** $-3x + y = 5$   **10.** $-2x + y = 6$

**11.** $4x - 5y = 2$   **12.** $-6x + 3y = -1$

In Exercises 13–16, find the slope-intercept equation for the lines with given slope and intercept.

**13.** slope $-7$, intercept $(0, 2)$   **14.** slope $\dfrac{1}{6}$, intercept $(0, -1)$

**15.** slope $-\dfrac{3}{8}$, intercept $\left(0, \dfrac{7}{3}\right)$   **16.** slope $4$, intercept $\left(0, \dfrac{2}{5}\right)$

Graph the lines in Exercises 17–18 on a coordinate system where one unit on the $y$-axis has twice the length of one unit on the $x$-axis.

**17.** $y = \dfrac{1}{2}x + \dfrac{2}{3}$   **18.** $y = -\dfrac{3}{5}x - 1$

In Exercises 19–22, write the equation of the line that passes through the indicated point and has the given slope.

**19.** $(-5, 3)$, $m = 8$   **20.** $(2, 4)$, $m = -\dfrac{6}{7}$

**21.** $(-4, -3)$, $m = \dfrac{2}{5}$   **22.** $(-3, 5)$, $m = -\dfrac{3}{7}$

In Exercises 23–26, use the given points to find the slope of the line that contains them. Find a point-slope equation for the line.

**23.** $(-2, -7)$, $(4, 9)$   **24.** $(3, 8)$, $(4, 1)$

**25.** $(1, 6)$, $(7, 6)$   **26.** $(34, 3)$, $(-2, 3)$

In Exercises 27–28, determine if the given points lie on a line.

**27.** (a) $(5, 1)$, $(7, 2)$, $(9, 3)$   (b) $(3, 4)$, $(4, 7)$, $(5, 9)$

**28.** (a) $(-2, 1)$, $(-1, -3)$, $(0, -4)$   (b) $(3, -2)$, $(1, 1)$, $(-1, 4)$

**29.** The equation $x/a + y/b = 1$, where $a \neq 0$, $b \neq 0$, is called the *intercept-intercept* form of the equation of the line. Show that the intercepts are $(a, 0)$ and $(0, b)$.

**30.** Write the equation $Ax + By = C$, where $A \neq 0$, $B \neq 0$, $C \neq 0$, in intercept-intercept form.

In Exercises 31–32, write the given equation in intercept-intercept form and graph the lines.

**31.** $4x + 2y = 5$　　　　　　　　**32.** $-3x + 5y = -2$

In Exercises 33–36, write the intercept-intercept form of the line through the given points.

**33.** $(0, 6), (-5, 0)$　　　　　　　　**34.** $(0, -4), (3, 0)$

**35.** $\left(0, \dfrac{1}{2}\right), \left(\dfrac{1}{6}, 0\right)$　　　　　　**36.** $\left(0, -\dfrac{3}{5}\right), \left(\dfrac{7}{4}, 0\right)$

**37.** Let a line have the equation $4x - 3y = 5$. Find the equation of a parallel line that passes through the point $(5, -1)$. Find the equation of a perpendicular line that passes through $(6, 2)$.

**38.** Let a line have the equation $-7x + 2y = 3$. Find the equation of a parallel line that passes through the point $(1, -2)$. Find the equation of a perpendicular line that passes through $(5, 3)$.

Convert the tabular information in Exercises 39–42 to points on an appropriately designed coordinate system. Plot the points and find a linear equation for the line of fit. Interpret the slope. Find the indicated predicted value.

**39.** Weekly costs for manufacturing typewriters at the Fancy Type Company are given below

| Number of typewriters | $ Costs per week |
|:---:|:---:|
| 0 | 950 |
| 1 | 1200 |
| 2 | 1450 |
| 3 | 1700 |

What is the predicted cost of manufacturing five typewriters per week?

**40.** Slick Auto Sales has done business as shown in the following table.

| Car sales (100 units) | Year |
|:---:|:---:|
| 287 | 1954 |
| 296 | 1955 |
| 305 | 1956 |

What would you predict car sales to have been in 1959?

**41.** The town of Myra had population figures as shown.

| Year | Population |
|------|-----------|
| 1962 | 1500 |
| 1963 | 1200 |
| 1964 | 900 |

Barring unforeseen developments, when would you conclude that Myra became empty?

**42.** The Alpha Corp. held a tract of land that had values as shown below.

| $ Value | Year |
|---------|------|
| 52,000 | 1972 |
| 53,500 | 1973 |
| 55,000 | 1974 |

Find the projected value of the land in 1977.

**43.** Karen Reed purchased a rental unit in 1975 for $140,000. She will fully depreciate it on a S/L basis over a 20-year period. Let the initial point be represented as $(0, 140)$, and find the linear equation that gives the value $y$ of the property at any time $x$, $0 \leqslant x \leqslant 20$. Find the value after 7.5 years.

**44.** Mudd Excavation bought a dump truck for $25,000 in 1979. In four years the truck will have a scrap value of $5000. If the initial point is represented as $(0, 25)$ and if the depreciation is S/L, find an equation giving the value in terms of the years of use. Find the value after two years.

## 1.2 LINEAR SYSTEMS IN TWO VARIABLES

*The Method of Elimination, Algebraic Analysis, Applications*

A linear equation in two variables $x$, $y$ can be viewed as a restraint on the freedom of the variables to act independently. If one variable has a particular value, then the other variable is forced by the equation to attain a specific value. In geometric terms the point $(x, y)$ is not allowed to roam freely around the plane; it is restricted to a line. If a second equation is brought into the scene, then it may impose a further restriction on the variables. It can happen that the two equations restrain $(x, y)$ to a single point, but it can also happen that the second equation is not compatible with the first, or it can happen that the second equation is redundant and imposes no further constraint on the variables.

In this section we examine the possible outcomes from both geometric and algebraic viewpoints. We will see that a system of two linear equations in two variables possesses either a unique solution, or no solution, or infinitely many solutions. These three different possibilities for the solution set are typical for linear systems, and we will see in Chapter 2 that the same possibilities hold for systems involving more equations and variables.

## THE METHOD OF ELIMINATION

Consider a system of two linear equations in two variables, $x$ and $y$:

$$ax + by = e$$
$$cx + dy = f$$

An ordered pair $(x_0, y_0)$ is a solution of the system if both equations are satisfied simultaneously by the values $x = x_0$, $y = y_0$.

A common method of solving a system of this type, one that the reader has probably used in previous courses, is to eliminate one of the variables by multiplying the equations by appropriate constants and then subtracting one equation from the other. This procedure, called the method of elimination, is illustrated in the following example.

**EXAMPLE 1**    Solve the system of linear equations

$$2x - y = 3$$
$$3x + 2y = -1$$

SOLUTION    The graphs of the equations are shown in Figure 1.9 on the next page. The two lines intersect in a single point, which corresponds to the solution of the system. The coordinates of the point are not evident, so we will find them algebraically.

To eliminate the variable $x$, we multiply the first equation by 3 and the second by 2 to get the system

$$6x - 3y = 9$$
$$6x + 4y = -2$$

We now subtract the first equation from the second to get the system

$$6x - 3y = 9$$
$$7y = -11$$

The second equation has the obvious solution $y = -\frac{11}{7}$. We now find the corresponding value of $x$ by substituting this value of $y$ back into the first equation. The back substitution gives us $x = \frac{5}{7}$. Thus the solution of this system is $(\frac{5}{7}, -\frac{11}{7})$.    ∎

For systems of linear equations that involve more equations and variables, it will be necessary to systematize the elimination method. This will be done in Chapter 2. Also, the fact that the elimination procedure actually delivers all solutions will be justified there. At this stage we wish to use the elimination method

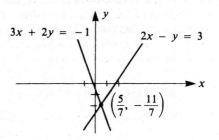

**FIGURE 1.9**                    *The solution is $(\frac{5}{7}, -\frac{11}{7})$*

to discuss the different possibilities that can arise in connection with a system of two linear equations in two variables.

It can happen that a system of linear equations has no solutions. For example, the system of equations

$$x + y = 1$$
$$x + y = 4$$

clearly imposes impossible demands on $x$ and $y$, since the existence of a solution would imply the false statement $1 = 4$. Geometrically, this occurs because the lines determined by the equations are parallel and distinct. See Figure 1.10.

In general, a system of linear equations that has no solutions is called **inconsistent**. If a system has one or more solutions, then it is called **consistent**.

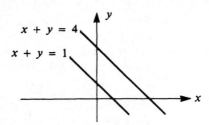

**FIGURE 1.10**                    *An inconsistent system*

It is possible to have infinitely many solutions because the two equations in a system may simply be a single equation in disguise. For example, in the system of equations

$$x + 2y = 3$$
$$2x + 4y = 6$$

the second equation is twice the first equation. If we multiply the first equation by 2 and subtract, we obtain the true statement $0 = 0$. Thus the system can be reduced to a single equation. In this case, every point on the line $x + 2y = 3$ gives us a solution of the system; consequently, there are infinitely many solutions. If we graphed the two equations in the system, we would simply trace the same line twice. In such a case, either equation can be thought of as redundant, since the other equation contains full information concerning solutions of the system. As we shall see later, in larger systems the issue of redundancy is somewhat more complicated and not as easily recognized as in the case of two equations.

## ALGEBRAIC ANALYSIS

We will now see how the different situations can be recognized and handled by algebraic means. Later, when we encounter more complicated systems, the geometric viewpoint will be inadequate, and the algebraic approach will be essential. The analysis that follows is a foreshadowing of more general techniques that will come later.

Consider the system

$$ax + by = e$$
$$cx + dy = f$$

We assume that $a \neq 0$ and $c \neq 0$, so that $x$ is present in both equations. Proceeding as before, we eliminate $x$ by multiplying the first equation by $c$ and the second by $a$. This gives us the system

$$(ac)x + (bc)y = ce$$
$$(ac)x + (ad)y = af$$

We now subtract the first equation from the second to get the system

$$(ac)x + (bc)y = ce$$
$$(ad - bc)y = af - ce$$

Looking at the coefficient of $y$ in the second equation, we see that there are two cases to consider.

*Case 1.*   $ad - bc \neq 0$. In this case we have from the second equation that $y = (af - ce)/(ad - bc)$, and back substitution gives, after some algebraic manipulation, the value $x = (de - bf)/(ad - bc)$. Thus a solution exists, and it is unique. Geometrically, we have two nonparallel lines intersecting in a single point. The formulas for $x$ and $y$ are not worth memorizing, since the method of elimination is quick and easy when only two equations are present.

*Case 2.*   $ad - bc = 0$. In this case the second equation is $0y = af - ce$. Two possibilities arise, depending on whether the constant $af - ce$ is zero or not. These subcases are treated as follows.

(a) $af - ce \neq 0$. This presents us with the contradictory statements that $af - ce \neq 0$ and $af - ce = 0$. We conclude that the system has no solutions and hence is inconsistent. This corresponds to the geometric situation in which the two lines are parallel and distinct. Note that if $b \neq 0$ and $d \neq 0$, then the condition $ad - bc = 0$ implies that $a/b = c/d$, which means that the slopes of the two lines are equal.

(b) $af - ce = 0$. This produces the trivial equation $0y = 0$, which is satisfied by every value of $y$. Consequently, the system reduces to one equation, and infinitely many solutions of the system exist. Geometrically, the two lines are not only parallel, but they coincide.

If either $a = 0$ or $c = 0$, the same cases arise, and they are handled in the same manner as above. In practice, the different cases are easily recognized when the method of elimination is applied and the results are obtained in a natural manner.

**EXAMPLE 2**  Solve the systems

(a)  $\begin{aligned} x - 3y &= 2 \\ -2x + 6y &= 3 \end{aligned}$     (b)  $\begin{aligned} x - 3y &= 2 \\ -2x + 6y &= -4 \end{aligned}$

**SOLUTION**  Note that the left-hand sides of both systems are the same, but the constant terms on the right-hand sides are different. By adding twice the first equation to the second in each of the systems, we obtain

(a)  $\begin{aligned} x - 3y &= 2 \\ 0y &= 7 \end{aligned}$     (b)  $\begin{aligned} x - 3y &= 2 \\ 0y &= 0 \end{aligned}$

Here we see that system (a) is inconsistent, since $0 \neq 7$.

System (b) reduces to one equation, and thus it has infinitely many solutions. The solutions can be represented as ordered pairs as follows. We let $y = t$, where $t$ represents an arbitrary real number, and we use the first equation to express $x$ in terms of $t$. Then we have

$$x = 3t + 2$$
$$y = t$$

so the solutions can be expressed as the set of ordered pairs

$$\{(3t + 2, t): \quad t \text{ any real number}\}$$

Note that each value of $t$ gives us a point on the line; for example, $t = 1$ gives us the point $(5, 1)$, and $t = -2$ gives us $(-4, -2)$.

The independent variable $t$ is usually referred to as a **parameter**. Note that we could also let $x$ equal a parameter, say $x = s$. This would give us the ordered pairs $(s, (s - 2)/3)$, where $s$ can take on any value. We will say more about parameters in Chapter 2. ▋▋

Although we have discussed only systems having two equations in two variables, it is certainly possible to have more than two equations in a system even if there are just two variables. The same three possibilities for the solution set still remain, although the situation of having no solutions can arise in different ways. The reader should draw all the possible types of configurations of three lines in the plane to see how the different types of solution sets can arise. The following example illustrates two of the possibilities.

**EXAMPLE 3**    Consider the system of three equations

$$x + 2y = 4$$
$$2x - y = 3$$
$$3x + y = k$$

where $k$ is a constant. Find the value of $k$ for which the system is consistent.

SOLUTION    If we examine the first two equations, those not involving $k$, we find that $x = 2$, $y = 1$ is the unique solution of the system consisting of those two equations. Upon substitution into the third equation, we obtain $3 \cdot 2 + 1 = k$. Hence if $k = 7$, then $(2, 1)$ satisfies all three equations, and therefore it is the solution of the system of three equations. However, if $k \neq 7$, then $(2, 1)$ does not satisfy the third equation. We conclude that the system has no solutions if $k \neq 7$. The situation is illustrated by Figure 1.11 for the cases $k = 7$ and $k = 9$.  ∎

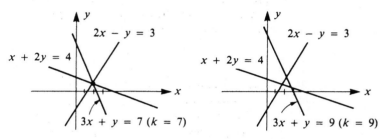

**FIGURE 1.11**                    *The system is consistent if k = 7 and inconsistent otherwise*

## APPLICATIONS

We now describe a few elementary linear models. In many applications there are quantities that must satisfy several different conditions at once, and thus we have the problem of finding values that are compatible with the different conditions. When the conditions can be expressed as linear equations, we have a system of equations to solve.

There is a broad class of problems known as *mixing problems* that involve combining different quantities to certain specifications. Many industrial processes entail the mixing of different raw materials; consequently, this type of problem occurs frequently.

**EXAMPLE 4**    The Elegant Electroplating Company uses two different mixtures of gold dust and silver dust in its electroplating process. The Premium mixture uses 7 ounces of gold to 3 ounces of silver, while the Standard mixture uses 4 ounces of gold to 6 ounces of silver. The company wishes to prepare mixtures that will exhaust its current stock of 250 ounces of gold and 300 ounces of silver. How much of each type of mixture should be made so that the two metals in stock are completely used?

**SOLUTION**   To solve the problem, it is first necessary to introduce variables and units of measure. It is convenient to use 10-ounce units; that is, we let 1 unit denote 10 ounces of metal. Now let $x$ be the number of units of Premium mix and let $y$ be the number of units of Standard mix. Then there are $7x$ ounces (not units) of gold in the Premium mix and $4y$ ounces of gold in the Standard mix, so that the total amount of gold in the two mixtures is $7x + 4y$ ounces. Since 250 ounces of gold are to be used we get the gold equation $7x + 4y = 250$. In a similar way we get the silver equation $3x + 6y = 300$. Thus we obtain the system

|        | Premium | | Standard | |
|--------|---------|---|----------|------|
| Gold   | $7x$ | $+$ | $4y$ | $= 250$ |
| Silver | $3x$ | $+$ | $6y$ | $= 300$ |

The system has the solution $x = 10$, $y = 45$. Hence there should be 100 ounces of Premium mixture and 450 ounces of Standard mixture.  ∎

A second example deals with what is called a **break-even analysis** of a company with respect to a product. The problem is to determine the production level, or output, that will generate just enough revenue to offset the cost of production. Suppose that the output for a product is $x$ units per week. If the $x$ units are sold at a price $P$ dollars per unit, then the resulting revenue is $R = Px$ dollars. The cost of production can be separated into two types: fixed costs and unit costs. **Fixed costs** are those expenses that do not depend on the exact level of production and include costs such as plant rental, managerial wages, and cost of durable equipment. **Unit cost** is the cost of producing one unit of the product; it depends on the cost of raw materials, labor, and other items that go into the actual production. If the company has fixed cost $F$ per week and unit cost $V$, then the **total cost** is $C = F + Vx$ dollars per week.

The **break-even point** is the value of $x$ for which cost equals revenue. Consequently, if the output is not at least up to the break-even point, the company will suffer a loss. To plot both cost and revenue against output on the same set of coordinate axes, we can use $y$ to denote both revenue and cost. See Figure 1.12. Then the break-even point is found by solving the system

$$y = F + Vx$$
$$y = Px$$

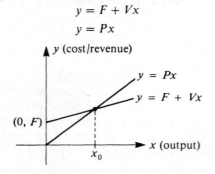

**FIGURE 1.12**          *The break-even point*

**EXAMPLE 5**   The Tough Hide Shoe Company has fixed costs of $5600 per week and a unit cost of $13 per pair of shoes. The company sells the shoes at a wholesale price of $20 per pair. Find the break-even point and the revenue at that point.

SOLUTION   We let $x$ denote the output, and we get the system of equations

$$y = 5600 + 13x \quad \text{(cost)}$$
$$y = \qquad 20x \quad \text{(revenue)}$$

This leads to the equation $7x = 5600$, so $x = 800$. Thus the company will break even at a production level of 800 pairs of shoes a week. The revenue is $y = 16,000$ dollars. ∎

A similar analysis may also be used when comparing the efficiency of two machines for various production run sizes. Let machine 1 have a setup cost $s_1$ and a per unit cost of $c_1$, while machine 2 has the corresponding costs $s_2$ and $c_2$. If $y$ is the total cost on a production run of $x$ units, then the variables are related as follows:

$$\text{machine 1} \quad y = s_1 + c_1 x$$
$$\text{machine 2} \quad y = s_2 + c_2 x$$

The value of $x$ for which the two costs are the same is called the **break point**. Whichever machine is cheaper to operate for a run smaller than the break point will be more expensive to operate when the production quantity is greater than the break point.

**EXAMPLE 6**   The Excellent Machine Shop has two machines that can mill a certain brass plate. Machine 1 has a setup cost of $700 and a cost per plate of $2, while machine 2 has a setup cost of $1200 and a unit cost of $1.50. Find the break point and determine the cheaper machine to use for runs on each side of the break point.

SOLUTION   The model is given by the system of equations

$$\text{machine 1} \quad y = \ 700 + \ 2x$$
$$\text{machine 2} \quad y = 1200 + 1.5x$$

We solve the system by subtracting the second equation from the first, thereby obtaining the equation $0 = -500 + 0.5x$. The break point is therefore $x = 1000$. The total cost at the break point is $y = 700 + 2(1000) = 2700$ dollars. For runs of less than 1000 plates, the company should use machine 1. For runs larger than 1000, it should use machine 2. Note that machine 1 has the smaller setup cost, while machine 2 has smaller unit cost. See Figure 1.13. ∎

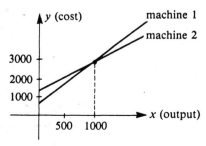

**FIGURE 1.13**   *The break point is $x = 1000$*

## EXERCISES 1.2

In Exercises 1–4, solve the given systems of equations and graph.

**1.** $-7x + 2y = \phantom{-}3$
$\phantom{-7}x - 3y = -2$

**2.** $-2x + 8y = \phantom{-}5$
$\phantom{-}5x + 2y = -4$

**3.** $-6x - 9y = \phantom{-}14$
$\phantom{-}5x + 4y = \phantom{-1}2$

**4.** $4x + 3y = \phantom{-}7$
$2x + 8y = -3$

In Exercises 5–8, show that the systems of equations have no solutions and graph.

**5.** $-12x + 5y = \phantom{-}5$
$\phantom{-}4x - \dfrac{5}{3}y = 14$

**6.** $-3x + 3y = \phantom{-}7$
$\phantom{-}6x - 6y = 15$

**7.** $5x + 2y = 33$
$10x + 4y = 10$

**8.** $\phantom{3}x + \phantom{2}7y = 4$
$3x + 21y = 8$

In Exercises 9–12, find all solutions to the given systems of equations.

**9.** $\phantom{-1}4x \phantom{1}- 7y = \phantom{-1}5$
$-12x + 21y = -15$

**10.** $\phantom{-1}5x \phantom{2}+ y = \phantom{-1}17$
$-10x - 2y = -34$

**11.** $18x - 3y = 5$
$\phantom{1}9x - \dfrac{3}{2}y = \dfrac{5}{2}$

**12.** $\phantom{-}2x + 3y = \phantom{-}4$
$-4x - 6y = -8$

In Exercises 13–18, find all solutions or show that none exist.

**13.** $\phantom{1}6x + \phantom{1}5y = \phantom{-}7$
$18x + 15y = 22$

**14.** $3x - 4y = \phantom{-}1$
$\phantom{3}x + 2y = -3$

**15.** $x + 8y = 5$
$x + 9y = 5$

**16.** $\phantom{-}4x - 3y = \phantom{-1}5$
$-8x + 6y = -10$

**17.** $\phantom{1}6x \phantom{1}- 7y = 4$
$12x - 14y = 8$

**18.** $-2x - 3y = \phantom{-}2$
$\phantom{-}4x + 6y = \phantom{-}1$

In Exercises 19–20 there are an infinite number of solutions to the given systems of equations. First set $y$ equal to a parameter $t$ and express the solution points in terms of $t$. Then set $x$ equal to a parameter $s$ and express the solution points in terms of $s$.

**19.** $\phantom{1}5x \phantom{1}- y = 3$
$10x - 2y = 6$

**20.** $3x + 2y = 2$
$6x + 4y = 4$

**21.** In Exercise 19, find any two points on the solution line and the values of $s$ and $t$ that correspond to each point.

**22.** In Exercise 20, find any two points on the solution line and the values of $s$ and $t$ that correspond to each point.

Solve the systems of equations in Exercises 23–24.

**23.**  $2x - 3y = 6$  
$-2x + 5y = -2$  
$4x - 10y = 4$

**24.**  $4x - 3y = 1$  
$7x - 6y = 3$  
$-8x + 6y = -2$

In Exercises 25–26, find the value of $k$ for which the given system is consistent.

**25.**  $x - y = 2$  
$x + 2y = 8$  
$kx + y = 0$

**26.**  $x + y = 1$  
$2x - y = 5$  
$x + ky = -1$

**27.** Charlies Bait Shop packages two mixes of worms (with a quantity of dirt). The Still Day mix uses 2 pounds of night crawlers and 1 pound of red wrigglers per 5-pound can, while their Breezy mix has 1 pound of night crawlers and 3 pounds of red wrigglers per 5-pound can. Charlie has 48 pounds of night crawlers and 54 pounds of red wrigglers on hand. Find a linear model that describes the quantity of night crawlers and red wrigglers in the two mixes if the worms are to be completely used up. Find a combination of the two mixes that will satisfy the model.

**28.** Suppose that oats and wheat are to be blended (with a quantity of bulk material) into two different feeds. Feed A has 60 pounds of oats and 15 pounds of wheat per 100 pounds of feed, while feed B uses 35 pounds of oats and 40 pounds of wheat per 100 pounds of feed. Suppose also that there are 14,550 pounds of oats and 8250 pounds of wheat on hand. Find a linear model that describes the use of oats and wheat in the two feeds if the materials are to be completely used. Find a combination of the two feeds that will satisfy the model.

**29.** The Perfect Pencil Company has a fixed cost of $4600 per week and a per unit cost of $4 a carton of pencils manufactured. If the pencils wholesale for $8 a carton, find the break-even point for the company. What is the total revenue at the break-even point?

**30.** Smackers Candy Shop has a fixed cost of $550 per week and a per unit cost of $2 per pound of candy. If the candy sells for $3 per pound, find the break-even point for the shop. What is the total revenue at the break-even point?

**31.** The Brighter Siding Company has two presses that stamp aluminum siding. Machine A has a setup cost of $400 and a per unit cost of $6 per 5000 pieces of siding, and machine B has a setup cost of $300 and a per unit cost of $7 per 5000 pieces of siding. Set up the mathematical model for the problem. Find the break point for the production run sizes. Which machine should be used for a run of 750,000 pieces of siding? Graph.

**32.** A tire company has two molds that are used to form tires. Mold A has a setup cost of $700 and a per unit cost of $10 per tire, while mold B has a setup cost of $1000 and a per unit cost of $8 per tire. Set up the mathematical model for the problem. Find the break point for the production run sizes. Which machine should be used for a production run of 950 tires? Graph.

## 1.3 LINEAR INEQUALITIES IN THE PLANE

*Linear Inequalities and Half-Planes, Systems of Linear Inequalities, Feasibility Regions*

If the equality sign in a linear equation is replaced by an inequality symbol, then we get a linear inequality. In this section we discuss linear inequalities in two variables and the associated geometry of half-planes. First we look at a single linear inequality, and then we consider systems of linear inequalities. This section provides the necessary background to discuss linear programming in two variables, the subject of the next section.

Before discussing linear inequalities, let us pause to recall a few basic facts about manipulating inequalities. The symbolism $a < b$ (equivalently, $b > a$) means that the number $a$ is strictly less than the number $b$, while $a \leqslant b$ (equivalently, $b \geqslant a$) means that $a$ is less than or equal to $b$. We shall be using the following familiar properties of inequalities:

1. If $a < b$ and $c$ is any number, then $a + c < b + c$.

2. If $a < b$ and $c > 0$, then $ac < bc$.

3. If $a < b$ and $c < 0$, then $ac > bc$.

Properties 2 and 3 state that if both sides of an inequality are multiplied by a number $c$, then the sense of the inequality is preserved if $c$ is positive but is reversed if $c$ is negative. The same properties hold if $<$ is replaced by $\leqslant$.

For example, to solve $5 - 2x < 1$ for $x$, we first add $-5$ to both sides of the inequality to get $-2x < -4$, and we then multiply both sides by $-\frac{1}{2}$ to get $x > 2$. Note that the inequality is reversed in the last step.

### LINEAR INEQUALITIES AND HALF-PLANES

There are several types of linear inequalities in two variables. If we use strict inequalities, then we have the linear inequalities

$$ax + by < c, \qquad ax + by > c$$

The case of equality is permitted in the linear inequalities

$$ax + by \leqslant c, \qquad ax + by \geqslant c$$

We want to describe the sets of points in the plane that are determined by the different types of linear inequalities. Since the case of equality gives us a line and since a line cuts the plane into two halves, it seems reasonable to expect that a linear inequality would determine one of the two halves. We can examine this expectation by looking at an example. In the following example it should be observed that the answer hinges on the sign of the coefficient of $y$.

**EXAMPLE 1**  Show that a point $(x, y)$ in the plane satisfies the linear inequality

$$2x + 3y > 7$$

if and only if it lies *above* the line $2x + 3y = 7$.

SOLUTION  Let $L$ denote the line with equation $2x + 3y = 7$. For the moment, consider a particular point on the line $L$, say, the point $(2, 1)$, and the other points $(2, y)$ having the same $x$-coordinate. If $x = 2$, then the linear inequality becomes $4 + 3y > 7$. To solve this inequality for $y$, we first get $3y > 7 - 4 = 3$; since $3 > 0$, we then conclude that $y > 1$. Thus a point $(2, y)$ satisfies the linear inequality if and only if $y > 1$, which means that the point lies above the point $(2, 1)$. See Figure 1.14.

The argument can be applied for any value $x_0$ of $x$. Note that any point $(x_0, y)$ not on the line $L$ lies either above or below a point $(x_0, y_0)$ on the line $L$. If we let $x = x_0$, then we have the inequality

$$2x_0 + 3y > 7$$

Solving this inequality for $y$ gives us

$$y > \frac{1}{3}(7 - x_0) = y_0$$

Hence the inequality holds for exactly those points $(x_0, y)$ such that $y > y_0$. That is, we again obtain the points $(x_0, y)$ that lie *above* the point $(x_0, y_0)$ on the line $L$. See Figure 1.14. In general, the point $(x, y)$ satisfies $2x + 3y > 7$ if and only if it lies above the line $L$.  ∎

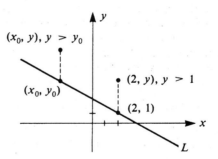

**FIGURE 1.14**

*The linear inequality $2x + 3y > 7$ determines the region above $L$*

If we carry the preceding example a little further, we see that the three relations

$$2x + 3y > 7, \qquad 2x + 3y = 7, \qquad 2x + 3y < 7$$

partition the plane into three sets, with the line $2x + 3y = 7$ being the boundary line between the other two sets. See Figure 1.15 on the next page. The set of points that lie on or above the line is determined by the linear inequality $2x + 3y \geqslant 7$, where equality is allowed. Similarly, the linear inequality $2x + 3y \leqslant 7$ determines the set of points that lie on or below the line.

In general, linear inequalities in two variables determine regions in the plane that are called half-planes. The following terminology is used in this connection.

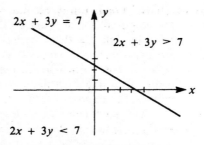

**FIGURE 1.15**                    *The line partitions the plane*

We have the two **open half-planes** determined by the strict inequalities

$$ax + by > c, \qquad ax + by < c$$

and the **boundary line** $ax + by = c$ that lies between them. The regions determined by the linear inequalities

$$ax + by \geqslant c, \qquad ax + by \leqslant c$$

are called **closed half-planes**. The boundary line is included in a closed half-plane but not in an open half-plane. We will be interested primarily in closed half-planes in what follows.

Since a linear inequality will give us one of two possible half-planes, the problem is to determine which one. There are two ways to solve the problem. One way is to solve the inequality for $y$, being careful to notice the sign of the coefficient of $y$. If $b$ is positive, then the inequality $ax + by > c$ can be written

$$y > \frac{c - ax}{b}$$

and we conclude as in Example 1 of this section that it determines the half-plane *above* the boundary line. If $b < 0$, then the inequality reverses, and the half-plane *below* the boundary line is obtained. For the opposite inequality $ax + by < c$, the roles are reversed.

However, there is a another way to answer the question of which half-plane is the correct one. The method consists of choosing a particular point that is not on the boundary line and testing to see if it satisfies the inequality. If the "test point" does satisfy the inequality, then all points on the same side of the boundary line must also satisfy the inequality. If the test point fails to satisfy the inequality, then the opposite side of the boundary line is the correct half-plane. The origin is a convenient test point as long as it does not lie on the line. This method is illustrated in the next example.

**EXAMPLE 2**    Graph the closed half-plane $x - 3y \leqslant 4$.

SOLUTION   We first draw the boundary line; the intercepts are $(4, 0)$ and $(0, -\frac{4}{3})$. The origin $(0, 0)$ does not lie on the line, so we can test it in the inequality. Setting $x = 0$, $y = 0$, we obtain $0 - 3 \cdot 0 < 4$, and we see that the inequality is satisfied. Therefore the origin and all points on the same side of the line as the origin are in the half-plane determined by the linear inequality. See Figure 1.16, where arrows and shading are used to indicate the proper half-plane. Note that if the point $(6, 0)$ had been chosen as the test point, then we would have obtained $6 - 3 \cdot 0 = 6 > 4$, so the given inequality would *not* have been satisfied. Then this test point, along with all other points on the same side of the line, are *not* in the half-plane determined by the inequality. ∎

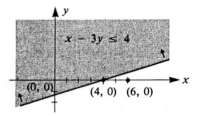

**FIGURE 1.16**                    *The closed half-plane $x - 3y \leqslant 4$*

**EXAMPLE 3**   Graph the closed half-plane $4x - 5y \geqslant 0$.

SOLUTION   We first graph the boundary line $4x - 5y = 0$. Note that the line passes through $(0, 0)$ and $(5, 4)$. Since the origin lies on the boundary line, it cannot be used as a test point. If we consider the point $(0, 1)$, we get $4 \cdot 0 - 5 \cdot 1 = -5 < 0$. Thus the inequality $4x - 5y \geqslant 0$ is *not* satisfied by $(0, 1)$. Therefore the point $(0, 1)$ and all other points above the line are *not* in the half-plane we want. Consequently, the half-plane below the line is the correct one. See Figure 1.17. ∎

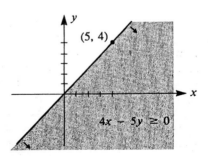

**FIGURE 1.17**                    *The closed half-plane $4x - 5y \geqslant 0$*

## SYSTEMS OF LINEAR INEQUALITIES

We now turn to the analysis of systems of linear inequalities in two variables. The nature of the solution set of systems of linear inequalities is much different from that of a system of linear equations. Since each linear inequality determines a half-plane, the set of solutions of a system will be an intersection of half-planes. Thus instead of a point or line, as in the case of systems of linear equations, we normally obtain a region in the plane when solving a system of linear inequalities.

The procedure for graphing the solution region of a system of linear inequalities is straightforward. We take the linear inequalities one at a time, graphing the boundary line and indicating which side of the line is determined by the inequality. The points common to all of the half-planes are those that satisfy all of the inequalities simultaneously. This region, the intersection of the half-planes, is the solution set of the system of inequalities.

**EXAMPLE 4**   Graph the solution set of the system of linear inequalities

$$5x - 7y \geqslant 8$$
$$-5x + y \leqslant 2$$

**SOLUTION**   We approach the system by considering each inequality in turn. For the first inequality we graph the boundary line $5x - 7y = 8$, using the intercepts $(\frac{8}{5}, 0)$ and $(0, -\frac{8}{7})$. Next we need to find which side of the line is determined. Testing the origin, we get $5 \cdot 0 - 7 \cdot 0 = 0 < 8$, so $(0, 0)$ does *not* satisfy the first inequality. Thus we want the half-plane below the line, and we indicate this region by using short arrows as in Figure 1.18.

Next we graph the boundary line $-5x + y = 2$, using the intercepts $(-\frac{2}{5}, 0)$ and $(0, 2)$. Since $-5 \cdot 0 + 0 < 2$, we see that the origin satisfies the second inequality, so we want the half-plane below the line. This is also indicated by arrows in Figure 1.18. The intersection of the two half-planes is the set of points that belong to both half-planes. This region is shaded in Figure 1.18.

The description of the solution region is completed by finding the point where the boundary lines meet, called a "corner point" of the region. The coordinates of the corner point are found by solving the system of equations

$$5x - 7y = 8$$
$$-5x + y = 2$$

where the case of equality is taken in each of the linear inequalities. We obtain the coordinates $(-\frac{11}{15}, -\frac{5}{3})$. ▮▮

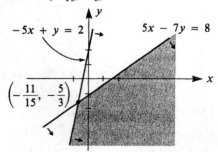

**FIGURE 1.18**                    *Solving the system of Example 4*

If there are more than two inequalities in the system, we continue the procedure. The corner points of the solution region are obtained by using the appropriate boundary line equations, taken two at a time, as in the following example.

**EXAMPLE 5**   Graph the solution region of the system

$$2x - 3y \leqslant -6$$
$$3x - 2y \geqslant -6$$
$$3x + 2y \leqslant 12$$

and find all corner points of the region.

SOLUTION   The procedure for graphing each of the half-planes in the system can be compiled in a brief table as follows.

| Half-plane | Intercepts of line | Origin in half-plane? |
|---|---|---|
| $2x - 3y \leqslant -6$ | $(-3, 0), (0, 2)$ | No |
| $3x - 2y \geqslant -6$ | $(-2, 0), (0, 3)$ | Yes |
| $3x + 2y \leqslant 12$ | $(4, 0), (0, 6)$ | Yes |

The results are displayed in Figure 1.19, where the solution region is the shaded polygon. The corner points of the polygon are labeled $P_1, P_2, P_3$ in the figure.

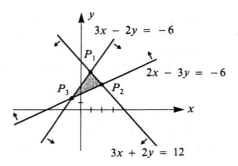

**FIGURE 1.19**                    *The solution region of Example 5*

To find the coordinates of the corner points, we solve the corresponding pairs of linear equations. The corner point $P_1$ is found by solving the system

$$P_1 \qquad \begin{array}{l} 3x - 2y = -6 \\ 3x + 2y = \phantom{-}12 \end{array}$$

By adding the equations we obtain $6x = 6$, so that $x = 1$; then we find $y = \frac{9}{2}$. Hence $P_1$ is the point $(1, \frac{9}{2})$.

To find the corner point $P_2$, we solve the system of equations

$$P_2 \qquad \begin{aligned} 2x - 3y &= -6 \\ 3x + 2y &= 12 \end{aligned}$$

Multiplying the first equation by 2, the second equation by 3, and subtracting, we get $13y = 42$, so $y = \frac{42}{13}$. Then we find $x = \frac{24}{13}$, and thus $P_2$ is the point $(\frac{24}{13}, \frac{42}{13})$.

Finally, by solving the system

$$P_3 \qquad \begin{aligned} 2x - 3y &= -6 \\ 3x - 2y &= -6 \end{aligned}$$

we find the corner point $P_3$ to be the point $(-\frac{6}{5}, \frac{6}{5})$.

Thus the solution region is the triangular region with corner points $(1, \frac{9}{2})$, $(\frac{24}{13}, \frac{42}{13})$ and $(-\frac{6}{5}, \frac{6}{5})$. ∎

## FEASIBILITY REGIONS

In applications, each linear inequality in a system represents a constraint that the variables must satisfy. Points that satisfy all of the constraints are called **feasible points,** since they do not violate any of the conditions and could possibly solve the problem being considered. The solution set of a system of linear inequalities is therefore called the **feasibility region** for the system. In anticipation of future applications we will use these terms in this section.

The feasibility region for a system of linear inequalities in the plane is a polygonal region, which means that the boundary of the region consists of straight line segments. If the region is unbounded or infinite in some direction, it is called a **polygonal wedge**. The region in Figure 1.18 is a polygonal wedge. However, if the region is bounded in all directions, then it is simply called a **polygon**. The feasibility region in Figure 1.19 is a polygon. The points of intersection of boundary lines of a feasibility region are called **corner points** of the region. The corner points of a feasibility region play a vital role in applications.

**EXAMPLE 6** The Crestline Company manufactures two jackets out of ripstop nylon cloth and suede leather. Their climber jacket uses 1.5 yards of cloth and 15 square inches of leather, while their hiker jacket uses 3 yards of cloth and 60 square inches of leather. If there are 258 yards of cloth and 4800 square inches of leather on hand, find the linear model that describes the feasible combinations of the two types of jackets that can be made from the available materials.

**SOLUTION** We let $x$ be the number of climber jackets and $y$ be the number of hiker jackets to be made. Then $1.5x$ yards of cloth are used in the former, and $3y$ yards of cloth are used in the latter for a total cloth usage of $1.5x + 3y$ yards. Since there are 258 yards of cloth on hand, the cloth constraint is $1.5x + 3y \leqslant 258$. Similarly, the leather constraint is found to be $15x + 60y \leqslant$

4800. Further, the inequalities $x \geqslant 0$ and $y \geqslant 0$ are necessary, since negative quantities of the jackets have no meaning. These latter inequalities limit the feasibility region to the first quadrant.

Thus the model of the production problem is the system

|  | Climber | Hiker |  |
|---|---|---|---|
| Nylon cloth | $1.5x$ | $+ \quad 3y$ | $\leqslant \quad 258$ |
| Suede leather | $15x$ | $+ \quad 60y$ | $\leqslant 4800$ |
|  | $x \geqslant 0,$ | $y \geqslant 0$ |  |

We display the feasibility region graphically in Figure 1.20. Each point in the region represents numbers of jackets that could actually be manufactured from the available raw materials, that is, a feasible production combination. Each point outside the region represents a production combination that is impossible to achieve from the given raw materials.

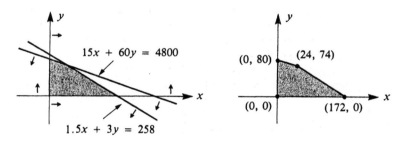

**FIGURE 1.20**          *The feasibility region for the Crestline*
*Company*

Three of the corners of the region are given by the intercepts $(0, 80)$, $(172, 0)$, and $(0, 0)$, while the fourth corner, $(24, 74)$, is found by solving the system of equations

$$1.5x + \phantom{0}3y = \phantom{0}258$$
$$15x + 60y = 4800 \quad \blacksquare\blacksquare$$

Sometimes we are given the converse problem. That is, we are given a polygonal region, and we are asked to describe the region as a system of linear inequalities.

**EXAMPLE 7**   Consider the region bounded by the triangle with vertices $(4, 3)$, $(6, -1)$, and $(1, 1)$. Find a system of linear inequalities having this feasibility region. See Figure 1.21.

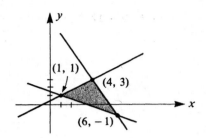

**FIGURE 1.21**                          *The region of Example 7*

SOLUTION   For each pair of points we first find the boundary line and then determine the direction of the inequality.

| Point pair | Slope | Line |
|---|---|---|
| $(4, 3), (6, -1)$ | $-2$ | $y - 3 = -2(x - 4), \quad 2x + y = 11$ |
| $(4, 3), (1, 1)$ | $\frac{2}{3}$ | $y - 1 = \frac{2}{3}(x - 1), \quad -2x + 3y = 1$ |
| $(1, 1), (6, -1)$ | $-\frac{2}{5}$ | $y - 1 = -\frac{2}{5}(x - 1), \quad 2x + 5y = 7$ |

To determine the direction of the inequalities, we use the origin as a test point. The feasibility region lies below the line $2x + y = 1$, and the origin also lies below this line. Therefore since $0 < 11$, the desired inequality must be $2x + y \leqslant 11$. Similarly, since the region and the origin lie on the same side of the line $-2x + 3y = 1$, we have the inequality $-2x + 3y \leqslant 1$. Finally, since the region and the origin lie on opposite sides of the line $2x + 5y = 7$, we get the inequality $2x + 3y \geqslant 7$. Thus the system of linear inequalities that has the specified feasibility region is

$$2x + \phantom{3}y \leqslant 11$$
$$-2x + 3y \leqslant \phantom{1}1$$
$$2x + 5y \geqslant \phantom{1}7 \quad \blacksquare\blacksquare$$

## EXERCISES 1.3

In Exercises 1–4, solve the given inequality for an explicit bound on $x$.

**1.**  $3x + 2 > \phantom{-}3$                    **2.**  $-5x + 3 > -7$

**3.**  $-2x - 4 < -5$                    **4.**  $6x + 7 < \phantom{-}10$

In Exercises 5–16, graphically display the region described by the inequality.

**5.**  $x \geqslant 2$                              **6.**  $y \leqslant -3$

**7.**  $3x + 7y \leqslant 4$                    **8.**  $2x + 5y \leqslant 6$

**9.**  $-5x + 2y \geqslant 3$                   **10.**  $-3x + 4y \geqslant 5$

**11.**  $4x - 6y \geqslant -12$         **12.**  $6x - 2y \geqslant -3$

**13.**  $-6x - 3y \leqslant 15$         **14.**  $-5x - 3y \leqslant 2$

**15.**  $4x - 3y \geqslant 0$         **16.**  $-3x + 5y \leqslant 0$

In Exercises 17–26, graphically display the region described by the inequalities. Find the coordinates of the corner points.

**17.**  $-5x + 2y \geqslant 10$
$6x + 3y \leqslant 7$

**18.**  $5x + 7y \leqslant -2$
$4x - 3y \geqslant 3$

**19.**  $-x + 2y \geqslant -2$
$4x + 3y \geqslant 12$

**20.**  $x + 2y \geqslant 4$
$-2x + 3y \geqslant -6$

**21.**  $2x - 3y \leqslant -3$
$4x + 2y \geqslant -6$
$4x + 6y \leqslant 2$

**22.**  $2x - 5y \geqslant -17$
$5x + 7y \geqslant 16$
$7x + 2y \leqslant 38$

**23.**  $5x + y \geqslant 5$
$2x + y \leqslant 4$
$x + y \geqslant 3$

**24.**  $3x + y \geqslant 6$
$x + 2y \leqslant 6$
$x + 4y \geqslant 8$

**25.**  $-2x + 3y \leqslant 6$
$2x + y \leqslant 4$
$x \geqslant 0, \quad y \geqslant 0$

**26.**  $3x - 2y \geqslant -6$
$5x + 4y \leqslant 20$
$x \geqslant 0, \quad y \geqslant 0$

In Exercises 27–30, find the linear mathematical model that describes the feasible combinations of the given materials into the given products. Graph the feasibility region and find the corner points.

**27.** The J. Sprat Sausage Company manufactures two types of sausages from pork and beef. Their Country Goodness line is 80% pork and 20% beef, while their Fast Start brand is 40% pork and 60% beef. They have 1000 pounds of pork and 840 pounds of beef in stock.

**28.** Chalet Roofing Materials manufactures two grades of shingle from asphalt and stone chips. Their Alpine shingle uses 250 pounds of asphalt and 100 pounds of stone, while their Green Meadows shingle uses 200 pounds of asphalt and 25 pounds of stone per bundle. They have on hand 40,000 pounds of asphalt and 10,000 pounds of stone.

**29.** American Sporting Goods constructs softballs and hardballs from leather and yarn. A softball requires 100 square inches of leather and 12 ounces of yarn, while a hardball uses 30 square inches of leather and 8 ounces of yarn. There are 3000 square inches of leather and 720 ounces of yarn available.

**30.** Quality Toys Inc. produces "Bucking Bronco" and "Locomotive" rider toys from a mixture of grade A plastic stock and floor scraps. Bucking Bronco is 60% grade A stock and 40% floor scraps, while Locomotive is 20% grade A stock and 80% floor scraps. Each toy weighs five pounds. They have on hand 540 pounds of grade A stock and 400 pounds of floor scraps.

In Exercises 31–32, find the system of linear inequalities that describes the triangular region with the given corner points.

**31.** $(5, 2)$ $(-3, -2)$, $(-1, 3)$         **32.** $(-4, 1)$, $(4, 3)$, $(1, -2)$

## 1.4 LINEAR PROGRAMMING IN THE PLANE

*Linear Functions, Maximum and Minimum Values, Linear Programming*

Linear programming is concerned with the determination of maximum values and minimum values of linear functions where the variables of the function are restricted, or constrained, by linear equations and inequalities. It provides a powerful method of constructing mathematical models involving production, distribution, and economic planning in which the principal purpose is to find the most efficient way of using available resources to attain specified goals.

Although its conceptual roots go back to Jean Fourier (1768–1830) in the early 1800s, linear programming as a distinct mathematical discipline was created in the 1940s by George Dantzig and others as part of a research project sponsored by the Air Force. World War II had presented enormously complicated problems of distributing men, weapons, and supplies to widely separated fronts, and military needs had to be met in as economical and efficient a manner as possible under the circumstances—a mammoth problem in the allocation of resources. Great amounts of data and large numbers of variables and equations were involved. The growth of computer technology in the 1940s motivated Dantzig to develop a systematic procedure that could take advantage of a computer's ability to perform calculations at high speed. The simplex algorithm, which is discussed in later chapters, was devised, and its refinements, extensions, and theoretical ramifications led to the area of mathematics now called linear programming.

The term "programming" in the expression linear programming should not be confused with computer programming. The term is used in the sense of having a procedure or plan of action to solve problems. However, the computer does play an important role in the applications of linear programming, since complicated problems involving many variables require computer assistance to handle the many computations that are needed. In this book we will not discuss computer programs in connection with linear programming.

Although the initial applications of linear programming dealt with the deployment of armed forces, it was quickly recognized that the methods could be applied to a wide range of economic and industrial problems. The 1975 Nobel Prize in Economics was awarded to Tjalling Koopmans of the United States and Leonid Kantorovich of the Soviet Union for "their contributions to the theory of optimum allocation of resources." Each had independently employed the tools of linear programming to analyze problems of economic planning and use of scarce resources.

In this section we will introduce some of the basic notions of linear programming in a geometric context. The problem is to determine the maximum or minimum value of a function of two variables when the variables are subjected to constraints. The term "linear" refers to the fact that the given function is linear and the constraints are all given by linear inequalities and linear equations. The initial restriction to two variables enables us to visualize the situation in the plane and thereby grasp the basic ideas with the help of geometric intuition. In higher dimensions, as our geometric intuition falters, we will be forced to rely on algebraic procedures. The general method, known as the simplex method, will be described in later chapters. By first examining linear programming in the plane, we can develop an insight into the nature of the problems and methods that will help us to understand the subject in a more general setting.

## LINEAR FUNCTIONS

If $z$ can be written as $z = ax + by$, then we say that $z$ is a **linear function** of the variables $x$ and $y$. For example, $z = 3x - 2y$ is a linear function. Its value at the point $(4, 1)$, that is, when $x = 4$ and $y = 1$, is $z = 3 \cdot 4 - 2 \cdot 1 = 10$. The alternative notation $f(x, y) = ax + by$ is sometimes used in textbooks, so that we would have $z = f(x, y)$, but we do not use that notation in this book.

Each value of a linear function corresponds to a line in the plane. If we have a linear function $z = ax + by$ and if the particular value $z = c$ is specified, then the line with equation $ax + by = c$ is obtained. In other words, a point $(x, y)$ produces the value $z = c$ if and only if $(x, y)$ lies on the line $ax + by = c$. Lines that correspond to particular values of $z$ are called **lines of constancy** for the function.

Since the slope is determined by $a$ and $b$, not $c$, the lines of constancy determined by different values of $c$ are all parallel. These ideas are illustrated in the following example.

**EXAMPLE 1**   For the linear function $z = 3x - 2y$, draw the lines of constancy corresponding to the values $z = 10$, $z = 4$, and $z = -6$.

**SOLUTION**   If the value $z = 10$ is specified, we get the linear equation $3x - 2y = 10$. Writing the equation as $y = \frac{3}{2}x - 5$, we see that the line has slope $\frac{3}{2}$ and $y$-intercept $(0, -5)$. For the value $z = 4$ we get $3x - 2y = 4$, which can be written $y = \frac{3}{2}x - 2$. The slope is again $\frac{3}{2}$, but the $y$-intercept is now $(0, -2)$. Finally, if $z = -6$, then we get $y = \frac{3}{2}x + 3$, which is a line with slope $\frac{3}{2}$ and $y$-intercept $(0, 3)$. This table summarizes the information.

| Value of $z$ | Equation of line | $y$-intercept |
|:---:|:---:|:---:|
| 10 | $y = \frac{3}{2}x - 5$ | $(0, -5)$ |
| 4 | $y = \frac{3}{2}x - 2$ | $(0, -2)$ |
| $-6$ | $y = \frac{3}{2}x + 3$ | $(0, 3)$ |

The three parallel lines of constancy are shown in Figure 1.22.   ∎

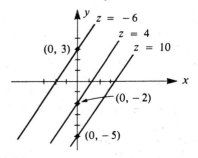

**FIGURE 1.22**                    *Lines of constancy for $z = 3x - 2y$*

The role played by lines of constancy in applications is indicated in the next example.

**EXAMPLE 2** A company markets two products. Product A sells for 12 dollars per unit, and product B sells for 8 dollars per unit. Suppose that $x$ units of product A and $y$ units of product B are sold each day. Express the daily revenue $R$ generated by the sales as a linear function of $x$ and $y$, and find the sales combinations that result in a revenue of $R = 2000$ dollars.

**SOLUTION** Since there are $12x$ dollars generated by product A and $8y$ dollars from product B, the total daily revenue is given by

$$R = 12x + 8y$$

Thus the same level of revenue can be achieved by many different sales configurations. For example, if either $x = 120$, $y = 70$ or $x = 50$, $y = 175$, then a quick calculation reveals that $R = 2000$. Many other sales figures can be chosen that also yield a revenue of $R = 2000$. In fact, any point on the line $12x + 8y = 2000$, where both $x$ and $y$ are nonnegative, can be chosen. Thus we have a **line of constant revenue**, which means that a variety of sales combinations schedules are possible. See Figure 1.23 for the line $R = 2000$ and three possible selections of points. The choice of "best" values for $x$ and $y$ is often determined by other factors, such as cost of materials and labor and cost of distribution. ∎

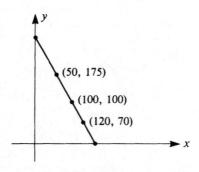

**FIGURE 1.23**    $R = 12x + 8y = 2000$, $x \geqslant 0$, $y \geqslant 0$

## MAXIMUM AND MINIMUM VALUES

The lines of constancy of a linear function can be used to examine the values of the function on regions in the plane. If we think of the lines as moving across the plane, then the associated values of the function are either getting larger or getting smaller, depending on the function at hand. If attention is restricted to a region in the plane, then only those lines that cut the region should be considered. The search for maximum or minimum values of a linear function on a region is made rather easy in this way, as the next example shows.

**EXAMPLE 3**    Find the maximum value of the linear function $z = x + y$ when $(x, y)$ is restricted to the unit square $0 \leqslant x \leqslant 1$, $0 \leqslant y \leqslant 1$.

SOLUTION    Let $S$ denote the unit square, which is shaded in Figure 1.24. Each value of $z$ corresponds to the line $z = x + y$. Writing $y = -x + z$, we see that it is a line of slope $-1$ and $y$-intercept $(0, z)$. Several lines of constancy are graphed in Figure 1.24, corresponding to the values $z = 0$, $z = 1$, $z = \frac{3}{2}$, and $z = 2$. (Lines that do not intersect $S$ are of no interest.)

It is easily seen that as $z$ increases, the lines move from left to right across the square. Since we want a maximum value of $z$ on $S$, we want to slide the line as far to the right as possible while still intersecting the region $S$. This extreme position is the corner point $(1, 1)$. Therefore the maximum value of $z = x + y$ over the region $S$ is $z = 1 + 1 = 2$. It is similarly seen that the minimum value of $z$ on $S$ is attained at the corner point $(0, 0)$. ▐▌

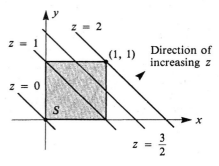

**FIGURE 1.24**    *Values of $z = x + y$ on $S$*

It is no accident that the maximum value of a linear function was attained at a corner point in the preceding example. Since the increase of function values corresponds to the shifting of the lines of constancy in a certain direction, we can slide the lines through a given region, in that direction, until the boundary of the region is reached. If the region is a polygon, then the line in this extreme position will pass through a corner point (perhaps two corner points if the line contains an entire segment of the boundary). Thus we see that the maximum value occurs at a corner point. By sliding the lines in the opposite direction, we get a similar conclusion for the minimum value.

The geometric notion of moving lines can be made into a rigorous proof of the following theorem, but we omit formal details.

**THEOREM 1**

Let $z = ax + by$ be a linear function, and let $P$ be a polygon in the plane. Then the maximum value and the minimum value of $z$ are attained at corner points of $P$.

To apply this theorem to Example 3, we would list the corner points $(0, 0)$, $(0, 1)$, $(1, 0)$, and $(1, 1)$ of the region and then calculate the respective values of $z$ to obtain $z = 0$, $z = 1$, and $z = 2$. The maximum value is therefore $z = 2$, which occurs at the point $(1, 1)$. Similarly, the minimum value is $z = 0$, which occurs at $(0, 0)$.

## LINEAR PROGRAMMING

The problem of optimizing (maximizing or minimizing) a linear function when the variables are restricted by a system of linear constraints is called a **linear program**. The constraints, which can be linear inequalities or linear equalities, determine a region called the **feasibility region**. The function to be optimized over the feasibility region is called the **objective function**. Consider the following linear program.

**EXAMPLE 4**  Solve the linear program:

$$\text{minimize} \quad z = -2x + y \quad \text{(objective function)}$$
$$
\begin{aligned}
\text{subject to} \quad & x - y \geqslant -3 \\
& x + y \leqslant 5 \quad \text{(constraints)} \\
& x \geqslant 0, \quad y \geqslant 0
\end{aligned}
$$

**SOLUTION**  The first step is to graph the feasibility region determined by the constraints. Using the methods of Section 1.3, we obtain the region shown in Figure 1.25. Recall that the corner points are found by using the appropriate constraints in pairs, taking the case of equality in each constraint. If we solve the resulting systems of linear equations, we get the following corner points.

| System | Corner point |
|---|---|
| $x - y = -3$<br>$x + y = \phantom{-}5$ | $(1, 4)$ |
| $x - y = -3$<br>$x \phantom{+ y} = \phantom{-}0$ | $(0, 3)$ |
| $x + y = \phantom{-}5$<br>$\phantom{x +} y = \phantom{-}0$ | $(5, 0)$ |
| $x \phantom{+ y} = \phantom{-}0$<br>$\phantom{x +} y = \phantom{-}0$ | $(0, 0)$ |

We next list the corner points of the region and calculate the corresponding values of the objective function.

| Corner point | Value of $z = -2x + y$ |
|---|---|
| $(1, 4)$ | $2$ |
| $(0, 3)$ | $3$ |
| $(5, 0)$ | $-10$ |
| $(0, 0)$ | $0$ |

According to Theorem 1, the smallest value of $z$ in this list will be the minimum value over the region. Thus the minimum value is $z = -10$, and it is attained at the corner point $(5, 0)$. (Similarly, the maximum value is $z = 3$, which is attained at the corner point $(0, 3)$.)  ▮▮

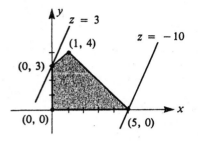

**FIGURE 1.25**                    *The minimum of $z = -2x + y$ is $z = -10$*

An alternative method of solving the problem in Example 4 is to draw a few lines of constancy of $z$ and note the direction in which the values decrease. Moving to an extreme position of the region then reveals the minimum value. Either method effectively deals with linear programs in the plane, but the use of Theorem 1 is systematic and easily performed.

**EXAMPLE 5**   Solve the linear program:

$$\text{maximize} \qquad z = 4x + 5y$$
$$\text{subject to} \qquad x + 2y \leqslant 6$$
$$5x + 4y \leqslant 20$$
$$x \geqslant 0, \quad y \geqslant 0$$

**SOLUTION**   As before, we first draw the feasibility region and find the co-ordinates of the corner points. Then we list the corner points and the corresponding values of $z$.

| Corner point | Value of $z = 4x + 5y$ |
|:---:|:---:|
| $(0, 0)$ | 0 |
| $(0, 3)$ | 15 |
| $(\frac{8}{3}, \frac{5}{3})$ | 19 |
| $(4, 0)$ | 16 |

Hence the maximum value of $z$ subject to the constraints is $z = 19$, attained at the point $(\frac{8}{3}, \frac{5}{3})$. The region and the line corresponding to $z = 19$ are shown in Figure 1.26.  ▮▮

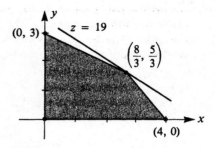

**FIGURE 1.26**

*The maximum of z = 4x + 5y is z = 19*

## EXERCISES 1.4

In Exercises 1–4, use the given linear function and draw the line corresponding to each of the given constants.

1. $z = 2x - 4y$; $z = -8$, $z = 4$, $z = 8$.
2. $z = -3x + y$; $z = -3$, $z = -6$, $z = 3$.
3. $z = 4x + y$; $z = 6$, $z = -4$, $z = 0$.
4. $z = -x - 2y$; $z = 0$, $z = 6$, $z = -1$.

In Exercises 5–6, find the line of constant revenue for each part. In each case, graph the segment of the line that shows feasible combinations, and find three feasible combinations for each revenue.

5. Easy Auto Rental rents sedans for $10 per day and station wagons for $15 per day. Let $x$ be the number of sedans rented per day, and let $y$ be the number of station wagons rented per day. (a) revenue = $990 and (b) revenue = $1500.

6. Jack's Produce sells honeydew melons for $1 and cantaloupes for 75¢. Let $x$ be the number of honeydew melons sold per day, and let $y$ be the number of cantaloupes sold per day. (a) revenue = $300 and (b) revenue = $450.

Solve Exercises 7–10 by graphing lines of constancy.

7. Maximize $z = 3x - 2y$ when $(x, y)$ is restricted to the rectangle with the corners $(1, 2)$, $(-2, 2)$, $(-2, -1)$, $(1, -1)$.

8. Maximize $z = -x + 3y$ when $(x, y)$ is restricted to the rectangle with the corners $(-1, 2)$, $(4, 2)$, $(-1, -3)$, $(4, -3)$.

9. Minimize $z = 4x + y$ when $(x, y)$ is restricted to the rectangle with corners $(3, 4)$, $(5, 4)$, $(3, 2)$, $(5, 2)$.

10. Minimize $z = -2x - y$ when $(x, y)$ is restricted to the rectangle with corners $(-3, 1)$, $(-1, 1)$, $(-3, -4)$, $(-1, -4)$.

In Exercises 11–16, find the indicated maximum or minimum by applying Theorem 1.

11. For the feasibility region of Exercise 21 of Section 1.3,
    (a) maximize $z = 3x - y$, (b) minimize $z = x + 4y$.

12. For the feasibility region of Exercise 22 of Section 1.3,
    (a) maximize $z = -2x + 3y$ (b) minimize $z = 3x + y$.

13. For the feasibility region of Exercise 23 of Section 1.3,
    (a) maximize $z = 5x + 2y$, (b) maximize $z = 2x + 4y$.

14. For the feasibility region of Exercise 24 of Section 1.3,
    (a) maximize $z = 3x + 6y$, (b) maximize $z = x + 4y$.

15. For the feasibility region of Exercise 25 of Section 1.3,
    (a) maximize $z = 4x + 5y$, (b) maximize $z = x + 6y$.

16. For the feasibility region of Exercise 26 of Section 1.3,
    (a) maximize $z = 7x + 6y$, (b) maximize $z = 5x + y$.

In Exercises 17–26, graph the feasibility region and then find the optimal value for each objective function by computing its value at each of the corner points.

17. (a) Maximize     $z = 6x - 4y$
    subject to     $5x - 10y \leqslant 20$
    $-x + 3y \leqslant 3$
    $x \geqslant 0, \quad y \geqslant 0$
    (b) Use the same feasibility region and minimize the objective function $z = x - 2y$.

18. (a) Maximize     $z = x - 3y$
    subject to     $8x + 16y \leqslant 32$
    $-4x + 8y \leqslant 8$
    $x \geqslant 0, \quad y \geqslant 0$
    (b) Use the same feasibility region and minimize the objective function $z = -3x + y$.

19. (a) Maximize     $z = 4x - y$
    subject to     $7x + 2y \leqslant 14$
    $-3x + y \leqslant 3$
    $y \geqslant 0$
    (b) Use the same feasibility region and minimize the objective function $z = x - 3y$.

20. (a) Maximize     $z = -x + 3y$
    subject to     $5x + 10y \leqslant 20$
    $x - 4y \leqslant 4$
    $x \geqslant 0$
    (b) Use the same feasibility region and minimize the objective function $z = -5x + 2y$.

21. (a) Minimize     $z = -2x + 3y$
    subject to     $-x + y \leqslant 1$
    $x + 2y \geqslant 4$
    $4x + 5y \leqslant 20$

(b) Use the same feasibility region and maximize the objective function $z = 5x - 2y$.

22. (a) Minimize $\quad z = -2x + 3y$

   subject to
   $$-3x + y \leqslant 3$$
   $$5x + 4y \leqslant 20$$
   $$-x + 2y \geqslant 2$$

   (b) Use the same feasibility region and maximize the objective function $z = 4x - y$.

23. (a) Maximize $\quad z = 5x + y$

   subject to
   $$4x + 3y \leqslant 12$$
   $$x + 3y \leqslant 6$$
   $$x \geqslant 0, \quad y \geqslant 0$$

   (b) Use the same feasibility region and maximize the objective function $z = 3x + 2y$.

24. (a) Maximize $\quad z = 2x + 4y$

   subject to
   $$4x + y \leqslant 8$$
   $$2x + y \leqslant 6$$
   $$x \geqslant 0, \quad y \geqslant 0$$

   (b) Use the same feasibility region and maximize the objective function $z = 4x + 5y$.

25. (a) Maximize $\quad z = 7x + 2y$

   subject to
   $$-4x + y \geqslant -4$$
   $$2x - 3y \geqslant -6$$
   $$x \geqslant 0, \quad y \geqslant 0$$

   (b) Use the same feasibility region and minimize the objective function $z = 3x - 4y$.

26. (a) Maximize $\quad z = 5x + 2y$

   subject to
   $$2x - 5y \geqslant -10$$
   $$-2x + y \geqslant -6$$
   $$x \geqslant 0, \quad y \geqslant 0$$

   (b) Use the same feasibility region and minimize the objective function $z = -5x + 4y$.

## 1.5 APPLICATIONS OF LINEAR PROGRAMMING

*Production Schedules, Maximizing Revenue, The Diet Problem*

There is a great variety of applications of linear programming. This section consists of a number of examples of applications of linear programming in the plane. We will look at production problems in which the objective function is either cost of production (to be minimized) or revenue (to be maximized) and in which the constraints arise from availability of raw materials, demand for the product, contract conditions, and other aspects of the production process. We will also look at an example of the classical diet problem in which a nutritionally adequate diet is to be designed at minimum cost.

The various problems may appear at first sight to be different from one another, but the mathematical structures are essentially identical. The similarities become apparent when the problems are modeled as linear programs. One great value of mathematics is its ability to strip away irrelevancies and identify common aspects of seemingly different problems.

Setting up a verbally described problem as a linear program takes several steps. First, we must name and define the appropriate variables. Second, we must determine the objective function and express it in terms of the variables. Third, we must convert each condition that constrains the variables into an inequality (the phrases "at least" and "at most" are often used). At this stage the methods of Section 1.4 can be employed to solve the resulting linear program. The solution must then be interpreted in the context of the original problem.

## PRODUCTION SCHEDULES

A production process consists of many activities, each with its own operating costs. Moreover, the various production activities often run for different lengths of time to achieve a specified production goal. A **production schedule** stipulates the amount of time, or the activity level, for each part of the production process. The activities can involve labor, machines, or different plants, and the time can be measured in hours or days or weeks, depending on the products under consideration. One important goal in determining a production schedule is the minimization of costs.

**EXAMPLE 1**  The Carbon Coal Company has two mines, a surface mine and a deep mine. It costs 200 dollars a day to operate the surface mine and 250 dollars a day to operate the deep mine. Each mine produces a medium grade and a medium-hard grade of coal, but in different proportions. The surface mine produces 12 tons of medium grade and 6 tons of medium-hard grade coal a day, and the deep mine produces 4 tons of medium grade and 8 tons of medium-hard grade coal a day. The company has a contract to deliver at least 600 tons of medium grade and 480 tons of medium-hard grade coal within 60 days. How many days should each mine be operated so that the contract can be filled at minimum cost?

**SOLUTION**  We seek a production schedule to minimize cost. We will set up the linear program in three steps.

First, we define the necessary variables. Let $x$ be the number of days of operation for the surface mine, and let $y$ be the number of days of operation for the deep mine.

Second, we define the objective function. The total cost $C$ of operation is found by multiplying the daily cost times the number of days of operation for each mine and adding the two together. Thus the total cost is

$$C = 200x + 250y \quad \text{(objective function)}$$

Third, we determine the constraints. It is very helpful to construct a table that displays the pertinent information concerning the production of each grade of coal. In such a table we always label the rows so that they correspond to the materials or products that are being constrained.

|  | Surface mine | Deep mine | Tons needed |
|---|---|---|---|
| Medium grade | 12 | 4 | 600 |
| Medium-hard grade | 6 | 8 | 480 |

Each row of the table determines a constraint. Each of the first two columns gives the daily production level for a mine, and the numbers must be multiplied by the number of days of operation to give total production. Thus the production of medium grade coal will be $12x + 4y$ tons; since at least 600 tons are needed, we have the constraint

$$12x + 4y \geqslant 600 \qquad \text{(medium grade)}$$

Similarly, the constraint corresponding to the medium-hard grade of coal is

$$6x + 8y \geqslant 480 \qquad \text{(medium-hard grade)}$$

We also have $0 \leqslant x \leqslant 60$, $0 \leqslant y \leqslant 60$. Putting all of the parts together, we obtain the following linear program:

$$\begin{aligned} \text{minimize} \quad & C = 200x + 250y \\ \text{subject to} \quad & 12x + 4y \geqslant 600 \\ & 6x + 8y \geqslant 480 \\ & 0 \leqslant x \leqslant 60 \\ & 0 \leqslant y \leqslant 60 \end{aligned}$$

The feasibility region determined by the constraints is shown in Figure 1.27.

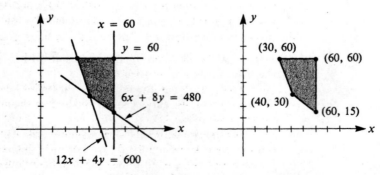

**FIGURE 1.27**    *The feasibility region for the Carbon Coal Company*

We next evaluate the objective function at the corner points and construct the following table of values

| Corner point | Value of $C$ |
|:---:|:---:|
| (40, 30) | 15,500 |
| (30, 60) | 21,000 |
| (60, 60) | 27,000 |
| (60, 15) | 15,750 |

Thus we find that a minimum cost of $C = 15,500$ dollars is obtained when $x = 40$ and $y = 30$. This means that we should operate the surface mine for 40 days and the deep mine for 30 days.  ∎

**EXAMPLE 2**    Roamer Motors, Inc. has two plants where it manufactures trucks in three different sizes: quarter-ton, half-ton, and three-quarter-ton. The number of trucks that each plant can produce per week and the total production costs per week are given in the following table.

| | Plant I | Plant II |
|:---|:---:|:---:|
| Quarter-ton | 100 | 50 |
| Half-ton | 75 | 100 |
| Three-quarter-ton | 50 | 150 |
| Cost | 0.2 million | 0.3 million |

The company has a military contract to deliver at least 5000 quarter-ton, 7500 half-ton, and 7500 three-quarter-ton trucks. Find a production schedule (number of weeks per plant) that will produce the trucks at minimum cost.

**SOLUTION**    Let $x$ be the number of weeks of operation for Plant I, and let $y$ be the number of weeks of operation for Plant II. The cost for Plant I will be $0.2x$ million dollars, and the cost for Plant II will be $0.3y$ million dollars. The total cost of production, our objective function, is given by $C = 0.2x + 0.3y$.

The minimum demand for each type of truck gives us the following constraints. Referring to the first row in the table, we see that $100x + 50y$ quarter-ton trucks will be produced; since at least 5000 are demanded, we have the constraint $100x + 50y \geqslant 5000$. Similarly, using the second row and the demand for half-ton trucks, we get the constraint $75x + 100y \geqslant 7500$. For three-quarter-ton trucks we get the constraint $50x + 150y \geqslant 7500$. Also, there are the obvious constraints $x \geqslant 0$, $y \geqslant 0$.

The constraint inequalities can be simplified by canceling common factors. Thus we obtain the following linear program:

$$\text{minimize} \quad C = 0.2x + 0.3y$$

$$
\begin{array}{lll}
\text{subject to} & 2x + \phantom{4}y \geqslant 100 & \text{(quarter-ton)} \\
& 3x + 4y \geqslant 300 & \text{(half-ton)} \\
& \phantom{3}x + 3y \geqslant 150 & \text{(three-quarter-ton)} \\
& x \geqslant 0, \ y \geqslant 0 &
\end{array}
$$

The feasibility region is shown in Figure 1.28.

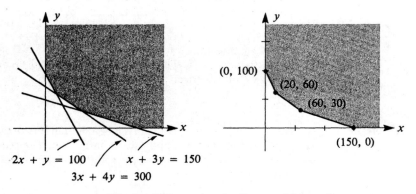

**FIGURE 1.28**            *The feasibility region for Roamer Motors, Inc.*

Observe that the region is not a polygon, but an unbounded wedge-shaped region. Therefore we cannot apply Theorem 1 of Section 1.4 directly. The objective function can be made arbitrarily large by taking $x$ and $y$ to be large, and hence no maximum value can exist. Fortunately, we seek a minimum value, and the minimum will occur at one of the corner points. (See the Note that follows this example.)

If we evaluate the objective function at the corner points of the region, we get the following values

| Corner point | Value of $C$ |
|:---:|:---:|
| $(0, 100)$ | 30 million |
| $(20, 60)$ | 22 million |
| $(60, 30)$ | 21 million |
| $(150, 0)$ | 30 million |

Hence a minimum cost of $C = 21$ million dollars occurs when Plant I operates for $x = 60$ weeks and Plant II operates for $y = 30$ weeks. Note that this schedule results in an overproduction of quarter-ton trucks (7500 instead of 5000 quarter-ton trucks), yet cost is minimized for the contract as a whole.                                                      ▮▮

*NOTE:*   There are two possible ways to see that a minimum value is attained at one of the corner points in Example 2 even though the region is unbounded. One way is to examine the lines of constancy of the objective function and observe that the values of $C$ decrease as the lines slide through the region toward the origin. The smallest value on the feasibility region therefore occurs as the line is about to exit the region at a corner point. It could also be noted that since $x$ and $y$ are both nonnegative, the objective function $C = 0.2x + 0.3y$ cannot be less than 0, and therefore smaller values for $C$ cannot be obtained by pushing the line away from the origin.

Another way is to impose a time restriction in the contract, thereby making the feasibility region into a polygon. For example, if the trucks are to be delivered within 200 weeks, we get the feasibility region shown in Figure 1.29. We can now apply Theorem 1 of Section 1.4 to conclude that maximum and minimum values occur at the corner points. Checking the values, we find that the minimum value occurs at one of the corner points of the original region. The maximum occurs at the far corner of the new region.

A word of caution is in order. If the time constraints are too severe, then it may happen that the minimum will occur at one of the newly introduced corner points. See Exercises 5–8 for examples of this phenomenon. However, if the imposed time constraints do not delete any of the original corners, then the location of the minimum point is not affected.

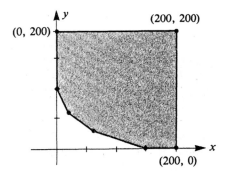

**FIGURE 1.29**

*Roamer Motors, Inc., with the additional constraints $x \leqslant 200$, $y \leqslant 200$*

## MAXIMIZING REVENUE

Most products require a combination of raw materials in their manufacture. If given amounts of resources are available, then it must be decided how to use the resources to best advantage. In the next example the raw materials can be used to make two different products, which are sold at different prices, and the goal is to maximize revenue. Recall that the revenue generated by a product is the number of units sold times the price per unit.

**EXAMPLE 3**   The Easy Mix Cement Company produces their Red Seal and Black Seal cements from a mixture of ground limestone, clay, and shale. The Red Seal mixture uses 1 part of limestone to 1 part clay and 2 parts shale, while the Black Seal mixture requires 4 parts limestone to 1 part clay and 1 part shale. There are 8 tons of limestone, 3.5 tons of clay, and 6 tons of shale on hand. Red Seal sells for 200 dollars a ton, while Black Seal sells for 250 dollars a ton. Assuming that the company can sell all that they produce, set up and solve the linear program to find the amount of each mixture that should be formed for maximum revenue.

**SOLUTION**   Let $x$ be the number of tons of Red Seal cement to be made, and let $y$ be the number of tons of Black Seal cement to be made. Since Red Seal sells for 200 dollars a ton, the revenue from $x$ tons is $200x$ dollars. Similarly, the revenue from $y$ tons of Black Seal is $250y$ dollars. The total revenue $R$ is then $R = 200x + 250y$, which is the objective function.

The following table displays the given information; each row corresponds to a raw material. Each of the first two columns displays the amount of each raw material needed to make one ton of the product.

|  | Red Seal (one ton) | Black Seal (one ton) | Tons on hand |
|---|---|---|---|
| Limestone | $\frac{1}{4}$ | $\frac{4}{6}$ | 8 |
| Clay | $\frac{1}{4}$ | $\frac{1}{6}$ | 3.5 |
| Shale | $\frac{2}{4}$ | $\frac{1}{6}$ | 6 |

Each raw material will have a corresponding constraint. In the case of limestone we note that one fourth of the Red Seal mixture and two thirds of the Black Seal mixture are limestone, so that $\frac{1}{4}x + \frac{2}{3}y$ tons of limestone will be used. Since 8 tons of limestone are available, we have the constraint $\frac{1}{4}x + \frac{2}{3}y \leqslant 8$, which can be written $3x + 8y \leqslant 96$. In a similar way we obtain the clay constraint $\frac{1}{4}x + \frac{1}{6}y \leqslant 3.5$, or $3x + 2y \leqslant 42$, and the shale constraint $\frac{1}{2}x + \frac{1}{6}y \leqslant 6$, or $3x + y \leqslant 36$. Of course, we also have constraints $x \geqslant 0$ and $y \geqslant 0$.

Thus we obtain the following linear program:

$$\begin{array}{lll} \text{maximize} & R = 200x + 250y & \\ \text{subject to} & 3x + 8y \leqslant 96 & \text{(limestone)} \\ & 3x + 2y \leqslant 42 & \text{(clay)} \\ & 3x + \phantom{2}y \leqslant 36 & \text{(shale)} \\ & x \geqslant 0,\ y \geqslant 0 & \end{array}$$

The feasibility region and the corner points determined by the constraints are shown in Figure 1.30. Note that each point $(x, y)$ inside the region is a "feasible" production level, since the corresponding amounts of raw materials are within the availability limits.

Next we evaluate $R$ at the corner points of the feasibility region, neglecting the origin, since no production yields zero revenue.

| Corner point | Value of $R$ |
|:---:|:---:|
| $(0, 12)$ | 3000 |
| $(8, 9)$ | 3850 |
| $(10, 6)$ | 3500 |
| $(12, 0)$ | 2400 |

We see that a maximum revenue of $R = 3850$ dollars is attained when $x = 8$ tons and $y = 9$ tons. It is interesting to note that the production level $x = 8$, $y = 9$ utilizes 8 tons of limestone, 3.5 tons of clay, and 5.5 tons of shale. While all of the limestone and clay will be used, there will be a half ton of surplus shale. Thus the raw materials need not be entirely used in order to maximize revenue. ∎

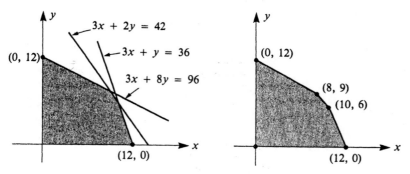

**FIGURE 1.30**

The feasibility region for the Easy Mix
Cement Company

## THE DIET PROBLEM

The diet problem is one of the earliest and most straightforward illustrations of the methods of linear programming. We are given a number of foods, and each food is composed of a number of nutrients. There is a unit cost for each food and a minimum daily allowance (MDA) for each nutrient. The problem is to find a diet that meets the given nutritional requirements at minimum cost.

**EXAMPLE 4**    We are given two foods bread and milk, and we want to consider two nutrients protein and food energy (calories). Suppose that one slice of bread has 1 gram of protein and 60 calories and that one cup of milk has 9 grams of protein and 90 calories. Further suppose that the cost of bread is 2 cents per slice and the cost of milk is 10 cents per cup. To guard against too much of a good thing, we restrict the diet to at most 100 slices of bread and at most 40 cups of milk. Find a daily bread-milk diet that contains at least 90 grams of protein and 2700 calories such that the cost is a minimum.

SOLUTION   Let $x$ be the number of slices of bread and let $y$ be the number of cups of milk. Then the cost of bread is $2x$ and the cost of milk is $10y$, so that the total cost is our objective function

$$C = 2x + 10y$$

As usual, we display the information in a table.

|  | Bread | Milk | Minimum needed |
|---|---|---|---|
| Protein | 1 | 9 | 90 |
| Calories | 60 | 90 | 2700 |

The first row of the table gives us the protein constraint $x + 9y \geqslant 90$. The second row of the table gives us the calorie constraint $60x + 90y \geqslant 2700$, or $2x + 3y \geqslant 90$. Also, the upper limit constraints are $x \leqslant 100$ and $y \leqslant 40$; and since negative quantities of bread and milk do not make sense, we have $x \geqslant 0$, $y \geqslant 0$.

The resulting linear program is as follows:

$$\begin{array}{lll} \text{minimize} & C = 2x + 10y & \\ \text{subject to} & x + 9y \geqslant 90 & \text{(protein)} \\ & 2x + 3y \geqslant 90 & \text{(calories)} \\ & 0 \leqslant x \leqslant 100 & \\ & 0 \leqslant y \leqslant 40 & \end{array}$$

The feasibility region is shown in Figure 1.31. Evaluation of the cost at the corner points reveals that the minimum occurs at $(36, 6)$. Hence a diet of 36 slices of bread and 6 cups of milk provides the stated nutritional requirements at a minimum cost of $C = 132$ cents per day. ▮▮

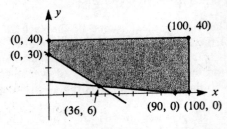

**FIGURE 1.31**

*The feasibility region for the bread-milk diet*

## EXERCISES 1.5

In Exercises 1–4, set up and solve the linear program to meet the given demands at minimum cost.

1. Country Mills produces two types of soy-nut flour at their North Fork and East Bend mills. Each mill produces both coarse grind and medium grind flour, but in different proportions. The North Fork mill will produce 3000 pounds of coarse grind and 2000 pounds of medium grind per day at a cost of $50, while the East Bend mill produces 1000 pounds of coarse grind and 6000 pounds of medium grind per day at a cost of $75. They have a contract to deliver 30,000 pounds of coarse grind and 60,000 pounds of medium grind flour within 40 days.

2. The B.C.K. Griwatz Company Ltd. mines rubies and emeralds in two locations. Both gems are found in each location but in different proportions. The Aakland location produces a daily average of 15 ounces of rubies and 5 ounces of emeralds at a cost of $2200, while the Graustein location produces a daily average of 10 ounces of rubies and 10 ounces of emeralds at a cost of $2600. The Sultan of Sharaef has placed an order for 150 ounces of rubies and 100 ounces of emeralds and wants them delivered within 25 days.

3. The Paris brickyard manufactures three types of brick in their two kilns. Kiln A can produce 2000 standard bricks, 1000 oversize bricks, and 500 glazed bricks per day, while kiln B can produce 1000 standard bricks, 1500 oversize bricks, and 2500 glazed bricks per day. The daily cost of operating kiln A is 500 dollars, and the daily cost of operating kiln B is 400 dollars. They have an order for 10,000 standard, 9000 oversize, and 7500 glazed bricks.

4. Quantron Watch Company manufactures three brands of watches at both their Westlawn and Bayview plants. The Westlawn plant can produce 100 Slim-n-Trim, 60 Super Sport, and 35 Petite watches per day at a cost of 3000 dollars, while the Bayview plant produces 50 Slim-n-Trim, 90 Super Sport, and 105 Petite watches per day at a cost of 3300 dollars. They have orders for 5000 Slim-n-Trim, 5400 Super Sport, and 4200 Petite watches.

In Exercises 5–8, solve the indicated exercise from 1–4 with the given time limitations

5. Exercise 1 with (a) 15 days for each,  (b) 5 days on North Fork and 40 days on East Bend.

6. Exercise 2 with (a) 10 days for each,  (b) 2 days at Aakland and 25 days at Graustein.

7. Exercise 3 with (a) 20 days each, (b) 2 days on kiln A, 9 days on kiln B.

8. Exercise 4 with (a) 100 days each, (b) 90 days at Westlawn, 30 days at Bayview.

In Exercises 9–12, set up and solve the linear program to maximize revenue from available resources.

9. Stullon Steel Company manufactures two types of truck bumpers from iron

and nickel. Their A bumper uses 10 pounds of iron and 2 pounds of nickel, while their B bumper uses 12 pounds of iron and 1 pound of nickel. Their A bumper sells for 50 dollars, and their B bumper sells for 60 dollars. There are on hand 2400 pounds of iron and 305 pounds of nickel.

10. The Corner Bakery makes two cakes from sugar and flour (and other ingredients in lesser amounts). Their Frosted Angel Cake requires 2 cups of sugar and 1 cup of flour, while their Chiffon Cake uses 1 cup of sugar and 3 cups of flour. An Angel Cake will sell for $3.50, while a Chiffon Cake will sell for $3.00. There are 80 cups of sugar and 90 cups of flour on hand.

11. The Chewey Candy Shoppe makes two types of caramel candy from sugar, cream, and molasses. A package of Heavenly Chew requires 1 cup of sugar, 2 cups of cream, and 2 cups of molasses, while a package of Rich-n-Chew uses 1 cup of sugar, 1 cup of cream, and 3 cups of molasses. A package of Heavenly Chew sells for $2, and a package of Rich-n-Chew sells for $1.50. There are on hand 425 cups of sugar, 800 cups of cream, and 1200 cups of molasses.

12. The Brilliant Jewelry Company produces two tiaras from gold, platinum, and diamonds. Their Starluster tiara is composed of 5 ounces gold, 2 ounces platinum, and 5 ounces diamonds, while their Galaxy Glow tiara is composed of 1 ounce gold, 3 ounces platinum, and 3 ounces diamonds. The Starluster tiara sells for 12,000 dollars, and the Galaxy Glow tiara sells for 4000 dollars. There are 60 ounces of gold, 72 ounces of platinum, and 90 ounces of diamonds on hand.

In Exercises 13–16, set up and solve the given diet problems.

13. Mrs. Brown wants to blend the cereals VIVA and Flaky Oats to obtain a nutritious breakfast with at least 10 grams of protein and 3 milligrams of iron at the least cost. One ounce of VIVA contains 5 grams of protein and 1 milligram of iron and costs 7 cents, while one ounce of Flaky Oats contains 5 grams of protein and 3 milligrams of iron and costs 9 cents.

14. Superintendent McBee has decided that school lunches are too expensive. In order to reduce costs he has elected to serve a tasty blend of peanut butter and jelly. One ounce of peanut butter has 5 grams of protein and 100 calories, while one ounce of jelly has no protein and 60 calories. McBee feels that a lunch should have no more than 5 ounces of peanut butter or 3 ounces of jelly and should provide at least 20 grams of protein and 500 calories. If peanut butter costs 10 cents per ounce and jelly costs 6 cents per ounce, find the cheapest blend that will meet the constraints.

15. Suppose that fruit and vegetable salads are to be blended to meet requirements on vitamins A and D. Let fruit salad have 10% of the necessary vitamin A and 40% of the vitamin D per serving, while vegetable salad has 30% of the necessary vitamin A and 20% of the vitamin D per serving. If the cost per serving is 10 cents for fruit salad and 7 cents for vegetable salad, find the cheapest blend that will meet 100% of the requirements.

16. Mike's Mightyfine Mixture is made from a blend of choice jelly beans. He has determined that his flavor and aroma standards are met if certain quantities

of sugar and spice are present. There are two principal jelly beans used for the blend: Southern Balm and Mexican Taco. One ounce of Southern Balm contains 40% of the necessary sugar and 20% of the spice, while one ounce of Mexican Taco contains 25% of the sugar and 50% of the spice. The cost per ounce is 15 cents for Southern Balm and 20 cents for Mexican Taco. Find the cheapest blend that meets 100% of the sugar and spice requirements.

# 2

# Linear Systems in Higher Dimensions

In Chapter 1 we solved systems of linear equations in two variables by combining the equations in such a way that one of the variables was eliminated. Once the elimination was accomplished, finding the solutions was quite easy. The same basic idea of elimination is appropriate in large and more complicated systems, but the additional complexity necessitates a more organized approach. Unless there is a systematic method of attack, the result can be calculational chaos. The resulting disorganized flurries of activity often lead nowhere and can be very discouraging.

In Section 2.1 we will discuss the method of Gaussian elimination, named for Carl Friedrich Gauss (1777–1855), for solving linear systems of equations. This is a precise, step-by-step procedure for solving systems; it works without fail, if no errors in calculation are made. Since there is no ambiguity in going from one step to the next in these methods, it is possible to program a computer to carry out the labor. We will not pursue this area in this book, but computer assistance is often the only feasible way to solve extremely large linear systems.

In Section 2.2 we will continue the discussion of Gaussian elimination and consider the problem of solving several suitably related systems simultaneously. An application to contingency planning illustrates the usefulness of the technique. Section 2.3 deals with linear systems that have either no solutions or infinitely many solutions. The notion of row rank of a matrix is introduced to help analyze the problem of consistency of linear systems.

Section 2.4 is devoted to the geometry of three dimensions. The ability to work with planes in space provides a geometric understanding of linear systems in three variables and thereby enhances the understanding of linear systems in general. It also paves the way for the discussion of vector spaces in Chapter 4.

Section 2.5 is a short section on a second elimination method known as Gauss–Jordan elimination. It is a modification of Gaussian elimination due to Camille Jordan (1838–1922) that is based on the idea of pivoting, a procedure that is also used in the next section on linear programming.

In Section 2.6 we will resume the discussion of linear programming and develop the simplex method for solving linear programs. A discussion of linear production models is included as an application of the simplex method. A discussion of the reasoning that underlies the simplex method is given in Section 2.7, along with brief descriptions of some extensions of the simplex method. This section is somewhat theoretical in nature and can be omitted on a first reading.

## 2.1    ROW OPERATIONS AND GAUSSIAN ELIMINATION

*Elementary Operations, the Matrix of a System, Elementary Row Operations, Gaussian Elimination, Row Echelon Form*

Gaussian elimination is a systematic method of solving linear systems. In this method a given system of linear equations is replaced by successively simpler systems until one is reached that is easily solved. It is crucial in passing from one system to the next that the solution set remain exactly the same. Thus the first order of business is to clearly specify the operations that are allowed and to see that these operations preserve the solution set.

Anyone who works with a system that involves more than two variables soon tires of all the writing and realizes that only the numbers, not the names of the variables, are important. It is very convenient to list the coefficients and constants in a rectangular array, called a matrix, and operate on the matrix of numbers. The variables are restored at the end. The matrix notation allows one to focus on the essential features of a system. We will use matrix notation in the discussion of Gaussian elimination, restoring the variables when they are needed.

Since we wish to emphasize the mechanics of Gaussian elimination, all of the systems in this section will have unique solutions. In Section 2.3 we will discuss how to recognize and handle systems that have either no solutions or infinitely many solutions. Though the methods are basically the same, there are subtleties that are best encountered after the fundamental techniques are mastered.

### ELEMENTARY OPERATIONS

Since we will be working with systems of equations that have different numbers of variables in them, we will use a subscript notation for the variables. For instance, in a system that has three variables we will write $x_1, x_2, x_3$ for the variables. When a system is written, the variables should be aligned in columns, the variable $x_1$ coming first, $x_2$ coming second, and so on.

In working with a system of linear equations to obtain a solution, there are three operations that are permitted. These operations, called **elementary operations**, are as follows.

1. The interchange of two equations

2. The multiplication of an equation by a nonzero constant

3. The addition of a multiple of one equation to another equation

The first operation enables us to rearrange the equations in the system. By performing successive interchanges we can arrange the equations into any desired order. Since the individual equations are not changed, the rearranged system will have exactly the same solutions as the original system.

The second operation enables us to change the coefficient of any particular term in an equation by multiplying the entire equation by an appropriate constant. Of course, multiplication by zero is not permitted, since that would wipe out an equation and thereby change the system. Since the introduced constant is not zero, it can easily be cancelled so that the solutions of the system are not changed.

The third operation is the most important of the three. It enables us to eliminate a variable from one equation by adding or subtracting a multiple of a different equation. The next example shows just how this operation works.

**EXAMPLE 1** Suppose the following two equations are part of a system of equations:

$$x_1 + 2x_2 - 3x_3 = 4$$
$$2x_1 + 3x_2 + x_3 = 5$$

Use the first equation to eliminate the variable $x_1$ from the second equation.

**SOLUTION**  To eliminate $x_1$ from the second equation, we add $-2$ times the first equation to the second. (We can also think of this as subtracting 2 times the first equation from the second.) The old second equation is then replaced by the new second equation as follows:

$$(2x_1 + 3x_2 + x_3) - 2(x_1 + 2x_2 - 3x_3) = 5 - 2 \cdot 4$$

Note that both sides of the equation are affected. After combining terms we obtain the new second equation

$$-x_2 + 7x_3 = -3$$

The new pair of equations is thus

$$x_1 + 2x_2 - 3x_3 = \quad 4$$
$$-x_2 + 7x_3 = -3$$

The first equation has not been changed. The first equation was used to operate on the second equation, but the first equation remains untouched. Only the second equation is modified by the operation.  ▌▌

It is important to realize that the third operation does not change the solution set of the system. Any solution of the original system will also be a solution of the new system obtained by applying the third operation. This is because any solution of the system will satisfy both equations involved in the operation, and thus it will satisfy the new equation. Moreover, since the operation can be reversed by using the negative of the given multiplier, the original system can be restored; thus any solution of the new system will be a solution of the original system. Hence the third operation, as well as the first and second operations, leaves the solution set of a system unchanged.

These observations are summarized in the following theorem.

## *THEOREM 1*

If a system of linear equations is derived from another system by applying any of the three elementary operations, then the solution sets of the two systems are identical.

Thus if we are given a system of linear equations, we can perform a chain of elementary operations with full confidence that we are not creating new solutions or destroying old ones. The idea is to keep changing a system with these solution-preserving operations until the system has been simplified to the point at which the solution is very easily obtained. But before pursuing this further, we first introduce an extremely useful notational device.

## THE MATRIX OF A SYSTEM

When a system is written so that the variables are aligned in columns, it is really not necessary to keep writing the variables as we apply the elementary operations. These operations do not shift the variables out of their columns. Since all of the numerical work is done on the coefficients and the constant terms, it is very convenient to strip away the variables and retain only the essential numbers.

A **matrix** (plural: matrices) is a rectangular array of numbers enclosed in brackets. For a given system of linear equations, if we list the coefficients of the variables and maintain their relative positions, we obtain the **coefficient matrix** of the system. For example, the system

$$\begin{aligned} x_1 + 2x_2 - 3x_3 &= 5 \\ 3x_1 - x_2 \phantom{- 3x_3} &= 3 \\ 2x_1 \phantom{- x_2} + 4x_3 &= -1 \end{aligned}$$

has the coefficient matrix

$$\begin{array}{ccc} x_1 & x_2 & x_3 \end{array}$$
$$\begin{bmatrix} 1 & 2 & -3 \\ 3 & -1 & 0 \\ 2 & 0 & 4 \end{bmatrix}$$

Here we have written the variable names above their corresponding columns for emphasis, but we will usually not make these labels explicit. Note that if a variable does not appear in an equation, then the coefficient 0 is used in the matrix.

If we include the column of constant terms lying to the right of the equal signs, then we obtain the **augmented coefficient matrix** or, more simply, the **augmented matrix** of the system. We separate the coefficients of the variables from the constant terms by putting a vertical bar between them. For example, the augmented matrix of the above system is

$$\begin{array}{ccc} x_1 & x_2 & x_3 \end{array}$$
$$\left[\begin{array}{ccc|c} 1 & 2 & -3 & 5 \\ 3 & -1 & 0 & 3 \\ 2 & 0 & 4 & -1 \end{array}\right]$$

Each **row** of the augmented matrix corresponds to an equation of the system. Each **column** of the matrix corresponds to a variable, except for the last column, which corresponds to the constant terms of the system.

## ELEMENTARY ROW OPERATIONS

The elementary operations performed on the equations of the system now become operations on the rows of the matrix. Thus we have the following row operations on matrices.

### Elementary Row Operations

1. The interchange of two rows of a matrix

2. The multiplication of a row by a nonzero constant

3. The addition of a multiple of one row to another row of a matrix

It is possible to interpret the third operation in terms of subtraction when the multiple is negative. That is, adding a negative multiple of a row to another row is the same as subtracting the positive multiple of the row. For example, the addition of $-3$ times row 1 to row 2 can be regarded as exactly the same as the subtraction of 3 times row 1 from row 2. Note that in this instance row 1 is not itself changed; it is used only for the purpose of modifying row 2.

The following example illustrates the mechanics of the elementary row operations. The systems of equations and the corresponding matrices are shown in parallel to exhibit the connection. Though this example is primarily practice in using the row operations, there is a method to the selection of the operations that will be explained shortly.

**EXAMPLE 2**   Solve the linear system

$$\begin{aligned} 2x_1 - x_2 + 3x_3 &= 6 \\ x_1 \phantom{{}- x_2} - x_3 &= 3 \\ x_1 - x_2 + x_3 &= 2 \end{aligned}$$

**SOLUTION**   The first step is to write down the augmented matrix of the system.

$$\left[\begin{array}{ccc|c} 2 & -1 & 3 & 6 \\ 1 & 0 & -1 & 3 \\ 1 & -1 & 1 & 2 \end{array}\right]$$

It is convenient to have a 1 in the leading corner position, so we can interchange the first and third rows (equations).

$$\begin{bmatrix} 1 & -1 & 1 & | & 2 \\ 1 & 0 & -1 & | & 3 \\ 2 & -1 & 3 & | & 6 \end{bmatrix} \qquad \begin{aligned} x_1 - x_2 + x_3 &= 2 \\ x_1 \quad\;\;\; - x_3 &= 3 \\ 2x_1 - x_2 + 3x_3 &= 6 \end{aligned}$$

We next subtract the first row (equation) from the second row (equation), which is the same as adding $-1$ times the first row (equation) to the second. This gives us the following.

$$\begin{bmatrix} 1 & -1 & 1 & | & 2 \\ 0 & 1 & -2 & | & 1 \\ 2 & -1 & 3 & | & 6 \end{bmatrix} \qquad \begin{aligned} x_1 - x_2 + x_3 &= 2 \\ x_2 - 2x_3 &= 1 \\ 2x_1 - x_2 + 3x_3 &= 6 \end{aligned}$$

We next add $-2$ times the first row (equation) to the third row (equation) to obtain the following.

$$\begin{bmatrix} 1 & -1 & 1 & | & 2 \\ 0 & 1 & -2 & | & 1 \\ 0 & 1 & 1 & | & 2 \end{bmatrix} \qquad \begin{aligned} x_1 - x_2 + x_3 &= 2 \\ x_2 - 2x_3 &= 1 \\ x_2 + x_3 &= 2 \end{aligned}$$

Note that the first column (the $x_1$ column) has zeros except for the top entry, so that $x_1$ has been eliminated from the first and second equations. The next step is to subtract the second row from the third row. This gives us the following.

$$\begin{bmatrix} 1 & -1 & 1 & | & 2 \\ 0 & 1 & -2 & | & 1 \\ 0 & 0 & 3 & | & 1 \end{bmatrix} \qquad \begin{aligned} x_1 - x_2 + x_3 &= 2 \\ x_2 - 2x_3 &= 1 \\ 3x_3 &= 1 \end{aligned}$$

We now multiply the third row by $\frac{1}{3}$.

$$\begin{bmatrix} 1 & -1 & 1 & | & 2 \\ 0 & 1 & -2 & | & 1 \\ 0 & 0 & 1 & | & 1/3 \end{bmatrix} \qquad \begin{aligned} x_1 - x_2 + x_3 &= 2 \\ x_2 - 2x_3 &= 1 \\ x_3 &= 1/3 \end{aligned}$$

At this step it is apparent that $x_3 = \frac{1}{3}$, but the values of $x_2$ and $x_3$ have yet to be found. This can be accomplished by first writing the last system as follows:

$$\begin{aligned} x_1 &= x_2 - x_3 + 2 \\ x_2 &= \qquad 2x_3 + 1 \\ x_3 &= \qquad\quad \frac{1}{3} \end{aligned}$$

Then if we substitute the value for $x_3$ back into the second equation, we get $x_2 = \frac{2}{3} + 1 = \frac{5}{3}$. And if we substitute the values of $x_3$ and $x_2$ back into the first equation, we get $x_1 = \frac{5}{3} - \frac{1}{3} + 2 = \frac{10}{3}$. Hence the solution is $x_1 = \frac{10}{3}$, $x_2 = \frac{5}{3}$, $x_3 = \frac{1}{3}$, which we can write as $(\frac{10}{3}, \frac{5}{3}, \frac{1}{3})$. ∎

The reader should examine each step in the preceding example to verify that the calculations are correct. It is wise to verify the solution by substituting the values back into the original system to be sure that a solution was actually obtained. Many calculations are done while performing row operations, and checking the result is the best way to see if any mistakes in arithmetic have been made. If the answer that was obtained turns out not to be a solution, then it is necessary to retrace the steps and find the error.

## GAUSSIAN ELIMINATION

The general idea of Gaussian elimination is to introduce zeros in the augmented coefficient matrix by means of elementary row operations. This corresponds to the elimination of variables in the system of equations. The process is done in a systematic manner as in Example 2. The step-by-step procedure for Gaussian elimination is to operate on the augmented coefficient matrix as follows.

*Step 1.* Find the leftmost variable column that has a nonzero entry in it. Choose a nonzero entry in this column and interchange rows, if necessary, to put this entry in the top row.

*Step 2.* Divide the top row by the nonzero entry found in step 1 so that the leftmost entry in the row is 1. This entry is called a **leading** 1 for the row.

*Step 3.* Add (or subtract) multiples of the top row to the rows beneath it to obtain 0s beneath the leading 1.

*Step 4.* Cover the top row and repeat steps 1 through 3. Stop when all rows have been covered or when only zero entries remain in the uncovered rows.

If all of the rows are now uncovered, the solution of the system can be found by using back substitution as in Example 2. Of course, it is not necessary to physically cover the rows as one proceeds down the staircase, but it may be helpful to do so the first few times to prevent confusion. After a little practice, however, the covering of rows should become a mental process.

**EXAMPLE 3** Use Gaussian elimination to solve the system

$$3x_1 - 7x_2 + 11x_3 = 4$$
$$x_1 - 2x_2 + 3x_3 = 1$$
$$-2x_1 + 8x_2 - 16x_3 = 4$$

SOLUTION We first write down the augmented matrix of the system:

$$\begin{bmatrix} 3 & -7 & 11 & | & 4 \\ 1 & -2 & 3 & | & 1 \\ -2 & 8 & -16 & | & 4 \end{bmatrix}$$

The first goal is to get a leading 1 in the top row. This can be accomplished in one step by interchanging the first and second rows. This gives us the matrix

$$\begin{bmatrix} 1 & -2 & 3 & | & 1 \\ 3 & -7 & 11 & | & 4 \\ -2 & 8 & -16 & | & 4 \end{bmatrix}$$

We next clear the first column of nonzero entries (step 3) as follows: add $-3$ times row 1 to row 2; add 2 times row 1 to row 3. This gives us the matrix

$$\begin{bmatrix} 1 & -2 & 3 & | & 1 \\ 0 & -1 & 2 & | & 1 \\ 0 & 4 & -10 & | & 6 \end{bmatrix}$$

We next cover row 1 (mentally) and repeat the steps for rows 2 and 3. To get a leading 1 in the second row (our new "top" row), we multiply the row by $-1$. This gives us the matrix

$$\begin{bmatrix} 1 & -2 & 3 & | & 1 \\ 0 & 1 & -2 & | & -1 \\ 0 & 4 & -10 & | & 6 \end{bmatrix}$$

We next add $-4$ times row 2 to row 3 to get the matrix

$$\begin{bmatrix} 1 & -2 & 3 & | & 1 \\ 0 & 1 & -2 & | & -1 \\ 0 & 0 & -2 & | & 10 \end{bmatrix}$$

If we cover the first two rows, then we are left with one row, in which we need a leading 1. If we multiply that row by $-\frac{1}{2}$, we get

$$\begin{bmatrix} 1 & -2 & 3 & | & 1 \\ 0 & 1 & -2 & | & -1 \\ 0 & 0 & 1 & | & -5 \end{bmatrix}$$

The last matrix has the associated system of equations

$$x_1 - 2x_2 + 3x_3 = 1$$
$$x_2 - 2x_3 = -1$$
$$x_3 = -5$$

The solution is now found by using the method of back substitution. We substitute the value of $x_3$ back into the second equation to get $x_2$, and then we substitute the values of $x_2$ and $x_3$ back into the first equation to get $x_1$. Thus since we have $x_3 = -5$, we get

$$x_2 = 2(-5) - 1 = -11$$

and then we get

$$x_1 = 2(-11) - 3(-5) + 1 = -6$$

Hence the solution is $(-6, -11, -5)$. ▮▮

## ROW ECHELON FORM

The process of creating zeros in the columns of a matrix as prescribed in steps 1 through 4 leads naturally to a matrix with zeros in the lower left-hand portion.

The resulting matrix has a very precise form, which is described as follows.

---

### DEFINITION

A matrix is said to be in **row echelon form** if

(*i*) the leftmost nonzero entry in each row is a 1 (its leading 1),

(*ii*) the entries below any leading 1 are all 0,

(*iii*) the leading 1 for each row is to the left of the leading 1 for any row below it,

(*iv*) any row of all zeros is located below the rows that have leading 1s.

---

In effect, a matrix in row echelon form has the appearance of a staircase, with a 1 on each step and 0s underneath. The two matrices shown below are both in row echelon form, where ∗ indicates that any number can be present.

$$
\begin{bmatrix} 1 & * & * & * \\ 0 & 1 & * & * \\ 0 & 0 & 1 & * \end{bmatrix}
\qquad
\begin{bmatrix} 1 & * & * & * & * \\ 0 & 0 & 1 & * & * \\ 0 & 0 & 0 & 1 & * \\ 0 & 0 & 0 & 0 & 0 \end{bmatrix}
$$

The significance of row echelon form is that when the augmented coefficient matrix is reduced to this form via row operations, the solution of the system is easily obtained by successive substitutions back up the staircase of the associated system. This technique of back substitution was used at the end of Example 2 and Example 3.

It should be noted that a row echelon form of a matrix is not unique. It depends on the sequence of row operations that one uses to produce it. It is possible for two different people to put the same matrix into row echelon form and get two different answers, both of which are correct. The leading 1s are uniquely determined, but other entries are not. Indeed, given a row echelon form for a matrix, another can be obtained from it by adding the lowest row with a leading 1 to any row above it. For example, the two matrices below are both row echelon forms for the same matrix, the one to the right being obtained by adding the third row to the second row of the one to the left.

$$
\begin{bmatrix} 1 & 2 & 3 & 4 \\ 0 & 1 & 5 & 6 \\ 0 & 0 & 1 & 2 \end{bmatrix}
\qquad
\begin{bmatrix} 1 & 2 & 3 & 4 \\ 0 & 1 & 6 & 8 \\ 0 & 0 & 1 & 2 \end{bmatrix}
$$

In performing row operations on a matrix, it is worthwhile to keep track of what has been done at each step. We will employ the following notation to record the operations that are used.

1. $R_i \leftrightarrow R_j$ means interchange row i and row j.

2. $R_i' = aR_i$ means that the new row i is $a$ times the old row i.

3. $R_i' = R_i + bR_j$ means that the new row i is the old row i plus $b$ times row j.

In the next example, the row operations listed to the right of a matrix describe how to obtain the next matrix located beneath it. The operations are given in the order that they are to be performed.

**EXAMPLE 4**    Use Gaussian elimination to solve

$$
\begin{aligned}
x_1 - 2x_2 - x_3 &= 3 \\
-x_1 + 2x_2 + 4x_3 &= -1 \\
3x_1 - 4x_2 + x_3 &= 5
\end{aligned}
$$

List the row operations that are used to put the augmented matrix into row echelon form.

SOLUTION    We start with the augmented matrix, and we use the row operations that are listed to the right.

$$
\left[\begin{array}{ccc|c}
1 & -2 & -1 & 3 \\
-1 & 2 & 4 & -1 \\
3 & -4 & 1 & 5
\end{array}\right]
\quad
\begin{array}{l}
R'_2 = R_2 + R_1 \\
R'_3 = R_3 - 3R_1
\end{array}
$$

$$
\left[\begin{array}{ccc|c}
1 & -2 & -1 & 3 \\
0 & 0 & 3 & 2 \\
0 & 2 & 4 & -4
\end{array}\right]
\quad
R_2 \leftrightarrow R_3
$$

$$
\left[\begin{array}{ccc|c}
1 & -2 & -1 & 3 \\
0 & 2 & 4 & -4 \\
0 & 0 & 3 & 2
\end{array}\right]
\quad
\begin{array}{l}
R'_2 = 1/2 R_2 \\
R'_3 = 1/3 R_3
\end{array}
$$

$$
\left[\begin{array}{ccc|c}
1 & -2 & -1 & 3 \\
0 & 1 & 2 & -2 \\
0 & 0 & 1 & 2/3
\end{array}\right]
$$

We have arrived at a row echelon form. If we now use back substitution, starting with $x_3 = \frac{2}{3}$, we get $x_2 = -2(\frac{2}{3}) - 2 = -\frac{10}{3}$ and then $x_1 = 2(-\frac{10}{3}) + \frac{2}{3} + 3 = -3$. Hence the solution is $(-3, -\frac{10}{3}, \frac{2}{3})$. ∎

*REMARK:*  Gaussian elimination is an organized procedure in which the successive steps are precisely specified. A procedure such as this is called an *algorithm;* we will discuss other algorithms in later sections. Algorithms are important because they provide methods of solving problems regardless of the number of variables, and since the steps are unambiguous, they can be carried out by computers. Thus Gaussian elimination works for very large systems as well as the small systems we will encounter in this book. Of course, in solving a small system of equations by hand, it is possible for us to find shortcuts and simplify arithmetic by using different combinations of row operations. Unfortunately, shortcuts usually change from problem to problem, and one that works in one place might not work in another. Also, in a large system the search for shortcuts is usually fruitless and wastes more time than it saves.

Each of the algorithms we will discuss has a definite structure, and the reader should be aware when variations are introduced. For example, to eliminate the entry 2 in the first column of the matrix

$$\begin{bmatrix} 1 & 4 & -3 \\ 2 & 3 & 1 \end{bmatrix}$$

we would use the row operation $R_2' = R_2 - 2R_1$ and obtain

$$\begin{bmatrix} 1 & 4 & -3 \\ 0 & -5 & 7 \end{bmatrix}$$

The elimination can also be accomplished by changing the signs in the second row and then adding 2 times the first row. This would give us

$$\begin{bmatrix} 1 & 4 & -3 \\ 0 & 5 & -7 \end{bmatrix}$$

However, this is *not* Gaussian elimination. Note that the signs in the second row are different and that two row operations were used ($R_2' = -R_2$ and $R_2' = R_2 + 2R_1$) instead of one. The distinction may seem minor in this small example, but in fact the difference is significant when viewed from the perspective of larger systems or more complex algorithms.

## EXERCISES 2.1

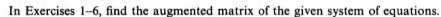

In Exercises 1–6, find the augmented matrix of the given system of equations.

**1.** 
$$4x_1 - 3x_2 + x_3 = 5$$
$$x_1 + 5x_2 - 2x_3 = -7$$
$$-5x_1 + 7x_2 - 6x_3 = 9$$

**2.** 
$$-2x_1 + 6x_2 - 4x_3 = -6$$
$$5x_1 + 8x_2 + 3x_3 = 8$$
$$4x_1 - 3x_2 + x_3 = 2$$

**3.** 
$$5x_1 - 3x_2 + x_3 - x_4 = 5$$
$$2x_1 + 4x_2 - 5x_3 + 3x_4 = -6$$
$$-3x_1 + 3x_2 - 4x_3 + 2x_4 = 1$$

**4.** 
$$-x_1 + 4x_2 - 6x_3 + 9x_4 = -6$$
$$6x_1 - 3x_2 + x_3 - 5x_4 = -2$$
$$2x_1 + 5x_2 + 4x_3 - 6x_4 = -3$$

**5.** 
$$4x + 2y + 3z - w = 10$$
$$8x + 5y - 2z + 4w = -2$$
$$7x + 4y + 5z + 3w = 4$$
$$2x - y + 3z + w = -5$$

**6.** 
$$-5x + 3y - 2z + 4w = 8$$
$$6x + 8y + 5z - 3w = 4$$
$$x + 2y - 7z - 5w = -1$$
$$-3x - 7y + 6z + 2w = 2$$

In Exercises 7–12, find a system of equations for which the given matrix is the augmented matrix of the system. Use the variable names $x_1, x_2, x_3, x_4$, as needed.

**7.** 
$$\begin{bmatrix} 4 & 2 & -3 & | & 8 \\ 1 & 5 & 2 & | & -6 \\ -6 & 1 & 7 & | & 2 \end{bmatrix}$$

**8.** 
$$\begin{bmatrix} 8 & 1 & 3 & | & 1 \\ 9 & 2 & 6 & | & 5 \\ -7 & 4 & 6 & | & -7 \end{bmatrix}$$

**9.** 
$$\begin{bmatrix} 5 & -1 & 4 & | & 3 \\ 6 & 0 & -4 & | & -2 \\ 1 & 2 & 5 & | & 6 \\ 3 & 1 & 4 & | & 2 \end{bmatrix}$$

**10.** 
$$\begin{bmatrix} 8 & 2 & 6 & | & 1 \\ 2 & 9 & 4 & | & -6 \\ 1 & -3 & -6 & | & -2 \\ 5 & -7 & 4 & | & 3 \end{bmatrix}$$

**11.** $\begin{bmatrix} 6 & 1 & 8 & 3 & | & -2 \\ -4 & 2 & 0 & 4 & | & 8 \\ 2 & 7 & 4 & 5 & | & 7 \end{bmatrix}$   **12.** $\begin{bmatrix} 1 & 4 & -8 & -2 & | & 3 \\ 5 & -7 & 0 & 2 & | & -5 \\ 6 & 3 & 9 & 1 & | & 6 \end{bmatrix}$

In Exercises 13–18, use back substitution to find the solution to the system of equations that has the given augmented matrix. Use the variable names $x_1, x_2, x_3, x_4$, as needed.

**13.** $\begin{bmatrix} 1 & 4 & | & -3 \\ 0 & 1 & | & 6 \end{bmatrix}$   **14.** $\begin{bmatrix} 1 & -2 & | & 5 \\ 0 & 1 & | & -3 \end{bmatrix}$

**15.** $\begin{bmatrix} 1 & 3 & -2 & | & 1 \\ 0 & 1 & 4 & | & 7 \\ 0 & 0 & 1 & | & 3 \end{bmatrix}$   **16.** $\begin{bmatrix} 1 & -4 & 1 & | & -4 \\ 0 & 1 & -3 & | & 3 \\ 0 & 0 & 1 & | & -2 \end{bmatrix}$

**17.** $\begin{bmatrix} 1 & 2 & 4 & -4 & | & 5 \\ 0 & 1 & -1 & 3 & | & -2 \\ 0 & 0 & 1 & -2 & | & 1 \\ 0 & 0 & 0 & 1 & | & 2 \end{bmatrix}$   **18.** $\begin{bmatrix} 1 & 5 & -1 & -4 & | & -5 \\ 0 & 1 & 3 & 2 & | & 1 \\ 0 & 0 & 1 & 4 & | & 4 \\ 0 & 0 & 0 & 1 & | & 3 \end{bmatrix}$

In Exercises 19–24, determine whether or not the matrices are in echelon form. For those that are not, apply elementary row operations to put them in echelon form.

**19.** $\begin{bmatrix} 1 & 2 & -1 & 4 \\ 0 & 0 & 1 & -3 \\ 0 & 0 & 0 & 1 \end{bmatrix}$   **20.** $\begin{bmatrix} 1 & 4 & 3 & 5 \\ 0 & 0 & 1 & -2 \\ 0 & 0 & 0 & 1 \end{bmatrix}$

**21.** $\begin{bmatrix} 1 & 2 & 0 & 5 \\ 0 & 0 & 0 & 0 \\ 0 & 0 & 1 & 4 \end{bmatrix}$   **22.** $\begin{bmatrix} 1 & 0 & 4 & -6 \\ 0 & 0 & 0 & 0 \\ 0 & 1 & 6 & 2 \end{bmatrix}$

**23.** $\begin{bmatrix} 1 & 2 & 4 & -3 \\ 0 & 1 & -2 & -1 \\ 0 & 0 & 3 & -4 \end{bmatrix}$   **24.** $\begin{bmatrix} 1 & 3 & 5 & -2 \\ 0 & 1 & 3 & 4 \\ 0 & 0 & 2 & 5 \end{bmatrix}$

In Exercises 25–26, perform each row operation on the indicated matrix.

**25.** For the matrix of Exercise 7,
(a) $R'_1 = R_1 - 4R_2$
(b) $R'_2 = R_2 - 5R_3$

**26.** For the matrix of Exercise 8,
(a) $R'_2 = R_2 - 2R_1$
(b) $R'_2 = R_2 - R_3$

In Exercise 27–28, perform the row operations in the given sequence on the indicated matrix.

**27.** For the matrix of Exercise 9,
$R'_1 = R_1 - 5R_3$
$R'_2 = R_2 - 6R_3$
$R'_4 = R_4 - 3R_3$
$R_1 \leftrightarrow R_3$

**28.** For the matrix of Exercise 10,
$R'_1 = R_1 - 8R_3$
$R'_2 = R_2 - 2R_3$
$R'_4 = R_4 - 5R_3$
$R_1 \leftrightarrow R_3$

In Exercises 29–34, (a) use Gaussian elimination to find a row echelon form for

*way am I thee*

*what makes me better than anyone else*

the augmented matrix of the given system, and (b) use back substitution to find the solution of the system.

**29.** $\quad x_1 + 2x_2 - 4x_3 = 1$
$\quad\quad 2x_1 + 5x_2 - 6x_3 = 0$
$\quad\quad -x_1 + 3x_2 + 6x_3 = -3$

**30.** $\quad x_1 + 3x_2 - 2x_3 = -2$
$\quad\quad 3x_1 + 8x_2 - 4x_3 = -6$
$\quad\quad -x_1 + 4x_2 - 7x_3 = 7$

**31.** $\quad 2x_1 + 4x_2 - 6x_3 = -2$
$\quad\quad 3x_1 + 5x_2 - 12x_3 = 2$
$\quad\quad -5x_1 - 3x_2 + 8x_3 = -2$

**32.** $\quad 3x_1 - 6x_2 + 9x_3 = 6$
$\quad\quad 4x_1 - 9x_2 + 6x_3 = 2$
$\quad\quad -2x_1 + 3x_2 - 5x_3 = -3$

**33.** $\quad x + 2y - 3z + w = 2$
$\quad\quad -3x - 8y + 4z - 4w = -5$
$\quad\quad -2x - 4y + 5z - 5w = -7$
$\quad\quad 2x + 4y - 4z - 2w = -10$

**34.** $\quad x + 3y + 5z + 3w = -24$
$\quad\quad 2x + 7y + 11z + 7w = -54$
$\quad\quad -x - y \quad\quad - 7w = -6$
$\quad\quad -2x - 9y - 14z - 5w = 74$

## 2.2 REDUCED ECHELON FORM

*Back Addition, Reduced Echelon Form, Multisystems, Application*

In this section we will continue the discussion of Gaussian elimination. We will introduce the technique of back addition to replace the method of back substitution used in the preceding section. In back addition the substitution of variables is accomplished by means of additional row operations. Instead of stopping at echelon form and using substitutions to find the solution of a system, we continue the row operations until the matrix is put into a simpler form. In effect, the substitutions are accomplished by means of row operations on the matrix. The resulting new matrix is said to be in "reduced" echelon form.

To illustrate the usefulness of the reduced echelon form of a matrix, we will see that under certain circumstances it is possible to solve several linear systems at once by operating on a single matrix. The technique is applied to an example in contingency planning. Further applications will be presented in the next section.

### BACK ADDITION

In the previous section we outlined Gaussian elimination as a two-stage procedure. The first stage consisted of putting the augmented matrix of a linear system into row echelon form. The second stage consisted of using back substitution to find the solution of the system.

Actually, the process of back substitution can be performed by simply using additional row operations after the matrix has been put into row echelon form. The idea is to start with the last row and operate upwards to create 0s above as well as below the leading 1s. This alternative method, which we call **back addition**, is illustrated in the following example.

**EXAMPLE 1** Suppose that the augmented matrix of a linear system has been put into row echelon form and the following matrix was obtained:

$$\begin{bmatrix} 1 & 5 & -4 & | & 8 \\ 0 & 1 & -3 & | & -1 \\ 0 & 0 & 1 & | & 2 \end{bmatrix}$$

Use back addition to find the solution of the system.

SOLUTION    We first concentrate on the bottom row and use row operations to obtain 0s above the leading 1 in the third column. If we add 3 times row 3 to row 2 ($R'_2 = R_2 + 3R_3$) and then add 4 times row 3 to row 1 ($R'_1 = R_1 + 4R_3$), we obtain the matrix

$$\begin{bmatrix} 1 & 5 & 0 & | & 16 \\ 0 & 1 & 0 & | & 5 \\ 0 & 0 & 1 & | & 2 \end{bmatrix}$$

Note that the entries in the first two columns were not affected because the first two entries in the third row are zero.

We next wish to get a zero above the leading 1 in the second column. To accomplish this, we subtract 5 times row 2 from row 1 ($R'_1 = R_1 - 5R_2$). We get the matrix

$$\begin{bmatrix} 1 & 0 & 0 & | & -9 \\ 0 & 1 & 0 & | & 5 \\ 0 & 0 & 1 & | & 2 \end{bmatrix}$$

The system represented by the last matrix is

$$
\begin{aligned}
x_1 \quad &= \quad -9 \\
x_2 \quad &= \quad 5 \\
x_3 &= \quad 2
\end{aligned}
$$

Thus the solution is obviously $(-9, 5, 2)$.  ∎

We suggest that the reader return to Examples 2, 3, and 4 in the preceding section and apply back addition instead of back substitution to find the solutions of the systems. Comparison of the two methods is instructive. Of course, the solutions should be the same as those obtained earlier.

## REDUCED ECHELON FORM

After applying back addition to a matrix in row echelon form, we get a new matrix in which the entries above and below the leading 1s are all zero. Thus a matrix in row echelon form is "reduced" to a new form. The precise definition is as follows.

---

**DEFINITION**

. A matrix is said to be in **reduced echelon form** if, in addition to having the properties of row echelon form, it also has the property

($v$) all entries above any leading 1 are zero.

---

The matrices shown below are examples of reduced echelon form, where the * indicates that the entry can be any number.

$$\begin{bmatrix} 1 & 0 & 0 & * \\ 0 & 1 & 0 & * \\ 0 & 0 & 1 & * \end{bmatrix} \qquad \begin{bmatrix} 1 & 0 & * & 0 & * \\ 0 & 1 & * & 0 & * \\ 0 & 0 & 0 & 1 & * \end{bmatrix}$$

It was noted in Section 2.1 that a matrix does not determine a unique row echelon form. It is an interesting fact that the reduced echelon form of a matrix is uniquely determined. In other words, if two people start with a given matrix and perform different sequences of row operations until a reduced echelon form is obtained, then their final matrices will be identical. Though we will not include a proof, we record this important fact as a theorem.

---

**THEOREM 1**

The reduced row echelon form associated with a matrix is uniquely determined.

---

To convert a matrix from row echelon form to reduced echelon form, we can employ the steps of back addition and proceed as follows. First, select the lowest row that contains a leading 1, which is the rightmost leading 1, and row operate to eliminate all nonzero entries above it. Then select the next lowest leading 1 and similarly eliminate the nonzero entries above it. In this manner we proceed up the echelon of leading 1s from right to left until the first column is reached and reduced echelon form is attained. The procedure is illustrated in the next example.

**EXAMPLE 2** Put the following matrix in reduced echelon form:

$$\begin{bmatrix} 1 & -2 & 4 & 5 & -3 \\ 0 & 1 & 3 & -1 & 7 \\ 0 & 0 & 0 & 1 & 2 \end{bmatrix}$$

**SOLUTION** The matrix is in row echelon form with leading 1s in the first, second, and fourth columns. We start with the leading 1 in the lowest row, which is the one in the fourth column, and use it to eliminate the entries $-1$ and

5 above it. The row operations $R_2' = R_2 + R_3$ and $R_1' = R_1 - 5R_3$ give us the matrix

$$\begin{bmatrix} 1 & -2 & 4 & 0 & -13 \\ 0 & 1 & 3 & 0 & 9 \\ 0 & 0 & 0 & 1 & 2 \end{bmatrix}$$

Next we move to the second row and locate the leading 1 in the second column. We use the row operation $R_1' = R_1 + 2R_2$ and get

$$\begin{bmatrix} 1 & 0 & 10 & 0 & 5 \\ 0 & 1 & 3 & 0 & 9 \\ 0 & 0 & 0 & 1 & 2 \end{bmatrix}$$

Thus we have arrived at reduced echelon form. In the columns that contain leading 1s, all other entries are zero. ■■

The notion of reduced echelon form will prove to be very useful. For instance, in the next section we will use it to solve systems that have infinitely many solutions. Finding the solutions of such systems, which require parametric representation, is facilitated by using the reduced echelon form. At this point we employ it to solve certain related systems of equations in one operation.

### MULTISYSTEMS

Reduced echelon form has the advantage that the solution of the associated system is more readily obtained than with row echelon form. This is particularly useful when there are several systems to solve in which the coefficients of the variables are the same in both systems. Systems that are related in this manner will be called **multisystems**. When the systems differ only in the constant terms to the right of the equals signs, they can be neatly solved at the same time by enlarging the augmented matrix so that it includes the different columns of constant terms. Consider the following example of solving multisystems.

**EXAMPLE 3**   Solve the two systems

$$\begin{array}{ccc} x_1 + 2x_2 - x_3 = & 4 & \qquad x_1 + 2x_2 - x_3 = -2 \\ 3x_1 + 7x_2 - 2x_3 = & 1 & \text{and} \quad 3x_1 + 7x_2 - 2x_3 = & 5 \\ -2x_1 + 3x_2 + 3x_3 = -1 & \qquad -2x_1 + 3x_2 + 3x_3 = & 3 \end{array}$$

SOLUTION   We could solve each of these systems independently, but this would lead to repeating many computations, since the coefficient matrix is the same for both systems. Alternatively, we can write both columns of equation constants in the augmented matrix and solve the two systems simultaneously as follows.

$$\left[\begin{array}{ccc|cc} 1 & 2 & -1 & 4 & -2 \\ 3 & 7 & -2 & 1 & 5 \\ -2 & 3 & 3 & -1 & 3 \end{array}\right] \quad \begin{array}{l} R_2' = R_2 - 3R_1 \\ R_3' = R_3 + 2R_1 \end{array}$$

$$\begin{bmatrix} 1 & 2 & -1 & 4 & -2 \\ 0 & 1 & 1 & -11 & 11 \\ 0 & 7 & 1 & 7 & -1 \end{bmatrix} \quad R'_3 = R_3 - 7R_2$$

$$\begin{bmatrix} 1 & 2 & -1 & 4 & -2 \\ 0 & 1 & 1 & -11 & 11 \\ 0 & 0 & -6 & 84 & -78 \end{bmatrix} \quad R'_3 = -1/6 R_3$$

$$\begin{bmatrix} 1 & 2 & -1 & 4 & -2 \\ 0 & 1 & 1 & -11 & 11 \\ 0 & 0 & 1 & -14 & 13 \end{bmatrix} \quad \begin{matrix} R'_1 = R_1 + R_3 \\ R'_2 = R_2 - R_3 \end{matrix}$$

$$\begin{bmatrix} 1 & 2 & 0 & -10 & 11 \\ 0 & 1 & 0 & 3 & -2 \\ 0 & 0 & 1 & -14 & 13 \end{bmatrix} \quad R'_1 = R_1 - 2R_2$$

$$\begin{bmatrix} 1 & 0 & 0 & -16 & 15 \\ 0 & 1 & 0 & 3 & -2 \\ 0 & 0 & 1 & -14 & 13 \end{bmatrix}$$

Thus the solutions to the first and second systems, respectively, are

$$x_1 = -16, \quad x_2 = 3, \quad x_3 = -14$$

and

$$x_1 = 15, \quad x_2 = -2, \quad x_3 = 13 \quad \blacksquare\blacksquare$$

## APPLICATION

The following example illustrates how the technique of multisystems can be applied to contingency planning.

**EXAMPLE 4**  Soymeal, chickpea, and bulgur wheat flours are blended into wholesome and savory meat substitutes by the Greenfields Company. The products STARPRO, CHICKROAST, and BRAWNAR are made up from the flours as shown in the table of percentages below:

|  | STARPRO | CHICKROAST | BRAWNAR |
|---|---|---|---|
| Soymeal | 50% | 10% | 20% |
| Chickpea | 30% | 50% | 20% |
| Bulgur wheat | 20% | 40% | 60% |

The foods sell very well, and everything that can be manufactured will be sold. Therefore the management wants to completely exhaust the supplies during production. However, because of uncertainties in shipping, they are unsure of the exact supplies that will be on hand at the beginning of the production period. They believe, with reasonable certainty, that the stocks will be one of the three possibilities in the following table.

|  | I | II | III |
|---|---|---|---|
| Soymeal | 2 | 4 | 6 |
| Chickpea | 3 | 3 | 6 |
| Bulgur wheat | 5 | 3 | 8 |

} (1000-pound units)

Determine the quantities of the products that should be made for each of the stock possibilities so that they will be ready when the production period starts.

SOLUTION    Let there be $a$ units of soymeal, $b$ units of chickpea, and $c$ units of bulgur wheat flour on hand, and let $x_1$, $x_2$, $x_3$ be the amounts of STARPRO, CHICKROAST, and BRAWNAR to be produced. Further, let each of these be in 1000-pound units. Then the equations are

Soymeal        $.50x_1 + .10x_2 + .20x_3 = a$

Chickpea      $.30x_1 + .50x_2 + .20x_3 = b$

Bulgur wheat    $.20x_1 + .40x_2 + .60x_3 = c$

where $a$, $b$, $c$ are taken to be any of the three possibilities in the table above.

We multiply all equations by 10 to clear decimals, write the augmented matrix of the three systems, and solve.

$$\begin{bmatrix} 5 & 1 & 2 & | & 20 & 40 & 60 \\ 3 & 5 & 2 & | & 30 & 30 & 60 \\ 2 & 4 & 6 & | & 50 & 30 & 80 \end{bmatrix} \quad \begin{array}{l} R_1 \leftrightarrow R_3 \\ R_1' = 1/2 R_1 \end{array}$$

$$\begin{bmatrix} 1 & 2 & 3 & | & 25 & 15 & 40 \\ 3 & 5 & 2 & | & 30 & 30 & 60 \\ 5 & 1 & 2 & | & 20 & 40 & 60 \end{bmatrix} \quad \begin{array}{l} R_2' = R_2 - 3R_1 \\ R_3' = R_3 - 5R_1 \end{array}$$

$$\begin{bmatrix} 1 & 2 & 3 & | & 25 & 15 & 40 \\ 0 & -1 & -7 & | & -45 & -15 & -60 \\ 0 & -9 & -13 & | & -105 & -35 & -140 \end{bmatrix} \quad \begin{array}{l} R_3' = R_3 - 9R_2 \\ R_2' = -R_2 \end{array}$$

$$\begin{bmatrix} 1 & 2 & 3 & | & 25 & 15 & 40 \\ 0 & 1 & 7 & | & 45 & 15 & 60 \\ 0 & 0 & 50 & | & 300 & 100 & 400 \end{bmatrix} \quad R_3' = 1/50 R_3$$

$$\begin{bmatrix} 1 & 2 & 3 & | & 25 & 15 & 40 \\ 0 & 1 & 7 & | & 45 & 15 & 60 \\ 0 & 0 & 1 & | & 6 & 2 & 8 \end{bmatrix} \quad \begin{array}{l} R_1' = R_1 - 3R_3 \\ R_2' = R_2 - 7R_3 \end{array}$$

$$\begin{bmatrix} 1 & 2 & 0 & | & 7 & 9 & 16 \\ 0 & 1 & 0 & | & 3 & 1 & 4 \\ 0 & 0 & 1 & | & 6 & 2 & 8 \end{bmatrix} \quad R_1' = R_1 - 2R_2$$

$$\begin{bmatrix} 1 & 0 & 0 & | & 1 & 7 & 8 \\ 0 & 1 & 0 & | & 3 & 1 & 4 \\ 0 & 0 & 1 & | & 6 & 2 & 8 \end{bmatrix}$$

Thus the three production schedules corresponding to the possible stocks are

|  | I | II | III |  |
|---|---|---|---|---|
| STARPRO | 1000 | 7000 | 8000 | |
| CHICKROAST | 3000 | 1000 | 4000 | (1-pound units) |
| BRAWNAR | 6000 | 2000 | 8000 | |

∎

## EXERCISES 2.2

In Exercises 1–6, use back addition to put the given augmented matrix into reduced echelon form. Use the variable names $x_1, x_2, x_3, x_4$ as needed and give the solution of the corresponding system of equations

**1.** $\begin{bmatrix} 1 & 5 & | & -3 \\ 0 & 1 & | & -2 \end{bmatrix}$

**2.** $\begin{bmatrix} 1 & -2 & | & 6 \\ 0 & 1 & | & -3 \end{bmatrix}$

**3.** $\begin{bmatrix} 1 & 4 & -2 & | & 5 \\ 0 & 1 & 3 & | & -3 \\ 0 & 0 & 1 & | & 2 \end{bmatrix}$

**4.** $\begin{bmatrix} 1 & -3 & 5 & | & -5 \\ 0 & 1 & 4 & | & -2 \\ 0 & 0 & 1 & | & 2 \end{bmatrix}$

**5.** $\begin{bmatrix} 1 & -1 & -2 & 4 & | & -6 \\ 0 & 1 & 0 & -3 & | & -1 \\ 0 & 0 & 1 & 2 & | & 4 \\ 0 & 0 & 0 & 1 & | & 3 \end{bmatrix}$

**6.** $\begin{bmatrix} 1 & -2 & 4 & 0 & | & 3 \\ 0 & 1 & -1 & 2 & | & -1 \\ 0 & 0 & 1 & -3 & | & 5 \\ 0 & 0 & 0 & 1 & | & -2 \end{bmatrix}$

In Exercises 7–10, solve the given systems of equations by using Gaussian elimination to put the augmented matrix of the system into row echelon form and then back addition to put the matrix into reduced echelon form. Give the solution.

**7.**
$$\begin{aligned} 2x + y &= 2 \\ 3y - z &= 1 \\ x + 2y + z &= 0 \end{aligned}$$

**8.**
$$\begin{aligned} 3x + 9y - 2z &= 16 \\ x + 4y + z &= 2 \\ 2x + 6y - z &= 12 \end{aligned}$$

**9.**
$$\begin{aligned} 4x_1 + 2x_2 - x_3 &= 1 \\ 2x_1 - 4x_2 - 2x_3 &= -4 \\ 3x_1 - x_2 + 2x_3 &= 4 \end{aligned}$$

**10.**
$$\begin{aligned} x_1 - 3x_2 + 2x_3 &= 4 \\ 5x_1 - 13x_2 + 8x_3 &= 19 \\ 3x_1 - 9x_2 + 8x_3 &= 13 \end{aligned}$$

In Exercises 11–14, use Gaussian elimination and back addition to solve the given systems of equations simultaneously.

**11.**
$$\begin{aligned} 4x - 11y + 13z &= 3 \\ 4x - 12y + 10z &= 0 \\ x - 3y + 2z &= -1 \end{aligned} \quad \text{and} \quad \begin{aligned} 4x - 11y + 13z &= 14 \\ 4x - 12y + 10z &= 10 \\ x - 3y + 2z &= 2 \end{aligned}$$

**12.** $2x + 4y - 6z = 4$    $2x + 4y - 6z = 2$
    $3x + 5y - 7z = -2$ and $3x + 5y - 7z = 6$
    $5x + 8y - 5z = 12$    $5x + 8y - 5z = -7$

**13.**   $x_1 - 2x_2 + 3x_3 = 2$    $x_1 - 2x_2 + 3x_3 = -2$
    $4x_1 - 9x_2 + 6x_3 = 2$ and $4x_1 - 9x_2 + 6x_3 = 1$
    $-2x_1 + 3x_2 - 5x_3 = -3$    $-2x_1 + 3x_2 - 5x_3 = -1$

**14.**   $x_1 + 2x_2 - 3x_3 = -1$    $x_1 + 2x_2 - 3x_3 = 2$
    $3x_1 + 5x_2 + 3x_3 = 2$ and $3x_1 + 5x_2 + 3x_3 = -3$
    $-5x_1 - 9x_2 + 8x_3 = 5$    $-5x_1 - 9x_2 + 8x_3 = -16$

**15.** The American Company manufacturers artillary shells (A), hand grenades (H), and bullets (B) from the raw materials gunpowder (G), lead (L), and steel (S). The materials are used as shown in percentage of weight in the following table

| %  | A  | H  | B  |
|----|----|----|----|
| G  | 60 | 50 | 50 |
| L  | 10 | 10 | 20 |
| S  | 30 | 40 | 30 |

The company will have a production run when the supply shipment arrives. There are two possible shipments, which we give in 1000–pound units:

  1. G–140,  L–30,  S–100
  2. G–170,  L–50,  S–110

The company wants to use all materials on the production run. Find the production schedule (amounts of A, H, and B) for each supply possibility. Solve the two problems simultaneously.

**16.** The Super Ball Company manufactures volleyballs (Vo), basketballs (B), and water polo balls (W) from the materials latex (L), nylon (N), and vinyl (Vi) as presented in the following table in ounces

|    | Vo | B | W |
|----|----|---|---|
| L  | 4  | 7 | 2 |
| N  | 1  | 2 | 1 |
| Vi | 2  | 5 | 5 |

The company will have a production run when the supply shipment arrives. There are two possible shipments which we give in ounces

  1. L–325,  N–100,  Vi–300
  2. L–400,  N–150,  Vi–600

Find the production schedule (amounts of Vo, B, and W) for each supply possibility. Solve the two problems simultaneously.

## 2.3 CONSISTENCY AND ROW RANK

*Inconsistent Systems, Row Rank, Parametrically Represented Solutions, Application, Homogeneous Systems*

Up to now we have seen only linear systems that have had unique solutions. It is also a common occurrence for a linear system to have either no solutions or infinitely many solutions, and in this section we expand our scope and examine these possibilities. In most cases it is not possible to tell just by looking at a system which of the three cases will occur. Therefore we proceed with the method of Gaussian elimination until a point is reached at which the situation becomes clear. This usually happens when the matrix has been put into row echelon form.

To help in the analysis of linear systems, we will introduce the concept of row rank of a matrix. This is the number of nonzero rows that are present after the matrix has been put into row echelon form. The notion of rank turns out to be important in other areas of linear algebra, and we will encounter it again in later chapters. In this section we use row rank to formulate a criterion for a system to be consistent.

For systems that have infinitely many solutions, it is useful to introduce auxiliary variables, called parameters, to describe the solution set. We will present a detailed account of the parametric representation of solution sets, and then we will apply this idea to a problem in production planning. We will also include a short discussion of special types of systems, called homogeneous systems, that utilizes all of the prior ideas in the section.

### INCONSISTENT SYSTEMS

A linear system is called **inconsistent** if it has no solutions. A system that has one or more solutions will be called **consistent**. If we think of each equation in a system as imposing a restriction on the freedom of the variables, it can happen that a system will overregulate the variables by imposing demands that are not compatible with one another. In this case we would have an inconsistent system.

If a system is inconsistent, this fact will become apparent during the process of putting the augmented coefficient matrix into row echelon form. A glaring contradiction will emerge, as in the following example.

**EXAMPLE 1**  Attempt to solve the system

$$
\begin{aligned}
x_1 + 3x_2 - x_3 + x_4 &= 1 \\
x_1 + 4x_2 + 2x_3 - 2x_4 &= 3 \\
2x_1 + 7x_2 + x_3 - x_4 &= 6
\end{aligned}
$$

SOLUTION  Since the system has more variables than equations, it may seem that the freedom of the variables is not overly restricted and that a solution should exist. But such is not the case, as we will see. Let us, as usual, put the augmented matrix in row echelon form. We form the row operations listed to the right.

$$\begin{bmatrix} 1 & 3 & -1 & 1 & | & 1 \\ 1 & 4 & 2 & -2 & | & 3 \\ 2 & 7 & 1 & -1 & | & 6 \end{bmatrix} \quad \begin{array}{l} R_2' = R_2 - R_1 \\ R_3' = R_3 - 2R_1 \end{array}$$

$$\begin{bmatrix} 1 & 3 & -1 & 1 & | & 1 \\ 0 & 1 & 3 & -3 & | & 2 \\ 0 & 1 & 3 & -3 & | & 4 \end{bmatrix} \quad R_3' = R_3 - R_2$$

$$\begin{bmatrix} 1 & 3 & -1 & 1 & | & 1 \\ 0 & 1 & 3 & -3 & | & 2 \\ 0 & 0 & 0 & 0 & | & 2 \end{bmatrix}$$

The last row represents the equation

$$0 \cdot x_1 + 0 \cdot x_2 + 0 \cdot x_3 + 0 \cdot x_4 = 2$$

Thus the existence of a solution to the system would imply that $0 = 2$. Since this is a contradiction, the system has no solution.  ∎

The occurrence of an impossible equation such as $0 = 2$ in the preceding example is typical for an inconsistent system. In progressing toward echelon form, a row of the form

$$0 \quad 0 \quad \dots \quad 0 \quad | \quad c \qquad (c \neq 0)$$

will appear. Since this row corresponds to the equation $0 = c$ and $c$ is known to be nonzero, we immediately conclude that a solution cannot exist and that the system is inconsistent. Once a row of this type makes its appearance, there is no need to continue.

## ROW RANK

The inconsistency of a system can be characterized in terms of a concept that has far-reaching utility. This is the notion of row rank, which we now define.

When we put a matrix into row echelon form, we get rows that either are all 0s or have a leading 1. That is, we get either zero rows or nonzero rows. Once we have reached row echelon form, we simply count the number of nonzero rows. This number is called the row rank of the matrix.

### *DEFINITION*

The **row rank** of a matrix is the number of nonzero rows in a row echelon form of the matrix.

There is one issue concerning the definition that must be clarified. The row echelon form of a matrix is not uniquely determined, and consequently we must be sure that the number of nonzero rows is not dependent on the particular echelon matrix we happen to obtain. However, the reduced echelon form of a matrix is uniquely determined, as we noted in Theorem 1 of the preceding section, and the number of nonzero rows in the reduced echelon form is the same as the number of nonzero rows in a row echelon form. This number is the number of leading 1 s that occur. Thus the row rank is determined when the matrix has reached the row echelon stage and the definition is unambiguous. The calculation of the row rank is a natural consequence of putting the matrix into row echelon form.

**EXAMPLE 2**   Determine the row rank of the matrix

$$\begin{bmatrix} 1 & 2 & 1 & 2 \\ 1 & 2 & 0 & 3 \\ 2 & 4 & 1 & 5 \end{bmatrix}$$

**SOLUTION**   We perform row operations to put the matrix into row echelon form. Subtracting row 1 from row 2 and twice row 1 from row 3, we get the matrix

$$\begin{bmatrix} 1 & 2 & 1 & 2 \\ 0 & 0 & -1 & 1 \\ 0 & 0 & -1 & 1 \end{bmatrix}$$

If we multiply row 2 by $-1$ and then add the new row 2 to row 3, we obtain the row echelon form

$$\begin{bmatrix} 1 & 2 & 1 & 2 \\ 0 & 0 & 1 & -1 \\ 0 & 0 & 0 & 0 \end{bmatrix}$$

We see that there are two nonzero rows, and so we conclude that the row rank of the matrix is 2. ∎

The relation of row rank to consistency is as follows. Suppose the augmented matrix of a system is put into row echelon form and the resulting matrix contains a row as shown below.

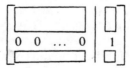

The exhibited row represents the contradictory equation $0 = 1$, so that the system is inconsistent. If we separate the coefficient matrix and the augmented matrix, we can make a side-by-side comparison.

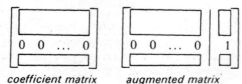

*coefficient matrix*      *augmented matrix*

The augmented matrix has at least one more nonzero row than the coefficient matrix. Therefore the row ranks of the two matrices are not equal.

Conversely, if the row ranks of the coefficient matrix and the augmented matrix are different, then there must be a row that entails the impossibility $0 = 1$. In this case the system is inconsistent. Thus we see that a system will be consistent if and only if the row ranks of the two matrices are equal. Though not a formal proof, the above discussion indicates the reasons behind the following theorem.

### THEOREM 1

A linear system is consistent if and only if the row rank of the coefficient matrix is equal to the row rank of the augmented matrix.

In practice the theorem is not really needed for a specific system, since the consistency or inconsistency of the system will become apparent as row operations are applied to put the augmented matrix in echelon form. However, it has theoretical significance and foreshadows future developments. It is also useful in understanding problems such as the following.

**EXAMPLE 3**   Find the value of the constant $k$ such that the following system is consistent.

$$x_1 + 2x_2 - x_3 = 1$$
$$-2x_1 - 3x_2 + 2x_3 = -1$$
$$-5x_1 - 8x_2 + 5x_3 = k$$

SOLUTION   If we form the augmented matrix and find an echelon form through the operations $R'_2 = R_2 + 2R_1$, $R'_3 = R_3 + 5R_1$, $R'_3 = R_3 - 2R_2$, then we obtain

$$\begin{bmatrix} 1 & 2 & -1 & | & 1 \\ 0 & 1 & 0 & | & 1 \\ 0 & 0 & 0 & | & k+3 \end{bmatrix}$$

The row rank of the coefficient matrix is 2. Thus the system will be consistent if and only if $0 = k + 3$, that is, if $k = -3$. ▪▪

## PARAMETRICALLY REPRESENTED SOLUTIONS

We now turn to the analysis of systems that have infinitely many solutions. The application of Gaussian elimination can lead to a reduced echelon form in which there are some columns in the coefficient matrix that do not contain leading 1s. In this case the variable associated with such a column is not uniquely determined and can be assigned any value whatever. However, the variable is related to the other variables of the system, and consequently the description of the solution set is affected. The following example clarifies these remarks and illustrates how the solution set is obtained.

**EXAMPLE 4**  Find all solutions of the system

$$
\begin{aligned}
x_1 + 2x_2 - 3x_3 &= 3 \\
-2x_1 - 5x_2 + 4x_3 &= 5 \\
-5x_1 - 13x_2 + 9x_3 &= 18
\end{aligned}
$$

**SOLUTION**  We proceed to put the augmented matrix in reduced echelon form

$$
\left[\begin{array}{ccc|c}
1 & 2 & -3 & 3 \\
-2 & -5 & 4 & 5 \\
-5 & -13 & 9 & 18
\end{array}\right]
\quad
\begin{aligned}
R'_2 &= R_2 + 2R_1 \\
R'_3 &= R_3 + 5R_1
\end{aligned}
$$

$$
\left[\begin{array}{ccc|c}
1 & 2 & -3 & 3 \\
0 & -1 & -2 & 11 \\
0 & -3 & -6 & 33
\end{array}\right]
\quad
\begin{aligned}
R'_2 &= -R_2 \\
R'_3 &= R_3 + 3R_2
\end{aligned}
$$

$$
\left[\begin{array}{ccc|c}
1 & 2 & -3 & 3 \\
0 & 1 & 2 & -11 \\
0 & 0 & 0 & 0
\end{array}\right]
\quad
R'_1 = R_1 - 2R_2
$$

Now the third row, which represents the equation $0 = 0$, is redundant and need not be explicitly displayed. With this convention we obtain the reduced echelon matrix

$$
\left[\begin{array}{ccc|c}
1 & 0 & -7 & 25 \\
0 & 1 & 2 & -11
\end{array}\right]
$$

The last matrix represents the system

$$
\begin{aligned}
x_1 \quad\ - 7x_3 &= 25 \\
x_2 + 2x_3 &= -11
\end{aligned}
$$

The system can be written as

$$
\begin{aligned}
x_1 &= 7x_3 + 25 \\
x_2 &= -2x_3 - 11
\end{aligned}
$$

We can assign any value to $x_3$ and calculate the values of $x_1$ and $x_2$, and the result will be a solution of the system. It is convenient to introduce a new letter and set $x_3 = t$. The solutions can then be written

$$
\begin{aligned}
x_1 &= 7t + 25 \\
x_2 &= -2t - 11 \\
x_3 &= t
\end{aligned}
$$

where $t$ is any number. Alternatively, we can write the solutions as $(7t + 25, -2t - 11, t)$ where $t$ is arbitrary.

Each value of $t$ produces a specific solution of the system. In the following table we exhibit a few values of $t$ and their corresponding solutions.

| Value of $t$ | Solution |
|:---:|:---:|
| 1 | $(32, -13, 1)$ |
| 0 | $(25, -11, 0)$ |
| $-2$ | $(11, -7, -2)$ |

∎

The introduction of the symbol $t$ in the preceding example emphasizes the fact that the variable is independent. The other variables are then expressed in terms of $t$ so that they are dependent on $t$. We say that $t$ is a **parameter** and that the solution set has been **parametrically represented** in terms of $t$. Some systems may require more than one parameter in the representation of the solution set, as in Example 5 below.

When the augmented matrix of a system has been put into reduced echelon form, a variable that corresponds to a leading 1 will be called a **leading variable**. The other variables will be called **nonleading variables**. Then the solution set of the system is obtained by replacing each nonleading variable by a parameter and expressing the leading variables in terms of the parameters. Thus the nonleading variables are independent variables, since their values are arbitrary, and the leading variables are dependent variables.

The procedure can be summarized as follows:

*Step 1.*   Put the augmented matrix of the system in reduced echelon form.

*Step 2.*   Write the system represented by the reduced echelon form.

*Step 3.*   Replace each nonleading variable by a parameter.

*Step 4.*   Express each leading variable in terms of the parameters.

The procedure is illustrated in the next example.

**EXAMPLE 5**   Solve the system

$$x_1 + 3x_2 + 4x_3 - 2x_4 = 3$$
$$2x_1 + 6x_2 + 9x_3 - 3x_4 = 8$$

SOLUTION   The augmented coefficient matrix is

$$\begin{bmatrix} 1 & 3 & 4 & -2 & | & 3 \\ 2 & 6 & 9 & -3 & | & 8 \end{bmatrix}$$

The operations $R_2' = R_2 - 2R_1$ and $R_1' = R_1 - 4R_2$ then produce the reduced echelon form

$$\begin{bmatrix} 1 & 3 & 0 & -6 & | & -5 \\ 0 & 0 & 1 & 1 & | & 2 \end{bmatrix}$$

The associated system is

$$x_1 + 3x_2 \qquad - 6x_4 = -5$$
$$x_3 + \ x_4 = \quad 2$$

The nonleading variables are $x_2$ and $x_4$. Let us introduce the parameters $x_2 = s$ and $x_4 = t$. Then $x_1 = -3s + 6t - 5$, and $x_3 = -t + 2$. Thus the solutions are given by

$$x_1 = -3s + 6t - 5$$
$$x_2 = \qquad s$$
$$x_3 = \quad -t + 2$$
$$x_4 = \qquad t$$

where $s, t$ are arbitrary numbers. We can also write the solutions as $(-3s + 6t - 5, s, -t + 2, t)$ where $s, t$ are arbitrary. The following table exhibits a few solutions that correspond to particular values of the parameters.

| Value of $s$ | Value of $t$ | Solution |
|:---:|:---:|:---:|
| 1 | 0 | $(-8, 1, 2, 0)$ |
| 0 | 1 | $(1, 0, 1, 1)$ |
| −1 | 2 | $(10, -1, 0, 2)$ |
| 2 | 3 | $(7, 2, -1, 3)$ |

∎

## APPLICATION

Linear systems that have infinitely many solutions can arise in very practical applications. However, in the context of applications the parameters are often restricted so that the solutions make practical sense. The following application to production planning illustrates this point.

**EXAMPLE 6** The Sudsy Detergent Company makes the laundry products SURF, CYCLONE, WASHO, and BRISK from the raw materials anionic surfactant (A.S.) for lifting, sodium phosphate (S.P.) for water softening, and sodium sulfate (S.S.) for anti-lumping. The products are made in large batches, and the batches differ in size and proportions of raw materials because of the different manufacturing processes and equipment used for the products. The amounts of the raw materials used to make one batch of each product and the total amounts on hand are given in the table below. The amounts are given in 100-pound units.

| | SURF | CYCLONE | WASHO | BRISK | On hand |
|:---|:---:|:---:|:---:|:---:|:---:|
| A.S. | 4 | 8 | 4 | 4 | 60 |
| S.P. | 2 | 5 | 2 | 3 | 36 |
| S.S. | 3 | 7 | 4 | 3 | 50 |

Find the possible number of batches of each product that can be made such that all of the available raw materials are used.

SOLUTION   If we let $x_1, x_2, x_3, x_4$ be the numbers of batches of the products, listed in the same order as in the above table, then we have the following system of equations.

$$4x_1 + 8x_2 + 4x_3 + 4x_4 = 60$$
$$2x_1 + 5x_2 + 2x_3 + 3x_4 = 36$$
$$3x_1 + 7x_2 + 4x_3 + 3x_4 = 50$$

The reader can verify that the reduced echelon form of the augmented matrix is given by

$$\begin{bmatrix} 1 & 0 & 0 & 0 & 4 \\ 0 & 1 & 0 & 1 & 6 \\ 0 & 0 & 1 & -1 & -1 \end{bmatrix}$$

$x = 4$

The corresponding system of equations is

$$x_1 \qquad\qquad\quad = 4$$
$$x_2 \qquad + x_4 = 6$$
$$x_3 - x_4 = -1$$

If we set $x_4 = t$, we obtain the one-parameter family of solutions

$$x_1 = \quad 4$$
$$x_2 = -t + 6$$
$$x_3 = \quad t - 1$$
$$x_4 = \quad t$$

In the context of the problem the parameter $t$ is not completely arbitrary. Since the variables represent nonnegative quantities, we must have

$$x_2 = -t + 6 \geqslant 0, \qquad x_3 = t - 1 \geqslant 0, \qquad x_4 = t \geqslant 0$$

Combining the inequalities, we find that $t$ must satisfy $1 \leqslant t \leqslant 6$. If $t$ is required to be an integer, then there are six possible choices for $t$. For example, if we choose $t = 1$, then the solution is $x_1 = 4, x_2 = 5, x_3 = 0, x_4 = 1$, which means that no WASHO would be made on the production run. If $t = 3$ is chosen, then we get $x_1 = 4, x_2 = 3, x_3 = 2, x_4 = 3$, which is a fairly balanced production arrangement. Note that for any choice of $t$, there will be four batches of SURF produced. The final decision for the production run would depend on additional considerations such as sales profiles, production costs, advertising budgets, and so on. ∎

## HOMOGENEOUS SYSTEMS

A linear system is called **homogeneous** if all of the constant terms are 0.

**EXAMPLE 7**   Solve the homogeneous system

$$x_1 - x_2 + \ x_3 = 0$$
$$2x_1 - x_2 + \ 4x_3 = 0$$
$$3x_1 + x_2 + 11x_3 = 0$$

**SOLUTION**   We note that $(0, 0, 0)$ is a solution, so that we know that the system is consistent. To see if there are more solutions, we apply Gaussian elimination to the augmented coefficient matrix.

$$\begin{bmatrix} 1 & -1 & 1 & \bigm| & 0 \\ 2 & -1 & 4 & \bigm| & 0 \\ 3 & 1 & 11 & \bigm| & 0 \end{bmatrix} \quad \begin{array}{l} R_2' = R_2 - 2R_1 \\ R_3' = R_3 - 3R_1 \end{array}$$

$$\begin{bmatrix} 1 & -1 & 1 & \bigm| & 0 \\ 0 & 1 & 2 & \bigm| & 0 \\ 0 & 4 & 8 & \bigm| & 0 \end{bmatrix} \quad R_3' = R_3 - 4R_2$$

$$\begin{bmatrix} 1 & -1 & 1 & \bigm| & 0 \\ 0 & 1 & 2 & \bigm| & 0 \\ 0 & 0 & 0 & \bigm| & 0 \end{bmatrix} \quad R_1' = R_1 + R_2$$

$$\begin{bmatrix} 1 & 0 & 3 & \bigm| & 0 \\ 0 & 1 & 2 & \bigm| & 0 \\ 0 & 0 & 0 & \bigm| & 0 \end{bmatrix}$$

The last matrix is in reduced echelon form, and the associated system is

$$x_1 \qquad + 3x_3 = 0$$
$$x_2 + 2x_3 = 0$$

If we set $x_3 = t$, then we get the infinitely many solutions $(-3t, -2t, t)$ where $t$ is arbitrary. Note that $t = 0$ gives us the solution $(0, 0, 0)$.  ∎

A homogeneous system is always consistent, since it always has the zero solution. Therefore a homogeneous system has either one solution or infinitely many solutions.

If there are infinitely many solutions, then one or more parameters are needed in the representation of the solutions. We can use row rank to tell how many parameters, if any, are required as follows. Consider a homogeneous system of $m$ equations in $n$ variables, and suppose the row rank of the system is $r$. Then there must be $r$ leading 1s in the reduced echelon form of the coefficient matrix (the column of zeros in the augmented matrix will have no effect on the row rank and thus can be ignored). It follows that there will be $n - r$ nonleading variables, and hence $n - r$ different parameters will be needed. To summarize, we have the following theorem.

### THEOREM 2

Suppose that a homogeneous system of $m$ equations in $n$ variables has row rank equal to $r$. If $r = n$, then only the zero solution exists. If $r < n$, then there are infinitely many solutions and there are $n - r$ parameters in the representation of the solution set.

For the system in Example 7 we had $n = 3$ and $r = 2$. Therefore we required $n - r = 1$ parameter.

There is an additional observation to be made about homogeneous systems. First note that the row rank $r$ cannot be greater than $m$, the number of equations, since $m$ is the total number of rows in the matrix. Thus we have $r \leqslant m$. In the case that $n$, the number of variables, exceeds the number of equations $m$, then we have $n > m \geqslant r$. It follows that $n - r > 0$, which implies that there must be one or more nonleading variables. Thus we are assured of infinitely many solutions in this case. The following theorem highlights this important conclusion.

### THEOREM 3

If there are more variables than equations in a homogeneous system, then the system has infinitely many solutions.

*CAUTION*:   The theorem applies only to homogeneous systems. The system in Example 1 of this section shows that the conclusion is not valid in general for non-homogeneous systems.

The above ideas are illustrated in the following example.

**EXAMPLE 8**   For the homogeneous system

$$x_1 + 2x_2 + 2x_3 + 3x_4 = 0$$
$$2x_1 + 4x_2 + 3x_3 + 7x_4 = 0$$
$$x_1 + 2x_2 + x_3 + 4x_4 = 0$$

determine if there are infinitely many solutions or not; if so, determine the number of parameters needed. Then solve the system.

SOLUTION   First we see that there are $n = 4$ variables but only $m = 3$ equations. We deduce from Theorem 3 that the system has infinitely many solutions.

To determine the number of parameters, we need to find the row rank $r$ of the coefficient matrix. The reader can verify that the augmented matrix can be put into the row echelon form

$$\begin{bmatrix} 1 & 2 & 2 & 3 & | & 0 \\ 0 & 0 & 1 & -1 & | & 0 \end{bmatrix}$$

where the bottom row of zeros has been suppressed. Hence the row rank is $r = 2$. Therefore by Theorem 2 there are $n - r = 4 - 2 = 2$ parameters needed for the solution set. The reduced echelon form is then found to be

$$\left[\begin{array}{cccc|c} 1 & 2 & 0 & 5 & 0 \\ 0 & 0 & 1 & -1 & 0 \end{array}\right]$$

Setting $x_2 = s$ and $x_4 = t$, we find that the family of solutions is given by

$$x_1 = -2s - 5t, \quad x_2 = s, \quad x_3 = t, \quad x_4 = t$$

where $s, t$ are arbitrary numbers. ∎

## EXERCISES 2.3

In Exercises 1–6, use Gaussian elimination to show that the given systems of equations are inconsistent.

**1.**
$$\begin{aligned} 2x_1 - 6x_2 + 8x_3 &= 2 \\ -4x_1 + 13x_2 + 3x_3 &= 6 \\ -6x_1 + 20x_2 + 14x_3 &= -2 \end{aligned}$$

**2.**
$$\begin{aligned} 3x_1 + 6x_2 - 3x_3 &= 9 \\ 6x_1 + 13x_2 - 4x_3 &= -5 \\ 12x_1 + 25x_2 - 10x_3 &= 19 \end{aligned}$$

**3.**
$$\begin{aligned} x_1 + 4x_2 - 2x_3 - 3x_4 + 2x_5 &= -1 \\ -2x_1 - 8x_2 + 5x_3 + 3x_4 + x_5 &= 4 \\ 5x_1 + 20x_2 - 12x_3 - 9x_4 &= 6 \end{aligned}$$

**4.**
$$\begin{aligned} -x_1 + 5x_2 + 2x_3 + 3x_4 - x_5 &= 6 \\ 3x_1 - 15x_2 - 6x_3 - 8x_4 + 5x_5 &= 2 \\ 5x_1 - 25x_2 - 10x_3 - 13x_4 + 9x_5 &= 4 \end{aligned}$$

**5.**
$$\begin{aligned} 2x_1 - 2x_2 + 4x_3 + 6x_4 &= 8 \\ -4x_1 + 5x_2 - 2x_3 - 7x_4 &= -10 \\ 2x_1 + x_2 + 22x_3 + 21x_4 &= 36 \\ -3x_1 + 5x_2 - 4x_3 + 11x_4 &= 10 \end{aligned}$$

**6.**
$$\begin{aligned} 3x_1 - 6x_2 + 9x_3 - 3x_4 &= 6 \\ 6x_1 - 12x_2 + 19x_3 - 4x_4 &= 17 \\ 3x_1 - 6x_2 + 12x_3 + 3x_4 &= 16 \\ 9x_1 - 18x_2 + 30x_3 - 2x_4 &= 12 \end{aligned}$$

In Exercises 7–12, find the rank of the coefficient matrix and the augmented coefficient matrix for the system of the indicated exercise.

**7.** Exercise 1        **8.** Exercise 2        **9.** Exercise 3

**10.** Exercise 4       **11.** Exercise 5       **12.** Exercise 6

In Exercises 13–16, use Gaussian elimination to find a solution to the given system or show that it is inconsistent.

**13.**
$$\begin{aligned} x - 3y - 2z &= 2 \\ 3x - 9y - 9z &= 9 \\ -x + 4y + 3z &= 3 \end{aligned}$$

**14.**
$$\begin{aligned} x + y - 2z &= 2 \\ -2x - y + 6z &= -7 \\ -x + 5z &= 4 \end{aligned}$$

**15.**
$$\begin{aligned} -2x + 4y + 2z &= 6 \\ 4x - 9y - 8z &= -5 \\ 8x - 19y - 20z &= 7 \end{aligned}$$

**16.**
$$\begin{aligned} -3x + 3y - 6z &= 9 \\ 3x - 4y + 5z &= -7 \\ 6x - 9y + 9z &= -10 \end{aligned}$$

In Exercises 17–18, find the value of $k$ for which the system of equations is consistent.

17.   $\begin{aligned} x_1 + 3x_2 + 5x_3 &= 2 \\ -3x_1 - 8x_2 - 13x_3 &= -5 \\ -x_1 - 2x_2 - 3x_3 &= k \end{aligned}$

18.   $\begin{aligned} x_1 - 6x_2 + 2x_3 &= 8 \\ 4x_1 - 25x_2 + 10x_3 &= 6 \\ 2x_1 - 13x_2 + 6x_3 &= k \end{aligned}$

In Exercises 19–20, find the relationship between $a$, $b$, and $c$ for which the system of equations will be consistent.

19.   $\begin{aligned} 2x + y - z &= a \\ x + 2y + z &= b \\ 5x + 4y - z &= c \end{aligned}$

20.   $\begin{aligned} 3x - 9y + 3z &= a \\ x - 2y - z &= b \\ 5x - 13y + z &= c \end{aligned}$

In Exercises 21–28, use Gaussian elimination to put the augmented matrix into reduced echelon form, and then parametrically represent the solutions. In each case, find two specific solutions. Check your specific solutions by substitution into the original system.

21.   $\begin{aligned} x_1 - 2x_2 + 2x_3 &= 3 \\ -3x_1 + 6x_2 - 5x_3 &= -4 \end{aligned}$

22.   $\begin{aligned} x_1 - 3x_2 + 2x_3 &= -1 \\ -4x_1 + 12x_2 - 7x_3 &= 8 \end{aligned}$

23.   $\begin{aligned} 3x + 8y - 13z &= -9 \\ 5x + 12y - 19z &= -11 \\ x + 2y - 3z &= -1 \end{aligned}$

24.   $\begin{aligned} -7x + 43y - 30z &= 19 \\ -2x + 12y - 8z &= 4 \\ x - 5y + 2z &= 3 \end{aligned}$

25.   $\begin{aligned} x_1 + 2x_2 + 2x_3 - 3x_4 &= -1 \\ 3x_2 - x_3 + 3x_4 &= 5 \\ 2x_1 + 5x_2 + 4x_3 + 2x_4 &= 10 \end{aligned}$

26.   $\begin{aligned} 4x_2 + 7x_3 + 10x_4 &= 6 \\ -3x_1 - 7x_2 - 17x_3 + 5x_4 &= -11 \\ x_1 + 2x_2 + 5x_3 - 3x_4 &= 3 \end{aligned}$

27.   $\begin{aligned} x_1 + 4x_2 - 6x_3 + x_4 - x_5 &= 3 \\ 2x_1 + 9x_2 - 8x_3 + x_5 &= 5 \\ 3x_1 + 12x_2 - 18x_3 + 4x_4 - 5x_5 &= 12 \end{aligned}$

28.   $\begin{aligned} x_1 - 3x_2 + 2x_3 + 2x_4 - 3x_5 &= -1 \\ -2x_1 + 7x_2 + 3x_3 - 6x_4 + 9x_5 &= 4 \\ 4x_1 - 12x_2 + 8x_3 + 10x_4 - 16x_5 &= -10 \end{aligned}$

In Exercises 29–30, find the possible number of batches of each product that can be made such that all of the available materials are used up.

**29.** Nutrina Feeds manufactures the dog foods RUFF, FLUFF, and PROWL from a blend of wheat and soybeans. A batch of RUFF uses 1000 pounds of wheat and 3000 pounds of soybeans; a batch of FLUFF uses 2000 pounds of wheat and 7000 pounds of soybeans; and a batch of PROWL uses 2000 pounds of wheat and 5000 pounds of soybeans. Suppose that there are 15,000 pounds of wheat and 50,000 pounds of soybeans on hand.

**30.** The Muffit Company produces breakfast, lunch, and dinner treats from a mixture of curds and whey. The breakfast treat uses 10 ounces of curds and 40 ounces of whey; the lunch treat uses 20 ounces of curds and 90 ounces of whey; and the dinner treat uses 30 ounces of curds and 30 ounces of whey per batch, respectively. Suppose that there are 300 ounces of curds and 500 ounces of whey on hand.

Solve the homogeneous systems of equations in Exercises 31–36 using Gaussian elimination followed by back addition. Give a parametric representation for the solutions when there is more than one. Verify that the row rank plus the number of parameters equals the number of variables.

**31.** $2x_1 + 6x_2 - 2x_3 = 0$
$\quad\;\; 5x_1 + 16x_2 - 3x_3 = 0$
$\quad\; 12x_1 + 38x_2 - 8x_3 = 0$

**32.** $-2x_1 + 4x_2 + 8x_3 = 0$
$\quad\;\; 3x_1 - 7x_2 + 5x_3 = 0$
$\quad\;\; 4x_1 - 10x_2 + 18x_3 = 0$

**33.** $2x + 4y - 4z = 0$
$\quad 2x + 5y - 2z = 0$
$\quad 4x + 7y - 11z = 0$

**34.** $-2x + 2y + 6z = 0$
$\quad -6x + 5y + 14z = 0$
$\quad\;\; 2x - y - 3z = 0$

**35.** $\quad x_1 + 3x_2 - 2x_3 + x_4 = 0$
$\quad -3x_1 - 9x_2 + 6x_3 - 4x_4 = 0$
$\quad\; -x_1 - 3x_2 + 2x_3 - 6x_4 = 0$

**36.** $\quad x_1 - 4x_2 + 3x_3 + 2x_4 = 0$
$\quad -4x_1 + 16x_2 - 12x_3 - 9x_4 = 0$
$\quad -6x_1 + 24x_2 - 18x_3 - 14x_4 = 0$

## 2.4 EUCLIDEAN 3-SPACE

*Coordinates in Space, Planes in Space, Intersection of Planes, Intersection of Three Planes, Finding the Equation of a Plane*

We have seen that linear systems have either a unique solution, no solution, or infinitely many solutions. To enhance one's understanding of these three different possibilities, it helps to visualize the situations and apply one's geometric intuition. The geometry of 3-space provides a setting for interpreting linear systems in three variables. A linear equation in three variables determines a plane in 3-space, and a linear system corresponds to the intersection of planes. In this section we look at the interplay between the algebra of linear systems and the geometry of planes in space.

### COORDINATES IN SPACE

To represent three-dimensional space in coordinates, we take three mutually perpendicular lines that intersect in a common point, called the origin. Each line is assumed to have a unit of length so that distances are measured from the origin. The lines are called **coordinate axes**, and the labels $x$, $y$, $z$ will be used for the axes. We draw the coordinate axes so that the $y$-axis and $z$-axis lie in the plane of the paper as shown in Figure 2.1. To create an illusion of depth on a flat page, the $x$-axis is drawn on a slant to indicate that it should come out of the page. The negative coordinate axes are drawn as dashed lines.

Pairs of coordinate axes determine three special planes called the **coordinate planes.** The $x$-axis and $y$-axis determine the **$xy$-plane**, the $y$-axis and $z$-axis determine the **$yz$-plane**, and the $x$-axis and $z$-axis determine the **$xz$-plane**. (See Figure 2.2). These three coordinate planes divide space into eight regions called **octants**. The

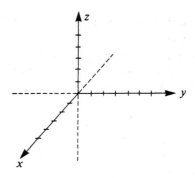

**FIGURE 2.1**                    *Coordinate axes in space*

octant determined by the positive coordinate axes is called the **first octant**. (See Figure 2.2.) We will not number the other octants.

To visualize the first octant, we can look toward the left corner of the classroom and think of the front wall as the $yz$-plane, the floor as the $xy$-plane, and the left wall as the $xz$-plane. The origin is in the corner, and the coordinate axes are the lines where the walls and floor meet.

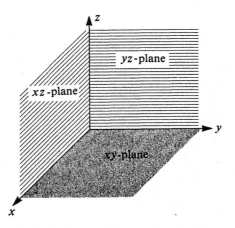

**FIGURE 2.2**                    *Coordinate planes in the first octant*

A point $(a, b, c)$ in space is determined by its three **coordinates**, where $a, b, c$ are the $x$-, $y$-, $z$-coordinates, respectively. The point $(a, b, c)$ can be located by measuring $a$ units along the $x$-axis, then $b$ units along a line parallel to the $y$-axis, and then $c$ units along a line parallel to the $z$-axis. Several points are located in this manner in Figure 2.3 on the next page.

The $yz$-coordinate plane consists of all points of the form $(0, y, z)$ where the $x$-coordinate is zero. Similarly, the $xz$-plane consists of all points $(x, 0, z)$, and the $xy$-plane consists of all points $(x, y, 0)$. A point on the $x$-axis has the form $(x, 0, 0)$ where both the $y$- and $z$-coordinates are zero. Points on the other axes are similarly represented.

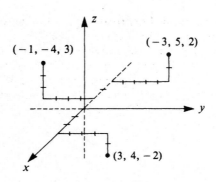

**FIGURE 2.3**                                    *Points in space*

If $a$, $b$, $c$ are all positive numbers, then the point $(a, b, c)$ is the corner of a box as shown in Figure 2.4. The reader is invited to supply the coordinates of the other corner points of the box.

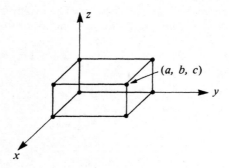

**FIGURE 2.4**                                    *A box and its corners*

## PLANES IN SPACE

In the 2-dimensional plane a linear equation in two variables determines a line. In 3-dimensional space a linear equation in three variables determines a plane. Thus a **plane** in space is given by a linear equation

$$Ax + By + Cz = D$$

where the coefficients $A$, $B$, $C$ are not all zero. Some of them may, of course, be zero. For example, if $B = 0$, $C = 0$, $D = 0$, and $A = 1$, then we obtain the equation $x = 0$, which is an equation of the $yz$-plane. Similarly, $y = 0$ and $z = 0$ are equations of the $xz$-plane and the $xy$-plane, respectively. The ceiling of the classroom might be represented by the equation $z = 9$.

It is not easy in general to sketch a plane in space. However, if a plane passes through the first octant, then it is not difficult to draw the first-octant portion of the plane, and this provides a fairly good picture of the position of the plane in space. In this brief treatment of 3-dimensional geometry we will restrict ourselves primarily to first-octant drawings. It must be kept in mind that planes go on forever and the sketches represent only small pieces of the planes.

It is helpful to locate any **intercepts** of the plane, that is, points at which the plane cuts the coordinate axes. If $D \neq 0$, then we can divide the equation by $D$; and if the coefficients $A$, $B$, $C$ are not 0, then the intercepts are conveniently displayed by writing the equation in the form

$$\frac{x}{a} + \frac{y}{b} + \frac{z}{c} = 1$$

where $a = D/A$, $b = D/B$, $c = D/C$. If we set $y = 0$, $z = 0$ in the above equation, then we get $x = a$, so that $(a, 0, 0)$ is the $x$-intercept. Similarly, the $y$-intercept and $z$-intercept are given by $b$ and $c$, respectively. The equation written in this way is called the **intercept form** of the plane.

**EXAMPLE 1**   Draw the plane $3x + 4y + 2z = 12$.

SOLUTION   If we divide both sides of the equation by 12, we get the intercept form

$$\frac{x}{4} + \frac{y}{3} + \frac{z}{6} = 1$$

Thus the intercepts are $(4, 0, 0)$, $(0, 3, 0)$, and $(0, 0, 6)$. If we plot these points and join them with lines, we obtain the sketch in Figure 2.5. ∎

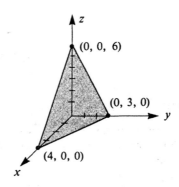

**FIGURE 2.5**                           *The plane $3x + 4y + 2z = 12$*

If a plane in space intersects a coordinate plane, then the resulting line in the coordinate plane is called a **trace** of the plane. The intersection of a plane with the $yz$-plane is called the *yz*-**trace** of the plane. The *xy*-**trace** and the *xz*-**trace** are defined in a similar way. The three line segments that outline the plane in Figure 2.5 are the first-octant portions of the traces. We see in the next example that traces can be very valuable when sketching planes.

**EXAMPLE 2**   Draw the plane $4x + 2y - z = 0$.

**SOLUTION**   Intercepts are little help for this plane. Since the constant term is $D = 0$, the plane contains the origin. In fact, it is readily seen that the origin is the only intercept for this plane.

To get the $yz$-trace, we set $x = 0$ and get the line $2y - z = 0$ in the $yz$-plane. Similarly, to get the $xz$-trace, we set $y = 0$ and get the line $4x - z = 0$ in the $xz$-plane. These two lines are shown in Figure 2.6. Since the $xy$-trace does not penetrate the first octant, we will ignore it.

To gain a better perspective for the inclination of the plane, we include in Figure 2.6 a line segment in the plane that lies above and parallel to the $xy$-plane. We can cut the plane at a height of 8 units above the $xy$-plane by setting $z = 8$ in the equation, thereby getting $4x + 2y - 8 = 0$. If we set $x = 0$ and solve for $y = 4$, we get the point $(0, 4, 8)$ in the $yz$-plane. Similarly, setting $y = 0$ and solving for $x = 2$ gives us the point $(2, 0, 8)$ in the $xz$-plane. By plotting these two points and drawing the line segment between them, we get the line 8 units above the $xy$-plane as shown in Figure 2.6.   ▋▋

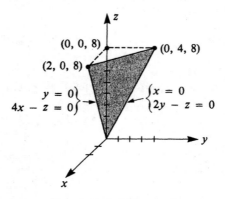

**FIGURE 2.6**   *The plane $4x + 2y - z = 0$*

If one or more of the coefficients $A$, $B$, $C$ are 0 in the equation

$$Ax + By + Cz = D, \qquad D \neq 0$$

then the corresponding term will be missing also in the intercept form. In this case the plane does not intersect the axis of any variable that is not present in the equation. For example, if $C = 0$, then it is not possible for the plane to intersect the $z$-axis, and there can be no $z$-intercept. To graph a plane of this type, we employ traces as in the following example.

**EXAMPLE 3**   Draw the plane $2x + y = 2$.

**SOLUTION**   Here we see that the only intercepts are $(1, 0, 0)$ and $(0, 2, 0)$. These two points are the endpoints of the first-octant segment of the $xy$-trace as shown in Figure 2.7. Also, the $xz$-trace is the line $x = 1$ in the $xz$-plane, and the $yz$-trace is the line $y = 2$ in the $yz$-plane. Since $z$ is missing from the equation of the plane, any point above or below the $xy$-trace is on the plane, so that the plane is perpendicular to the $xy$-plane. Thus the plane is parallel to the $z$-axis, and it passes through the $xy$-trace. It helps to visualize the first octant portion of the plane if we plot the points $(1, 0, 4)$ and $(0, 2, 4)$ and draw the line segment between them. See Figure 2.7.  ∎

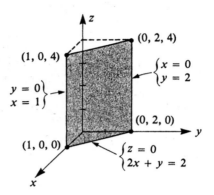

**FIGURE 2.7**                    *The plane $2x + y = 2$*

## INTERSECTION OF PLANES

Since a linear equation in $x$, $y$, $z$ determines a plane in space, a linear system in these variables is concerned with several planes at once. A solution of the system corresponds to a point at which all of the planes intersect. Thus the algebraic problem of solving a linear system corresponds to the geometric problem of determining the intersection of two or more planes.

We first look at the case of two planes in space.

**EXAMPLE 4**   Solve the linear system

$$x + \ y + 3z = \ \ 6$$
$$3x + 2y + 6z = 12$$

SOLUTION   We present two solutions. First we draw the planes determined by the equations and geometrically display the points in common. Let us call the planes $R$ and $S$ and write the equations in intercept form:

$$R: \quad \frac{x}{6} + \frac{y}{6} + \frac{z}{2} = 1$$

$$S: \quad \frac{x}{4} + \frac{y}{6} + \frac{z}{2} = 1$$

By plotting the intercepts we get the planes as shown in Figure 2.8. Note that the two planes have the same $y$-intercept $(0, 6, 0)$ and the same $z$-intercept

$(0, 0, 2)$. Therefore the line passing through these two points must be the line of intersection of the two planes. This line is just the common $yz$-trace of the planes. See Figure 2.8.

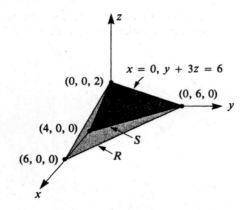

**FIGURE 2.8**                    *The intersection of R and S*

We now solve the problem algebraically. If the augmented matrix is reduced, we get the reduced echelon form

$$\begin{bmatrix} 1 & 0 & 0 & | & 0 \\ 0 & 1 & 3 & | & 6 \end{bmatrix}$$

The associated system for this matrix is

$$x \qquad\quad = 0$$
$$y + 3z = 6$$

Since $x = 0$, we again get the $yz$-trace of the plane. We wish to write the solution in parametric form. If we let $z = t$, then we can write

$$x = 0, \quad y = -3t + 6, \quad z = t$$

where $t$ is an arbitrary number. Thus the line of intersection is given by a one-parameter family of solutions.  ∎

Two planes are parallel if they do not intersect, that is, the system of equations has no solutions. A simple algebraic condition for two planes to be parallel is given in the next example.

**EXAMPLE 5**  Consider the planes

$$a_1 x + b_1 y + c_1 z = d_1$$
$$a_2 x + b_2 y + c_2 z = d_2$$

Show that if $a_2 = ka_1, b_2 = kb_1, c_2 = kc_1$ for some constant $k \neq 0$, then the planes are either identical or parallel.

SOLUTION   The augmented matrix for the system is the matrix

$$\begin{bmatrix} a_1 & b_1 & c_1 & \bigm| & d_1 \\ a_2 & b_2 & c_2 & \bigm| & d_2 \end{bmatrix}$$

If we subtract $k$ times the first row from the second row, then because of the assumed relation between the coefficients we get the matrix

$$\begin{bmatrix} a_1 & b_1 & c_1 & \bigm| & d_1 \\ 0 & 0 & 0 & \bigm| & d_2 - kd_1 \end{bmatrix}$$

If $d_2 - kd_1 = 0$, then the planes are identical, since the second equation is just $k$ times the first. However, if $d_2 - kd_1 \neq 0$, then the system has no solutions, which means that the planes do not intersect and hence are parallel. ∎

It can also be shown that the converse of Example 5 is true. That is, if the planes are identical or parallel, then the coefficients $a_2$, $b_2$, $c_2$ are a common nonzero multiple of $a_1$, $b_1$, $c_1$. (See Exercises 31 and 32.) Thus, for example, we can see at a glance that the planes

$$x + 2y + \phantom{1}3z = 1$$
$$4x + 8y + 12z = 7$$

are parallel because the coefficients have a common factor of 4, but the constant terms do not.

For reference we state the condition for parallelism as a theorem.

## THEOREM 1

Two planes are either identical or parallel if and only if the $x$, $y$, $z$ coefficients of the one plane are common multiples, respectively, of the $x$, $y$, $z$ coefficients of the other plane.

## INTERSECTION OF THREE PLANES

For three planes in space, there are a number of possible configurations. Several are shown in Figure 2.9. No matter how the planes are positioned, there will be either a unique point of intersection, no points of intersection, or a line of intersection, or all three planes will coincide. This is the geometric counterpart to the fact that a linear system has either a unique solution, no solution, or infinitely many solutions.

It is easy to find three planes that intersect in the same line. For example, if we adjoin the equation $2x + y + 3z = 6$ to the system in Example 4, the resulting system of three equations will have the same solutions as the original two equations. This can be seen by noting that the new plane has the same $yz$-trace as the other two planes. The reader can verify algebraically that the enlarged system has the same solutions as before.

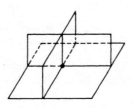

(a) Unique point of intersection

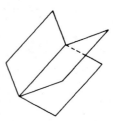

(b) Line of intersection

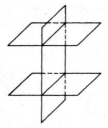

(c) No points of intersection

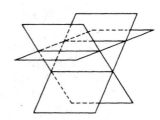

(d) No points of intersection

**FIGURE 2.9**                    *Three planes in space*

In the next two examples we see two ways in which three planes can fail to intersect.

**EXAMPLE 6**  Show that the three planes

$$R: \quad 2x + y + z = 4$$
$$S: \quad 4x + 2y + 2z = 20$$
$$T: \quad x + y - z = 0$$

have no points of intersection

**SOLUTION**  The quickest way to derive the conclusion is to observe that the planes $R$ and $S$ are parallel because the coefficients $4, 2, 2$ for $S$ are twice the coefficients $2, 1, 1$ for $R$, but the constant 20 is not twice 4. Hence the system has no solutions. Geometrically, the planes $R$ and $T$ intersect in a line $L$, and the planes $S$ and $T$ intersect in a line $M$, but the lines $L$ and $M$ are parallel. See Figure 2.10.

The lack of solutions may also be established algebraically. If 2 times the first row is subtracted from the second row in the augmented matrix, the result is the matrix

$$\begin{bmatrix} 2 & 1 & 1 & 4 \\ 0 & 0 & 0 & 12 \\ 1 & 1 & -1 & 0 \end{bmatrix}$$

The second row immediately reveals that the system has no solutions.  ∎

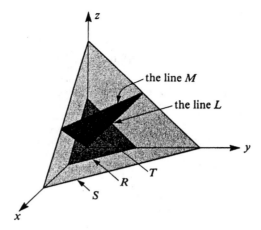

**FIGURE 2.10**                                    *The planes of Example 6*

It is not necessary for two of the three planes to be parallel for the three to fail to intersect. Consider the next example.

**EXAMPLE 7**   Find the points of intersection, if any, of the planes

$$x + 2y + 3z = 2$$
$$2x + 3y + 5z = 3$$
$$3x + 5y + 8z = 6$$

SOLUTION   Attempting to draw the planes in this case is not fruitful, so we will use algebraic methods. By row reducing the augmented matrix, we obtain

$$\begin{bmatrix} 1 & 2 & 3 & 2 \\ 0 & 1 & 1 & 1 \\ 0 & 0 & 0 & 1 \end{bmatrix}$$

A look at the third row reveals that there are no solutions. Therefore the three planes fail to have any points of intersection.

Geometrically, no two of the planes are parallel. This can be seen by drawing a sketch or by checking the coefficients in the equations. Each pair of planes intersects in a line, but the resulting lines of intersection are parallel. Thus the three planes have no points in common. ∎

Interpreting linear systems in three variables in terms of the geometry of planes in space can provide a feeling for the ways in which the different types of solution sets can occur. The last two examples illustrate ways in which a linear system can fail to have solutions. Three planes in space fail to intersect if (1) two of the planes are parallel or (2) pairs of planes intersect in parallel lines. Parallel planes are easily spotted by looking at the coefficients; and if no parallelism is apparent, then an algebraic analysis will solve the problem. A linear system will have a unique solution if no two of the planes are parallel and if the lines of intersection all meet in a single point. Examples of this kind of system are given in the exercises. The geometry of lines and planes in space will be studied further in later chapters when vector methods have been developed.

## FINDING THE EQUATION OF A PLANE

According to Euclidean geometry, if there are three points that do not all lie on a line, then there is a unique plane containing the three points. The next example shows how an equation of the plane can be found algebraically.

**EXAMPLE 8** Find an equation of the plane that contains the points $(1, -4, -6)$, $(2, -7, -9)$, and $(2, -8, -11)$.

**SOLUTION** We seek an equation $Ax + By + Cz = D$ where $A$, $B$, $C$, $D$ are to be determined. If we successively substitute the coordinates of the given points for $x$, $y$, $z$ in this equation, we obtain

$$A(1) + B(-4) + C(-6) = D$$
$$A(2) + B(-7) + C(-9) = D$$
$$A(2) + B(-8) + C(-11) = D$$

If we rewrite the equations, we have the following system of three homogeneous equations in the unknowns $A$, $B$, $C$, $D$.

$$A - 4B - 6C - D = 0$$
$$2A - 7B - 9C - D = 0$$
$$2A - 8B - 11C - D = 0$$

The reduced echelon form of the matrix is found to be

$$\begin{bmatrix} 1 & 0 & 0 & -3 & | & 0 \\ 0 & 1 & 0 & -2 & | & 0 \\ 0 & 0 & 1 & 1 & | & 0 \end{bmatrix}$$

Thus we obtain $A = 3D$, $B = 2D$, $C = -D$, where $D$ can be any value. If we choose $D = 1$, we get the equation $3x + 2y - z = 1$, which is the desired plane. If any other nonzero value of $D$ were chosen, then both sides of the equation would be multiplied by the same constant, and no essential change in the equation would result. ∎

## EXERCISES 2.4

In Exercises 1–4, plot the given points on a 3-dimensional coordinate system.

**1.** $(-1, -6, 3)$, $(1, -2, -1)$, $(5, 4, 1)$, $(-3, 3, 2)$

**2.** $(3, 4, 5)$, $(-4, -3, -1)$, $(2, -4, 3)$, $(-6, 3, 1)$

**3.** $(-5, -4, -2)$, $(4, -3, 2)$, $(3, 4, -1)$, $(-2, 2, -1)$

**4.** $(5, 6, -2)$, $(-2, 3, -1)$, $(3, -5, -2)$, $(-3, -4, 2)$

In Exercises 5–8, write the plane in intercept form and sketch the first-octant portion of the plane by drawing the lines between the intercepts.

**5.** $2x + 6y + 4z = 12$          **6.** $4x + 8y + 2z = 16$

**7.** $10x + 5y + 15z = 30$          **8.** $7x + 4y + 14z = 28$

In Exercises 9–20, sketch the first-octant portion of the indicated plane by locating the visible traces (those that can be seen when viewing the first octant). As an aid in visualizing the graph, show some line that lies in the given plane and that is parallel to the indicated coordinate plane.

**9.** $3x + 4y - 2z = 0$; $xy$-plane          **10.** $5x + 3y - 3z = 0$; $xy$-plane

**11.** $6x - 3y + 4z = 0$; $xz$-plane          **12.** $4x - 6y + 3z = 0$; $xz$-plane

**13.** $-2x + 4y + 5z = 0$; $yz$-plane          **14.** $-6x + y + 3z = 0$; $yz$-plane

**15.** $4x + 3y = 12$; $xy$-plane          **16.** $5x + 7y = 35$; $xy$-plane

**17.** $5x + 3z = 15$; $xz$-plane          **18.** $2x + 5z = 10$; $xz$-plane

**19.** $7y + 2z = 14$; $yz$-plane          **20.** $3y + 8z = 24$; $yz$-plane

Sketch the planes in Exercises 21–24, and then algebraically (Gaussian elimination) find the line of intersection.

**21.**  $\begin{aligned} x + 2y + 4z &= 8 \\ 2x + y + 2z &= 4 \end{aligned}$          **22.**  $\begin{aligned} x + 5y + 3z &= 15 \\ 3x + 10y + 6z &= 30 \end{aligned}$

**23.** $\begin{aligned} 2x + 4y + 5z &= 20 \\ 2x + 7y + 2z &= 14 \end{aligned}$          **24.** $\begin{aligned} 2x + 3y + 2z &= 5 \\ x + 2y + 6z &= 6 \end{aligned}$

Sketch the planes in Exercises 25–26 and show algebraically that they are parallel.

**25.** $\begin{aligned} 2x + y + 4z &= 8 \\ 6x + 3y + 12z &= 36 \end{aligned}$          **26.** $\begin{aligned} 3x + 2y + 5z &= 15 \\ 6x + 4y + 10z &= 16 \end{aligned}$

Graph the planes in Exercises 27–30. Show the lines of intersection between pairs of planes. Show algebraically that the planes have no common point.

**27.** $\begin{aligned} 4x + y + 3z &= 12 \\ 8x + 2y + 6z &= 16 \\ x + 2y - z &= 0 \end{aligned}$          **28.** $\begin{aligned} 3x + 2y + z &= 6 \\ 6x + 4y + 2z &= 24 \\ 3x + 3y - z &= 0 \end{aligned}$

**29.** $\begin{aligned} 6x + 3y + 4z &= 12 \\ 6x + 3y + 4z &= 24 \\ 8x + 12y + 3z &= 24 \end{aligned}$          **30.** $\begin{aligned} 2x + 5y + z &= 10 \\ 2x + 5y + z &= 20 \\ 3x + y + 3z &= 9 \end{aligned}$

In Exercises 31–32, consider the planes

$$P_1: \quad a_1x + b_1y + c_1z = d_1$$
$$P_2: \quad a_2x + b_2y + c_2z = d_2$$

**31.** Show that if $P_1$ and $P_2$ are parallel then

$$a_2 = ka_1, \quad b_2 = kb_1, \quad c_2 = kc_1, \quad d_2 \neq kd_1$$

for some nonzero $k$.

**32.** Show that if $P_1$ and $P_2$ are identical then

$$a_2 = ka_1, \quad b_2 = kb_1 \quad c_2 = kc_1, \quad d_2 = kd_1$$

for some nonzero $k$. (*Hint:* Consider the plane $a_2 x + b_2 y + c_2 z = d_2 + 1$ and use the result in Exercise 31.)

In Exercises 33–34, show algebraically that the planes have no common point. Are any pairs of planes parallel?

**33.**
$$\begin{aligned} x + 3y - 3z &= 4 \\ 2x + 7y + 4z &= 2 \\ 4x + 13y - 2z &= 6 \end{aligned}$$

**34.**
$$\begin{aligned} -x + 4y + 2z &= 5 \\ 3x - 13y + z &= 6 \\ 5x - 22y + 4z &= 20 \end{aligned}$$

Sketch the planes in Exercises 35–36. Display the line of intersection. Algebraically find the line of intersection.

**35.**
$$\begin{aligned} 3x + 6y + 4z &= 18 \\ 3x + 3y + 4z &= 15 \\ 3x + 2y + 4z &= 14 \end{aligned}$$

**36.**
$$\begin{aligned} x + 3y + 4z &= 12 \\ 2x + 5y + 2z &= 20 \\ 4x + 11y + 10z &= 44 \end{aligned}$$

Sketch the planes in Exercises 37–38. Display the lines of intersection between pairs of planes. Algebraically find the point of intersection.

**37.**
$$\begin{aligned} 4x + 12y + 3z &= 24 \\ 2x + 5y + 10z &= 20 \\ 2x + y + 2z &= 8 \end{aligned}$$

**38.**
$$\begin{aligned} x + 4y + 2z &= 8 \\ 3x + 10y + 10z &= 30 \\ 7x + 4y + 2z &= 28 \end{aligned}$$

In Exercises 39–40, find an equation of the plane that passes through the given points.

**39.** $(1, 3, -6), (-1, -2, -5), (-2, -6, 13)$

**40.** $(-1, 2, -2), (4, -7, 3), (-2, 6, -13)$

## 2.5 GAUSS-JORDAN ELIMINATION

*The Gauss-Jordan Method, Pivots*

In this short section we describe a modification of Gaussian elimination introduced by Camille Jordan (1838–1922) to solve linear systems. The method is appropriately called Gauss-Jordan elimination. The key feature of the method is a procedure called "pivoting." The notion of pivoting will also be very important in the next section when we discuss the simplex method in linear programming.

### THE GAUSS-JORDAN METHOD

To solve a system of linear equations by Gaussian elimination, first the augmented coefficient matrix is put into row echelon form and then the coefficients above the leading 1s are eliminated by either back substitution or back addition. An alternative procedure, called Gauss-Jordan elimination, is to eliminate the entries above as well as below each leading 1 as it is generated. In this way an entire column is swept out by row operations before moving to the next column.

We illustrate the procedure by an example and then describe it in more detail. The linear system in the following example was solved in Example 3 of Section 2.1 by Gaussian elimination. We now solve it using Gauss-Jordan elimination. The reader should look at the earlier example to see the difference in the two methods.

**EXAMPLE 1** Use Gauss-Jordan elimination to solve the linear system

$$3x - 7y + 11z = 4$$
$$x - 2y + 3z = 1$$
$$-2x + 8y - 16z = 4$$

SOLUTION   The sequence of matrices is as follows:

$$\left[\begin{array}{rrr|r} 3 & -7 & 11 & 4 \\ 1 & -2 & 3 & 1 \\ -2 & 8 & -16 & 4 \end{array}\right] \quad R_1 \leftrightarrow R_2$$

$$\left[\begin{array}{rrr|r} 1 & -2 & 3 & 1 \\ 3 & -7 & 11 & 4 \\ -2 & 8 & -16 & 4 \end{array}\right] \quad \begin{array}{l} R'_2 = R_2 - 3R_1 \\ R'_3 = R_3 + 2R_1 \end{array}$$

$$\left[\begin{array}{rrr|r} 1 & -2 & 3 & 1 \\ 0 & -1 & 2 & 1 \\ 0 & 4 & -10 & 6 \end{array}\right] \quad \begin{array}{l} R'_1 = R_1 - 2R_2 \\ R'_3 = R_3 + 4R_2 \\ R'_2 = -R_2 \end{array}$$

Here we have the difference in the two methods. The entry $-2$ in row 1 is eliminated *now* instead of later.

$$\left[\begin{array}{rrr|r} 1 & 0 & -1 & -1 \\ 0 & 1 & -2 & -1 \\ 0 & 0 & -2 & 10 \end{array}\right] \quad \begin{array}{l} R'_2 = R_2 - R_3 \\ R'_3 = -1/2R_3 \\ R'_1 = R_1 + R_3 \end{array}$$

$$\left[\begin{array}{rrr|r} 1 & 0 & 0 & -6 \\ 0 & 1 & 0 & -11 \\ 0 & 0 & 1 & -5 \end{array}\right]$$

Thus we have obtained the reduced echelon form. The solution of the system is $(-6, -11, -5)$ as before.  ∎

The change in procedure may seem minor, but in larger systems the difference is significant. In small systems that are solved by hand, the Gauss-Jordan method requires less writing than Gaussian elimination with back addition, since fewer matrices need to be written down. In general, however, Gauss-Jordan elimination requires more additions and multiplications than Gaussian elimination (in Example 1 the difference is very small). Consequently, the Gauss-Jordan method is not as desirable if one seeks only a numerical solution to a linear system, since more calculations are involved. This is especially true when computers are used, since round-off errors can accumulate and seriously affect the results. However, there are special algorithms in which the Gauss-Jordan procedure is necessary as well as instances in which it is preferred for theoretical reasons.

We now introduce some terminology that is used in conjunction with Gauss-Jordan elimination as well as other areas of linear algebra, including linear programming.

## PIVOTS

The idea of pivoting is simply to select a nonzero entry in a matrix and then use it to eliminate all other nonzero entries from the chosen column. The steps can be listed as follows.

### Pivoting

**Step 1.**   Choose a nonzero entry in the matrix. This entry is called the **pivot**.

**Step 2.**   Multiply the **pivot row** (the row that contains the pivot) by the reciprocal \ of the pivot to get 1 in the pivot position.

**Step 3.**   Add multiples of the pivot row to each of the other rows to obtain zeros above and below the 1 in the **pivot column** (the column that contains the pivot).

In the examples that follow, we will circle the entry to be used as a pivot. The selection of a pivot (step 1) then implicitly specifies a number of row operations. To carry out the arithmetic, it is sometimes helpful to first write the multiplied pivot row (step 2) in the new matrix and then add multiples of it to the other rows (step 3).

We highlight the procedure in the following example by performing the pivoting process on a single column of the matrix.

**EXAMPLE 2**   Use the circled term as pivot in the matrix

$$\begin{bmatrix} 2 & 1 & -1 & 3 \\ -4 & 6 & \boxed{-2} & 1 \\ 7 & -5 & 3 & 2 \end{bmatrix}$$

**SOLUTION**   We multiply the pivot row by $-\frac{1}{2}$ and write down the new second row.

$$\begin{bmatrix} 2 & -3 & 1 & -1/2 \end{bmatrix}$$

Then we add $-3$ times the new second row to the third row ($R_3' = R_3 - 3R_2$) to get

$$\begin{bmatrix} 2 & -3 & 1 & -1/2 \\ 1 & 4 & 0 & 7/2 \end{bmatrix}$$

Finally, we add the second row to the first row $(R_1' = R_1 + R_2)$ to get

$$\begin{bmatrix} 4 & -2 & 0 & 5/2 \\ 2 & -3 & 1 & -1/2 \\ 1 & 4 & 0 & 7/2 \end{bmatrix}$$

The third column now has 1 in the pivot position, and all other entries in the pivot column are 0. The pivoting is done.  ▮▮

In Gauss-Jordan elimination, pivoting proceeds in a systematic manner from left to right across the columns of the augmented matrix of a linear system. The pivots become the leading 1s in the reduced echelon form.

In the next two examples we both circle the pivot and explicitly describe the row operations that are dictated by the pivot.

**EXAMPLE 3**   Use Gauss-Jordan elimination to solve the system

$$\begin{aligned} x + 2y - 3z + w &= 2 \\ 3x + 8y - 4z + 4w &= 5 \\ 2x + 4y - 5z + 5w &= 7 \\ x + 2y - 2z - w &= -5 \end{aligned}$$

**SOLUTION**   We have the following sequence of pivots. The row operations listed to the right of a matrix are used to get the matrix beneath it.

$$\left[\begin{array}{cccc|c} ① & 2 & -3 & 1 & 2 \\ 3 & 8 & -4 & 4 & 5 \\ 2 & 4 & -5 & 5 & 7 \\ 1 & 2 & -2 & -1 & -5 \end{array}\right] \quad ① \begin{cases} R_2' = R_2 - 3R_1 \\ R_3' = R_3 - 2R_1 \\ R_4' = R_4 - R_1 \end{cases}$$

$$\left[\begin{array}{cccc|c} 1 & 2 & -3 & 1 & 2 \\ 0 & ② & 5 & 1 & -1 \\ 0 & 0 & 1 & 3 & 3 \\ 0 & 0 & 1 & -2 & -7 \end{array}\right] \quad ② \begin{cases} R_1' = R_1 - R_2 \\ R_2' = 1/2 R_2 \end{cases}$$

$$\left[\begin{array}{cccc|c} 1 & 0 & -8 & 0 & 3 \\ 0 & 1 & 5/2 & 1/2 & -1/2 \\ 0 & 0 & ① & 3 & 3 \\ 0 & 0 & 1 & -2 & -7 \end{array}\right] \quad ① \begin{cases} R_1' = R_1 + 8R_3 \\ R_2' = R_2 - 5/2 R_3 \\ R_4' = R_4 - R_3 \end{cases}$$

$$\left[\begin{array}{cccc|c} 1 & 0 & 0 & 24 & 27 \\ 0 & 1 & 0 & -7 & -8 \\ 0 & 0 & 1 & 3 & 3 \\ 0 & 0 & 0 & ⊝5 & -10 \end{array}\right] \quad ⊝5 \begin{cases} R_4' = -1/5 R_4 \\ R_1' = R_1 - 24R_4 \\ R_2' = R_2 + 7R_4 \\ R_3' = R_3 - 3R_4 \end{cases}$$

$$\left[\begin{array}{cccc|c} 1 & 0 & 0 & 0 & -21 \\ 0 & 1 & 0 & 0 & 6 \\ 0 & 0 & 1 & 0 & -3 \\ 0 & 0 & 0 & 1 & 2 \end{array}\right]$$

Thus the solution is $x = -21$, $y = 6$, $z = -3$, $w = 2$, which we write as $(-21, 6, -3, 2)$. ∎

**EXAMPLE 4** Use Gauss-Jordan elimination to solve the system

$$3x_1 + 6x_2 + 12x_3 - 9x_4 - 6x_5 = -3$$
$$-4x_1 - 8x_2 - 10x_3 + 18x_4 + 6x_5 = 16$$
$$-2x_1 - 4x_2 - 5x_3 + 9x_4 + 6x_5 = 11$$

**SOLUTION** We obtain the sequence of matrices

$$\left[\begin{array}{ccccc|c} ③ & 6 & 12 & -9 & -6 & -3 \\ -4 & -8 & -10 & 18 & 6 & 16 \\ -2 & -4 & -5 & 9 & 6 & 11 \end{array}\right] \quad ③\left\{\begin{array}{l} R_1' = 1/3R_1 \\ R_2' = R_2 + 4R_1 \\ R_3' = R_3 + 2R_1 \end{array}\right.$$

$$\left[\begin{array}{ccccc|c} 1 & 2 & 4 & -3 & -2 & -1 \\ 0 & 0 & ⑥ & 6 & -2 & 12 \\ 0 & 0 & 3 & 3 & 2 & 9 \end{array}\right] \quad ⑥\left\{\begin{array}{l} R_2' = 1/6R_2 \\ R_1' = R_1 - 4R_2 \\ R_3' = R_3 - 3R_2 \end{array}\right.$$

$$\left[\begin{array}{ccccc|c} 1 & 2 & 0 & -7 & -2/3 & -9 \\ 0 & 0 & 1 & 1 & -1/3 & 2 \\ 0 & 0 & 0 & 0 & ③ & 3 \end{array}\right] \quad ③\left\{\begin{array}{l} R_3' = 1/3R_3 \\ R_1' = R_1 + 2/3R_3 \\ R_2' = R_2 + 1/3R_3 \end{array}\right.$$

$$\left[\begin{array}{ccccc|c} 1 & 2 & 0 & -7 & 0 & -25/3 \\ 0 & 0 & 1 & 1 & 0 & 7/3 \\ 0 & 0 & 0 & 0 & 1 & 1 \end{array}\right]$$

Then we have the system

$$x_1 + 2x_2 \quad - 7x_4 \qquad = -\frac{25}{3}$$
$$x_3 + \quad x_4 \qquad = \frac{7}{3}$$
$$x_5 = \quad 1$$

If we set $x_2 = s$ and $x_4 = t$, we obtain the parametrically represented solutions

$$x_1 = -2s + 7t - \frac{25}{3}$$
$$x_2 = \quad s$$
$$x_3 = \quad -t + \frac{7}{3}$$
$$x_4 = \quad t$$
$$x_5 = \quad 1$$

where $s$, $t$ are arbitrary. ∎

## EXERCISES 2.5

In Exercises 1–6, perform the indicated pivot

1. $\begin{bmatrix} -6 & -2 & 8 \\ 2 & ① & -3 \\ 5 & 4 & -8 \end{bmatrix}$

2. $\begin{bmatrix} 10 & 3 & -7 \\ 4 & ① & -3 \\ -5 & -2 & 10 \end{bmatrix}$

3. $\left[\begin{array}{ccc|c} 5 & -2 & -3 & 7 \\ -5 & 3 & 1 & -1 \\ -2 & 4 & ② & -6 \end{array}\right]$

4. $\left[\begin{array}{ccc|c} -2 & 4 & -1 & -5 \\ 8 & -10 & 4 & 6 \\ 3 & -6 & ③ & 9 \end{array}\right]$

5. $\begin{bmatrix} 4 & 5 & 2 & -3 \\ -3 & 7 & 3 & -5 \\ -2 & 4 & ⊖① & 5 \\ 1 & -5 & -2 & 10 \end{bmatrix}$

6. $\begin{bmatrix} -6 & -3 & -5 & 7 \\ 3 & ⊖① & -4 & 2 \\ 8 & -4 & 7 & -6 \\ 4 & 3 & -5 & -2 \end{bmatrix}$

In Exercises 7–16, use Gauss-Jordan elimination to solve the given systems of equations.

7. $\begin{aligned} x + 3y - 2z &= 4 \\ 5x + 16y - 5z &= 27 \\ 4x + 13y - 6z &= 26 \end{aligned}$

8. $\begin{aligned} -x + 5y + 4z &= -3 \\ -2x + 6y + 4z &= -8 \\ -x + y + z &= -4 \end{aligned}$

9. $\begin{aligned} 2x_1 + 4x_2 + 8x_3 &= 42 \\ x_1 + 2x_2 + 3x_3 &= 16 \\ x_1 + 3x_2 + 5x_3 &= 29 \end{aligned}$

10. $\begin{aligned} 4x_1 + 5x_2 - 2x_3 &= -14 \\ x_1 + 2x_2 - 2x_3 &= -8 \\ -x_1 - x_2 - 3x_3 &= 5 \end{aligned}$

11. $\begin{aligned} x - 3y - 6z - 3w &= 7 \\ -2x + y + 4z &= 2 \\ -x + y + 3z + w &= -2 \\ x - 2y - 4z - 2w &= 6 \end{aligned}$

12. $\begin{aligned} x + 2y &= 5 \\ 3x + 8y + 2z + 4w &= 17 \\ -2x + 3z + 5w &= -1 \\ x - 5z - 11w &= 14 \end{aligned}$

13. $\begin{aligned} x_1 - 3x_2 + x_3 + x_4 + x_5 &= 3 \\ x_3 - 2x_4 + 3x_5 &= 9 \\ -x_1 + 3x_2 + x_3 - 5x_4 + 6x_5 &= 19 \end{aligned}$

14. $\begin{aligned} x_1 + 5x_2 - 3x_3 - 2x_4 + 3x_5 &= 5 \\ -2x_1 - 10x_2 + 7x_3 + 6x_4 - 9x_5 &= -12 \\ 2x_1 + 10x_2 - 8x_3 - 9x_4 + 8x_5 &= 6 \end{aligned}$

15. $\begin{aligned} 2x + 8y + 10z - 6w &= 12 \\ 3x + 12y + 19z - 17w &= 22 \\ -2x - 8y - 8z + 5w &= -16 \end{aligned}$

16. $\begin{aligned} 4x + 12y + 8z + 4w &= 20 \\ 2x + 8y + 12z + 6w &= 8 \\ 3x + 13y + 25z + 2w &= 5 \end{aligned}$

## 2.6 LINEAR PROGRAMMING: THE SIMPLEX ALGORITHM

*Maximum Programs, Slack Variables, The Initial Simplex Table, The Simplex Algorithm for Maximization, Simplex Tables and Basic Feasible Solutions, Linear Production Models*

In Chapter 1 we introduced the rudimentary ideas of linear programming in a geometric context. However, when more than two variables are involved, it is far more efficient to turn to algebraic methods. In this section we discuss the simplex algorithm for solving linear programs.

Since the operation of pivoting is central to the method, it is similar in spirit to the method of Gauss-Jordan elimination for solving systems of linear equations. Indeed, the first stage of the procedure is to convert a linear program into a system of linear equations. Then pivot operations are performed on the augmented matrix, which is called a simplex table in this context. The similarity of the two methods is limited, however, since linear programs impose conditions on the variables that are not present in general linear systems. Thus the selection of the pivots must be treated much more carefully.

Linear programs are of two types: maximum problems or minimum problems. That is, either the objective function is to be maximized or it is to be minimized. Since linear mathematical models that arise from maximization problems usually result in a more straightforward simplex treatment, we will deal with them initially and discuss in Section 4.7 how minimum programs are handled.

## MAXIMUM PROGRAMS

Recall that a linear program consists of a linear function, called the objective function, which is to be maximized or minimized subject to one or more constraints on the variables. A linear program in which the problem is to maximize the objective function will be called a **maximum program**. For example, the following linear program is a maximum program:

$$\text{Maximize} \quad z = 3x_1 + 2x_2$$
$$\text{subject to} \quad x_1 + 2x_2 \leqslant 8$$
$$4x_1 + x_2 \leqslant 11$$
$$x_1 \geqslant 0, \quad x_2 \geqslant 0$$

In order to apply the methods that will be given in this section, it is important that maximum programs be formulated in a standardized way. We will require that a maximum program satisfy the following conditions:

1. All variables $x_1, x_2, \ldots, x_n$ in the program are nonnegative

2. Each constraint is written in the form

$$a_1x_1 + \cdots + a_nx_n \leqslant b, \qquad b \geqslant 0$$

That is, the sense of the inequality is $\leqslant$ (not $\geqslant$) with the variables to the left and a nonnegative constant to the right of the inequality sign.

We note that the above maximum program is given in the proper form.

*REMARK:* It can be proved that any maximum program can be put into the form described above by manipulating constraints and variables. However, the necessary maneuvers can be complicated and would only cloud the main issue at this point. The linear programs in this chapter will be given in the proper form or can be put into the proper form quite easily.

## SLACK VARIABLES

The first step toward the solution of a maximum program consists of converting the program into a system of linear equations. This is accomplished by the introduction of some new variables, called "slack" variables, into the problem.

An inequality such as $4 \leqslant 7$ means that the left-hand side is short a certain amount of equaling the right-hand side. In this case, if we add 3 to the left-hand side, we get the equality $4 + 3 = 7$. We can think of the 3 as taking up the slack in the inequality.

In a similar spirit, if we have an inequality such as

$$2x_1 + x_2 \leqslant 7$$

then a nonnegative quantity can be added to the left-hand side to bring it up to the value 7. If we introduce a nonnegative variable $x_3$, then we can write the inequality as the equation

$$2x_1 + x_2 + x_3 = 7$$

where $x_3 \geqslant 0$. For each value of $x_1$ and $x_2$ that satisfy the inequality, there will be a nonnegative value of $x_3$ such that the equation is satisfied. For example, if we have the values $x_1 = 1$ and $x_2 = 1$, then $2x_1 + x_2 = 2 + 1 = 3$, so that we have $x_3 = 4$. Conversely, if we have any nonnegative solution of the equation, then the $x_1, x_2$ values will also satisfy the inequality. For example, the values $x_1 = 2, x_2 = 2, x_3 = 1$ produce the equation $4 + 2 + 1 = 7$, and the deletion of the $x_3$ variable results in the valid inequality $4 + 2 \leqslant 7$. The term **slack variable** is used for the variable $x_3$, since it "takes up the slack" in the inequality.

Slack variables are used to convert a system of linear constraints into a system of linear equations. A different slack variable is used for each constraint.

**EXAMPLE 1**   Use slack variables to convert the constraints

$$x_1 + 4x_2 \leqslant 20$$
$$2x_1 + 7x_2 \leqslant 35$$
$$x_1 \geqslant 0, \quad x_2 \geqslant 0$$

into a system of linear equations in nonnegative variables.

SOLUTION   We introduce the slack variable $x_3$ into the first inequality and $x_4$ into the second inequality. Then we obtain the system of linear equations

$$x_1 + 4x_2 + x_3 \qquad = 20$$
$$2x_1 + 7x_2 \qquad + x_4 = 35$$

where it is required that $x_1 \geqslant 0$, $x_2 \geqslant 0$, $x_3 \geqslant 0$, $x_4 \geqslant 0$. The requirement that the slack variables be nonnegative assures us that any solution of the two inequalities determines a solution of the system of equations and that the converse also holds. For example, the values $x_1 = 2, x_2 = 3$ satisfy the inequalities; and if the values are substituted into the system of equations, we obtain the values $x_3 = 6, x_4 = 10$ for the slack variables. Thus we get the solution $(2, 3, 6, 10)$ of the system of equations. Conversely, the solution

$(4, 1, 12, 20)$ of the system of equations determines the values $x_1 = 4$, $x_2 = 1$ that satisfy the inequalities. ▮▮

The system of equations obtained from the constraints by the introduction of slack variables will be called the **constraint system**, and the variables of this system will be called the **constraint variables**. The constraint variables thus include *both* the original variables and the slack variables.

The requirement that the constraint variables be nonnegative is not part of the system itself, but it is imposed on the solutions of the system. There may exist solutions of the constraint system that contain negative values and therefore do not satisfy this requirement. These solutions will be rejected. A solution of the constraint system whose values are all nonnegative is called a **feasible solution** of the system. The problem is to find a feasible solution that determines the largest possible value for the objective function from among all feasible solutions.

One feasible solution is easily found by setting the variables of the original program (nonslack variables) equal to zero. For instance, in Example 1 we can set $x_1 = 0$, $x_2 = 0$, which then determines the values $x_3 = 20$, $x_4 = 35$. Then $(0, 0, 20, 35)$ is a feasible solution of the constraint system. On the other hand, we note that $(-1, -1, 25, 44)$ is a solution of the constraint system, but it is *not* a feasible solution.

## THE INITIAL SIMPLEX TABLE

The objective function of a linear program can be written as a linear equation with all of the variables moved to the left-hand side of the equation. For example, the objective function

$$z = 3x_1 + 2x_2$$

can be written as the equation

$$z - 3x_1 - 2x_2 = 0$$

We will combine the equation of the objective function with the constraint system to obtain a single system of linear equations. The augmented matrix for this system is called the **initial simplex table**. To distinguish the equation of the objective function, it is given the position of the first equation, and a horizontal line is drawn beneath the first row of the simplex table. The following example clarifies the structure of the initial simplex table of a maximum program.

**EXAMPLE 2** Display the initial simplex table for the maximum program:

Maximize $\qquad z = 18x_1 + 20x_2 + 32x_3$

subject to $\qquad x_1 + 2x_2 + 2x_3 \leqslant 22$

$\qquad\qquad 3x_1 + 2x_2 + 4x_3 \leqslant 40$

$\qquad\qquad 3x_1 + x_2 + 2x_3 \leqslant 14$

$\qquad\qquad x_1 \geqslant 0, \quad x_2 \geqslant 0, \quad x_3 \geqslant 0$

SOLUTION   First we rewrite the objective function as the equation

$$z - 18x_1 - 20x_2 - 32x_3 = 0$$

Then we introduce the nonnegative slack variables $x_4$, $x_5$, $x_6$ to get the constraint system

$$
\begin{aligned}
x_1 + 2x_2 + 2x_3 + x_4 \quad\quad\quad\quad &= 22 \\
3x_1 + 2x_2 + 4x_3 \quad\quad + x_5 \quad\quad &= 40 \\
3x_1 + \ x_2 + 2x_3 \quad\quad\quad\quad + x_6 &= 14
\end{aligned}
$$

Putting the equations together, we get the combined system

$$
\begin{aligned}
z - 18x_1 - 20x_2 - 32x_3 \quad\quad\quad\quad\quad\quad &= \ 0 \\
x_1 + \ 2x_2 + \ 2x_3 + x_4 \quad\quad\quad\quad &= 22 \\
3x_1 + \ 2x_2 + \ 4x_3 \quad\quad + x_5 \quad\quad &= 40 \\
3x_1 + \ \ x_2 + \ 2x_3 \quad\quad\quad\quad + x_6 &= 14
\end{aligned}
$$

where it is understood that only feasible (that is, nonnegative) solutions are acceptable. The initial simplex table is the augmented matrix of the last system. It is written in the form

$$
\left[
\begin{array}{rrrr|rrr|r}
1 & -18 & -20 & -32 & 0 & 0 & 0 & 0 \\
\hline
0 & 1 & 2 & 2 & 1 & 0 & 0 & 22 \\
0 & 3 & 2 & 4 & 0 & 1 & 0 & 40 \\
0 & 3 & 1 & 2 & 0 & 0 & 1 & 14
\end{array}
\right]
$$

where a line is put under the top row and before the slack variable columns for ease in reading the table.   ∎

The initial simplex table for a linear program has the general appearance of the table shown below, where the boxed areas correspond to the expressions in the originally stated linear program.

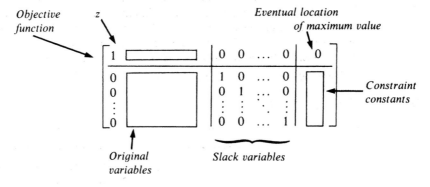

*The Initial Simplex Table*

After a sequence of pivot operations, performed according to the steps that will be given below, the maximum value will be located in the upper right-hand corner (initially occupied by a 0). Each pivot is performed in a row beneath the first row and in a column corresponding to a constraint variable. Then the new matrices are called simplex tables for the linear program (the precise form of these tables will be discussed shortly). Thus a sequence of simplex tables is obtained, each derived from the preceding one by a certain pivot operation, until the answer to the problem is found. We will now describe how the sequence of pivots is performed.

## THE SIMPLEX ALGORITHM FOR MAXIMIZATION

The simplex algorithm consists of a sequence of pivot operations on the simplex table much in the spirit of Gauss-Jordan elimination. However, the pivots must be chosen very carefully so that the nonnegativity condition on the variables is not violated and a maximum for the objective function is obtained. Since only feasible solutions are acceptable and since a maximum is sought for the objective function, the pivot operations cannot simply proceed from left to right, nor can they be done in random fashion.

The steps that constitute the simplex algorithm are given below. In the next section we will discuss the reasons behind them and explain why the procedure works. For now we will concentrate just on the mechanics of the algorithm.

After a maximum program in standardized form has been converted into a system of linear equations and the initial simplex table has been obtained, then the following steps are performed.

### The Simplex Algorithm for Maximum Programs

**Step 1.**   Select a negative entry in the first row of the table. This entry determines the pivot column. (This will always be in a column that corresponds to a constraint variable. Remember that constraint variables include the slack variables.)

**Step 2.**   Look at the quotients obtained by dividing each positive entry of the column of step 1 (the pivot column) into the corresponding entries of the last column. Select the entry that produces the smallest quotient. In case of a tie, choose either. This determines the pivot row. (These entries will always be in the rows corresponding to the constraint system.)

**Step 3.**   Use the entry found in step 2 as the pivot. (Multiply the row to make the entry 1, and then use row operations to get 0s above and below the pivot location.)

**Stopping Rule.**   Repeat steps 1–3 until there are no negative entries in the first row. This last matrix is called the **final simplex table.**

**Maximum Value.**   The maximum value of $z$ subject to the constraints will be the last entry in the first row of the final simplex table.

The sequence of steps may seem at first to be rather confusing. We suggest that the reader work through the following example and then review the steps given above. After a little practice, the procedure will become fairly routine. However, we warn the reader that the simplex algorithm almost always involves calculations with fractions. We suggest that a large scratch pad be used and that each calculation be performed carefully and patiently.

**EXAMPLE 3**   Use the simplex algorithm to solve the following linear program:

$$\text{Maximize} \qquad z = 18x_1 + 20x_2 + 32x_3$$

$$\text{subject to} \qquad x_1 + 2x_2 + 2x_3 \leqslant 22$$

$$3x_1 + 2x_2 + 4x_3 \leqslant 40$$

$$3x_1 + x_2 + 2x_3 \leqslant 14$$

$$x_1 \geqslant 0, \quad x_2 \geqslant 0, \quad x_3 \geqslant 0$$

SOLUTION   The initial simplex table for this linear program was obtained in Example 2. We repeat it here together with some annotations that are explained below.

(*Step 1*) Pivot column                                        (*Step 2*)

$$\begin{bmatrix} 1 & -18 & -20 & -32 & 0 & 0 & 0 & 0 \\ 0 & 1 & 2 & 2 & 1 & 0 & 0 & 22 \\ 0 & 3 & 2 & 4 & 0 & 1 & 0 & 40 \\ 0 & 3 & 1 & ② & 0 & 0 & 1 & 14 \end{bmatrix}$$

| Quotients |
|---|
| |
| $22/2 = 11$ |
| $40/4 = 10$ |
| $14/2 = 7$ |

Pivot

Step 1 requires that we choose a negative entry in the first row. We choose the entry $-32$, which specifies the fourth column as the pivot column. (It is often advantageous to choose the most negative entry.) Next, according to step 2, we divide each positive entry of the pivot column into the entries of the last column. The quotients can be calculated on scratch paper or off to the side of the table as shown above. We choose the smallest quotient, which is 7, and we see that it corresponds to the entry in the fourth row. Hence the entry 2 in the fourth row and fourth column is the pivot; it is circled in the initial simplex table.

We now move to step 3 and use the pivot to obtain 0s in the pivot column. After the appropriate row operations have been performed, we get the following simplex table. The annotations refer to the next phase of the procedure.

Pivot column

$$\begin{bmatrix} 1 & 30 & -4 & 0 & 0 & 0 & 16 & 224 \\ 0 & -2 & ① & 0 & 1 & 0 & -1 & 8 \\ 0 & -3 & 0 & 0 & 0 & 1 & -2 & 12 \\ 0 & 3/2 & 1/2 & 1 & 0 & 0 & 1/2 & 7 \end{bmatrix}$$

| Quotients |
|---|
| |
| $8/1 = 8$ |
| |
| $7/(1/2) = 14$ |

Since there is still a negative entry in the first row, we return to step 1 and make the selection of $-4$ (the only possible one) in the third column. For step 2 there are only two quotients to calculate, and they are shown to the right of the table. The smaller quotient determines the entry 1 in the second row and third column as pivot. It is circled in the above table. After the pivoting operation of step 3, we obtain the following simplex table.

$$
\begin{bmatrix}
1 & 22 & 0 & 0 & 4 & 0 & 12 & 256 \\
0 & -2 & 1 & 0 & 1 & 0 & -1 & 8 \\
0 & -3 & 0 & 0 & 0 & 1 & -2 & 12 \\
0 & 5/2 & 0 & 1 & -1/2 & 0 & 1 & 3
\end{bmatrix}
$$

There are no negative entries in the first row. Therefore we stop. This is the final simplex table. We now look at the last entry in the first row, and we assert that the answer is 256. That is, the maximum value of $z$ subject to the constraints is 256. The reasons for this will be explained in Section 2.7. ▮▮

*NOTE*: If a negative number ever appears in the last column, then either an arithmetic mistake was made or an incorrect pivot element was chosen. Recalculation is necessary.

The maximum value of $z$ is not a completely satisfying answer by itself. In most applications it is very important to know the values of the variables at which the maximum value of $z$ is attained. For example, products must be manufactured if revenue is to be realized. This information is actually contained in the final simplex table, and we now discuss how it is found. The solution for Example 3 will be given in Example 4.

## SIMPLEX TABLES AND BASIC FEASIBLE SOLUTIONS

If we start with the initial simplex table, then each application of steps 1–3 of the simplex algorithm produces a new matrix called a **simplex table**. Each simplex table will have some columns that have one entry equal to 1 and the other entries equal to 0, where the 1s correspond to the rows of the table that are beneath the top row. In the initial simplex table, columns of this type correspond to the slack variables. However, after a pivot operation the pivot column becomes a column of this type, and some column that was of this type changes form. The first column, which corresponds to $z$, is never changed.

For a specific simplex table we say that a variable (other than $z$) is **basic** if its column in the simplex table has one entry equal to 1 while the other entries are equal to 0. Thus a pivot column will represent a basic variable once the pivot operation is done. A **nonbasic** variable is one that is not basic. Thus on each pivot a nonbasic variable becomes basic, and a basic variable becomes nonbasic. Each different simplex table determines a different set of basic variables and nonbasic variables. We emphasize that the special variable $z$ is not regarded as either basic or nonbasic.

Each simplex table determines a **basic feasible solution** as follows. If we set the nonbasic variables equal to 0, then the values of the basic variables are determined by the system of equations associated with the simplex table. In fact, the values of the basic variables are determined by the corresponding entries in the last column of the simplex table. This is demonstrated in the next example. A value for $z$ is also determined in this manner. Since the entries in the last column are always nonnegative, these basic solutions are necessarily feasible.

**EXAMPLE 4**   Find the basic feasible solution determined by the simplex table

$$\left[ \begin{array}{cccc|ccc|c} 1 & 22 & 0 & 0 & 4 & 0 & 12 & 256 \\ \hline 0 & -2 & 1 & 0 & 1 & 0 & -1 & 8 \\ 0 & -3 & 0 & 0 & 0 & 1 & -2 & 12 \\ 0 & 5/2 & 0 & 1 & -1/2 & 0 & 1 & 3 \end{array} \right]$$

SOLUTION   This simplex table is the final one obtained in Example 3. The system of equations associated with the table is

$$\begin{aligned}
z + 22x_1 \qquad\qquad + 4x_4 \qquad + 12x_6 &= 256 \\
-2x_1 + x_2 \qquad + x_4 \qquad - x_6 &= 8 \\
-3x_1 \qquad\qquad\qquad + x_5 - 2x_6 &= 12 \\
\tfrac{5}{2}x_1 \qquad + x_3 - \tfrac{1}{2}x_4 \qquad + x_6 &= 3
\end{aligned}$$

The basic variables are $x_2$, $x_3$, $x_5$. Note that each of them appears in only one of the equations. If we set the nonbasic variables $x_1$, $x_4$, $x_6$ equal to 0, then the system becomes

$$\begin{aligned}
z \qquad\qquad\qquad &= 256 \\
x_2 \qquad\qquad &= 8 \\
x_5 &= 12 \\
x_3 \qquad &= 3
\end{aligned}$$

Thus the values of $x_2$, $x_3$, $x_5$, and $z$ are easily found to be $x_2 = 8$, $x_3 = 3$, $x_5 = 12$, and $z = 256$. Thus the values of the basic variables and the objective function are the appropriate values in the last column of the simplex table. The basic feasible solution is therefore $x_1 = 0$, $x_2 = 8$, $x_3 = 3$, $x_4 = 0$, $x_5 = 12$, $x_6 = 0$, which we can write as $(0, 8, 3, 0, 12, 0)$. If we drop the slack variables and consider only the original variables of the program, then we have $x_1 = 0$, $x_2 = 8$, $x_3 = 3$. Then the value of the objective function at $(0, 8, 3)$ is

$$z = 18x_1 + 20x_2 + 32x_3 = 18 \cdot 0 + 20 \cdot 8 + 32 \cdot 3 = 256$$

which is in agreement with the value of $z$ found above. ▮▮

In the preceding example the maximum value of $z$ was attained at the basic feasible solution obtained from the final simplex table. This phenomenon occurs in general. The reasons will be discussed in the next section.

We now consider an example in which all the links of the chain are joined. We first obtain the initial simplex table and then apply the simplex algorithm. We will list the sequence of simplex tables, find the basic feasible solution for each table, and observe that the value of $z$ is increased after each pivot. The reader should use pencil and paper to perform the calculations used in going from table to table.

**EXAMPLE 5**  Solve the linear program

$$\text{Maximize} \quad z = -15x_1 - 14x_2 + 24x_3$$
$$\text{subject to} \quad 4x_1 - 2x_2 + 2x_3 \leqslant 2$$
$$16x_1 - 2x_2 + 4x_3 \leqslant 10$$
$$15x_1 - 5x_2 + 6x_3 \leqslant 15$$
$$x_1 \geqslant 0, \quad x_2 \geqslant 0, \quad x_3 \geqslant 0$$

Your solution should include the basic feasible solution that maximizes $z$.

**SOLUTION**  We first introduce the slack variables $x_4, x_5, x_6$ and obtain the linear system

$$z + 15x_1 + 14x_2 - 24x_3 \qquad\qquad = 0$$
$$4x_1 - 2x_2 + 2x_3 + x_4 \qquad\qquad = 2$$
$$16x_1 - 2x_2 + 4x_3 \qquad + x_5 \qquad = 10$$
$$15x_1 - 5x_2 + 6x_3 \qquad\qquad + x_6 = 15$$

Then the initial simplex table is as follows.

$$\begin{bmatrix} 1 & 15 & 14 & -24 & 0 & 0 & 0 & 0 \\ 0 & 4 & -2 & ② & 1 & 0 & 0 & 2 \\ 0 & 16 & -2 & 4 & 0 & 1 & 0 & 10 \\ 0 & 15 & -5 & 6 & 0 & 0 & 1 & 15 \end{bmatrix}$$

| Quotients |
|-----------|
| 1 |
| 5/2 |
| 5/2 |

We set the nonbasic variables equal to zero, $x_1 = 0$, $x_2 = 0$, $x_3 = 0$, and obtain from the last column that $x_4 = 2$, $x_5 = 10$, $x_6 = 15$ with $z = 0$. Thus the initial basic feasible solution is $(0, 0, 0, 2, 10, 15)$ with the value $z = 0$.

The only choice for the pivot column is the fourth column, with a $-24$ in the top row. The minimum quotient is $\frac{2}{2} = 1$, which dictates that the 2 in the second row is the pivot. After pivoting we get the new simplex table

$$\begin{bmatrix} 1 & 63 & -10 & 0 & | & 12 & 0 & 0 & | & 24 \\ 0 & 2 & -1 & 1 & | & 1/2 & 0 & 0 & | & 1 \\ 0 & 8 & ② & 0 & | & -2 & 1 & 0 & | & 6 \\ 0 & 3 & 1 & 0 & | & -3 & 0 & 1 & | & 9 \end{bmatrix}$$

Quotients

$6/2 = 3$
$9/1 = 9$

The nonbasic variables are now $x_1$, $x_2$, $x_4$, and we set $x_1 = 0$, $x_2 = 0$, $x_4 = 0$. Then the values of the basic variables are $x_3 = 1$, $x_5 = 6$, $x_6 = 9$, and also $z = 24$. Thus the basic feasible solution is $(0, 0, 1, 0, 6, 9)$, and the objective function has increased in value by 24.

The third column has a $-10$ in the top row and is our only choice of pivot column. The minimum quotient $\frac{6}{2} = 3$ determines the 2 in the third row as the pivot. The next simplex table is as follows.

$$\begin{bmatrix} 1 & 103 & 0 & 0 & | & 2 & 5 & 0 & | & 54 \\ 0 & 6 & 0 & 1 & | & -1/2 & 1/2 & 0 & | & 4 \\ 0 & 4 & 1 & 0 & | & -1 & 1/2 & 0 & | & 3 \\ 0 & -1 & 0 & 0 & | & -2 & -1/2 & 1 & | & 6 \end{bmatrix}$$

We see that the final simplex table has been reached, since there are no negative entries in the first row. We set $x_1 = 0$, $x_4 = 0$, $x_5 = 0$, and we find from the last column that $x_3 = 4$, $x_2 = 3$, $x_6 = 6$, and $z = 54$. The basic feasible solution is $(0, 3, 4, 0, 0, 6)$, and the value of $z$ has increased by 30 to $z = 54$. Thus the optimal value of $z$ is 54, and it is attained at $x_1 = 0$, $x_2 = 3$, $x_3 = 4$. ∎

## LINEAR PRODUCTION MODELS

We will now illustrate the method of the simplex algorithm in the context of applications to production problems. The following examples serve to show how the simplex algorithm is used to solve linear programs as well as to indicate how linear programming arises in production decision making. The examples concern the use of limited resources to maximize profits.

**EXAMPLE 6**   Leather Products Ltd. has cutting machines, sewing machines, and a supply of leather with which they make shoes, purses, and coats. Suppose that the articles use the machines and leather as given in the table below:

|  | Shoes | Purse | Coat |
|---|---|---|---|
| Cutting machines (10 min) | 1 | 2 | 5 |
| Sewing machines (10 min) | 4 | 1 | 5 |
| Leather (square ft) | 2 | 4 | 10 |

Further, let there be a profit of \$22 on shoes, \$15 on purses, and \$50 on a coat, and suppose that there are 600 minutes available on the cutting machines, 810 minutes on the sewing machines, and 180 square feet of leather. Set up and solve the linear program to obtain the maximum profit from the available resources.

SOLUTION   Let $x_1$, $x_2$, $x_3$ be the numbers of shoes, coats, and purses to be made, respectively. Then the linear program to maximize profit subject to resources is

|          |       | *Shoes* | *Purses* | *Coats* | |
|----------|-------|---------|----------|---------|--|
| Maximize | $z =$ | $22x_1 +$ | $15x_2 +$ | $50x_3$ | profit |
| subject to | | $x_1 +$ | $2x_2 +$ | $5x_3 \leqslant 60$ | cutting machines |
| | | $4x_1 +$ | $x_2 +$ | $5x_3 \leqslant 81$ | sewing machines |
| | | $2x_1 +$ | $4x_2 +$ | $10x_3 \leqslant 180$ | leather |
| | | $x_1 \geqslant 0,$ | $x_2 \geqslant 0,$ | $x_3 \geqslant 0$ | |

In terms of equations we must find a solution to the following system where the constraint variables are nonnegative and $z$ is as large as possible:

$$
\begin{aligned}
z - 22x_1 - 15x_2 - 50x_3 && = 0 \\
x_1 + 2x_2 + 5x_3 + x_4 && = 60 \\
4x_1 + x_2 + 5x_3 \quad + x_5 && = 81 \\
2x_1 + 4x_2 + 10x_3 \quad\quad + x_6 && = 180
\end{aligned}
$$

The succession of simplex tables that leads to the solution is as follows. The initial simplex table is

$$
\begin{bmatrix}
1 & -22 & -15 & -50 & 0 & 0 & 0 & 0 \\
0 & 1 & 2 & ⑤ & 1 & 0 & 0 & 60 \\
0 & 4 & 1 & 5 & 0 & 1 & 0 & 81 \\
0 & 2 & 4 & 10 & 0 & 0 & 1 & 180
\end{bmatrix}
$$

In the initial table, $x_4$, $x_5$, $x_6$ are basic and $x_1$, $x_2$, $x_3$ are nonbasic. Therefore we let $x_1 = x_2 = x_3 = 0$, and we find that $x_4 = 60$, $x_5 = 81$, $x_6 = 180$. The initial basic feasible solution gives the value $z = 0$. That is, nothing is made and nothing is earned.

We may take any one of the $x_1$, $x_2$, or $x_3$ columns to be the pivot column, since they are headed by the negative entries $-22$, $-15$, $-50$. Here we choose the $x_3$ column, since $-50$ has the largest absolute value of the negative entries. There are three positive coefficients in the $x_3$ column, so we compute the quotients and find

$$
\frac{60}{5} < \frac{81}{5} < \frac{180}{10}
$$

Therefore the 5 in the second row is taken to be the pivot. We obtain the second table:

$$\begin{bmatrix} 1 & -12 & 5 & 0 & 10 & 0 & 0 & 600 \\ 0 & 1/5 & 2/5 & 1 & 1/5 & 0 & 0 & 12 \\ 0 & ③ & -1 & 0 & -1 & 1 & 0 & 21 \\ 0 & 0 & 0 & 0 & -2 & 0 & 1 & 60 \end{bmatrix}$$

The basic variables are now $x_3$, $x_5$, $x_6$. We set the nonbasic variables equal to zero so that $x_1 = x_2 = x_4 = 0$, and we find that $x_3 = 12$, $x_5 = 21$, $x_6 = 60$. Further, this basic feasible solution produces the value $z = 600$. In other words we can make 12 coats for a profit of $600, and we have 210 minutes for sewing and 60 square feet of leather left over.

The only possible choice for pivot column is the $x_1$ column. We check the quotients

$$\frac{21}{3} < \frac{12}{1/5}$$

and we pivot on the 3 in row three. We obtain

$$\begin{bmatrix} 1 & 0 & 1 & 0 & 6 & 4 & 0 & 684 \\ 0 & 0 & 7/15 & 1 & 4/15 & -1/15 & 0 & 53/5 \\ 0 & 1 & -(1/3) & 0 & -(1/3) & 1/3 & 0 & 7 \\ 0 & 0 & 0 & 0 & -2 & 0 & 1 & 60 \end{bmatrix}$$

The basic feasible solution is given by $x_2 = x_4 = x_5 = 0$, $x_3 = \frac{53}{5}$, $x_1 = 7$, $x_6 = 60$ with value $z = 684$. That is, we should make $\frac{53}{5}$ coats (finish the last one next week) and 7 pairs of shoes for a profit of $684. There are no negative entries left in the top row, so we conclude that the current basic feasible solution is the best possible. We make a maximum profit of $684 with 60 square feet of leather left over.  ∎

As the preceding example illustrates, the raw materials need not be exhausted to have maximum profit. Any amounts left over are determined by the values of the slack variables. Thus the slack variables have a genuine and important interpretation, though their initial insertion into the problem may have seemed somewhat contrived.

**EXAMPLE 7**   Pauls Pipe and Tobacco Shop blends Virginia, Turkish, and Mexican tobaccos into three aromatic house mixtures. A packet of Wild has 6 ounces Virginia, 4 ounces Turkish, and 14 ounces Mexican; Heather has 3 ounces Virginia, 1 ounce Turkish, and 2 ounces Mexican; and Silk has 4 ounces Virginia, 2 ounces Turkish, and 8 ounces Mexican. If Wild sells for $8, Heather for $10, and Silk for $16 per packet and if there are 32 ounces of Virginia, 10 ounces of Turkish, and 72 ounces of Mexican on hand, set up and solve the linear program to find the amounts of

Wild, Heather, and Silk that should be blended to maximize profit from the tobacco on hand.

**SOLUTION** We let $x_1$, $x_2$, $x_3$ denote the number of packets of Wild, Heather, and Silk, respectively. The linear program is:

$$
\begin{array}{llll}
 & & \textit{Wild} \quad \textit{Heather} \quad \textit{Silk} & \\
\text{Maximize} & z = & 8x_1 + 10x_2 + 16x_3 & \\
\text{subject to} & & 6x_1 + 3x_2 + 4x_3 \leqslant 32 & \text{(Virginia)} \\
 & & 4x_1 + x_2 + 2x_3 \leqslant 10 & \text{(Turkish)} \\
 & & 14x_1 + 2x_2 + 8x_3 \leqslant 72 & \text{(Mexican)} \\
 & & x_1 \geqslant 0, \quad x_2 \geqslant 0, \quad x_3 \geqslant 0 &
\end{array}
$$

The equations to be solved are

$$
\begin{array}{rl}
z - 8x_1 - 10x_2 - 16x_3 & = 0 \\
6x_1 + 3x_2 + 4x_3 + x_4 & = 32 \\
4x_1 + x_2 + 2x_3 + x_5 & = 10 \\
14x_1 + 2x_2 + 8x_3 + x_6 & = 72
\end{array}
$$

where $x_1$, $x_2$, $x_3$ and the slack variables $x_4$, $x_5$, $x_6$ are to be nonnegative and $z$ is to be as large as possible.

We now seek progressively better basic feasible solutions by pivoting from simplex table to simplex table. The initial table is:

$$
\begin{bmatrix}
1 & -8 & -10 & -16 & 0 & 0 & 0 & 0 \\
\hline
0 & 6 & 3 & 4 & 1 & 0 & 0 & 32 \\
0 & 4 & 1 & ② & 0 & 1 & 0 & 10 \\
0 & 14 & 2 & 8 & 0 & 0 & 1 & 72
\end{bmatrix}
\quad
\begin{array}{l}
\text{Quotients} \\
\\
8 \\
5 \\
9
\end{array}
$$

The initial basic feasible solution is given by $x_1 = x_2 = x_3 = 0$, $x_4 = 32$, $x_5 = 10$, $x_6 = 72$, with $z = 0$. A pivot can be made in any of the $x_1$, $x_2$, or $x_3$ columns. We take $x_3$, since $-16$ is the most negative of the first row entries. The quotients are $\frac{32}{4} = 8$, $\frac{10}{2} = 5$, and $\frac{72}{8} = 9$. The least quotient is 5, and we pivot on the 2 in row three.

$$
\begin{bmatrix}
1 & 24 & -2 & 0 & 0 & 8 & 0 & 80 \\
\hline
0 & -2 & 1 & 0 & 1 & -2 & 0 & 12 \\
0 & 2 & ①② & 1 & 0 & 1/2 & 0 & 5 \\
0 & -2 & -2 & 0 & 0 & -4 & 1 & 32
\end{bmatrix}
\quad
\begin{array}{l}
\text{Quotients} \\
\\
12 \\
10 \\
\end{array}
$$

The basic feasible solution is given by $x_1 = x_2 = x_5 = 0$, $x_3 = 5$, $x_4 = 12$, $x_6 = 32$, with value $z = 80$. A pivot may now be made in the $x_2$ column. The quotients are $\frac{12}{1} = 12$ and $\frac{5}{1/2} = 10$, and the pivot is made on the $\frac{1}{2}$ in row three. (The $-2$ in row three is not a candidate for pivot, since the new solution would not be feasible ($\frac{32}{-2} = -16$) and the value of $z$ would decrease as well.) We obtain the table

$$\begin{bmatrix} 1 & 32 & 0 & 4 & 0 & 10 & 0 & 100 \\ 0 & -6 & 0 & -2 & 1 & -3 & 0 & 2 \\ 0 & 4 & 1 & 2 & 0 & 1 & 0 & 10 \\ 0 & 6 & 0 & 4 & 0 & -2 & 1 & 52 \end{bmatrix}$$

The basic feasible solution is $x_1 = x_3 = x_5 = 0$, $x_2 = 10$, $x_4 = 2$, $x_6 = 52$, with value $z = 100$. There are no nonnegative entries left in the top row, so that this is a maximum solution, and we stop. The best that we can do is to make \$100 from 10 packets of Heather. There will be 2 ounces of Virginia and 52 ounces of Mexican left over.  ∎

# EXERCISES 2.6

In Exercises 1–4, find the slack produced in the given inequalities by the given solution.

**1.** $3x_1 - 4x_2 \leqslant 5$;  $(1, 2)$

**2.** $-2x_1 + 4x_2 \leqslant 7$;  $(3, 2)$

**3.** $6x_1 - 5x_2 + x_3 \leqslant 9$;  $(1, 2, 5)$

**4.** $-3x_1 + 4x_2 + 2x_3 \leqslant 8$;  $(3, 2, 4)$

In Exercises 5–8, use slack variables to convert the inequalities to systems of equations in nonnegative variables.

**5.** $2x_1 - x_2 \leqslant 20$
$3x_1 + 4x_2 \leqslant 5$
$x_1 \geqslant 0$,  $x_2 \geqslant 0$

**6.** $5x_1 + 3x_2 \leqslant 15$
$3x_1 - 4x_2 \leqslant 8$
$x_1 \geqslant 0$,  $x_2 \geqslant 0$

**7.** $6x_1 - 3x_2 + 2x_3 \leqslant 19$
$5x_1 + 2x_2 - 4x_3 \leqslant 8$
$-2x_1 + 3x_2 + 5x_3 \leqslant 11$
$x_1 \geqslant 0$,  $x_2 \geqslant 0$,  $x_3 \geqslant 0$

**8.** $7x_1 + 4x_2 - x_3 \leqslant 12$
$-9x_1 - 6x_2 + 6x_3 \leqslant 13$
$x_1 + 2x_2 - 5x_3 \leqslant 6$
$x_1 \geqslant 0$,  $x_2 \geqslant 0$,  $x_3 \geqslant 0$

In Exercises 9–16, display the initial simplex table for the given linear program.

**9.** Maximize  $z = 2x_1 + x_2$
subject to
$x_1 + 4x_2 \leqslant 8$
$3x_1 + 3x_2 \leqslant 9$
$x_1 \geqslant 0$,  $x_2 \geqslant 0$

**10.** Maximize  $z = 2x_1 + 3x_2$
subject to
$4x_1 + 2x_2 \leqslant 9$
$x_1 + 3x_2 \leqslant 7$
$x_1 \geqslant 0$,  $x_2 \geqslant 0$

**11.** Maximize  $z = 6x_1 + 3x_2 + x_3$
subject to
$4x_1 + 5x_2 + 2x_3 \leqslant 11$
$x_1 + 3x_2 + x_3 \leqslant 7$
$3x_1 + x_2 + 4x_3 \leqslant 8$
$x_1 \geqslant 0$,  $x_2 \geqslant 0$,  $x_3 \geqslant 0$

**12.** Maximize $\quad z = 2x_1 + 5x_2 + 4x_3$
subject to
$$3x_1 + 2x_2 + 4x_3 \leqslant 12$$
$$5x_1 + 3x_2 + 8x_3 \leqslant 16$$
$$x_1 + 6x_2 + 2x_3 \leqslant 4$$
$$x_1 \geqslant 0, \quad x_2 \geqslant 0, \quad x_3 \geqslant 0$$

**13.** Maximize $\quad z = 4x_1 - 3x_2$
subject to
$$x_1 \qquad\quad - 6x_3 \leqslant 10$$
$$3x_1 - 2x_2 + 4x_3 \leqslant 8$$
$$5x_1 + 4x_2 \qquad\; \leqslant 9$$
$$x_1 \geqslant 0, \quad x_2 \geqslant 0, \quad x_3 \geqslant 0$$

**14.** Maximize $\quad z = \qquad\quad -2x_2 + 4x_3$
subject to
$$3x_1 - 4x_2 \qquad\;\; \leqslant 7$$
$$-2x_1 + \qquad\; 6x_3 \leqslant 5$$
$$4x_1 + 7x_2 - 2x_3 \leqslant 13$$
$$x_1 \geqslant 0, \quad x_2 \geqslant 0, \quad x_3 \geqslant 0$$

**15.** Maximize $\quad z = 4x_1 + 7x_2 + 2x_3$
subject to
$$3x_1 + 4x_2 + 5x_3 \leqslant 19$$
$$2x_1 + 6x_2 + x_3 \leqslant 12$$
$$x_1 \geqslant 0, \quad x_2 \geqslant 0, \quad x_3 \geqslant 0$$

**16.** Maximize $\quad z = 3x_1 + 6x_2 + 9x_3$
subject to
$$5x_1 + x_2 + 3x_3 \leqslant 14$$
$$3x_1 + 4x_2 + 2x_3 \leqslant 11$$
$$x_1 \geqslant 0, \quad x_2 \geqslant 0, \quad x_3 \geqslant 0$$

In Exercises 17–24, use the simplex rules to find a pivot element. Perform the pivot to get another simplex table. If the new table is a final simplex table, give the maximum value of $z$.

**17.**
$$\begin{bmatrix} 1 & -6 & 2 & 0 & 0 & 0 \\ \hline 0 & 1 & 3 & 1 & 0 & 5 \\ 0 & 2 & 4 & 0 & 1 & 4 \end{bmatrix}$$

**18.**
$$\begin{bmatrix} 1 & 4 & -9 & 0 & 0 & 0 \\ \hline 0 & 6 & 3 & 1 & 0 & 9 \\ 0 & 4 & 1 & 0 & 1 & 4 \end{bmatrix}$$

**19.**
$$\begin{bmatrix} 1 & 7 & 4 & -6 & 0 & 0 & 0 \\ \hline 0 & -6 & 6 & 2 & 1 & 0 & 10 \\ 0 & 4 & -8 & 4 & 0 & 1 & 8 \end{bmatrix}$$

**20.**
$$\begin{bmatrix} 1 & -4 & 4 & 5 & 0 & 0 & 0 \\ \hline 0 & 2 & -4 & 2 & 1 & 0 & 6 \\ 0 & 1 & 1 & 1 & 0 & 1 & 10 \end{bmatrix}$$

**21.**
$$\begin{bmatrix} 1 & 4 & 13 & -6 & 0 & 0 & 0 & 0 \\ \hline 0 & 3 & -8 & 1 & 1 & 0 & 0 & 10 \\ 0 & -2 & -4 & 2 & 0 & 1 & 0 & 4 \\ 0 & -4 & 3 & -1 & 0 & 0 & 1 & 3 \end{bmatrix}$$

**22.**
$$\left[\begin{array}{cccc|ccc|c}
1 & -9 & 6 & 25 & 0 & 0 & 0 & 0 \\
\hline
0 & -1 & 2 & -2 & 1 & 0 & 0 & 5 \\
0 & 1 & -2 & 4 & 0 & 1 & 0 & 8 \\
0 & 3 & -3 & -6 & 0 & 0 & 1 & 6
\end{array}\right]$$

**23.**
$$\left[\begin{array}{cccc|ccc|c}
1 & 6 & 14 & -4 & 0 & 0 & 0 & 0 \\
\hline
0 & -4 & 4 & 2 & 1 & 0 & 0 & 12 \\
0 & -2 & -6 & 2 & 0 & 1 & 0 & 8 \\
0 & 3 & 3 & 1 & 0 & 0 & 1 & 6
\end{array}\right]$$

**24.**
$$\left[\begin{array}{cccc|ccc|c}
1 & -6 & 7 & 14 & 0 & 0 & 0 & 0 \\
\hline
0 & 3 & 5 & 1 & 1 & 0 & 0 & 12 \\
0 & 3 & -3 & -6 & 0 & 1 & 0 & 9 \\
0 & 1 & -2 & 4 & 0 & 0 & 1 & 7
\end{array}\right]$$

For the simplex table in each of Exercises 25–30, give the basic feasible solution and the value of $z$. Identify the basic and nonbasic variables. Is the solution optimal? Use the variable names $x_1, x_2, x_3, \ldots$ as needed.

**25.**
$$\left[\begin{array}{ccc|cc|c}
1 & 0 & -4 & 2 & 0 & 12 \\
\hline
0 & 1 & 2 & 1/6 & 0 & 1 \\
0 & 0 & 1 & -1/6 & 1 & 1
\end{array}\right]$$

**26.**
$$\left[\begin{array}{ccc|cc|c}
1 & -8 & 0 & 6/4 & 0 & 12 \\
\hline
0 & 3 & 1 & 1/4 & 0 & 2 \\
0 & -1 & 0 & -1/4 & 1 & 1
\end{array}\right]$$

**27.**
$$\left[\begin{array}{cccc|cc|c}
1 & 12 & 0 & 8 & 1 & 0 & 18 \\
\hline
0 & 2 & 1 & 1 & 1/6 & 0 & 3 \\
0 & -3 & 0 & 0 & -1/3 & 1 & 7
\end{array}\right]$$

**28.**
$$\left[\begin{array}{cccc|cc|c}
1 & 0 & 20 & 4 & 4 & 0 & 16 \\
\hline
0 & 1 & 3 & -2 & 1/2 & 0 & 2 \\
0 & 0 & -8 & 13 & -3 & 1 & 3
\end{array}\right]$$

**29.**
$$\left[\begin{array}{cccc|ccc|c}
1 & 2 & 0 & 4 & 0 & 0 & 2 & 8 \\
\hline
0 & 0 & 0 & 7 & 1 & 0 & 1/2 & 19 \\
0 & 2 & 0 & 0 & 0 & 1 & -1/4 & 2 \\
0 & -1 & 1 & 2 & 0 & 0 & 1/4 & 1
\end{array}\right]$$

**30.**
$$\left[\begin{array}{cccc|ccc|c}
1 & 0 & 4 & 6 & 0 & 1/2 & 0 & 2 \\
\hline
0 & 0 & 3 & 7 & 1 & -2 & 0 & 16 \\
0 & 1 & -1 & -2 & 0 & 1/4 & 0 & 1 \\
0 & 0 & 4 & -6 & 0 & 1/2 & 1 & 4
\end{array}\right]$$

In Exercises 31–36, use the simplex algorithm to solve the given linear program. Your solution should include both the maximum value of $z$ and the corresponding basic feasible solution.

**31.** Maximize $\quad z = 4x_1 + 8x_2$
subject to
$$5x_1 + x_2 \leqslant 8$$
$$6x_1 + 2x_2 \leqslant 4$$
$$x_1 \geqslant 0, \quad x_2 \geqslant 0$$

**32.** Maximize $\quad z = 8x_1 + 6x_2$
subject to
$$2x_1 + 4x_2 \leqslant 6$$
$$x_1 + 7x_2 \leqslant 4$$
$$x_1 \geqslant 0, \quad x_2 \geqslant 0$$

**33.** Maximize $\quad z = -6x_1 + 12x_2 - 8x_3$
subject to
$$10x_1 + 4x_2 - 2x_3 \leqslant 20$$
$$6x_1 + 3x_2 - 3x_3 \leqslant 9$$
$$-2x_1 + 2x_2 + x_3 \leqslant 24$$
$$x_1 \geqslant 0, \quad x_2 \geqslant 0, \quad x_3 \geqslant 0$$

**34.** Maximize $\quad z = 9x_1 - 16x_2 - 5x_3$
subject to
$$-3x_1 + 8x_2 - 4x_3 \leqslant 40$$
$$6x_1 - 10x_2 + 16x_3 \leqslant 36$$
$$3x_1 - 6x_2 + 9x_3 \leqslant 6$$
$$x_1 \geqslant 0, \quad x_2 \geqslant 0, \quad x_3 \geqslant 0$$

**35.** Maximize $\quad z = -10x_1 - 12x_2 + 8x_3$
subject to
$$-4x_1 - 8x_2 + 4x_3 \leqslant 16$$
$$4x_1 - 2x_2 + 2x_3 \leqslant 20$$
$$x_1 \geqslant 0, \quad x_2 \geqslant 0, \quad x_3 \geqslant 0$$

**36.** Maximize $\quad z = -2x_1 + 12x_2 - 12x_3$
subject to
$$-6x_1 + x_2 + 2x_3 \leqslant 8$$
$$6x_1 + 3x_2 - 6x_3 \leqslant 12$$
$$x_1 \geqslant 0, \quad x_2 \geqslant 0, \quad x_3 \geqslant 0$$

In Exercises 37–40, set up and solve the linear program to maximize income from available resources. Give the economic interpretation of your answer.

**37.** Mrs. Hill's Girl Scout troop is making bakery items for a sale. They have decided to bake apple cakes, pies, and cookies. The products use apples, sugar, and flour as shown in the following table:

|            | Cake | Pie | Cookies (12) |
|------------|------|-----|--------------|
| Apples (1) | 3    | 10  | 1            |
| Sugar (cup)| 1    | 2   | 3            |
| Flour (cup)| 2    | 3   | 1            |

They have 840 apples, 630 cups of sugar, and 450 cups of flour on hand and will sell cakes for 80¢ apiece, pies for 60¢ apiece and cookies for 50¢ per dozen.

**38.** The Lamia Toy Company manufactures Dracula, Frankenstein and Wolfman head masks from hair, plastic, and latex. A Dracula mask requires 8 ounces hair, 8 ounces plastic, and 4 ounces latex; a Frankenstein mask takes 4 ounces, 1 ounce, and 4 ounces; and a Wolfman mask needs 10 ounces, 2 ounces, and 4 ounces, respectively, of the same materials. The Dracula mask sells for 60¢, Frankenstein for 70¢, and Wolfman for 80¢, and there are on hand 500 ounces hair, 40 ounces plastic, and 140 ounces latex.

**39.** The Finest Furniture Factory makes beds, chairs, and couches from the raw materials time (man-hours), lumber (board feet), and cloth (yards). Let there be a profit of $18 per bed, $20 per chair, and $32 per couch, and let the supplies be 88 man-hours, 240 feet of lumber, and 28 yards of cloth. Further, assume that it takes 4 man-hours, 18 feet of lumber, and 6 yards of cloth to make a bed; 8 man-hours, 12 feet of lumber, and 2 yards of cloth to make a chair; and 8 man-hours, 24 feet of lumber, and 4 yards of cloth to make a couch.

**40.** Cold Start Electric produces three batteries from lead, acid, and plastic as shown in the table below:

|  | 24-month | 36-month | 48-month |
|---|---|---|---|
| Lead (pounds) | 4 | 6 | 8 |
| Acid (ounces) | 12 | 14 | 16 |
| Plastic (ounces) | 10 | 12 | 16 |

The selling prices are $40 for a 24-month, $48 for a 36-month, and $64 for a 48-month battery, and there are 7200 pounds of lead, 19,200 ounces of acid, and 28,200 ounces of plastic on hand.

In Exercises 41–42, use the simplex algorithm to solve the given linear program. Observe that it is possible for a slack variable to become nonbasic and then become basic again.

**41.** Maximize subject to

$$z = x_1 - x_2 - 6x_3$$
$$x_1 - 2x_2 - 2x_3 \leqslant 2$$
$$2x_1 - 3x_2 - 6x_3 \leqslant 6$$
$$2x_1 - 2x_2 - 4x_3 \leqslant 10$$
$$x_1 \geqslant 0, \quad x_2 \geqslant 0, \quad x_3 \geqslant 0$$

**42.** Maximize subject to

$$z = -6x_1 - 2x_2 + x_3$$
$$6x_1 - 5x_2 + 2x_3 \leqslant 5$$
$$2x_1 - 3x_2 + 1x_3 \leqslant 2$$
$$6x_1 - 4x_2 + 2x_3 \leqslant 10$$
$$x_1 \geqslant 0, \quad x_2 \geqslant 0, \quad x_3 \geqslant 0$$

## 2.7 SIMPLEX ALGORITHM: ADDITIONAL CONSIDERATIONS (OPTIONAL)

*Why It Works, When It Fails, The Geometry of the Simplex Method, Degeneracy*

The simplex algorithm involves the interplay of positive and negative values. The mechanics of the method may appear intricate at first, but once the terminology and techniques become familiar, it can be applied in a routine though sometimes messy manner. However, at this stage it may still seem somewhat mysterious. In this section we attempt to explain the reasons behind the method. We will examine the steps of the simplex algorithm and explain their purpose in arriving at a maximum value of the objective function. The possibility that the method cannot be applied because of the lack of an appropriate pivot will also be discussed, and we will see that no maximum value exists in this case.

The geometric method of linear programming in the plane that was discussed in Chapter 1 is closely related to the simplex algorithm, though the connection may not be apparent. We will compare the two approaches and see that the pivot operations on the simplex tables actually correspond to the locating of corner points of the feasibility region. Since the geometry of regions in higher dimensions can be complicated, the algebraic methods are superior in practice.

We will also mention briefly at the end of the section a difficulty that can arise in the simplex algorithm known as degeneracy. Though it is a problem that is not likely to occur in practice, it is a theoretical possibility that should be noted, and we will give an example to illustrate the phenomenon.

## WHY IT WORKS

We will discuss a sequence of key observations concerning the simplex algorithm and then summarize the method. The reader may wish to follow the discussion with an earlier example at hand to see how the different pieces fit together.

1. In the top row, as each pivot operation eliminates a negative entry, the entry in the last column either increases or remains the same. (The latter possibility is called degeneracy and will be discussed at the end of this section.)

   To see this, let us isolate one row operation for a pivot and watch what happens. Consider a pivot $b$ and the three numbers $a$, $c$, $d$ as shown below, where $a$, $b$ are positive and $d$ is nonnegative.

$$\begin{bmatrix} \cdots & -a & \cdots & \vline & c \\ \hline \cdots & \circled{b} & \cdots & \vline & d \end{bmatrix}$$

The negative entry $-a$ is eliminated by adding $a/b$ times the pivot row to the top row. In the process the entry $c$ is replaced by $c + (a/b)d$. Since $(a/b)d \geqslant 0$, the entry does not decrease. Further, if $d > 0$ (usually the case), then the entry has been made larger. For example, if $a = 2$, $b = 3$, $c = 15$, $d = 6$ in the table

$$\begin{bmatrix} \cdots & -2 & \cdots & \vline & 15 \\ \hline \cdots & \circled{3} & \cdots & \vline & 6 \end{bmatrix}$$

then the elimination of $-2$ increases the value 15 to the value $15 + (\frac{2}{3})6 = 19$.

2. Any nonzero entry in the top row of a simplex table, other than the first and last entry, corresponds to a nonbasic variable:

Recall that a column that corresponds to a basic variable has a single 1 and 0 otherwise. Initially, these are the columns of the slack variables, but in subsequent tables they are obtained by pivot operations. When a pivot is performed, the pivot column becomes 0 at the top, and the corresponding variable becomes basic. Some other column, which did correspond to a basic variable, will become positive at the top, and the corresponding variable will become nonbasic. In the table below, the basic variable $x_k$ becomes nonbasic, and the nonbasic variable $x_h$ becomes basic.

$$\begin{bmatrix} x_h & x_k & \\ -3 & 0 & \\ \textcircled{2} & 1 & \end{bmatrix} \rightarrow \begin{bmatrix} x_h & x_k & \\ 0 & 3/2 & \\ 1 & 1/2 & \end{bmatrix}$$

3. If the top row has no negative entries in the columns that correspond to constraint variables, then the entry in the last column is the maximum value of $z$.

Let us examine the assertion for a particular case. Suppose the top row is

$$1 \quad 0 \quad 8 \quad 0 \quad 0 \quad 3 \quad 0 \mid 125$$

This row represents the equation

$$z + 8x_2 + 3x_5 = 125$$

which can be written as

$$z = 125 - 8x_2 - 3x_5$$

The values of $x_2$ and $x_5$ are required to be nonnegative. If either were actually greater than zero, then we would subtract a positive amount from 125, and the value of $z$ would satisfy $z < 125$. Thus the value of $z$ is maximum if we set $x_2 = x_5 = 0$. In general, positive entries in the constraint variable portion of the top row correspond to negative coefficients in the expression for $z$. Therefore $z$ will take on its maximum value when these variables are 0.

4. In the final table the maximum value of $z$ is obtained by setting the nonbasic variables equal to 0.

This claim is verified by combining observations 2 and 3 and by recalling that the row operations do not change the solution set of a system of equations. Thus the maximum value of $z$ and the values for the constraint variables that produced it in the final table are valid for the initial table and therefore for the initial system of equations as well.

There is one gap that remains to be filled. It is crucial that the pivot operations used in going from one simplex table to the next do not introduce infeasible solutions. That is, the requirements of nonnegativity must be maintained. This is guaranteed by the rule of quotients in Step 2 of the simplex algorithm, as we now show.

**5.** The pivots are selected so that the basic solutions are always feasible.

In other words, when the nonbasic variables are taken to be 0, then the basic variables must have nonnegative values. This is assured as long as the entries below the first row in the last column do not become negative. This is accomplished by calculating the quotients with positive denominators and choosing the row with the smallest quotient as the pivot row.

In the table below, we consider two possible pivots and the entries in the last column, where $a$, $b$ are positive and $c$, $d$ are nonnegative (it may happen that $c$ or $d$ is 0). We suppose that the pivot is made on $a$.

$$\begin{bmatrix} \dots & \text{\textcircled{$a$}} & \dots & \bigm| & c \\ \dots & b & \dots & \bigm| & d \end{bmatrix}$$

We multiply the pivot row by $1/a$ and then subtract $b$ times the pivot row from the row containing $b$. This operation gives us

$$\begin{bmatrix} \dots & 1 & \dots & \bigm| & c/a \\ \dots & 0 & \dots & \bigm| & d - b(c/a) \end{bmatrix}$$

We must have

$$d - b(c/a) \geqslant 0$$

and this inequality can be written

$$\frac{d}{b} \geqslant \frac{c}{a}$$

Hence the quotient determined by the pivot row must be smaller than or equal to the quotient determined by the other row. For example, if the pivot is made on the entry 2 below, then the new solution is feasible.

$$\begin{bmatrix} \dots & \text{\textcircled{2}} & \dots & \bigm| & 4 \\ \dots & 1 & \dots & \bigm| & 5 \\ \dots & -2 & \dots & \bigm| & 3 \end{bmatrix} \rightarrow \begin{bmatrix} \dots & 1 & \dots & \bigm| & 2 \\ \dots & 0 & \dots & \bigm| & 3 \\ \dots & 0 & \dots & \bigm| & 7 \end{bmatrix}$$

But if the pivot is made on the 1 instead, then the new solution is not feasible. Notice the negative entry in the last column.

$$\begin{bmatrix} \dots & 2 & \dots & \bigm| & 4 \\ \dots & \text{\textcircled{1}} & \dots & \bigm| & 5 \\ \dots & -2 & \dots & \bigm| & 3 \end{bmatrix} \rightarrow \begin{bmatrix} \dots & 0 & \dots & \bigm| & -6 \\ \dots & 1 & \dots & \bigm| & 5 \\ \dots & 0 & \dots & \bigm| & 13 \end{bmatrix}$$

Finally, we observe that if $b < 0$ then

$$d - b(c/a) \geqslant d \geqslant 0$$

and thus negative entries in the pivot column do not need to be considered when comparing quotients.

*Summary.* Each pivot eliminates a negative entry in the top row and thereby increases the value of $z$ (barring the occurrence of degeneracy). The pivots are selected by the rule of quotients to preserve feasibility of solutions. When no negative entries appear in the top row, in a column corresponding to an $x_j$, then the value $z$ is maximized by setting the nonbasic variables equal to 0. The resulting values of the basic variables then yield the maximum value of $z$. Thus the simplex algorithm proceeds from one basic feasible solution to the next until the solution determined by the final table is obtained. If we discard the slack variables, then the original linear program has been solved.

## WHEN IT FAILS

Thus far we have carefully avoided the possibility that the simplex rules cannot be fully applied. It can happen, however, that a pivot column can be found but there is no pivot row to go with it. That is, we may come to a table with a negative entry in a constraint variable column of the top row, but there is no positive entry below it. We investigate this case in the following example and see that there is no maximum value for $z$.

**EXAMPLE 1**   Show that the linear program

$$\text{Maximize} \quad z = -6x_1 + 4x_2 - x_3$$
$$\text{subject to} \quad -2x_1 + x_2 - x_3 \leqslant 3$$
$$x_1 - 2x_2 + 2x_3 \leqslant 3$$
$$-x_1 + 2x_2 - 4x_3 \leqslant 8$$
$$x_1 \geqslant 0, \quad x_2 \geqslant 0, \quad x_3 \geqslant 0$$

has no solution because the feasibility region is not bounded on all sides and contains points that give a value of $z$ as large as we please.

**SOLUTION**   We adjoin the slack variables $x_4$, $x_5$, $x_6$ and form the initial simplex table

$$\begin{bmatrix} 1 & 6 & -4 & 1 & 0 & 0 & 0 & 0 \\ \hline 0 & -2 & ① & -1 & 1 & 0 & 0 & 3 \\ 0 & 1 & -2 & 2 & 0 & 1 & 0 & 3 \\ 0 & -1 & 2 & -4 & 0 & 0 & 1 & 8 \end{bmatrix}$$

Here the simplex rules dictate that a pivot made on the 1 in the $x_2$ column. We obtain the new simplex table

$$\begin{bmatrix} 1 & -2 & 0 & -3 & 4 & 0 & 0 & 12 \\ \hline 0 & -2 & 1 & -1 & 1 & 0 & 0 & 3 \\ 0 & -3 & 0 & 0 & 2 & 1 & 0 & 9 \\ 0 & 3 & 0 & -2 & -2 & 0 & 1 & 2 \end{bmatrix}$$

Now we see that the $x_3$ column is a potential pivot column, but there are no positive entries to choose for a pivot.

Let us examine the equations given by the last table. They are

$$
\begin{aligned}
z - \quad 2x_1 \qquad - 3x_3 + 4x_4 \qquad\qquad &= 12 \\
-2x_1 + x_2 - x_3 + x_4 \qquad\qquad &= 3 \\
-3x_1 \qquad\qquad + 2x_4 + x_5 \quad &= 9 \\
3x_1 \qquad - 2x_3 - 2x_4 \qquad + x_6 &= 2
\end{aligned}
$$

If we set the nonbasic variables other than $x_3$ equal to zero and if we write $z$ and the basic variables in terms of the constants and $x_3$, then we obtain

$$
\begin{aligned}
z &= 12 + 3x_3 \\
x_2 &= 3 + x_3 \\
x_5 &= 9 \\
x_6 &= 2 + 2x_3
\end{aligned}
$$

If we let $x_3 = t$, any nonnegative number, then we have

$$
\begin{aligned}
x_2 &= 3 + t > 0 \\
x_5 &= 9 > 0 \\
x_6 &= 2 + 2t > 0
\end{aligned}
$$

and $(0, 3 + t, t, 0, 9, 2 + 2t)$ is a nonnegative solution with value $z = 12 + 3t$. Therefore the feasibility region is unbounded in the $x_3$ coordinate direction (and others as well), and $z$ will get large without bound as $t$ is increased. For example, if $t = 1000$, then the solution $(0, 1003, 1000, 0, 9, 2002)$ will yield the value $z = 3012$, and if $t = 10,000$, then the solution $(0, 10003, 10000, 0, 9, 20002)$ will produce the value $z = 30012$. ∎

The method of the example can be generalized to furnish a proof for the following theorem.

---

### THEOREM 1

Let the linear program

$$
\begin{aligned}
\text{Maximize} \quad & z = c_1 x_1 + \cdots + c_n x_n \\
\text{subject to} \quad & a_{11} x_1 + \cdots + a_{1n} x_n \leqslant b_1 \\
& \qquad \vdots \qquad\qquad \vdots \qquad \vdots \\
& a_{m1} x_1 + \cdots + a_{mn} x_n \leqslant b_m \\
& x_1 \geqslant 0, \ldots, x_n \geqslant 0
\end{aligned}
$$

have a simplex table with a negative entry in a constraint variable position of the top row, but no positive entry below it. Then the feasibility region is unbounded in at least one coordinate direction, and nonnegative solutions of the constraint system can be found that give arbitrarily large values for $z$.

---

It is worthwhile to treat an example in the plane where it is easy to look at the problem geometrically as well as algebraically.

**EXAMPLE 2**   Use the simplex algorithm to show that the linear program

$$\text{Maximize} \quad z = 2x_1 - 2x_2$$
$$\text{subject to} \quad 4x_1 - 9x_2 \leqslant 11$$
$$x_1 - 2x_2 \leqslant 2$$
$$x_1 \geqslant 0, \quad x_2 \geqslant 0$$

has no solution, and then sketch the feasibility region and use lines of constancy to show that $z$ is not bounded. Find a feasible solution with $z \geqslant 6000$.

SOLUTION   We adjoin slack variables and form the initial simplex table

$$\begin{bmatrix} 1 & -2 & 2 & 0 & 0 & 0 \\ \hline 0 & 4 & -9 & 1 & 0 & 11 \\ 0 & \boxed{1} & -2 & 0 & 1 & 2 \end{bmatrix}$$

The pivot is made on the 1 in column 2 to obtain the table

$$\begin{bmatrix} 1 & 0 & -2 & 0 & 2 & 4 \\ \hline 0 & 0 & -1 & 1 & -4 & 3 \\ 0 & 1 & -2 & 0 & 1 & 2 \end{bmatrix}$$

Here column 3 is a potential pivot column, but there is no positive entry on which to pivot. Therefore we know that the feasibility region is unbounded and that nonnegative solutions can be found for which $z$ is arbitrarily large. We will use the method of the previous example and exhibit a nonnegative solution with a large $z$. Let $x_4 = 0$ and write the equations as

$$z = 4 + 2x_2$$
$$x_1 = 2 + 2x_2$$
$$x_3 = 3 + x_2$$

Thus $(6002, 3000, 3003, 0)$ is a nonnegative solution with $z = 6004$.

On the other hand, we may graph the feasibility region and display some lines of constancy, say, $z = -2$, $z = 2$, $z = 4$ (see Figure 2.11). We see

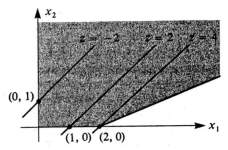

**FIGURE 2.11**                    *Unbounded feasibility region with unbounded z*

that the region is not bounded in the $x_2$ direction (and the $x_1$ direction as well) and that $z$ increases as the lines of constancy are moved to the right. Further, the lines intersect the feasibility region no matter how far to the right they are moved. Thus $z$ has no upper bound.  ▮▮

## THE GEOMETRY OF THE SIMPLEX METHOD

Despite appearances, the simplex algorithm is actually related to the geometric approach to linear programming that was discussed in Chapter 1. The relationship will be indicated by the following example. We will solve the linear program by using the simplex method, and at the same time we will draw the feasibility region in the plane and show how the two approaches are connected.

**EXAMPLE 3**   Solve the linear program

$$\text{Maximize} \quad z = 2x_1 + 3x_2$$
$$\text{subject to} \quad x_1 + 2x_2 \leqslant 8$$
$$4x_1 + x_2 \leqslant 11$$
$$x_1 \geqslant 0, \quad x_2 \geqslant 0$$

SOLUTION   We first apply the simplex algorithm. The simplex tables and basic feasible solutions are as follows.

$$
\begin{bmatrix}
1 & -2 & -3 & 0 & 0 & 0 \\
0 & 1 & ② & 1 & 0 & 8 \\
0 & 4 & 1 & 0 & 1 & 11
\end{bmatrix}
$$

Basic feasible solutions
$(0, 0, 8, 11)$
$z = 0$

$$
\begin{bmatrix}
1 & -1/2 & 0 & 3/2 & 0 & 12 \\
0 & 1/2 & 1 & 1/2 & 0 & 4 \\
0 & ⑦/② & 0 & -1/2 & 1 & 7
\end{bmatrix}
$$

$(0, 4, 0, 7)$
$z = 12$

$$
\begin{bmatrix}
1 & 0 & 0 & 10/7 & 1/7 & 13 \\
0 & 0 & 1 & 4/7 & -1/7 & 3 \\
0 & 1 & 0 & -1/7 & 2/7 & 2
\end{bmatrix}
$$

$(2, 3, 0, 0)$
$z = 13$

Thus the maximum value $z = 13$ is attained when $x_1 = 2$, $x_2 = 3$.

The feasibility region in the plane corresponding to the constraints is shown in Figure 2.12. Look at the $x_1$, $x_2$ values of the three basic feasible solutions we obtained above. First we have $x_1 = 0$, $x_2 = 0$, which gives us the corner point $(0, 0)$. Second, we have $x_1 = 0$, $x_2 = 4$, which gives us the adjacent corner point $(0, 4)$ in Figure 2.12. Finally, we have $x_1 = 2$, $x_2 = 3$, which gives us the corner point $(2, 3)$ adjacent to $(0, 4)$.

Thus the basic solutions move from the initial corner point $(0, 0)$ to a neighboring corner point $(0, 4)$ with an improved value of $z$, and finally to the neighboring corner point $(2,3)$, which yields the maximum $z = 13$. See Figure 2.12.

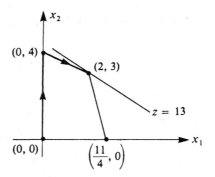

**FIGURE 2.12**                                    *Path of the simplex algorithm*

The sequence of corner points that we chose to reach the maximum was not unique. Indeed, the simplex algorithm can follow any path that leads from corner point to adjacent corner point with an improved objective function value. In this example the reader may check that a pivot on the 4 in the second column of the initial simplex table would lead to the basic feasible solution $(\frac{11}{4}, 0, \frac{21}{4}, 0)$ with $z = \frac{22}{4}$ and then to $(2, 3, 0, 0)$ with value $z = 13$ as before. That is, we move from $(0, 0)$ to the adjacent corner $(\frac{11}{4}, 0)$ and then to the adjacent corner $(2, 3)$.  ▋▌

The geometric interpretation of the simplex algorithm is more difficult to conceive in higher dimensions. We can still think of each linear equation in several variables as a bounding surface and of a feasibility region as a region bounded by these surfaces. The notions of corner point and adjacency can be appropriately extended to higher-dimensional feasibility regions. Basic feasible solutions then correspond to selected corner points. The simplex algorithm thus starts at some corner point (usually the origin) and moves from corner point to neighboring corner point, improving the value of the objective function with each move, until the solution corner point is reached. For problems that involve three variables, a polyhedral region in space can be drawn. These regions are usually too complex to visualize adequately, but we will present a simple example that conveys the above notions satisfactorily.

**EXAMPLE 4**   Geometrically and algebraically treat the linear program

$$\text{Maximize} \quad z = x_1 + 3x_2 + 4x_3$$
$$\text{subject to} \quad 6x_1 + 3x_2 + 2x_3 \leqslant 6$$
$$3x_1 + 2x_2 + 3x_3 \leqslant 6$$
$$x_1 \geqslant 0, \quad x_2 \geqslant 0, \quad x_3 \geqslant 0$$

SOLUTION   First we sketch the feasibility region. See Figure 2.13. It is the poly-
hedron in the corner of the first octant and bounded by the planes $x_1 = 0$,
$x_2 = 0$, $x_3 = 0$, $6x_1 + 3x_2 + 2x_3 = 6$, and $3x_1 + 2x_2 + 3x_3 = 6$. The corners
of the region are the points $O(0, 0, 0)$, $B(0, 2, 0)$, $C(1, 0, 0)$, $E(\frac{1}{2}, 0, \frac{3}{2})$, $F(0, \frac{6}{5}, \frac{6}{5})$
and $G(0, 0, 2)$.

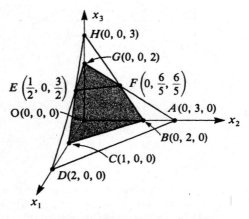

**FIGURE 2.13**                    *A feasibility region in three dimensions*

First we form a table of corners and their objective function values.

| Corner | Value of $z$ |
|--------|--------------|
| $O(0, 0, 0)$ | 0 |
| $B(0, 2, 0)$ | 6 |
| $C(1, 0, 0)$ | 1 |
| $E(\frac{1}{2}, 0, \frac{3}{2})$ | $\frac{13}{2}$ |
| $F(0, \frac{6}{5}, \frac{6}{5})$ | $\frac{42}{5}$ |
| $G(0, 0, 2)$ | 8 |

Next we will sketch a diagram of the paths that the simplex algorithm could
follow. See Figure 2.14.

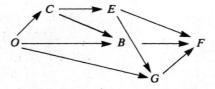

**FIGURE 2.14**                    *Paths of the simplex algorithm*

From this we see that the allowable paths are

$$OBF, \quad OCBF, \quad OCEF, \quad OCEGF, \quad OGF$$

There is a sequence of simplex pivots that corresponds to each of these paths. We display the simplex tables for the path $OGF$.

$$\begin{bmatrix} 1 & -1 & -3 & -4 & 0 & 0 & 0 \\ 0 & 6 & 3 & 2 & 1 & 0 & 6 \\ 0 & 3 & 2 & ③ & 0 & 1 & 6 \end{bmatrix} \quad \begin{array}{c} (0,0,0,6,6) \\ \text{or} \\ O(0,0,0) \end{array}$$

$$\begin{bmatrix} 1 & 3 & -1/3 & 0 & 0 & 4/3 & 8 \\ 0 & 4 & ⑤/③ & 0 & 1 & -2/3 & 2 \\ 0 & 1 & 2/3 & 1 & 0 & 1/3 & 2 \end{bmatrix} \quad \begin{array}{c} (0,0,2,2,0) \\ \text{or} \\ G(0,0,2) \end{array}$$

$$\begin{bmatrix} 1 & 19/5 & 0 & 0 & 1/5 & 6/5 & 42/5 \\ 0 & 12/5 & 1 & 0 & 3/5 & -2/5 & 6/5 \\ 0 & -3/5 & 0 & 1 & -2/5 & 3/5 & 6/5 \end{bmatrix} \quad \begin{array}{c} (0,6/5,6/5,0,0) \\ \text{or} \\ F(0,6/5,6/5) \end{array}$$

The reader may check that the other paths from $O$ to $F$ have a corresponding sequence of simplex pivots. ∎

## DEGENERACY

It is possible that a simplex pivot will not produce a new solution and therefore there will be no improvement in the objective function value. Specifically, this will be the case when the equation constant of the pivot row is 0. In this case we call the pivot **degenerate**. We illustrate this possibility with a simple example where degeneracy occurs.

**EXAMPLE 5**  Solve the linear program

$$\begin{aligned} \text{Maximize} \quad z = \quad & 8x_1 - 7x_2 - 16x_3 \\ \text{subject to} \quad & 2x_1 - 2x_2 - 4x_3 \leqslant 4 \\ & 4x_1 - 3x_2 - 10x_3 \leqslant 8 \\ & -2x_1 + 2x_2 + 6x_3 \leqslant 2 \\ & x_1 \geqslant 0, \quad x_2 \geqslant 0, \quad x_3 \geqslant 0 \end{aligned}$$

SOLUTION  After adjoining slack variables we obtain the initial simplex table

$$\begin{bmatrix} 1 & -8 & 7 & 16 & 0 & 0 & 0 & 0 \\ 0 & ② & -2 & -4 & 1 & 0 & 0 & 4 \\ 0 & 4 & -3 & -10 & 0 & 1 & 0 & 8 \\ 0 & -2 & 2 & 6 & 0 & 0 & 1 & 2 \end{bmatrix} \quad \begin{array}{c} 4/2 = 2 \\ 8/4 = 2 \end{array}$$

The pivot is to be made in column 2, and we have a tie in the ratios of interest. We can pivot on the 2 or on the 4. We arbitrarily choose the 2. We obtain the table

$$
\begin{bmatrix}
1 & 0 & -1 & 0 & 4 & 0 & 0 & 16 \\
0 & 1 & -1 & -2 & 1/2 & 0 & 0 & 2 \\
0 & 0 & \textcircled{1} & -2 & -2 & 1 & 0 & 0 \\
0 & 0 & 0 & 2 & 1 & 0 & 1 & 6
\end{bmatrix}
\quad 0/1 = 0
$$

The basic feasible solution is given by $x_2 = 0$, $x_3 = 0$, $x_4 = 0$ for the nonbasic variables and $x_1 = 2$, $x_5 = 0$, $x_6 = 6$ for the basic variables with $z = 16$. Column 3 is the pivot column. Here the pivot must be made on the 1. Since the equation constant of this row is 0, the numbers in the rightmost column remain the same. However, the table and the roles of $x_2$ and $x_5$ as nonbasic and basic variables will change.

$$
\begin{bmatrix}
1 & 0 & 0 & -2 & 2 & 1 & 0 & 16 \\
0 & 1 & 0 & -4 & -3/2 & 1 & 0 & 2 \\
0 & 0 & 1 & -2 & -2 & 1 & 0 & 0 \\
0 & 0 & 0 & \textcircled{2} & 1 & 0 & 1 & 6
\end{bmatrix}
$$

The basic feasible solution is given by $x_3 = 0$, $x_4 = 0$, $x_5 = 0$ for the nonbasic variables and $x_1 = 2$, $x_2 = 0$, $x_6 = 6$ for the basic variables with $z = 16$. The solution and objective function value have not changed, but $x_2$ has become basic and $x_5$ has become nonbasic. Now a pivot is made on the 2 in column 4 to obtain

$$
\begin{bmatrix}
1 & 0 & 0 & 0 & 3 & 1 & 1 & 22 \\
0 & 1 & 0 & 0 & 1/2 & 1 & 2 & 14 \\
0 & 0 & 1 & 0 & -1 & 1 & 1 & 6 \\
0 & 0 & 0 & 1 & 1/2 & 0 & 1/2 & 3
\end{bmatrix}
$$

The maximizing solution is now seen to be $(14, 6, 3, 0, 0, 0)$ with value $z = 22$. We see that although degeneracy forced a pivot that did not improve the objective function value, it did not stop the method from reaching the best solution. ∎

It is theoretically possible for a sequence of degenerate pivots to be made in such a way that a previously obtained simplex table will be attained again. If this should happen, then the same choice of pivots will cause this table to continue to appear from time to time, and the maximum will never be reached. This phenomenon is called **cycling**. In practice we do not worry about the possibility of cycling, since the likelihood of choosing a sequence of pivots that will produce it is very small.

## EXERCISES 2.7

In each of Exercises 1–8 a simplex table for a maximization program is given. Perform the indicated pivot and contrast the new and old basic solutions and objective function values. Tell why the indicated pivot is undesirable.

**1.**
$$\begin{bmatrix} 1 & -2 & 6 & 0 & 0 & 0 \\ 0 & 1 & 1 & 1 & 0 & 7 \\ 0 & 2 & ③ & 0 & 1 & 1 \end{bmatrix}$$

**2.**
$$\begin{bmatrix} 1 & 6 & 0 & 0 & 4 & 16 \\ 0 & 1 & 0 & 1 & 3 & 13 \\ 0 & ② & 1 & 0 & 1 & 4 \end{bmatrix}$$

**3.**
$$\begin{bmatrix} 1 & 0 & -2 & 0 & 6 & 12 \\ 0 & 0 & ③ & 1 & 6 & 18 \\ 0 & 1 & 2 & 0 & 2 & 4 \end{bmatrix}$$

**4.**
$$\begin{bmatrix} 1 & -6 & 4 & 0 & 0 & 0 \\ 0 & 2 & 1 & 1 & 0 & 4 \\ 0 & ④ & 8 & 0 & 1 & 12 \end{bmatrix}$$

**5.**
$$\begin{bmatrix} 1 & 0 & 4 & 8 & 0 & 4 \\ 0 & 1 & ⊝1 & 4 & 0 & 2 \\ 0 & 0 & 3 & -1 & 1 & 9 \end{bmatrix}$$

**6.**
$$\begin{bmatrix} 1 & 3 & 0 & 0 & 6 & 6 \\ 0 & 2 & 0 & 1 & 2 & 8 \\ 0 & ⊝3 & 1 & 0 & 3 & 3 \end{bmatrix}$$

**7.**
$$\begin{bmatrix} 1 & 8 & -2 & 0 & 0 & 0 \\ 0 & 6 & 2 & 1 & 0 & 8 \\ 0 & 4 & ⊝4 & 0 & 1 & 6 \end{bmatrix}$$

**8.**
$$\begin{bmatrix} 1 & -3 & 0 & 0 & 4 & 8 \\ 0 & ⊝3 & 0 & 1 & 6 & 15 \\ 0 & 6 & 1 & 0 & 2 & 4 \end{bmatrix}$$

In the systems of constraints in Exercises 9–10, what is the maximum value of $z$? Give a feasible solution that produces this value.

**9.** 
$$z - 3x_1 \quad\quad - x_3 - 4x_4 \quad\quad = 14$$
$$6x_1 + x_2 - 3x_3 - 3x_4 \quad\quad = 9$$
$$2x_1 \quad\quad + 5x_3 + 2x_4 + x_5 = 8$$
$$x_1 \geqslant 0, \quad x_2 \geqslant 0, \quad x_3 \geqslant 0, \quad x_4 \geqslant 0, \quad x_5 \geqslant 0$$

**10.** 
$$z \quad\quad - 2x_2 - 5x_3 - 7x_4 \quad\quad = 15$$
$$3x_2 + x_3 - 2x_4 + x_5 = 10$$
$$x_1 - x_2 + 6x_3 + 4x_4 \quad\quad = 6$$
$$x_1 \geqslant 0, \quad x_2 \geqslant 0, \quad x_3 \geqslant 0, \quad x_4 \geqslant 0, \quad x_5 \geqslant 0$$

In Exercises 11–14, use the simplex algorithm to show that there is no upper bound on the objective function value $z$. Then sketch the feasibility region in the plane and use lines of constancy to show that $z$ is not bounded.

**11.** Maximize $z = -4x_1 + 6x_2$
 subject to
$$-4x_1 + 2x_2 \leqslant 2$$
$$2x_1 - 4x_2 \leqslant 4$$
$$x_1 \geqslant 0, \quad x_2 \geqslant 0$$

**12.** Maximize $z = 4x_1 - x_2$
 subject to
$$-12x_1 + 6x_2 \leqslant 6$$
$$4x_1 - 4x_2 \leqslant 4$$
$$x_1 \geqslant 0, \quad x_2 \geqslant 0$$

**13.** Maximize $z = -22x_1 + 12x_2$
 subject to
$$9x_1 - 6x_2 \leqslant 3$$
$$-6x_1 + 3x_2 \leqslant 6$$
$$x_1 \geqslant 0, \quad x_2 \geqslant 0$$

**14.** Maximize $z = 10x_1 - 18x_2$
 subject to
$$5x_1 - 10x_2 \leqslant 10$$
$$-5x_1 + 2x_2 \leqslant 8$$
$$x_1 \geqslant 0, \quad x_2 \geqslant 0$$

In Exercises 15–16, use the simplex algorithm to show that $z$ has no upper bound over the given feasibility region. Find a specific solution with $z \geqslant 1000$.

**15.** Maximize $\quad z = \quad 2x_1 - 3x_2 - 4x_3$
   subject to
   $$x_1 - 2x_2 - 10x_3 \leqslant 3$$
   $$-2x_1 + x_2 + 10x_3 \leqslant 2$$
   $$x_1 - x_2 - 4x_3 \leqslant 2$$
   $$x_1 \geqslant 0, \quad x_2 \geqslant 0, \quad x_3 \geqslant 0$$

**16.** Maximize $\quad z = \quad 3x_1 - x_2 - 4x_3$
   subject to
   $$6x_1 - 19x_2 + 19x_3 \leqslant 13$$
   $$3x_1 - 9x_2 + 9x_3 \leqslant 6$$
   $$-3x_1 + 10x_2 - 11x_3 \leqslant 7$$
   $$x_1 \geqslant 0, \quad x_2 \geqslant 0, \quad x_3 \geqslant 0$$

In each of Exercises 17–18 a simplex table of a maximization program is given. Describe the most appropriate course of action and why it should be taken.

**17.**
$$\begin{bmatrix} 1 & -4 & -2 & 0 & 0 & 4 & 0 & 40 \\ \hline 0 & -2 & -1 & 0 & 1 & 1 & 0 & 4 \\ 0 & 1 & -3 & 1 & 0 & 1/5 & 0 & 2 \\ 0 & 3 & -5 & 0 & 0 & -2 & 1 & 7 \end{bmatrix}$$

**18.**
$$\begin{bmatrix} 1 & 0 & -2 & -6 & 0 & 2 & 0 & 18 \\ \hline 0 & 0 & 6 & -3 & 1 & -3 & 0 & 12 \\ 0 & 1 & 1 & -5 & 0 & 1/3 & 0 & 3 \\ 0 & 0 & -5 & -2 & 0 & 2 & 1 & 2 \end{bmatrix}$$

In Exercises 19–24, sketch the feasibility region for the given linear program, and then label the vertices and compute the objective function value for each. Determine all paths that the simplex algorithm could take from the initial vertex (the origin) to the maximum vertex, and follow a shortest path with the simplex algorithm.

**19.** Maximize $\quad z = 3x_1 + 4x_2$
   subject to
   $$-x_1 + x_2 \leqslant 1$$
   $$2x_1 + 4x_2 \leqslant 12$$
   $$x_1 \geqslant 0, \quad x_2 \geqslant 0$$

**20.** Maximize $\quad z = x_1 + 6x_2$
   subject to
   $$2x_1 - x_2 \leqslant 2$$
   $$3x_1 + 5x_2 \leqslant 15$$
   $$x_1 \geqslant 0, \quad x_2 \geqslant 0$$

**21.** Maximize $\quad z = 2x_1 + 3x_2$
   subject to
   $$-x_1 + 2x_2 \leqslant 6$$
   $$x_1 - 3x_2 \leqslant 3$$
   $$x_1 + x_2 \leqslant 4$$
   $$x_1 \geqslant 0, \quad x_2 \geqslant 0$$

**22.** Maximize $\quad z = 3x_1 + 2x_2$
   subject to
   $$-4x_1 + 3x_2 \leqslant 12$$
   $$2x_1 - 3x_2 \leqslant 6$$
   $$5x_1 + 6x_2 \leqslant 30$$
   $$x_1 \geqslant 0, \quad x_2 \geqslant 0$$

**23.** Maximize $\quad z = x_1 + x_2 + 4x_3$
   subject to
   $$3x_1 + 4x_2 + 6x_3 \leqslant 12$$
   $$15x_1 + 10x_2 + 6x_3 \leqslant 30$$
   $$x_1 \geqslant 0, \quad x_2 \geqslant 0, \quad x_3 \geqslant 0$$

**24.** Maximize     $z = x_1 + 2x_2 + x_3$
  subject to
$$3x_1 + 4x_2 + 3x_3 \leqslant 12$$
$$5x_1 + 4x_2 + 10x_3 \leqslant 20$$
$$x_1 \geqslant 0, \quad x_2 \geqslant 0, \quad x_3 \geqslant 0$$

In Exercises 25–28, solve the given linear program.

**25.** Maximize     $z = 8x_1 - 14x_2 - 2x_3$
  subject to
$$2x_1 - 4x_2 + 6x_3 \leqslant 0$$
$$4x_1 - 7x_2 + 14x_3 \leqslant 8$$
$$6x_1 - 10x_2 + 10x_3 \leqslant 18$$
$$x_1 \geqslant 0, \quad x_2 \geqslant 0, \quad x_3 \geqslant 0$$

**26.** Maximize     $z = -6x_1 - 4x_2 + 3x_3$
  subject to
$$5x_1 - x_2 + x_3 \leqslant 9$$
$$3x_1 - 9x_2 + 4x_3 \leqslant 4$$
$$6x_1 - 6x_2 + 3x_3 \leqslant 0$$
$$x_1 \geqslant 0, \quad x_2 \geqslant 0, \quad x_3 \geqslant 0$$

**27.** Maximize     $z = -2x_1 + 2x_2 - x_3$
  subject to
$$2x_1 + 2x_2 - 2x_3 \leqslant 4$$
$$-6x_1 + 4x_2 - 2x_3 \leqslant 8$$
$$6x_1 - 6x_2 + 4x_3 \leqslant 4$$
$$x_1 \geqslant 0, \quad x_2 \geqslant 0, \quad x_3 \geqslant 0$$

**28.** Maximize     $z = -10x_1 - 2x_2 + 6x_3$
  subject to
$$10x_1 - 18x_2 - 3x_3 \leqslant 1$$
$$-10x_1 - 4x_2 + 6x_3 \leqslant 6$$
$$-6x_1 + 3x_2 + 3x_3 \leqslant 3$$
$$x_1 \geqslant 0, \quad x_2 \geqslant 0, \quad x_3 \geqslant 0$$

# 3

# Matrices and Determinants

A matrix is a rectangular array of numbers. We have made extensive use of matrices as a convenient way of working with systems of linear equations, and we have used the matrices called simplex tables in linear programming. We have also displayed data in several production problems in the form of rectangular tables of numbers, although the term matrix was not used at the time. However, the value of matrices goes far beyond their being a shorthand for linear systems or a means of tabulating data.

Even though coefficient arrays of systems of equations had been studied since the early eighteenth century, it was not until the mid-nineteenth century that matrices were studied as distinct mathematical entities in their own right. This viewpoint was taken by Arthur Cayley (1821–1895) in the 1850s. He organized the known properties of matrices into a coherent theory and developed many new properties and applications of matrices. Today matrix theory is a thriving field of mathematics that has extensive applications in science and business.

In Section 3.1 we will introduce the basic operations of addition and multiplication of matrices. Many of the algebraic properties of numbers have counterparts in the context of matrices, but we will see that there are a few important properties that do not have matrix parallels.

Section 3.2 deals with the important notion of the inverse of a square matrix, which is the matrix analogue of the reciprocal of a number. Matrix inverses do not always exist, and we will see that the question of existence is related to the question of uniqueness of solutions of linear systems. In Section 3.3 we will apply the algebra of matrices and the concept of inverse to the Leontief model for economic planning.

Sections 3.4 and 3.5 are devoted to determinants of square matrices. The determinant function assigns a numerical value to each square matrix in an intriguingly complicated way. Fortunately, elementary row operations can be used to simplify the tedium of calculation. In Section 3.5 we will apply determinants to the calculation of inverses and to deriving a method, called Cramer's Rule, for solving linear systems.

As another application of matrices, we will present in Section 3.6 an introduction to Markov analysis. Although it was originally developed in the physical sciences, the method of Markov analysis now has significant applications in managerial decision making and long-range planning.

## 3.1  MATRIX OPERATIONS

*Matrices, Matrix Addition and Scalar Multiplication, Matrix Multiplication, Properties of Matrix Multiplication*

In this section we define the basic operations on matrices: addition of matrices, multiplication of a matrix by a number, and multiplication of matrices. We examine their properties and illustrate how they arise in applications. The first two operations are quite natural, but matrix multiplication is a little more complicated. The definition of matrix multiplication may seem awkward at first, but it is very appropriate for numerous applications. In addition, these operations lead to a rich and useful algebra of matrices. Matrix addition and multiplication have many properties that are analogous to properties of numbers, but there are some important exceptions. We will see one exception in this section and another in the next section.

### MATRICES

We will use capital letters for names of matrices. Normally, the letters $A$, $B$, $C$, and so on, will be used for matrices of numbers, and the letters $X$, $Y$, $Z$ will refer to matrices whose entries are variables. The letters $O$ and $I$ are reserved for special matrices that will be defined later.

If a matrix $A$ has $m$ rows and $n$ columns, then it is called an **$m \times n$ matrix**. If it is necessary to be explicit about the number of rows and columns in a matrix $A$, then we will write $A_{m \times n}$. Thus the notation $A_{3 \times 5}$ refers to a matrix with 3 rows and 5 columns.

We will often write $A = [a_{ij}]$, where $a_{ij}$ is the entry in the $i$th row and $j$th column. For example, if $A = [a_{ij}]$ is the $2 \times 4$ matrix

$$A = \begin{bmatrix} 1 & -6 & 3 & 2 \\ 4 & 8 & 1 & 9 \end{bmatrix}$$

then $a_{14} = 2$, $a_{23} = 1$, and so on. Similarly, if the $3 \times 2$ matrix $B = [b_{ij}]$ is given by

$$B = \begin{bmatrix} 1 & 7 \\ -1 & 8 \\ 3 & 6 \end{bmatrix}$$

then we have $b_{12} = 7$, $b_{31} = 3$, and so on.

Two matrices $A = [a_{ij}]$ and $B = [b_{ij}]$ are said to be **equal**, written $A = B$, if they have the same number of rows and columns and if $a_{ij} = b_{ij}$ for every $i$ and $j$. Thus equal matrices have the same dimensions, and they have equal entries in corresponding positions.

Data is frequently presented in matrix form. Indeed, whenever numbers are listed in rows and columns, we are dealing with matrices, even though the term may not be mentioned explicitly. For example, if daily sales of two brands of toothpaste are recorded according to size, then the information may be given in a matrix such as

$$A = \begin{bmatrix} \overset{\text{Regular}}{20} & \overset{\text{King}}{35} & \overset{\text{Family}}{57} \\ 17 & 42 & 51 \end{bmatrix} \begin{matrix} \text{Sparkle} \\ \text{Glisten} \end{matrix}$$

The information could also be displayed with rows and columns reversed. Then we would have the following matrix, which we denote by $A^t$.

$$A^t = \begin{bmatrix} \overset{\text{Sparkle}}{20} & \overset{\text{Glisten}}{17} \\ 35 & 42 \\ 57 & 51 \end{bmatrix} \begin{matrix} \text{Regular} \\ \text{King} \\ \text{Family} \end{matrix}$$

The matrix $A^t$ that is obtained by interchanging the rows and columns is called the **transpose** of $A$. In general, if $A = [a_{ij}]$, then the transpose of $A$ is the matrix $A^t = [a_{ji}]$ where the row and column indices are reversed. To go from $A$ to $A^t$, each row of $A$ becomes the corresponding column of $A^t$. For example, if $A$ is the $2 \times 3$ matrix

$$A = \begin{bmatrix} 1 & 2 & 3 \\ 4 & 1 & -5 \end{bmatrix}$$

then the transpose of $A$ is the $3 \times 2$ matrix

$$A^t = \begin{bmatrix} 1 & 4 \\ 2 & 1 \\ 3 & -5 \end{bmatrix}$$

In general, if $A$ is an $m \times n$ matrix, then the transpose $A^t$ is an $n \times m$ matrix.

## MATRIX ADDITION AND SCALAR MULTIPLICATION

Let $A$ be a matrix that shows the production by shifts for three types of automobiles at an assembly plant, and let $B$ be the corresponding matrix for a second plant, as follows:

$$\begin{matrix} \text{Plant 1} \end{matrix} \qquad \begin{matrix} \text{Shift} \\ 1 \quad 2 \quad 3 \end{matrix}$$

$$A = \begin{bmatrix} 14 & 12 & 9 \\ 26 & 23 & 18 \\ 8 & 7 & 5 \end{bmatrix} \begin{matrix} \text{4-door sedan} \\ \text{2-door sedan} \\ \text{Station wagon} \end{matrix}$$

Plant 2          Shift

$$B = \begin{bmatrix} 32 & 29 & 25 \\ 41 & 35 & 31 \\ 17 & 14 & 11 \end{bmatrix} \begin{array}{l} \text{4-door sedan} \\ \text{2-door sedan} \\ \text{Station wagon} \end{array}$$

Suppose that we want the total production (both plants) per car type, per shift. Then we would add the corresponding entries of the two matrices. If we call this matrix $A + B$, then we have

Shift

$$A + B = \begin{bmatrix} 14+32 & 12+29 & 9+25 \\ 26+41 & 23+35 & 18+31 \\ 8+17 & 7+14 & 5+11 \end{bmatrix} = \begin{bmatrix} 46 & 41 & 34 \\ 67 & 58 & 49 \\ 25 & 21 & 16 \end{bmatrix} \begin{array}{l} \text{4-door sedan} \\ \text{2-door sedan} \\ \text{Station wagon} \end{array}$$

In general, we have the following definition.

**DEFINITION**

If $A = [a_{ij}]$ and $B = [b_{ij}]$ have the same dimensions, then the **matrix sum** is defined by

$$A + B = [c_{ij}]$$

where

$$c_{ij} = a_{ij} + b_{ij}$$

for all $i, j$.

Thus to add two $m \times n$ matrices, we add the corresponding entries. We stress that the addition of two matrices is possible only if they have the same number of rows and columns.

Suppose now that we want to double the automobile production at Plant 1 given by the matrix $A$ above. If we write this output in matrix form and call the matrix $2A$, then we have

$$2A = \begin{bmatrix} 2\cdot14 & 2\cdot12 & 2\cdot9 \\ 2\cdot26 & 2\cdot23 & 2\cdot18 \\ 2\cdot8 & 2\cdot7 & 2\cdot5 \end{bmatrix} = \begin{bmatrix} 28 & 24 & 18 \\ 52 & 46 & 36 \\ 16 & 14 & 10 \end{bmatrix}$$

Thus the matrix $2A$ is obtained from $A$ by multiplying every entry of $A$ by 2.

When a matrix is multiplied by a constant, it is customary to call the constant a **scalar**. We have the following definition.

### DEFINITION

If $k$ is a scalar (constant) and if $A = [a_{ij}]$, then the **scalar multiplication** of the matrix $A$ by the scalar $k$ is defined by

$$kA = [c_{ij}]$$

where

$$c_{ij} = ka_{ij}$$

for all $i, j$.

---

In other words, if a matrix is multiplied by a constant, then the constant multiplies every entry of the matrix. That is, we have $kA = [ka_{ij}]$.

The **negative** $-A$ of a matrix $A$ is defined to be $(-1)A$. Then subtraction of matrices is defined as follows. If $A$ and $B$ are matrices of the same dimension, then the **difference** $A - B$ is defined by $A - B = A + (-1)B$. Thus the operation of subtraction is not a new operation but is defined in terms of addition and scalar multiplication.

The symbol $O$ will be used for the $m \times n$ matrix whose entries are all 0, and it will be called the **zero matrix**. Normally, the dimensions of the zero matrix are understood from the context and are not given explicitly.

There are a number of properties that hold for matrix addition and scalar multiplication, and we list them for convenient reference. These properties are analogous to familiar properties of addition and multiplication of numbers, and they follow from the properties of numbers by considering the individual entries of the matrices. Rather than memorize this list, we simply manipulate matrix expressions involving these two operations as experience with numbers dictates.

### THEOREM 1

If $a, b$ are scalars and if $A, B$ are $m \times n$ matrices, then we have the following properties:

(*i*)  $A + B = B + A$

(*ii*)  $A + (B + C) = (A + B) + C$

(*iii*)  $a(bA) = (ab)A$

(*iv*)  $(a + b)A = aA + bA$

(*v*)  $a(A + B) = aA + aB$

(*vi*)  $A + O = A$, and $aO = O$

---

Property (*i*) is called the commutative property of addition, and property (*ii*) is called the associative property of addition. From these properties it follows that three matrices of the same dimensions can be added in any order. Consequently, the sum of three matrices can be written unambiguously without parentheses as $A + B + C$ or in any other arrangement. This property can be extended to the sum of any finite number of matrices.

**EXAMPLE 1**   Let

$$A = \begin{bmatrix} -2 & 1 \\ 1 & 0 \end{bmatrix}, \quad B = \begin{bmatrix} 4 & -2 \\ 2 & 3 \end{bmatrix}, \quad C = \begin{bmatrix} 1 & 4 \\ -5 & 2 \end{bmatrix}$$

Find (a) $A + B + C$, and (b) $3A - 2B$

**SOLUTION**   (a) The sum $A + B + C$ can be found either as

$$A + (B + C) = \begin{bmatrix} -2 & 1 \\ 1 & 0 \end{bmatrix} + \begin{bmatrix} 5 & 2 \\ -3 & 5 \end{bmatrix} = \begin{bmatrix} 3 & 3 \\ -2 & 5 \end{bmatrix}$$

or as

$$(A + B) + C = \begin{bmatrix} 2 & -1 \\ 3 & 3 \end{bmatrix} + \begin{bmatrix} 1 & 4 \\ -5 & 2 \end{bmatrix} = \begin{bmatrix} 3 & 3 \\ -2 & 5 \end{bmatrix}$$

(b) We first perform the scalar multiplications and then add to get

$$3A + (-2)B = \begin{bmatrix} -6 & 3 \\ 3 & 0 \end{bmatrix} + \begin{bmatrix} -8 & 4 \\ -4 & -6 \end{bmatrix} = \begin{bmatrix} -14 & 7 \\ -1 & -6 \end{bmatrix} \quad \blacksquare$$

## MATRIX MULTIPLICATION

To multiply a matrix $A$ times a matrix $B$ to get the matrix product $AB$, we think of the left factor $A$ as consisting of rows and the right factor $B$ as consisting of columns.

The entries of the product matrix $AB$ are found by multiplying the rows of $A$ times the columns of $B$ as follows. To multiply a row times a column, we multiply the corresponding entries and add. For example, we have

$$[5 \quad 2 \quad 4] \begin{bmatrix} 1 \\ 2 \\ 3 \end{bmatrix} = 5 \cdot 1 + 2 \cdot 2 + 4 \cdot 3 = 21$$

We will state the formal definition of matrix multiplication after we present an example that motivates the way in which matrices are multiplied.

**EXAMPLE 2**   The Famous Afarr Department Store has tabulated the sales of ties, belts, and wallets in the men's accessories department of the downtown, north mall, and south mall stores by means of the matrix

$$A = \begin{bmatrix} \overset{\text{Ties}}{72} & \overset{\text{Belts}}{54} & \overset{\text{Wallets}}{47} \\ 37 & 28 & 33 \\ 43 & 32 & 25 \end{bmatrix} \begin{matrix} \text{Downtown} \\ \text{North mall} \\ \text{South mall} \end{matrix}$$

The wholesale and retail prices for these items are given by the matrix

$$B = \begin{bmatrix} \overset{\text{Wholesale}}{3} & \overset{\text{Retail}}{5} \\ 4 & 7 \\ 8 & 15 \end{bmatrix} \begin{matrix} \text{Ties} \\ \text{Belts} \\ \text{Wallets} \end{matrix}$$

Find a matrix tabulation that shows total receipts, both wholesale and retail, for the three stores.

SOLUTION   There are six totals to find, but they are all found in the same manner. For example, to find the total downtown wholesale receipts, we multiply the entries of row 1 of $A$ times the corresponding entries of column 1 of $B$ and add the results. Thus we have

Downtown     Wholesale     Ties     Belts     Wallets     Total wholesale

$$\begin{bmatrix} 72 & 54 & 47 \end{bmatrix} \begin{bmatrix} 3 \\ 4 \\ 8 \end{bmatrix} = 72\cdot3 + 54\cdot4 + 47\cdot8 = 808$$

To find the total retail receipts for the downtown store, we use column 2 of $B$ and get

Downtown     Retail     Ties     Belts     Wallets     Total retail

$$\begin{bmatrix} 72 & 54 & 47 \end{bmatrix} \begin{bmatrix} 5 \\ 7 \\ 15 \end{bmatrix} = 72\cdot5 + 54\cdot7 + 47\cdot15 = 1443$$

The other totals are found by multiplying the rows of $A$ times the columns of $B$ in the same way. If we call the resulting matrix $AB$, then we have the following, where we use initials to label the rows and columns.

$$AB = \begin{matrix} \text{dt} \\ \text{nm} \\ \text{sm} \end{matrix} \begin{bmatrix} \overset{t}{72} & \overset{b}{54} & \overset{w}{47} \\ 37 & 28 & 33 \\ 43 & 32 & 25 \end{bmatrix} \begin{bmatrix} \overset{w}{3} & \overset{r}{5} \\ 4 & 7 \\ 8 & 15 \end{bmatrix} \begin{matrix} t \\ b \\ w \end{matrix}$$

$$= \begin{bmatrix} \overset{\text{Wholesale}}{72\cdot3 + 54\cdot4 + 47\cdot8} & \overset{\text{Retail}}{72\cdot5 + 54\cdot7 + 47\cdot15} \\ 37\cdot3 + 28\cdot4 + 33\cdot8 & 37\cdot5 + 28\cdot7 + 33\cdot15 \\ 43\cdot3 + 32\cdot4 + 25\cdot8 & 43\cdot5 + 32\cdot7 + 25\cdot15 \end{bmatrix} \begin{matrix} \text{dt} \\ \text{nm} \\ \text{sm} \end{matrix}$$

$$= \begin{bmatrix} \overset{w}{808} & \overset{r}{1443} \\ 487 & 876 \\ 457 & 814 \end{bmatrix} \begin{matrix} \text{dt} \\ \text{nm} \\ \text{sm} \end{matrix} \quad \blacksquare$$

The method of combining the rows of $A$ and the columns of $B$ in the preceding example gave us the matrix product of $A$ and $B$. The general definition of matrix multiplication is as follows.

## DEFINITION

If $A = [a_{ij}]$ is an $m \times n$ matrix and $B = [b_{ij}]$ is an $n \times p$ matrix, then the **matrix product** $AB$ is the $m \times p$ matrix defined by

$$AB = [c_{ij}]$$

where

$$c_{ij} = a_{i1}b_{1j} + a_{i2}b_{2j} + \cdots + a_{in}b_{nj}$$

$$= \sum_{k=1}^{n} a_{ik}b_{kj}$$

for all $i, j$.

To show matrix multiplication more clearly, we can write the matrices as

$$\begin{bmatrix} a_{11} & a_{12} & \cdots & a_{1k} & \cdots & a_{1n} \\ & & & & & \\ a_{i1} & a_{i2} & \cdots & a_{ik} & \cdots & a_{in} \\ & & & & & \\ a_{m1} & a_{m2} & \cdots & a_{mk} & \cdots & a_{mn} \end{bmatrix} \begin{bmatrix} b_{11} & \cdots & b_{1j} & \cdots & b_{1p} \\ b_{21} & \cdots & b_{2j} & \cdots & b_{2p} \\ & & & & \\ b_{k1} & \cdots & b_{kj} & \cdots & b_{kp} \\ & & & & \\ b_{n1} & \cdots & b_{nj} & \cdots & b_{np} \end{bmatrix}$$

The $ij$th entry of the product $AB$ is found by working across the $i$th row of $A$ and down the $j$th column of $B$, multiplying the corresponding entries and adding.

It is important to note that the matrix product $AB$ is defined only when the number of columns of $A$ is equal to the number of rows of $B$—that is, when the number of entries in each row of $A$ is equal to the number of entries in each column of $B$. Further note that the number of rows of $AB$ is the same as the number of rows of $A$, and the number of columns of $AB$ is the same as the number of columns of $B$. We can diagram the relations as

$$A_{(m) \times (n)} B_{(n) \times (p)} = C_{(m) \times (p)}$$

Thus if $A$ is a $3 \times 5$ matrix and $B$ is a $5 \times 7$ matrix, then the product $AB$ is a $3 \times 7$ matrix; the product $BA$ in the opposite order is not defined.

**EXAMPLE 3**   Find the product $AB$ of the matrices

$$A = \begin{bmatrix} 5 & -1 & 6 & 2 \\ 4 & 3 & -3 & -2 \\ -4 & 6 & 1 & 7 \end{bmatrix}, \quad B = \begin{bmatrix} 2 & -5 \\ -3 & -2 \\ 1 & 4 \\ -5 & 3 \end{bmatrix}$$

**SOLUTION** Since $A$ is a $3 \times 4$ matrix and $B$ is a $4 \times 2$ matrix, their product $AB$ is defined, and it will be a $3 \times 2$ matrix. We have

$$AB = \begin{bmatrix} 10 + 3 + 6 - 10 & -25 + 2 + 24 + 6 \\ 8 - 9 - 3 + 10 & -20 - 6 - 12 - 6 \\ -8 - 18 + 1 - 35 & 20 - 12 + 4 + 21 \end{bmatrix} = \begin{bmatrix} 9 & 7 \\ 6 & -44 \\ -60 & 33 \end{bmatrix}$$

Note that the product $BA$ is not defined. ∎

If we multiply a matrix $A$ on the right by a matrix $B$ to get the product $AB$, then we say that $B$ **postmultiplies** $A$. On the other hand, if we multiply $A$ on the left by a matrix $C$ to get the product $CA$, then we say that $C$ **premultiplies** $A$. We can often combine the entries in the rows or columns of a matrix by appropriate pre- or postmultiplication. For example, suppose we have the matrix

$$A = \begin{bmatrix} 3 & 2 \\ 5 & 4 \\ 7 & 6 \end{bmatrix}$$

To add the entries in each column and thereby find the column sums, we can premultiply $A$ as follows:

$$\begin{bmatrix} 1 & 1 & 1 \end{bmatrix} \begin{bmatrix} 3 & 2 \\ 5 & 4 \\ 7 & 6 \end{bmatrix} = \begin{bmatrix} 3 + 5 + 7 & 2 + 4 + 6 \end{bmatrix} = \begin{bmatrix} 15 & 12 \end{bmatrix}$$

To find the row sums, we can postmultiply $A$ as follows:

$$\begin{bmatrix} 3 & 2 \\ 5 & 4 \\ 7 & 6 \end{bmatrix} \begin{bmatrix} 1 \\ 1 \end{bmatrix} = \begin{bmatrix} 3 + 2 \\ 5 + 4 \\ 7 + 6 \end{bmatrix} = \begin{bmatrix} 5 \\ 9 \\ 13 \end{bmatrix}$$

If we wish to subtract column 2 from column 1, this can be accomplished by postmultiplication of $A$ as follows:

$$\begin{bmatrix} 3 & 2 \\ 5 & 4 \\ 7 & 6 \end{bmatrix} \begin{bmatrix} 1 \\ -1 \end{bmatrix} = \begin{bmatrix} 3 - 2 \\ 5 - 4 \\ 7 - 6 \end{bmatrix} = \begin{bmatrix} 1 \\ 1 \\ 1 \end{bmatrix}$$

## PROPERTIES OF MATRIX MULTIPLICATION

We now extend our list of properties of matrix operations to include matrix multiplication. The properties are analogous to properties of operations on numbers, and we can continue to rely on experience with numbers to manipulate matrix expressions correctly. The formal proofs, which involve the manipulation of summation indices, will be omitted.

## *THEOREM 2*

Let $a$, $b$ be numbers and let $A$, $B$, $C$ be matrices. Assume that the matrix dimensions are such that the sums and products in each of the following are defined. Then we have

(i)   $A(BC) = (AB)C$

(ii)  $(A + B)C = AC + BC$

(iii) $A(B + C) = AB + AC$

(iv)  $OA = O, \ AO = O$

(v)   $(aA)(bB) = abAB$

---

Property (*i*) is called the associative property of multiplication. Properties (*ii*) and (*iii*) are the distributive properties of multiplication with respect to addition. The next two examples, which continue with the Famous Afarr Department Store, illustrate these properties. We first consider the associative property.

**EXAMPLE 4**   Net receipts are found by subtracting wholesale receipts from retail receipts. Find the total net receipts for each store in Example 2.

SOLUTION   The matrix

$$
N = \begin{bmatrix} -1 \\ 1 \end{bmatrix} \quad \begin{matrix} \text{Wholesale} \\ \text{Retail} \end{matrix}
$$

expresses the information that net is retail minus wholesale. The net receipts for each store can be obtained by postmultiplying the matrix $AB$ found in Example 2 by the matrix $N$ as follows.

$$
(AB)N = \begin{matrix} \text{dt} \\ \text{nm} \\ \text{sm} \end{matrix} \begin{bmatrix} 808 & 1443 \\ 487 & 876 \\ 457 & 814 \end{bmatrix} \begin{bmatrix} -1 \\ 1 \end{bmatrix} = \begin{bmatrix} 635 \\ 389 \\ 357 \end{bmatrix} \begin{matrix} \text{dt} \\ \text{nm} \\ \text{sm} \end{matrix}
$$

On the other hand, we could find the net receipts for each article first by

$$
BN = \begin{matrix} \text{t} \\ \text{b} \\ \text{w} \end{matrix} \begin{bmatrix} 3 & 5 \\ 4 & 7 \\ 8 & 15 \end{bmatrix} \begin{bmatrix} -1 \\ 1 \end{bmatrix} = \begin{bmatrix} 2 \\ 3 \\ 7 \end{bmatrix} \begin{matrix} \text{t} \\ \text{b} \\ \text{w} \end{matrix}
$$

and then compute the net for each store by

$$
A(BN) = \begin{array}{c} \text{dt} \\ \text{nm} \\ \text{sm} \end{array}
\begin{array}{ccc} \text{t} & \text{b} & \text{w} \\ \left[\begin{array}{ccc} 72 & 54 & 47 \\ 37 & 28 & 33 \\ 43 & 32 & 25 \end{array}\right] \end{array}
\begin{array}{c} \text{Net} \\ \left[\begin{array}{c} 2 \\ 3 \\ 7 \end{array}\right] \end{array}
\begin{array}{c} \text{t} \\ \text{b} \\ \text{w} \end{array}
=
\begin{array}{c} \text{Net} \\ \left[\begin{array}{c} 635 \\ 389 \\ 357 \end{array}\right] \end{array}
\begin{array}{c} \text{dt} \\ \text{nm} \\ \text{sm} \end{array}
$$

Thus we see that the results are the same:

$$
(AB)N = \begin{bmatrix} 635 \\ 389 \\ 357 \end{bmatrix} = A(BN)
$$

This is an example of the associative property of matrix multiplication. ∎

A similar analysis can be used to give an example of distributive property (*ii*) in Theorem 2.

**EXAMPLE 5** Suppose that the sales matrix *A* (we are still working with the Famous Afarr example) is for a period before Christmas and that many of the items are returned after New Years. Specifically, let the return matrix be

$$
R = \begin{array}{c} \text{dt} \\ \text{nm} \\ \text{sm} \end{array}
\begin{array}{ccc} \text{t} & \text{b} & \text{w} \\ \left[\begin{array}{ccc} 21 & 18 & 15 \\ 12 & 10 & 8 \\ 14 & 20 & 7 \end{array}\right] \end{array}
$$

Compute the total receipts, both wholesale and retail, for all three stores after adjustment for returns.

**SOLUTION** On the one hand we can compute sales revenue and refunds separately and then subtract. This gives us

$$
AB - RB = \begin{array}{c} \text{dt} \\ \text{nm} \\ \text{sm} \end{array}
\begin{array}{cc} \text{w} & \text{r} \\ \left[\begin{array}{cc} 808 & 1443 \\ 487 & 876 \\ 457 & 814 \end{array}\right] \end{array}
-
\begin{array}{c} \text{dt} \\ \text{nm} \\ \text{sm} \end{array}
\begin{array}{ccc} \text{t} & \text{b} & \text{w} \\ \left[\begin{array}{ccc} 21 & 18 & 15 \\ 12 & 10 & 8 \\ 14 & 20 & 7 \end{array}\right] \end{array}
\begin{array}{cc} \text{w} & \text{r} \\ \left[\begin{array}{cc} 3 & 5 \\ 4 & 7 \\ 8 & 15 \end{array}\right] \end{array}
$$

$$
= \begin{bmatrix} 808 & 1443 \\ 487 & 876 \\ 457 & 814 \end{bmatrix}
- \begin{bmatrix} 255 & 456 \\ 140 & 250 \\ 178 & 315 \end{bmatrix}
= \begin{array}{cc} \text{w} & \text{r} \\ \left[\begin{array}{cc} 553 & 987 \\ 347 & 626 \\ 279 & 499 \end{array}\right] \end{array}
\begin{array}{c} \text{dt} \\ \text{nm} \\ \text{sm} \end{array}
$$

We can also compute sales-less-returns and then postmultiply by prices. Then we obtain

$$
(A - R)B = \left\{ \begin{array}{c} \text{dt} \\ \text{nm} \\ \text{sm} \end{array}
\begin{array}{ccc} \text{t} & \text{b} & \text{w} \\ \left[\begin{array}{ccc} 72 & 54 & 47 \\ 37 & 28 & 33 \\ 43 & 32 & 25 \end{array}\right] \end{array}
-
\begin{array}{ccc} \text{t} & \text{b} & \text{w} \\ \left[\begin{array}{ccc} 21 & 18 & 15 \\ 12 & 10 & 8 \\ 14 & 20 & 7 \end{array}\right] \end{array} \right\}
\begin{array}{cc} \text{w} & \text{r} \\ \left[\begin{array}{cc} 3 & 5 \\ 4 & 7 \\ 8 & 15 \end{array}\right] \end{array}
\begin{array}{c} \text{t} \\ \text{b} \\ \text{w} \end{array}
$$

$$
= \begin{matrix} \text{dt} \\ \text{nm} \\ \text{sm} \end{matrix}
\begin{bmatrix} \overset{t}{51} & \overset{b}{36} & \overset{w}{32} \\ 25 & 18 & 25 \\ 29 & 12 & 18 \end{bmatrix}
\begin{bmatrix} \overset{w}{3} & \overset{r}{5} \\ 4 & 7 \\ 8 & 15 \end{bmatrix}
\begin{matrix} t \\ b \\ w \end{matrix}
= \begin{bmatrix} \overset{w}{553} & \overset{r}{987} \\ 347 & 626 \\ 279 & 499 \end{bmatrix}
\begin{matrix} \text{dt} \\ \text{nm} \\ \text{sm} \end{matrix}
$$

Hence we have

$$
AB - RB = \begin{bmatrix} 553 & 987 \\ 347 & 626 \\ 279 & 499 \end{bmatrix} = (A - R)B
$$

This illustrates the distributive property (*ii*). ∎

There is one major property of number multiplication that matrix multiplication does *not* have. Number multiplication is **commutative**; that is, $ab = ba$, and the order of the factors is immaterial. However, matrix multiplication is *not* commutative. The matrix product in the reverse order may not even be defined. That is,

$$
A_{m \times n} B_{n \times p}
$$

is a proper multiplication, but

$$
B_{n \times p} A_{m \times n}
$$

is not, except when $p = m$. Even if both products are defined, $AB$ will equal $BA$ only rarely. For example, we have

$$
AB = \begin{bmatrix} 2 & 1 \\ -3 & 4 \end{bmatrix} \begin{bmatrix} 6 & -7 \\ 5 & 2 \end{bmatrix} = \begin{bmatrix} 17 & -12 \\ 2 & 29 \end{bmatrix}
$$

but in the opposite order we have

$$
BA = \begin{bmatrix} 6 & -7 \\ 5 & 2 \end{bmatrix} \begin{bmatrix} 2 & 1 \\ -3 & 4 \end{bmatrix} = \begin{bmatrix} 33 & -22 \\ 4 & 13 \end{bmatrix}
$$

Thus the two products are not the same, so that matrix multiplication is not commutative.

A **square matrix** is a matrix that has equal numbers of rows and columns. A square matrix can be multiplied by itself, and the result is again a square matrix of the same size. Thus if $A$ is an $n \times n$ matrix, then the **powers** $A^2 = AA$, $A^3 = A^2 A$, ... of $A$ are defined, and they are also $n \times n$ matrices.

**EXAMPLE 6**   Find $A^2$ and $A^3$ for the matrix

$$
A = \begin{bmatrix} 0 & 1 \\ 2 & -1 \end{bmatrix}
$$

**SOLUTION** We have

$$A^2 = \begin{bmatrix} 0 & 1 \\ 2 & -1 \end{bmatrix} \begin{bmatrix} 0 & 1 \\ 2 & -1 \end{bmatrix} = \begin{bmatrix} 2 & -1 \\ -2 & 3 \end{bmatrix}$$

$$A^3 = \begin{bmatrix} 2 & -1 \\ -2 & 3 \end{bmatrix} \begin{bmatrix} 0 & 1 \\ 2 & -1 \end{bmatrix} = \begin{bmatrix} -2 & 3 \\ 6 & -5 \end{bmatrix} \quad ∎$$

## EXERCISES 3.1

In the exercises of this section, $A, B, C, D, E, F, G$ refer to the matrices below

$$A = \begin{bmatrix} 5 & -1 & 6 \\ -4 & 3 & 2 \end{bmatrix}, \quad B = \begin{bmatrix} -2 & 3 & -5 \\ -3 & 4 & 1 \end{bmatrix}, \quad G = \begin{bmatrix} 5 & -2 \\ -1 & 3 \end{bmatrix}$$

$$C = \begin{bmatrix} 1 & 6 \\ 5 & 2 \\ -1 & 3 \end{bmatrix}, \quad D = \begin{bmatrix} 7 \\ 5 \\ 4 \end{bmatrix}, \quad E = \begin{bmatrix} -3 & 4 \\ 8 & -9 \\ 2 & 1 \end{bmatrix}, \quad F = \begin{bmatrix} 7 \\ 9 \\ -5 \end{bmatrix}$$

In Exercises 1–8, find the indicated entries or matrices.

**1.** $a_{12}, a_{23}$  **2.** $b_{11}, b_{22}$  **3.** $c_{32}, c_{21}$  **4.** $d_{11}, d_{31}$
**5.** $A^t$  **6.** $B^t$  **7.** $C^t$  **8.** $E^t$

In Exercises 9–12, display the given information in matrix form

**9.** Brown's Hardware Company has 1500 saws, 750 axes, and 350 hatchets in stock in their downtown store and 1245 saws, 875 axes, and 200 hatchets in their suburban store.

**10.** Continental Nut Mix Company produces a Thrift mix, which is 75% peanuts, 6% almonds, 12% filberts, and 7% cashews, and a Splendor mix, which is 23% peanuts, 36% almonds, 14% filberts, and 27% cashews.

**11.** Paul has test scores of 97, 93, 87, 84; Jim has 59, 72, 63, 85; and Ann has 74, 83, 95, 87.

**12.** Jack has quiz grades of 6, 8, 4; Mary has scores of 7, 10, 3; Mark has scores of 5, 9, 1; and Sue has scores of 9, 10, 6.

In Exercises 13–34, find the indicated matrices.

**13.** $A + B$  **14.** $C + E$  **15.** $4A$  **16.** $3B$
**17.** $-2D, 4C$  **18.** $-5F, 3E$  **19.** $B - A, A - B$  **20.** $C - E, E - C$
**21.** $A + 2B, B - 2A, -3(6A)$  **22.** $E - 3C, 4(-2B), 2A + B$
**23.** $B + C^t$  **24.** $E + A^t$
**25.** $AD, AE$  **26.** $BC, BF$  **27.** $AC, AF$  **28.** $BE, BD$
**29.** $A(CB), (AC)B$  **30.** $(BE)A, B(EA)$
**31.** $AD + BD, (A + B)D$  **32.** $BE + AE, (B + A)E$
**33.** $CA + CB, C(A + B)$  **34.** $EB + EA, E(B + A)$

**35.** In Exercise 9, let saws, axes, and hatchets wholesale for $5, $7, $4, and retail for $9, $13, $7, respectively. Set up a matrix product that will give both the wholesale value and the retail value of the stock in each store.

**36.** In Exercise 10, suppose that the purchase prices per pound of the nuts are $1.35 for peanuts, $1.85 for almonds, $1.75 for filberts, and $2.10 for cashews. Set up a matrix product that will give the purchase cost for both a pound of Thrift and a pound of Splendor.

**37.** In Exercise 11, find a matrix product that will give (a) the sum of the scores for each person and (b) the sum of the scores on each test.

**38.** In Exercise 12, find a matrix product that will give (a) the sum of the scores for each person and (b) the sum of the scores for each quiz.

**39.** In Exercise 35, set up a matrix product that will give the wholesale value of the stock for both stores and the retail value of the stock for both stores. Express the result in two ways.

**40.** In Exercise 36, set up a matrix product that will give the total cost for a pound of Thrift and a pound of Splendor. Express the result in two ways.

**41.** In Exercise 37, find a matrix product that will give the average score for (a) each person and (b) each test.

**42.** In Exercise 38, find a matrix product that will give the average score for (a) each person and (b) each quiz.

**43.** Find $G^2$, $G^4$          **44.** Find $G^3$, $G^5$

In Exercises 45–50, find the values of $x$ and $y$ such that equality holds.

**45.** $\begin{bmatrix} 1 & x \\ y & 3 \end{bmatrix} + \begin{bmatrix} 2 & 4 \\ 1 & -2 \end{bmatrix} = \begin{bmatrix} 3 & 5 \\ 4 & 1 \end{bmatrix}$

**46.** $\begin{bmatrix} 4 & y \\ x & 2 \end{bmatrix} + \begin{bmatrix} 5 & 1 \\ 6 & 5 \end{bmatrix} = \begin{bmatrix} 9 & 6 \\ 3 & 7 \end{bmatrix}$

**47.** $\begin{bmatrix} 1 & x \\ 2 & 3 \end{bmatrix} \begin{bmatrix} 2 & 4 \\ 1 & -1 \end{bmatrix} = \begin{bmatrix} 4 & 2 \\ 7 & 5 \end{bmatrix}$

**48.** $\begin{bmatrix} 3 & 1 \\ y & -1 \end{bmatrix} \begin{bmatrix} -2 & 2 \\ 4 & 3 \end{bmatrix} = \begin{bmatrix} -2 & 9 \\ -2 & -5 \end{bmatrix}$

**49.** $\begin{bmatrix} x & 2 \\ 1 & y \end{bmatrix} \begin{bmatrix} 3 & 2 \\ -2 & 1 \end{bmatrix} = \begin{bmatrix} 8 & 10 \\ 9 & -1 \end{bmatrix}$

**50.** $\begin{bmatrix} 1 & 2 \\ 3 & 4 \end{bmatrix} \begin{bmatrix} 1 & y \\ x & 1 \end{bmatrix} = \begin{bmatrix} 5 & 3 \\ 11 & 7 \end{bmatrix}$

## 3.2 THE INVERSE OF A MATRIX

*Cancellation, Inverse Matrices, Finding the Inverse of a Matrix, Inverses and Linear Systems, Proofs of the Theorems*

Matrix multiplication has many properties in common with algebraic properties of numbers, but there are important exceptions. We have already encountered one exception, namely, that matrix multiplication is not commutative, since $AB = BA$ does not hold in general. In this section we examine another property that holds for some but not all matrices.

The notion of the inverse of a square matrix corresponds to that of the multiplicative inverse (i.e., reciprocal) of a number. We will see that not every nonzero square matrix has an inverse. Nevertheless, in spite of this limitation, the concept of an inverse matrix is one of the most important tools in linear algebra. The existence of the inverse of a matrix is closely tied to the idea of consistency of linear systems. In fact, a procedure very similar to Gaussian elimination is used to calculate the inverse of a square matrix, when the inverse exists. It will also be seen that if the coefficient matrix of a linear system has an inverse, then the inverse matrix provides a means of solving the system.

### CANCELLATION

An important property of numbers is the fact that nonzero numbers can be cancelled. For example, by cancelling the factor 5 in the equation $5x = 5y$, we can conclude that $x = y$. The number 0 is singular in the realm of numbers; it is the only number that may not be cancelled. For instance, we may *not* deduce from $0 \cdot 4 = 0 \cdot 7$ that $4 = 7$ by cancelling the 0.

Unfortunately, matrices cannot be cancelled as freely as numbers. For example, if we have the matrices

$$A = \begin{bmatrix} 1 & 2 \\ 2 & 4 \end{bmatrix}, \quad B = \begin{bmatrix} -1 \\ 1 \end{bmatrix}, \quad C = \begin{bmatrix} 5 \\ -2 \end{bmatrix}$$

then the products $AB$ and $AC$ are equal, since

$$AB = \begin{bmatrix} 1 & 2 \\ 2 & 4 \end{bmatrix} \begin{bmatrix} -1 \\ 1 \end{bmatrix} = \begin{bmatrix} 1 \\ 2 \end{bmatrix} = \begin{bmatrix} 1 & 2 \\ 2 & 4 \end{bmatrix} \begin{bmatrix} 5 \\ -2 \end{bmatrix} = AC$$

However, we cannot cancel the $A$ in the equality $AB = AC$ because it is not true that $B = C$. Thus the cancellation property is not valid for matrices in general. In fact, it is possible to get the zero matrix by multiplying two nonzero matrices, a result that cannot occur with numbers. For example, we have

$$\begin{bmatrix} 1 & 2 \\ 2 & 4 \end{bmatrix} \begin{bmatrix} 2 & -2 \\ -1 & 1 \end{bmatrix} = \begin{bmatrix} 0 & 0 \\ 0 & 0 \end{bmatrix}$$

There do exist matrices for which cancellation is valid. We will soon find conditions that guarantee that the cancellation of certain square matrices is permissible. The approach is to examine the matrix analogue of reciprocals of numbers.

## INVERSE MATRICES

Cancellation of nonzero numbers is a consequence of the fact that for each nonzero number $a$ there is a number $a^{-1} = 1/a$ such that $aa^{-1} = a^{-1}a = 1$. Thus to cancel the 5 in the equation $5x = 5y$, we multiply both sides of the equation by $\frac{1}{5}$ and conclude that $x = y$. The number $a^{-1}$ is called the multiplicative inverse (or the reciprocal) of $a$.

The number 1 has the special property that $1 \cdot a = a \cdot 1 = a$ for any number $a$. The number 1 is the multiplicative identity for the number system. To define the notion of matrix inverse, it is necessary to have a matrix analogue that serves as an identity for matrix multiplication.

The $n \times n$ **identity matrix** is the matrix

$$I = I_n = \begin{bmatrix} 1 & 0 & \dots & 0 & 0 \\ 0 & 1 & \dots & 0 & 0 \\ \vdots & & \ddots & & \vdots \\ 0 & 0 & \dots & 1 & 0 \\ 0 & 0 & \dots & 0 & 1 \end{bmatrix}$$

This matrix has 1s down the main diagonal and 0s elsewhere. It is a square matrix, since it has an equal number of rows and columns. If it is important to emphasize the dimension, we will write $I_n$, but otherwise we will simply write $I$.

The identity matrix plays the role of 1 in multiplication. For example, for the $2 \times 2$ identity matrix $I_2$ we have

$$\begin{bmatrix} 1 & 0 \\ 0 & 1 \end{bmatrix} \begin{bmatrix} 1 & 2 \\ 3 & 4 \end{bmatrix} = \begin{bmatrix} 1 & 2 \\ 3 & 4 \end{bmatrix} \begin{bmatrix} 1 & 0 \\ 0 & 1 \end{bmatrix} = \begin{bmatrix} 1 & 2 \\ 3 & 4 \end{bmatrix}$$

In general, we have for any $m \times n$ matrix $A$ that

$$I_m A = A I_n = A$$

If $A$ is a square matrix, then we have $IA = AI = A$ where it is assumed that $I$ has the correct dimensions for multiplying $A$.

We now define the notion of inverse of a matrix. Note that the following definition applies only to square matrices.

### DEFINITION

A square matrix $A$ is said to be **invertible** if there exists a matrix $A^{-1}$ such that

$$A^{-1}A = I = AA^{-1}$$

The matrix $A^{-1}$ is called the **inverse** of $A$.

For example, a direct multiplication will show that the matrices

$$A = \begin{bmatrix} 1 & 1 \\ 2 & 3 \end{bmatrix}, \quad A^{-1} = \begin{bmatrix} 3 & -1 \\ -2 & 1 \end{bmatrix}$$

satisfy the relations $A^{-1}A = I$ and $AA^{-1} = I$, so that $A$ is invertible and has inverse $A^{-1}$.

Thus if $A$ is an $n \times n$ matrix and if $A$ is invertible, then its inverse $A^{-1}$ is also an $n \times n$ matrix, and the product of $A$ with its inverse in either order is the $n \times n$ identity matrix $I$. A matrix that is not invertible is sometimes said to be **singular**. Some basic properties of inverses are given in the following theorem.

### THEOREM 1

Let $A$ and $B$ be square matrices. Then:

(*i*)  If $A$ is invertible, then the inverse $A^{-1}$ is unique. That is, if $B$ is a matrix such that $BA = AB = I$, then $B = A^{-1}$.

(*ii*)  If $A$ is invertible, then $A^{-1}$ is invertible, and the inverse of $A^{-1}$ is $A$. That is, $(A^{-1})^{-1} = A$.

(*iii*)  If $A$ and $B$ are invertible, then the product $AB$ is invertible and $(AB)^{-1} = B^{-1}A^{-1}$.

The proofs of these statements are straightforward, but for the moment we want to concentrate on the use of the inverse, and so we will defer them to the end of the section.

If a matrix $B$ is alleged to be the inverse of a matrix $A$, then according to the uniqueness property (*i*) in Theorem 1, the allegation can be checked by seeing if it is true that $AB = I$ and $BA = I$. Actually, as the next theorem states, it suffices to verify only one of these equalities to show that one matrix is the inverse of another. This labor-saving theorem will be established at the end of the section.

### THEOREM 2

Let $A$ and $B$ be $n \times n$ matrices. If $AB = I$, then $BA = I$ and $B = A^{-1}$.

Thus to check if $B$ is the inverse of $A$, we need only see if $AB = I$. Note that it then follows from Theorem 1(*ii*) that if $B = A^{-1}$, then $A = (A^{-1})^{-1} = B^{-1}$. Thus inverse matrices come in pairs.

**EXAMPLE 1**   Show that if

$$A = \begin{bmatrix} 2 & 1 \\ 5 & 3 \end{bmatrix} \quad \text{and} \quad B = \begin{bmatrix} 3 & -1 \\ -5 & 2 \end{bmatrix}$$

then $B = A^{-1}$ and $A = B^{-1}$.

**SOLUTION**   Both conclusions follow from the single calculation

$$AB = \begin{bmatrix} 2 & 1 \\ 5 & 3 \end{bmatrix} \begin{bmatrix} 3 & -1 \\ -5 & 2 \end{bmatrix} = \begin{bmatrix} 1 & 0 \\ 0 & 1 \end{bmatrix} = I \quad \blacksquare$$

The cancellation property that was discussed earlier is now seen to be valid for invertible matrices. Invertible matrices can be cancelled by simply multiplying by their inverses. Suppose that we have a matrix equation $AB = AC$ and $A$ is invertible. Then if we multiply on the left by $A^{-1}$, we get $A^{-1}AB = A^{-1}AC$. Since $A^{-1}A = I$, it follows that $IB = IC$, and hence $B = C$. Thus $AB = AC$ implies that $B = C$ if $A$ has an inverse.

Many square matrices do not have inverses. We earlier encountered the matrix

$$A = \begin{bmatrix} 1 & 2 \\ 2 & 4 \end{bmatrix}$$

that had the property that

$$A \begin{bmatrix} -1 \\ 1 \end{bmatrix} = A \begin{bmatrix} 5 \\ -2 \end{bmatrix}$$

The matrix $A$ cannot be invertible, for the existence of $A^{-1}$ would imply that

$$A^{-1}A \begin{bmatrix} -1 \\ 1 \end{bmatrix} = A^{-1}A \begin{bmatrix} 5 \\ -2 \end{bmatrix}$$

and since $A^{-1}A = I$, it would follow that

$$\begin{bmatrix} -1 \\ 1 \end{bmatrix} = \begin{bmatrix} 5 \\ 2 \end{bmatrix}$$

Since this is *not* true, the matrix $A$ cannot possess an inverse.

## FINDING THE INVERSE OF A MATRIX

We are faced with two questions: How can we tell if a matrix is invertible? How do we find the inverse when it exists? We will describe a method that answers both questions. The procedure will first be illustrated by finding the inverse of a particular matrix.

Consider the matrix

$$A = \begin{bmatrix} 1 & 2 & 3 \\ -1 & -3 & -2 \\ 2 & -1 & 1 \end{bmatrix}$$

and let the supposed inverse be the matrix of unknowns

$$A^{-1} = \begin{bmatrix} x_1 & y_1 & z_1 \\ x_2 & y_2 & z_2 \\ x_3 & y_3 & z_3 \end{bmatrix}$$

Then the property that $AA^{-1} = I$ gives us

$$\begin{bmatrix} 1 & 2 & 3 \\ -1 & -3 & -2 \\ 2 & -1 & 1 \end{bmatrix} \begin{bmatrix} x_1 & y_1 & z_1 \\ x_2 & y_2 & z_2 \\ x_3 & y_3 & z_3 \end{bmatrix} = \begin{bmatrix} 1 & 0 & 0 \\ 0 & 1 & 0 \\ 0 & 0 & 1 \end{bmatrix}$$

From the construction of the matrix product, this can be separated into three systems of equations. We must have $A$ times the first column of unknowns equal to the first column of $I$, and $A$ times the second column of unknowns equal to the second column of $I$, and so on. That is, we have the three systems

$$A\begin{bmatrix} x_1 \\ x_2 \\ x_3 \end{bmatrix} = \begin{bmatrix} 1 \\ 0 \\ 0 \end{bmatrix}, \quad A\begin{bmatrix} y_1 \\ y_2 \\ y_3 \end{bmatrix} = \begin{bmatrix} 0 \\ 1 \\ 0 \end{bmatrix}, \quad A\begin{bmatrix} z_1 \\ z_2 \\ z_3 \end{bmatrix} = \begin{bmatrix} 0 \\ 0 \\ 1 \end{bmatrix}$$

We see that finding the inverse matrix is equivalent to solving the three systems of equations above, and the coefficient matrix is the same in each system, namely, the matrix $A$. In other words, we have a multisystem. If it happens that $A^{-1}$ does not exist, then at least one of the systems will be inconsistent.

Since all three systems have the same coefficient matrix, we can treat them simultaneously with Gauss or Gauss-Jordan elimination on the augmented matrix $[A|I]$. We perform row operations as follows.

$$\left[\begin{array}{rrr|rrr} 1 & 2 & 3 & 1 & 0 & 0 \\ -1 & -3 & -2 & 0 & 1 & 0 \\ 2 & -1 & 1 & 0 & 0 & 1 \end{array}\right] \quad \begin{array}{l} R_2' = R_2 + R_1 \\ R_3' = R_3 - 2R_1 \end{array}$$

$$\left[\begin{array}{rrr|rrr} 1 & 2 & 3 & 1 & 0 & 0 \\ 0 & -1 & 1 & 1 & 1 & 0 \\ 0 & -5 & -5 & -2 & 0 & 1 \end{array}\right] \quad \begin{array}{l} R_3' = R_3 - 5R_2 \\ R_2' = -R_2 \end{array}$$

$$\left[\begin{array}{rrr|rrr} 1 & 2 & 3 & 1 & 0 & 0 \\ 0 & 1 & -1 & -1 & -1 & 0 \\ 0 & 0 & -10 & -7 & -5 & 1 \end{array}\right] \quad \begin{array}{l} R_3' = -1/10R_3 \\ R_1' = R_1 - 3R_3 \\ R_2' = R_2 + R_3 \end{array}$$

$$\left[\begin{array}{rrr|rrr} 1 & 2 & 0 & -11/10 & -15/10 & 3/10 \\ 0 & 1 & 0 & -3/10 & -5/10 & -1/10 \\ 0 & 0 & 1 & 7/10 & 5/10 & -1/10 \end{array}\right] \quad R_1' = R_1 - 2R_2$$

$$\left[\begin{array}{rrr|rrr} 1 & 0 & 0 & -5/10 & -5/10 & 5/10 \\ 0 & 1 & 0 & -3/10 & -5/10 & -1/10 \\ 0 & 0 & 1 & 7/10 & 5/10 & -1/10 \end{array}\right]$$

Thus we have that

$$\begin{bmatrix} x_1 \\ x_2 \\ x_3 \end{bmatrix} = \begin{bmatrix} -5/10 \\ -3/10 \\ 7/10 \end{bmatrix}, \quad \begin{bmatrix} y_1 \\ y_2 \\ y_3 \end{bmatrix} = \begin{bmatrix} -5/10 \\ -5/10 \\ 5/10 \end{bmatrix}, \quad \begin{bmatrix} z_1 \\ z_2 \\ z_3 \end{bmatrix} = \begin{bmatrix} 5/10 \\ -1/10 \\ -1/10 \end{bmatrix}$$

Therefore the inverse matrix is given by

$$A^{-1} = \begin{bmatrix} -5/10 & -5/10 & 5/10 \\ -3/10 & -5/10 & -1/10 \\ 7/10 & 5/10 & -1/10 \end{bmatrix}$$

In general, the procedure for finding the inverse of a square matrix $A$ is as follows. We start with the augmented matrix $[A|I]$ and use row operations to put it into reduced echelon form. Then one of two possibilities will occur.

***Case 1.*** The matrix $A$ can be row reduced to $I$. In this case the augmented matrix $[A|I]$ will be transformed into $[I|A^{-1}]$, and $A$ will be invertible.

***Case 2.*** The matrix $A$ cannot be row reduced to $I$, but rather a row of zeros will appear in the left-hand portion of the augmented matrix as row operations are applied. In this case there is an inconsistency, and $A^{-1}$ does not exist.

We will illustrate the method by two examples.

**EXAMPLE 2**   Find the inverse of the matrix

$$A = \begin{bmatrix} 2 & -4 & 6 \\ 3 & -5 & 8 \\ -2 & 6 & -10 \end{bmatrix}$$

SOLUTION   We form the augmented matrix $[A|I]$ and perform the pivots indicated by the circled entries. For convenience, when inverting matrices, we will not enclose the matrices in brackets, but simply separate the successive matrices with a horizontal line.

$$[A|I] = \begin{array}{ccc|ccc} ② & -4 & 6 & 1 & 0 & 0 \\ 3 & -5 & 8 & 0 & 1 & 0 \\ -2 & 6 & -10 & 0 & 0 & 1 \end{array} \quad \begin{array}{l} R'_1 = 1/2R_1 \\ R'_2 = R_2 - 3R_1 \\ R'_3 = R_3 + 2R_1 \end{array}$$

$$\begin{array}{ccc|ccc} 1 & -2 & 3 & 1/2 & 0 & 0 \\ 0 & ① & -1 & -3/2 & 1 & 0 \\ 0 & 2 & -4 & 1 & 0 & 1 \end{array} \quad \begin{array}{l} R'_1 = R_1 + 2R_2 \\ R'_3 = R_3 - 2R_2 \end{array}$$

$$\begin{array}{ccc|ccc} 1 & 0 & 1 & -5/2 & 2 & 0 \\ 0 & 1 & -1 & -3/2 & 1 & 0 \\ 0 & 0 & ⟨-2⟩ & 4 & -2 & 1 \end{array} \quad \begin{array}{l} R'_3 = -1/2R_3 \\ R'_1 = R_1 - R_3 \\ R'_2 = R_2 + R_3 \end{array}$$

$$\begin{array}{ccc|ccc} 1 & 0 & 0 & -1/2 & 1 & 1/2 \\ 0 & 1 & 0 & -7/2 & 2 & -1/2 \\ 0 & 0 & 1 & -2 & 1 & -1/2 \end{array} = [I|A^{-1}]$$

Thus we obtain the inverse matrix

$$A^{-1} = (1/2)\begin{bmatrix} -1 & 2 & 1 \\ -7 & 4 & -1 \\ -4 & 2 & -1 \end{bmatrix}$$

We may check our work by multiplying the matrices together as in

$$AA^{-1} = \begin{bmatrix} 2 & -4 & 6 \\ 3 & -5 & 8 \\ -2 & 6 & -10 \end{bmatrix}\begin{bmatrix} -1 & 2 & 1 \\ -7 & 4 & -1 \\ -4 & 2 & -1 \end{bmatrix}(1/2) = (1/2)\begin{bmatrix} 2 & 0 & 0 \\ 0 & 2 & 0 \\ 0 & 0 & 2 \end{bmatrix} = I$$

Thus $A^{-1}$ is indeed the inverse of $A$.  ∎

If an inverse fails to exist, then at least one of the systems of equations must be inconsistent. This will be reflected in the procedure by the occurrence of a row that signifies $0 = a \neq 0$.

**EXAMPLE 3**  If possible, invert the matrix

$$A = \begin{bmatrix} -1 & 2 & 1 \\ 0 & 1 & 3 \\ -1 & 4 & 7 \end{bmatrix}$$

SOLUTION  We form the augmented matrix $[A|I]$ and attempt to row reduce $A$ to the identity.

| | | | | | | |
|---|---|---|---|---|---|---|
| $-1$ | 2 | 1 | 1 | 0 | 0 | $R_1' = -R_1$ |
| 0 | 1 | 3 | 0 | 1 | 0 | $R_3' = R_3 + R_1$ |
| $-1$ | 4 | 7 | 0 | 0 | 1 | |

| | | | | | | |
|---|---|---|---|---|---|---|
| 1 | $-2$ | $-1$ | $-1$ | 0 | 0 | |
| 0 | 1 | 3 | 0 | 1 | 0 | $R_3' = R_3 - 2R_2$ |
| 0 | 2 | 6 | $-1$ | 0 | 1 | |

| | | | | | |
|---|---|---|---|---|---|
| 1 | $-2$ | $-1$ | $-1$ | 0 | 0 |
| 0 | 1 | 3 | 0 | 1 | 0 |
| 0 | 0 | 0 | $-1$ | $-2$ | 1 |

Here the bottom row gives us the equation

$$0x_1 + 0x_2 + 0x_3 = -1$$

which implies that the system is inconsistent. In fact, we also have from the bottom row that

$$0y_1 + 0y_2 + 0y_3 = -2$$

and

$$0z_1 + 0z_2 + 0z_3 = 1$$

Thus none of the systems is consistent. We conclude from any one of the inconsistencies that the matrix does not have an inverse.  ∎

The validity of the procedure for finding the inverse of a matrix rests on Theorem 2. Note that if the augmented matrix $[A|I]$ can be transformed into a matrix $[I|B]$, then the matrix $B$ satisfies $AB = I$. Therefore by Theorem 2 we have $BA = I$ so that $B = A^{-1}$.

The two cases that distinguish between the existence and nonexistence of the inverse of a matrix can be described in terms of row rank. The relation is essentially the same as that in Theorem 1 of Section 2.3 in Chapter 2 on consistency of systems of equations. Suppose that $A$ is an $n \times n$ matrix. In Case 1 the reduced echelon form of $A$ is $I$, so that the row rank of $A$ is $n$. Since the row rank of $[A|I]$ is necessarily equal to $n$, we see that $A$ and the augmented matrix $[A|I]$ both have row rank $n$ in this case. In Case 2 the reduced echelon form of $A$ contains a row of zeros, so that the row rank of $A$ is less than $n$. Note that the row rank of $A$ is strictly less than the row rank of $[A|I]$ in this case.

## INVERSES AND LINEAR SYSTEMS

By using matrix multiplication we can write any system of linear equations as a matrix equation. For example, the linear system

$$5x_1 + 2x_2 - 3x_3 = 4$$
$$-x_1 + 4x_2 + 5x_3 = 5$$

can be written as

$$\begin{bmatrix} 5x_1 + 2x_2 - 3x_3 \\ -x_1 + 4x_2 + 5x_3 \end{bmatrix} = \begin{bmatrix} 4 \\ 5 \end{bmatrix}$$

which, using matrix multiplication, can be written as

$$\begin{bmatrix} 5 & 2 & -3 \\ -1 & 4 & 5 \end{bmatrix} \begin{bmatrix} x_1 \\ x_2 \\ x_3 \end{bmatrix} = \begin{bmatrix} 4 \\ 5 \end{bmatrix}$$

Thus if $A = [a_{ij}]$ is the coefficient matrix of the system, if $X = [x_j]$ is the matrix of variables, and if $B = [b_i]$ is the matrix of constants, then the system can be written as

$$AX = B$$

Each of the matrices $X$ and $B$ consists of a single column, and matrices of this type are often called **vectors**. Here we have

$$X = \begin{bmatrix} x_1 \\ \vdots \\ x_n \end{bmatrix}, \quad B = \begin{bmatrix} b_1 \\ \vdots \\ b_m \end{bmatrix}$$

where $X$ is the vector of variables and $B$ is the vector of constant terms.

If the system has the same number of equations as variables, then the coefficient matrix $A$ is a square matrix. If $A$ happens to be invertible, then the matrix $A^{-1}$ can be used to solve the system. The solution is found by multiplying both sides of the system $AX = B$ on the left by $A^{-1}$. Then we get

$$(A^{-1}A)X = A^{-1}B$$
$$IX = A^{-1}B$$
$$X = A^{-1}B$$

Hence the solution is given by $X = A^{-1}B$. Note that the existence of the inverse implies that the system has a unique solution.

**EXAMPLE 4**   Suppose a matrix $A$ and its inverse $A^{-1}$ are given by

$$A = \begin{bmatrix} 4 & 1 \\ 7 & 2 \end{bmatrix}, \quad A^{-1} = \begin{bmatrix} 2 & -1 \\ -7 & 4 \end{bmatrix}$$

Solve the system

$$4x_1 + x_2 = 5$$
$$7x_1 + 2x_2 = 8$$

SOLUTION   We first write the system in matrix form as

$$\begin{bmatrix} 4 & 1 \\ 7 & 2 \end{bmatrix} \begin{bmatrix} x_1 \\ x_2 \end{bmatrix} = \begin{bmatrix} 5 \\ 8 \end{bmatrix}$$

We then multiply on the left by $A^{-1}$ to get

$$\begin{bmatrix} x_1 \\ x_2 \end{bmatrix} = A^{-1} \begin{bmatrix} 5 \\ 8 \end{bmatrix} = \begin{bmatrix} 2 & -1 \\ -7 & 4 \end{bmatrix} \begin{bmatrix} 5 \\ 8 \end{bmatrix} = \begin{bmatrix} 2 \\ -3 \end{bmatrix}$$

Hence the unique solution is $x_1 = 2$, $x_2 = -3$. ∎

As we have seen, the process of calculating the inverse of a matrix is tantamount to solving systems of equations. Consequently, unless the inverse is already available, finding the inverse just to solve a single system is not labor efficient. However, there are linear models that give rise to multiple systems in which the constant terms differ but the coefficient matrix is the same in each system. (See Section 2.2 for a discussion of multisystems.) In this type of situation the inverse of the coefficient matrix can be useful.

*REMARK*:   It is possible to write a square matrix $A$ as a product of square matrices $LU$ where $L$ is lower triangular and $U$ is upper triangular. If $A$ is invertible, then $A^{-1} = U^{-1}L^{-1}$, and the solution of the system $AX = B$ can be written as

$$X = A^{-1}B = (U^{-1}L^{-1})B = U^{-1}(L^{-1}B)$$

The products $L^{-1}B$ and $U^{-1}(L^{-1}B)$ can then be formed in an implicit manner with a great savings on the number of calculations. This technique is called *L/U decomposition*. Its main use is in connection with computer solution of multisystems where the number of calculations can affect accuracy because of accumulated round-off error. We will not discuss the details in this book.

For a $2 \times 2$ matrix the inverse is very easily found by using the formula given below. The formula can be derived by the methods that were discussed above, but we will simply state it and verify that it works.

### Formula for 2 × 2 inverses

If the matrix

$$A = \begin{bmatrix} a & b \\ c & d \end{bmatrix}$$

is such that $D = ad - bc \neq 0$, then $A$ is invertible, and the inverse is given by

$$A^{-1} = (1/D) \begin{bmatrix} d & -b \\ -c & a \end{bmatrix}$$

Thus the inverse $A^{-1}$ is obtained from $A$ by interchanging $a$ and $d$, negating $b$ and $c$, and dividing by $D$. To verify the formula, we note that

$$\begin{bmatrix} a & b \\ c & d \end{bmatrix} \begin{bmatrix} d & -b \\ -c & a \end{bmatrix} = \begin{bmatrix} D & 0 \\ 0 & D \end{bmatrix}$$

Therefore if $D \neq 0$, then we can multiply by $1/D$ and thereby obtain $A^{-1}$.

**EXAMPLE 5**   Let

$$A = \begin{bmatrix} 1 & -4 \\ 2 & -5 \end{bmatrix}, \quad X = \begin{bmatrix} x_1 \\ x_2 \end{bmatrix}$$

Find $A^{-1}$ and use it to solve the systems

$$AX = \begin{bmatrix} 2 \\ 3 \end{bmatrix}, \quad AX = \begin{bmatrix} -1 \\ 1 \end{bmatrix}, \quad AX = \begin{bmatrix} 7 \\ 11 \end{bmatrix}$$

**SOLUTION**   We first find $A^{-1}$. Since $D = -5 + 8 = 3$, we know that $A^{-1}$ exists, and the above formula gives us

$$A^{-1} = (1/3) \begin{bmatrix} -5 & 4 \\ -2 & 1 \end{bmatrix} = \begin{bmatrix} -5/3 & 4/3 \\ -2/3 & 1/3 \end{bmatrix}$$

The solutions to the system are then given by

$$A^{-1} \begin{bmatrix} 2 \\ 3 \end{bmatrix} = \begin{bmatrix} 2/3 \\ -1/3 \end{bmatrix}, \quad A^{-1} \begin{bmatrix} -1 \\ 1 \end{bmatrix} = \begin{bmatrix} 3 \\ 1 \end{bmatrix}, \quad A^{-1} \begin{bmatrix} 7 \\ 11 \end{bmatrix} = \begin{bmatrix} 3 \\ -1 \end{bmatrix}$$

Hence the solutions are $(\frac{2}{3}, -\frac{1}{3})$, $(3, 1)$, $(3, -1)$, respectively.   ▌▐

The issue of whether a matrix is invertible or not is related to the row rank of the matrix, as we noted earlier. It is also related to the issue of uniqueness of solutions of linear systems. The relationships are summarized in the following theorem.

## THEOREM 3

If $A$ is an $n \times n$ matrix, then the following statements are equivalent:

(*i*)   The row rank of $A$ is $n$.

(*ii*)   $A$ is invertible.

(*iii*)   For any vector $B$, the system $AX = B$ has a unique solution.

## PROOFS OF THE THEOREMS

### Theorem 1 (proof)

(*i*)   Suppose that we have $AB = I$. Then, since $B = IB$ and $I = A^{-1}A$, we have

$$B = IB = (A^{-1}A)B = A^{-1}(AB) = A^{-1}I = A^{-1}$$

(*ii*)   Since $A$ satisfies $AA^{-1} = A^{-1}A = I$ and since the inverse of $A^{-1}$ is unique, we must have $(A^{-1})^{-1} = A$.

(*iii*)   We must show that $B^{-1}A^{-1}$ satisfies the property of the inverse of $AB$. We have

$$(B^{-1}A^{-1})(AB) = B^{-1}(A^{-1}A)B = B^{-1}IB = B^{-1}B = I$$

Similarly, we get $(AB)(B^{-1}A^{-1}) = I$. Hence we have shown that $B^{-1}A^{-1}$ is the inverse of $AB$, that is, $B^{-1}A^{-1} = (AB)^{-1}$. ∎

### Theorem 2 (proof)

If $AB = I$, then the matrix $[A|I]$ can be row reduced to $[I|B]$, so that $A$ is row reduced to $I$ and $I$ is row reduced to $B$. Since row operations can be reversed by other row operations, it follows that $B$ can be row reduced to $I$. Thus the matrix $[B|I]$ can be row reduced to $[I|C]$ for some matrix $C$ such that $BC = I$. Then

$$C = IC = (AB)C = A(BC) = AI = A$$

Therefore we have that $AB = BA = I$; and since inverses are unique by Theorem 1, we conclude that $B = A^{-1}$. ∎

### Theorem 3 (proof)

The equivalence of (*i*) and (*ii*) was discussed in this section (see page 154). The equivalence of (*ii*) and (*iii*) can be seen as follows. If $A^{-1}$ exists, then $X = A^{-1}B$ is a solution of $AX = B$. Suppose that there are two solutions, say, $X_1$ and $X_2$. Then $AX_1 = B = AX_2$, and multiplication on the left by $A^{-1}$ yields $A^{-1}AX_1 = A^{-1}AX_2$. Therefore $X_1 = X_2$, and the solution is unique. Thus (*ii*) implies (*iii*). Conversely, if $AX = B$ has a unique solution for each choice of $B$, then the systems

$$AX = \begin{bmatrix} 1 \\ 0 \\ 0 \end{bmatrix}, \quad AX = \begin{bmatrix} 0 \\ 1 \\ 0 \end{bmatrix}, \quad AX = \begin{bmatrix} 0 \\ 0 \\ 1 \end{bmatrix}$$

have unique solution vectors. Then the matrix with these three vectors as its columns is $A^{-1}$, as we observed earlier.

Thus we see that the three statements about $A$ are equivalent. ∎

## EXERCISES 3.2

In Exercises 1–4, show that the given matrices are inverses.

1. $\begin{bmatrix} 7 & 6 \\ 6 & 5 \end{bmatrix}$, $\begin{bmatrix} -5 & 6 \\ 6 & -7 \end{bmatrix}$

2. $\begin{bmatrix} 3 & 4 \\ 8 & 11 \end{bmatrix}$, $\begin{bmatrix} 11 & -4 \\ -8 & 3 \end{bmatrix}$

3. $\begin{bmatrix} -4 & -3 & 2 \\ 4 & 3 & -1 \\ -3 & -2 & 1 \end{bmatrix}$, $\begin{bmatrix} 1 & -1 & -3 \\ -1 & 2 & 4 \\ 1 & 1 & 0 \end{bmatrix}$

4. $\begin{bmatrix} 1 & 2 & -3 \\ -1 & -1 & 4 \\ 1 & 4 & 0 \end{bmatrix}$, $\begin{bmatrix} -16 & -12 & 5 \\ 4 & 3 & -1 \\ -3 & -2 & 1 \end{bmatrix}$

In Exercises 5–8, match inverses. (Note: the matching need not be complete.)

**5.** $A = \begin{bmatrix} 5 & 3 \\ -2 & 4 \end{bmatrix}$,    $B = \begin{bmatrix} 5 & 4 \\ -2 & 3 \end{bmatrix}$,    $C = \begin{bmatrix} 4 & -3 \\ 5 & 2 \end{bmatrix}$

$D = \begin{bmatrix} 3 & 5 \\ 4 & 2 \end{bmatrix}$,    $E = \begin{bmatrix} 2/26 & -5/26 \\ -4/26 & 3/26 \end{bmatrix}$,    $F = \begin{bmatrix} 3/23 & -4/23 \\ 2/23 & 5/23 \end{bmatrix}$

$G = \begin{bmatrix} 4/26 & -3/26 \\ 2/26 & 5/26 \end{bmatrix}$,    $H = \begin{bmatrix} 2/23 & 3/23 \\ -5/23 & 4/23 \end{bmatrix}$

**6.** $A = \begin{bmatrix} -2 & 2 \\ 4 & 1 \end{bmatrix}$,    $B = \begin{bmatrix} 2 & -2 \\ 1 & 4 \end{bmatrix}$,    $C = \begin{bmatrix} 4 & 1 \\ -2 & 2 \end{bmatrix}$

$D = \begin{bmatrix} 4 & 2 \\ -2 & -1 \end{bmatrix}$,    $E = \begin{bmatrix} 4/10 & 2/10 \\ -1/10 & 2/10 \end{bmatrix}$,    $F = \begin{bmatrix} -1/10 & 2/10 \\ 4/10 & 2/10 \end{bmatrix}$

$G = \begin{bmatrix} 4/10 & -1/10 \\ 2/10 & 2/10 \end{bmatrix}$,    $H = \begin{bmatrix} 2/10 & -1/10 \\ 2/10 & 4/10 \end{bmatrix}$

**7.** $A = \begin{bmatrix} 3 & -1 & -3 \\ -3 & -2 & -4 \\ 1 & 2 & 4 \end{bmatrix}$,    $B = \begin{bmatrix} 3 & -2 & 2 \\ 1 & -3 & -4 \\ 4 & -3 & -1 \end{bmatrix}$

$C = \begin{bmatrix} 3 & 2 & -3 \\ 1 & -1 & 4 \\ -3 & -4 & -2 \end{bmatrix}$,    $D = \begin{bmatrix} -9/21 & -8/21 & 14/21 \\ -15/21 & -11/21 & 14/21 \\ 9/21 & 1/21 & -7/21 \end{bmatrix}$

$E = \begin{bmatrix} 14/15 & 18/15 & -2/15 \\ 15/15 & -21/15 & -14/15 \\ -9/15 & 4/15 & -8/15 \end{bmatrix}$,    $F = \begin{bmatrix} 0 & -2/4 & -2/4 \\ 8/4 & 15/4 & 21/4 \\ -4/4 & -7/4 & -9/4 \end{bmatrix}$

**8.** $A = \begin{bmatrix} 4 & 1 & -4 \\ -1 & -3 & -2 \\ -2 & -1 & 2 \end{bmatrix}$,    $B = \begin{bmatrix} 2 & -3 & -2 \\ -1 & 1 & -1 \\ -4 & -2 & 4 \end{bmatrix}$

$C = \begin{bmatrix} -4 & -1 & -2 \\ -2 & 1 & -3 \\ -1 & 2 & 4 \end{bmatrix}$,    $D = \begin{bmatrix} -16/19 & 6/19 & -1/19 \\ -14/19 & 0 & -5/19 \\ 8/19 & 12/19 & 16/19 \end{bmatrix}$

$E = \begin{bmatrix} 8/6 & -2/6 & 14/6 \\ -6/6 & 0 & -12/6 \\ 5/6 & -2/6 & 11/6 \end{bmatrix}$,    $F = \begin{bmatrix} -2/32 & -16/32 & -5/32 \\ -8/32 & 0 & -4/32 \\ -6/32 & -16/32 & 1/32 \end{bmatrix}$

In Exercises 9–20, use row operations to find the inverse of the given matrix or to determine that none exists.

**9.** $\begin{bmatrix} 2 & 6 \\ -4 & 3 \end{bmatrix}$    **10.** $\begin{bmatrix} 1 & -5 \\ 2 & 4 \end{bmatrix}$    **11.** $\begin{bmatrix} 3 & -2 \\ 3 & 6 \end{bmatrix}$

**12.** $\begin{bmatrix} 4 & -5 \\ -8 & 10 \end{bmatrix}$    **13.** $\begin{bmatrix} 2 & -7 \\ -8 & 28 \end{bmatrix}$    **14.** $\begin{bmatrix} 4 & -12 \\ -4 & 8 \end{bmatrix}$

**15.** $\begin{bmatrix} 1 & -2 & 4 \\ 2 & -5 & 6 \\ -3 & 9 & -8 \end{bmatrix}$    **16.** $\begin{bmatrix} 1 & 3 & -2 \\ -3 & -10 & 8 \\ 2 & 9 & -12 \end{bmatrix}$    **17.** $\begin{bmatrix} 3 & -6 & -3 \\ 4 & 2 & -2 \\ 11 & -2 & -7 \end{bmatrix}$

**18.** $\begin{bmatrix} 3 & -6 & 9 \\ 6 & -13 & 17 \\ -3 & 8 & -10 \end{bmatrix}$    **19.** $\begin{bmatrix} 2 & -4 & 6 \\ 4 & -9 & 14 \\ -2 & 6 & -9 \end{bmatrix}$    **20.** $\begin{bmatrix} -2 & -8 & 4 \\ 5 & 3 & -1 \\ 1 & -13 & 7 \end{bmatrix}$

In Exercises 21–26, determine $A$, $X$, and $B$ if the system is written as $AX = B$.

**21.**  $\begin{aligned} 6x_1 + 4x_2 - 3x_3 &= -7 \\ -5x_1 + 3x_2 + 2x_3 &= 4 \end{aligned}$

**22.** $\begin{aligned} -3x_1 - 8x_2 + 4x_3 &= -2 \\ 2x_1 + 4x_2 - 6x_3 &= 8 \end{aligned}$

**23.**  $\begin{aligned} 6x + 4y - 3z &= 10 \\ 3x - 8y + 2z &= 4 \\ -7x - 3y + 9z &= -2 \end{aligned}$

**24.** $\begin{aligned} 4x - 2y + 5z &= -4 \\ 5x + 3y - 2z &= 5 \\ 7x - y - 3z &= 1 \end{aligned}$

**25.**  $\begin{aligned} 2x_1 + 3x_2 + 7x_3 &= 2 \\ 4x_1 + 5x_2 - 2x_3 &= -1 \\ -x_1 + 2x_2 + 4x_3 &= 4 \\ -6x_1 - x_2 + 3x_3 &= 8 \end{aligned}$

**26.**  $\begin{aligned} 3x_1 + 3x_2 - 2x_3 &= -8 \\ -8x_1 + 6x_2 - 4x_3 &= 1 \\ -7x_1 + 2x_2 + x_3 &= 5 \\ 6x_1 - 5x_2 + 3x_3 &= -1 \end{aligned}$

In Exercises 27–30, write the given matrix equation as a system of scalar equations.

**27.** $\begin{bmatrix} 2 & 4 \\ -3 & 1 \end{bmatrix} \begin{bmatrix} x_1 \\ x_2 \end{bmatrix} = \begin{bmatrix} 7 \\ 4 \end{bmatrix}$    **28.** $\begin{bmatrix} 5 & -7 \\ 4 & 3 \end{bmatrix} \begin{bmatrix} x_1 \\ x_2 \end{bmatrix} = \begin{bmatrix} -2 \\ 5 \end{bmatrix}$

**29.** $\begin{bmatrix} 6 & 4 & -2 \\ 8 & 1 & 7 \\ 5 & 2 & -2 \end{bmatrix} \begin{bmatrix} x_1 \\ x_2 \\ x_3 \end{bmatrix} = \begin{bmatrix} 8 \\ -3 \\ 1 \end{bmatrix}$

**30.** $\begin{bmatrix} 2 & 4 & 1 \\ -6 & 8 & 9 \\ -2 & -7 & 3 \end{bmatrix} \begin{bmatrix} x_1 \\ x_2 \\ x_3 \end{bmatrix} = \begin{bmatrix} 5 \\ -7 \\ 4 \end{bmatrix}$

In Exercises 31–36, use the given information to solve the given system of equations.

**31.** $\begin{aligned} 3x - 4y &= 7 \\ 2x + 7y &= -2 \end{aligned}$  $\begin{bmatrix} 3 & -4 \\ 2 & 7 \end{bmatrix} \begin{bmatrix} 7/29 & 4/29 \\ -2/29 & 3/29 \end{bmatrix} = I$

**32.** $\begin{aligned} 6x - 3y &= 4 \\ 5x + 2y &= -3 \end{aligned}$  $\begin{bmatrix} 6 & -3 \\ 5 & 2 \end{bmatrix} \begin{bmatrix} 2/27 & 3/27 \\ -5/27 & 6/27 \end{bmatrix} = I$

**33.** $\begin{aligned} -7x + 3y &= -2 \\ 2x + 8y &= 6 \end{aligned}$  $\begin{bmatrix} -7 & 3 \\ 2 & 8 \end{bmatrix} \begin{bmatrix} -8/62 & 3/62 \\ 2/62 & 7/62 \end{bmatrix} = I$

**34.** $\begin{aligned} 2x + 4y &= -3 \\ 5x - 6y &= 7 \end{aligned}$  $\begin{bmatrix} 2 & 4 \\ 5 & -6 \end{bmatrix} \begin{bmatrix} 6/32 & 4/32 \\ 5/32 & -2/32 \end{bmatrix} = I$

**35.** $\begin{aligned} x_1 - 2x_2 + 3x_3 &= 4 \\ 3x_1 - 5x_2 + 14x_3 &= -2 \\ 2x_1 - 4x_2 + 7x_3 &= 5 \end{aligned}$  $\begin{bmatrix} 1 & -2 & 3 \\ 3 & -5 & 14 \\ 2 & -4 & 7 \end{bmatrix} \begin{bmatrix} 21 & 2 & -13 \\ 7 & 1 & -5 \\ -2 & 0 & 1 \end{bmatrix} = I$

**36.**  $\begin{array}{r} x_1 + 2x_2 + 3x_3 = \phantom{-}2 \\ 2x_1 + 5x_2 + 3x_3 = -1 \\ x_1 \phantom{+ 5x_2} + 8x_3 = \phantom{-}1 \end{array}$  $\begin{bmatrix} 1 & 2 & 3 \\ 2 & 5 & 3 \\ 1 & 0 & 8 \end{bmatrix}$  $\begin{bmatrix} -40 & 16 & 9 \\ 13 & -5 & -3 \\ 5 & -2 & -1 \end{bmatrix} = I$

In Exercises 37–42, let $A$ and $B$ be the coefficient matrix and equation constant vector for the matrix equation $AX = B$. Find the solution vector $X = A^{-1}B$.

**37.**  $A = \begin{bmatrix} 2 & -10 \\ 4 & -12 \end{bmatrix}$, $B = \begin{bmatrix} 8 \\ -3 \end{bmatrix}$

**38.**  $A = \begin{bmatrix} 3 & -9 \\ 6 & -15 \end{bmatrix}$, $B = \begin{bmatrix} -4 \\ 7 \end{bmatrix}$

**39.**  $A = \begin{bmatrix} 1 & 1 & -1 \\ 4 & 6 & -2 \\ 4 & 5 & -1 \end{bmatrix}$, $B = \begin{bmatrix} -4 \\ -8 \\ -3 \end{bmatrix}$

**40.**  $A = \begin{bmatrix} 1 & 4 & -2 \\ 3 & 11 & -4 \\ -2 & -5 & -3 \end{bmatrix}$, $B = \begin{bmatrix} 6 \\ -4 \\ 3 \end{bmatrix}$

In Exercises 41–42, let

$$\text{(a) } B = \begin{bmatrix} -1 \\ 2 \\ 4 \end{bmatrix}, \quad \text{(b) } B = \begin{bmatrix} 2 \\ -3 \\ 1 \end{bmatrix}$$

**41.**  $A = \begin{bmatrix} 3 & 0 & 8 \\ -1 & -4 & 10 \\ 0 & -2 & 6 \end{bmatrix}$

**42.**  $A = \begin{bmatrix} -5 & -1 & 0 \\ 1 & -3 & -4 \\ 0 & -2 & -4 \end{bmatrix}$

In Exercises 43–46, use the formula for $2 \times 2$ matrices to find the inverse of the given matrix.

**43.** $\begin{bmatrix} 6 & 2 \\ 8 & 1 \end{bmatrix}$

**44.** $\begin{bmatrix} 4 & 10 \\ 5 & 3 \end{bmatrix}$

**45.** $\begin{bmatrix} 7 & 3 \\ 5 & 6 \end{bmatrix}$

**46.** $\begin{bmatrix} 8 & 2 \\ 1 & 4 \end{bmatrix}$

In Exercises 47–48, find the inverse of each matrix, where $a, b, c, d$ are nonzero numbers.

**47.** $\begin{bmatrix} 0 & 0 & a \\ 0 & b & 0 \\ c & 0 & 0 \end{bmatrix}$

**48.** $\begin{bmatrix} 0 & 0 & 0 & a \\ 0 & 0 & b & 0 \\ 0 & c & 0 & 0 \\ d & 0 & 0 & 0 \end{bmatrix}$

In Exercises 49–50, find the values of $k$ such that the matrix is *not* invertible.

**49.** $\begin{bmatrix} 1 & k \\ k & 1 \end{bmatrix}$

**50.** $\begin{bmatrix} 1 & 2 & -1 \\ 2 & 0 & 2 \\ -1 & 2 & k \end{bmatrix}$

**51.** Multiply $A^t$ by $(A^{-1})^t$ to verify that $(A^t)^{-1} = (A^{-1})^t$. (Use the fact that $(AB)^t = B^t A^t$.)

**52.** Multiply $A^2$ by $(A^{-1})^2$ to verify that $(A^2)^{-1} = (A^{-1})^2$. (Recall that $A^2 = AA$.)

## 3.3 THE LEONTIEF OPEN MODEL
*Consumption, Demand, and Production*

In this section we apply the concept of inverse matrix to the analysis of industrial interdependence in an economy. A portion of the output of one industry is used as input by another industry in the manufacture of its output. The study of the relationship between industrial activities in an economy is called input–output analysis. This type of analysis was created by Harvard economist Wassily W. Leontief (1906–   ) who received the 1973 Nobel Prize in Economic Science "for the development of the input–output method and for its application to important economic problems."

### CONSUMPTION, DEMAND, AND PRODUCTION

Suppose that we have an economy that consists of a number of industries, each of which produces a single product. Further assume that a portion of the output of the economy is used within the economy itself in the production process. For example, part of the output of an oil company will be used by a utility to generate electricity, and part of the electricity is used in turn in the oil company's production process.

If an external demand, such as consumer usage, is to be filled by the economy, then enough goods must be produced to meet this external demand as well as the internal requirements of production. We then have the problem: How much needs to be produced in all? The Leontief open model of an economy assists in answering this question.

We shall illustrate the ideas by means of an example. To have common units for the commodities of the various industries, we will measure production and demand in dollars.

**EXAMPLE 1** Let an economy contain three industries: electric, oil, and pipeline. For each $1 of electricity generated, let there be charges of 20¢ for electricity to run auxiliary equipment, 40¢ for oil to power the generators, and 10¢ in pipeline usage. For each $1 of oil produced, suppose that 10¢ is spent on electricity and 40¢ for oil to produce steam that is pumped into the well. Finally, for each $1 in pipeline usage, suppose that 30¢ is spent on electricity while 20¢ is spent on oil to heat the pipeline. Suppose that there is an outside demand for $4200 worth of electricity, $8400 worth of oil, and $12,600 in pipeline usage. How much should each industry produce?

SOLUTION   We will first organize the information in a **consumption matrix**, where each entry represents a portion of $1. We list each industry's cost in columns as follows.

$$
\begin{array}{ccc}
\text{Electricity} & \text{Oil} & \text{Pipeline}
\end{array}
$$
$$
C = \begin{bmatrix} .2 & .1 & .3 \\ .4 & .4 & .2 \\ .1 & 0 & 0 \end{bmatrix} \begin{array}{l} \text{Electricity} \\ \text{Oil} \\ \text{Pipeline} \end{array}
$$

Since the rows and columns have the same headings, some confusion may result. Remember that the numbers down each column represent the input costs for producing \$1 worth of the product that heads the column. The entries of the matrix $C$ are sometimes called *input coefficients*.

We shall now derive the equations that must be solved. Let $x_1$, $x_2$, and $x_3$, respectively, be the dollar value of the electricity, oil, and pipeline usage produced. Then we have

$$
\begin{array}{cccc}
\text{Internal usage} & \text{Demand} & \text{Total} & \\
\text{E} \quad \text{O} \quad \text{P} & & & \\
.2x_1 + .1x_2 + .3x_3 + & 4200 & = x_1 & \text{Electricity} \\
.4x_1 + .4x_2 + .2x_3 + & 8400 & = x_2 & \text{Oil} \\
.1x_1 + 0x_2 + 0x_3 + & 12600 & = x_3 & \text{Pipeline}
\end{array}
$$

This system can be rewritten as

$$
\begin{aligned}
x_1 \quad - .2x_1 - .1x_2 - .3x_3 &= 4200 \\
x_2 \quad - .4x_1 - .4x_2 - .2x_3 &= 8400 \\
x_3 - .1x_1 - 0x_2 - 0x_3 &= 12600
\end{aligned}
$$

In matrix form we have

$$
\begin{bmatrix} 1 & 0 & 0 \\ 0 & 1 & 0 \\ 0 & 0 & 1 \end{bmatrix} \begin{bmatrix} x_1 \\ x_2 \\ x_3 \end{bmatrix} - \begin{bmatrix} .2 & .1 & .3 \\ .4 & .4 & .2 \\ .1 & 0 & 0 \end{bmatrix} \begin{bmatrix} x_1 \\ x_2 \\ x_3 \end{bmatrix} = \begin{bmatrix} 4200 \\ 8400 \\ 12600 \end{bmatrix}
$$

We now let

$$
D = \begin{bmatrix} 4200 \\ 8400 \\ 12600 \end{bmatrix}
$$

be the **demand vector**, and we let

$$
X = \begin{bmatrix} x_1 \\ x_2 \\ x_3 \end{bmatrix}
$$

be the **production vector**. Then the system can be written as the matrix equation

$$
IX - CX = D
$$

or as

$$
(I - C)X = D
$$

If $(I - C)^{-1}$ exists, then we can multiply both sides of the last equation by $(I - C)^{-1}$ to obtain the solution

$$
X = (I - C)^{-1}D
$$

Accordingly, we find $I - C$ and compute its inverse. Now

$$I - C = \begin{bmatrix} 1 & 0 & 0 \\ 0 & 1 & 0 \\ 0 & 0 & 1 \end{bmatrix} - \begin{bmatrix} .2 & .1 & .3 \\ .4 & .4 & .2 \\ .1 & 0 & 0 \end{bmatrix} = \begin{bmatrix} .8 & -.1 & -.3 \\ -.4 & .6 & -.2 \\ -.1 & 0 & 1 \end{bmatrix}$$

and we perform the indicated pivots to obtain $(I - C)^{-1}$.

| .8 | −.1 | −.3 | 1 | 0 | 0 | $R_1 \leftrightarrow R_3$ |
|---|---|---|---|---|---|---|
| −.4 | .6 | −.2 | 0 | 1 | 0 | |
| (−.1) | 0 | 1 | 0 | 0 | 1 | |

| 1 | 0 | −10 | 0 | 0 | −10 | $R_2 \leftrightarrow R_3$ |
|---|---|---|---|---|---|---|
| 0 | .6 | −4.2 | 0 | 1 | −4 | |
| 0 | (.1) | 7.7 | 1 | 0 | 8 | |

| 1 | 0 | −10 | 0 | 0 | −10 | |
|---|---|---|---|---|---|---|
| 0 | 1 | −77 | −10 | 0 | −80 | |
| 0 | 0 | (42) | 6 | 1 | 44 | |

| 1 | 0 | 0 | 60/42 | 10/42 | 20/42 |
|---|---|---|---|---|---|
| 0 | 1 | 0 | 42/42 | 77/42 | 28/42 |
| 0 | 0 | 1 | 6/42 | 1/42 | 44/42 |

Thus we have

$$(I - C)^{-1} = (1/42) \begin{bmatrix} 60 & 10 & 20 \\ 42 & 77 & 28 \\ 6 & 1 & 44 \end{bmatrix}$$

so that the solution is

$$X = (100/42) \begin{bmatrix} 60 & 10 & 20 \\ 42 & 77 & 28 \\ 6 & 1 & 44 \end{bmatrix} \begin{bmatrix} 42 \\ 84 \\ 126 \end{bmatrix} = 100 \begin{bmatrix} 60 & 10 & 20 \\ 42 & 77 & 28 \\ 6 & 1 & 44 \end{bmatrix} \begin{bmatrix} 1 \\ 2 \\ 3 \end{bmatrix} = \begin{bmatrix} 14000 \\ 28000 \\ 14000 \end{bmatrix}$$

Therefore the **production schedule** is $x_1 = 14,000$, $x_2 = 28,000$, $x_3 = 14,000$. In other words, the economy should produce $14,000 electricity, $28,000 oil, and $14,000 pipeline usage. ∎

The method of the example is completely general, so that we may formulate from it a procedure for finding the production schedule for the demand on any economy:

**Step 1.** Find the consumption matrix $C$.

**Step 2.** Find $I - C$.

**Step 3.** Invert $I - C$.

**Step 4.** The production vector is given by

$$X = (I - C)^{-1} D$$

where $D$ is the demand vector.

A critical requirement that the solution must satisfy is that all of the $x_j$ must be nonnegative to have a meaningful production schedule. We say that a matrix $A$ is **nonnegative**, written $A \geqslant O$, if all of its entries are nonnegative. If $D$ is a nonnegative demand vector and if $(I - C)^{-1}$ exists and is nonnegative as well, then $X = (I - C)^{-1}D$ will also be nonnegative. That is, if we have

$$(I - C)^{-1} \geqslant O$$

than a nonnegative production vector can be found for any given nonnegative demand. In this case we say that the economy and the consumption matrix $C$ are **productive**.

**EXAMPLE 2**   Suppose that we have an economy with labor, transportation, and food industries. Let \$1 in labor require 40¢ in transportation and 20¢ in food, while \$1 in transportation takes 50¢ in labor and 30¢ in transportation, and \$1 in food production uses 50¢ in labor, 5¢ in transportation, and 35¢ in food. Let the demand for the current production period be \$10,000 labor, \$20,000 transportation, and \$10,000 food. Find the production schedule for the economy.

SOLUTION   The consumption matrix is given by

$$C = \begin{bmatrix} 0 & .5 & .5 \\ .4 & .3 & .05 \\ .2 & 0 & .35 \end{bmatrix} \begin{matrix} \text{Labor} \\ \text{Transportation} \\ \text{Food} \end{matrix}$$

with column headings Labor, Transportation, Food

and from this we find

$$I - C = \begin{bmatrix} 1 & -.5 & -.5 \\ -.4 & .7 & -.05 \\ -.2 & 0 & .65 \end{bmatrix}$$

Next we invert $I - C$. We use Gaussian elimination with back addition.

| 1 | −.5 | −.5 | 1 | 0 | 0 |
|---|---|---|---|---|---|
| −.4 | .7 | −.05 | 0 | 1 | 0 |
| −.2 | 0 | .65 | 0 | 0 | 1 |

| 1 | −.5 | −.5 | 1 | 0 | 0 |
|---|---|---|---|---|---|
| 0 | .5 | −.25 | .4 | 1 | 0 |
| 0 | −.1 | .55 | .2 | 0 | 1 |

| 1 | −.5 | −.5 | 1 | 0 | 0 |
|---|---|---|---|---|---|
| 0 | 1 | −.5 | .8 | 2 | 0 |
| 0 | 0 | .5 | .28 | .2 | 1 |

| 1 | −.5 | 0 | 1.28 | .2 | 1 |
|---|---|---|---|---|---|
| 0 | 1 | 0 | 1.08 | 2.2 | 1 |
| 0 | 0 | 1 | .56 | .4 | 2 |

| 1 | 0 | 0 | 1.82 | 1.3 | 1.5 |
|---|---|---|---|---|---|
| 0 | 1 | 0 | 1.08 | 2.2 | 1 |
| 0 | 0 | 1 | .56 | .4 | 2 |

Thus the inverse is

$$(I - C)^{-1} = \begin{bmatrix} 1.82 & 1.3 & 1.5 \\ 1.08 & 2.2 & 1 \\ .56 & .4 & 2 \end{bmatrix}$$

We see that the entries are all positive, so the economy is productive. For the given demand vector the required production vector is given by

$$X = (1/100) \begin{bmatrix} 182 & 130 & 150 \\ 108 & 220 & 100 \\ 56 & 40 & 200 \end{bmatrix} \begin{bmatrix} 1 \\ 2 \\ 1 \end{bmatrix} 10{,}000 = 100 \begin{bmatrix} 592 \\ 648 \\ 336 \end{bmatrix}$$

That is, production schedule should be $59,200 labor, $64,800 transportation, and $33,600 food.

Note that once the matrix $(I - C)^{-1}$ is found, it can be used as demand changes. For example, suppose that in the next month the outside demand is for $10,000 labor, $40,000 transportation, and $20,000 food. Then the production for this period is

$$X = (1/100) \begin{bmatrix} 182 & 130 & 150 \\ 108 & 220 & 100 \\ 56 & 40 & 200 \end{bmatrix} \begin{bmatrix} 1 \\ 4 \\ 2 \end{bmatrix} 10{,}000 = 100 \begin{bmatrix} 1002 \\ 1188 \\ 616 \end{bmatrix}$$

so $100,200 in labor, $118,800 in transportation, and $61,600 in food are to be produced. ∎

There are several conditions on the matrix $C$ that will ensure that it is a productive consumption matrix. One concerns the columns of $C$. If a column in the matrix $C$ sums to less than 1, then the corresponding industry consumes less than $1 to produce $1 worth of its output. In this case the industry is said to be **profitable**. It should be intuitively easy to believe that an economy will be productive if all the industries are profitable, and it can be proved that this is in fact the case. However, the converse assertion is not true, as we will see in Example 3. That is, it is possible for an economy to be productive even though one or more of the industries are not profitable.

A second condition for productivity is given in terms of row sums. The row sums are the total amounts needed as input for the economy as a whole to produce $1 worth of each commodity as output. If all row sums are less than 1, then the economy can output $1 of each commodity while internally using less. If there is some excess in each commodity after internal consumption has been accounted for, then it is reasonable to expect that the economy will be productive. The two conditions for productivity are given in the following theorem, whose proof we omit.

**THEOREM 1**

If a consumption matrix $C$ for an economy is such that either (a) all column sums are less than 1 or (b) all row sums are less than 1, then the economy is productive.

We note that while either of these two criteria is sufficient for an economy to be productive, neither is actually necessary. The next example shows a productive economy in which both conditions fail to hold.

**EXAMPLE 3**  Let an economy contain agriculture, manufacturing, and labor industries. Let $1 of agriculture require 50¢ in agriculture, 20¢ in manufacturing, and 100¢ in labor. Let $1 of manufacturing use 80¢ in manufacturing and 40¢ labor, while $1 labor takes 25¢ agriculture and 10¢ manufacturing. Show that the economy is productive, and find the production schedule if demand is for $100 agriculture, $500 manufacturing, and $700 labor.

SOLUTION   The consumption matrix is

$$C = \begin{bmatrix} .5 & 0 & .25 \\ .2 & .8 & .1 \\ 1 & .4 & 0 \end{bmatrix} \begin{matrix} \text{Agriculture} \\ \text{Manufacturing} \\ \text{Labor} \end{matrix}$$

with column headings A  M  L.

Note that two of the columns have sums greater than 1 and two of the rows have sums greater than 1.

We invert $I - C$ by using the indicated pivots.

| | | | | | |
|---|---|---|---|---|---|
| .5 | 0 | -.25 | 1 | 0 | 0 |
| -.2 | .2 | -.10 | 0 | 1 | 0 |
| -1 | -.4 | 1 | 0 | 0 | 1 |
| 1 | 0 | -.5 | 2 | 0 | 0 |
| 0 | .2 | -.2 | .4 | 1 | 0 |
| 0 | -.4 | .5 | 2 | 0 | 1 |
| 1 | 0 | -.5 | 2 | 0 | 0 |
| 0 | 1 | -1 | 2 | 5 | 0 |
| 0 | 0 | .1 | 2.8 | 2 | 1 |
| 1 | 0 | 0 | 16 | 10 | 5 |
| 0 | 1 | 0 | 30 | 25 | 10 |
| 0 | 0 | 1 | 28 | 20 | 10 |

$= (I - C)^{-1}$

Thus we have $(I - C)^{-1} \geqslant O$, and the economy is productive. Then since the demand is $100 agriculture, $500 manufacturing, and $700 labor, the production vector is

$$X = \begin{bmatrix} 16 & 10 & 5 \\ 30 & 25 & 10 \\ 28 & 20 & 10 \end{bmatrix} \begin{bmatrix} 1 \\ 5 \\ 7 \end{bmatrix} 100 = 100 \begin{bmatrix} 101 \\ 225 \\ 198 \end{bmatrix}$$

Thus the production schedule is for $10,100 agriculture, $22,500 manufacturing, and $19,800 labor. We observe that this is a large amount of production for a very small external output; such an economy would probably be considered marginal. ∎

Finally, we close with a necessary and sufficient condition for a consumption matrix (or economy) to be productive.

### THEOREM 2

A consumption matrix $C$ is productive if and only if there is some production schedule $X \geqslant O$ such that $CX < X$.

The condition $CX < X$ means that every entry of $CX$ is strictly less than the corresponding entry of $X$, which is the same as saying that $X - CX > O$. Economically, the condition states that for some particular production schedule, each industry will produce more than it consumes. The theorem states that if one such production schedule exists, then $C$ is productive; that is, given *any* outside demand, there will exist a (possibly different) production schedule such that the demand can be met. Conversely, if $C$ is productive, then the inequality is satisfied for some production vector $X$.

Note that if the inequality of the theorem is satisfied for the particular production vector $X = (1, 1, \ldots, 1)$ of all 1s, then the economy will be productive. In this case $CX$ gives us the row sums of $C$ so that the condition $CX < X$ is simply condition (b) of Theorem 1. In general the condition of Theorem 2 is not easy to test in practice unless a rather simple case such as this one happens to work. In some cases the search for a vector $X$ that satisfies the inequality of Theorem 2 may be more work than finding the inverse of $I - C$ and seeing if the entries are nonnegative. The conditions of Theorem 1 are easily applied, but as we have seen, they are not equivalent to the matrix being productive.

## EXERCISES 3.3

In Exercises 1–10, find the consumption matrix $C$ and then compute $I - C$, the inverse $(I - C)^{-1}$, and the production vector for the given external demand. What dollar amount must each industry produce in a given time period?

1. An autobody repairman (AR) and a mechanic (M) each has a company. For each $1 of business that AR does, he uses $.25 of his own services and $.25 of M's services. For each $1 of business that M does, he uses $.1 of AR's service and

$.2 of his own. In a certain week AR receives $690 worth of outside business, and M receives $460 worth of outside business.

2. Jack Spratt is a producer of fat and his wife is a producer of lean. For each $1 of fat that Jack produces, he uses 50¢ worth of fat and 25¢ of lean. For each $1 of lean that Mrs. Spratt produces, she uses 10¢ worth of fat and 25¢ worth of lean. In a certain week Jack receives orders for $840 worth of fat, while his wife obtains orders for $980 worth of lean.

3. Let a simple economy have two industries: food and labor. Let the production of $1 in food require 90¢ in food and 10¢ in labor, while the production of $1 in labor requires 20¢ in food and 60¢ in labor. Let there be an external demand for $100 in food and $200 in labor.

4. Let a simple economy have two industries: electric and oil. Let the production of $1 in electricity require $.90 in electricity and $.20 in oil, while the production of $1 in oil requires $.40 in electricity and $.10 in oil. Let the external demand be for $300 electricity and $100 oil.

5. The Alpha Omega Company produces atomic energy and labor. Let each $1 in energy require 40¢ in labor while each $1 in labor requires $1 in energy and 50¢ in labor. Suppose that there is an outside demand for $23,000 in energy and $14,000 in labor. How much of each product is used internally?

6. The Renewit Company has the products labor and lumber. Let each $1 in labor require 30¢ in lumber, while each $1 in lumber requires $2 in labor and 10¢ in lumber. Suppose that there is an outside demand for $600 labor and $1200 lumber. How much of each product will be used internally?

7. The Kaanian economy has the goods plastic and oil. Let $1 in plastic require $.20 in oil, while each $1 in oil uses $3 in plastic and $.30 in oil. Suppose that there is an outside demand for $18 million in plastic and $15 million in oil.

8. The Caramban economy has two industries: bananas and coconut oil. Let each $1 in bananas require 40¢ in bananas and 10¢ in oil while $1 in coconut oil requires 20¢ in bananas and 80¢ in oil. The outside demand is for $400 in bananas and $100 in oil.

9. Let an economy contain clothing, housing, and food industries. Let $1 in clothing require 30¢ in clothing, 30¢ in housing, and 10¢ in food, while $1 in housing takes 10¢ in clothing and 50¢ in housing, and $1 in food uses 50¢ in clothing, 10¢ in housing, and 70¢ in food. Let the demand be for $700 in clothing, $1400 in housing, and $2100 in food for the first quarter and $1400 in clothing, $700 in housing, and $1400 in food in the second quarter.

10. Suppose that an economy consists of three interdependent firms: a computing service, a statistical service, and an engineering service. For each $1 of computing that is provided, 30¢ is spent on computing, 10¢ on statistical services, and 30¢ on engineering. For each $1 of statistical service, 20¢ is spent on computing, 40¢ on statistics, and 20¢ on engineering. Each $1 in engineering takes 30¢ in computing, 10¢ in statistical service, and 30¢ in engineering. Let the May demand be $1000 computing, $1500 statistical service, and $1800

engineering and the June demand be $800 computing, $1200 statistics, and $1400 engineering.

Use Theorem 1 to show that the consumption matrices in Exercises 11–18 are productive. Determine if the industries are profitable in each case.

**11.**
$$\begin{bmatrix} .1 & .6 & .4 \\ .3 & .2 & .3 \\ .4 & .1 & .2 \end{bmatrix}$$

**12.**
$$\begin{bmatrix} .3 & .5 & .1 \\ .1 & .1 & .7 \\ .1 & .2 & .4 \end{bmatrix}$$

**13.**
$$\begin{bmatrix} .1 & .3 & .2 \\ .6 & .2 & .1 \\ .1 & .3 & .4 \end{bmatrix}$$

**14.**
$$\begin{bmatrix} .1 & .1 & .2 \\ .6 & .2 & .1 \\ .1 & .3 & .4 \end{bmatrix}$$

**15.**
$$\begin{bmatrix} .3 & .4 & .2 \\ .2 & .2 & .5 \\ .8 & .1 & 0 \end{bmatrix}$$

**16.**
$$\begin{bmatrix} .2 & .5 & .1 \\ 4 & .1 & .3 \\ .3 & .2 & .4 \end{bmatrix}$$

**17.**
$$\begin{bmatrix} .2 & .3 & .1 \\ .1 & .1 & .2 \\ .1 & .2 & .1 \end{bmatrix}$$

**18.**
$$\begin{bmatrix} .4 & .3 & .3 \\ .2 & .5 & .4 \\ .3 & .1 & .2 \end{bmatrix}$$

Show that the consumption matrices in Exercises 19–20 are not productive. (Apply Theorem 2; show that an $X$ that satisfies the condition of the theorem cannot exist.)

**19.**
$$\begin{bmatrix} .1 & 0 & .2 \\ .3 & 2 & .1 \\ 0 & .2 & .2 \end{bmatrix}$$

**20.**
$$\begin{bmatrix} 3 & .1 & 0 \\ .3 & .2 & .1 \\ .2 & 0 & .4 \end{bmatrix}$$

In Exercises 21–22, let $C$ be a consumption matrix.

**21.** Show there can be no $X \geqslant O$ such that $X > CX$ if some diagonal entry, say, $c_{kk}$, of $C$ is greater than or equal to 1.

**22.** Show that the conditions $X \geqslant O$, $X > CX$ imply that $X > O$.

## 3.4  DETERMINANTS

*Determinants of 2 × 2 and 3 × 3 Matrices, Cofactor Expansions, Triangular Matrices, Determinants and Row Operations*

In the eighteenth century, formulas were devised by Colin Maclaurin (1698–1746) for the solution of systems of linear equations in two, three, and four unknowns. Maclaurin's work was extended by Gabriel Cramer (1704–1752), and the method of solution is now called Cramer's Rule (see Section 3.5). The quantities in the formulas were called determinants, since they determined the solutions of the systems. The general properties of determinants were then studied, and the work of Pierre-Simon deLaplace (1749–1827) in the 1770s became the basis of the general theory. Since that time determinants have been applied in many areas of mathematics and science.

The first part of this section is devoted to defining the determinant of square matrices. The definition, due to Laplace, is inductive in nature as it proceeds from determinants of one size to the next size in a systematic way. The definition may seem complicated, but the repetitious pattern is quickly recognized. As a method of actually computing determinants, the definition is cumbersome and not very efficient for $4 \times 4$ or larger matrices. Fortunately, the determinant function interacts very well with elementary row operations, and we will show how they can be used to greatly simplify the computations.

Although it is important to know how to compute determinants, it should be realized that their main significance lies in the fact that they can replace procedures with formulas. That is, a number of quantities found earlier by algorithms can be compactly expressed in terms of determinants, and they also provide criteria for various properties to hold. We will apply determinants in this manner to inverses and linear systems in the next section. In this section we are primarily concerned with the computational aspects of determinants.

## DETERMINANTS OF $2 \times 2$ AND $3 \times 3$ MATRICES

The determinant function will be defined in stages. For completeness we begin by defining the determinant of a $1 \times 1$ matrix $[a]$ to be

$$\det[a] = a$$

Thus we have $\det[5] = 5$ and $\det[-3] = -3$.

We next define the determinant of a $2 \times 2$ matrix by

$$\det\begin{bmatrix} a & b \\ c & d \end{bmatrix} = a \cdot \det[d] - b \cdot \det[c] = ad - bc$$

For example, we have

$$\det\begin{bmatrix} 4 & 3 \\ -1 & 2 \end{bmatrix} = (4)(2) - (3)(-1) = 11$$

We can picture this operation as taking the product of the entries on the left-to-right diagonal and subtracting the entries on the right-to-left diagonal as shown below.

To save space, we sometimes use the notation $|A|$ in place of $\det(A)$. That is, the brackets used for matrices are replaced by straight lines to denote determinants. With this notation we would write

$$\begin{vmatrix} 3 & 7 \\ 2 & 6 \end{vmatrix} = 18 - 14 = 4$$

The determinant of a $3 \times 3$ matrix $A = [a_{ij}]$ is defined in terms of determinants of $2 \times 2$ matrices as follows:

$$\det(A) = \begin{vmatrix} a_{11} & a_{12} & a_{13} \\ a_{21} & a_{22} & a_{23} \\ a_{31} & a_{32} & a_{33} \end{vmatrix}$$

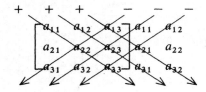

$$= a_{11} \begin{vmatrix} a_{22} & a_{23} \\ a_{32} & a_{33} \end{vmatrix} - a_{12} \begin{vmatrix} a_{21} & a_{23} \\ a_{31} & a_{33} \end{vmatrix} + a_{13} \begin{vmatrix} a_{21} & a_{22} \\ a_{31} & a_{32} \end{vmatrix}$$

Note that the entries in the first row are multiplied by the determinants of $2 \times 2$ submatrices obtained by deleting the first row and appropriate columns from $A$. Also, in this expansion along the first row, the sign of the second term has been adjusted.

If we evaluate the determinants of the submatrices and carry out the multiplications, we can express $\det(A)$ in terms of the entries of $A$ as follows.

$$\det(A) = a_{11}[a_{22}a_{33} - a_{23}a_{32}] - a_{12}[a_{21}a_{33} - a_{23}a_{31}] + a_{13}[a_{21}a_{32} - a_{22}a_{31}]$$
$$= a_{11}a_{22}a_{33} - a_{11}a_{23}a_{32} - a_{12}a_{21}a_{33}$$
$$+ a_{12}a_{23}a_{31} + a_{13}a_{21}a_{32} - a_{13}a_{22}a_{31}$$

A diagram can help to find the terms in this expression for $\det(A)$. If we copy the first two columns of $A$ to the right of the matrix, then we add the products on the left-to-right diagonals and subtract the products on the right-to-left diagonals as shown.

$$\begin{array}{cccccc} + & + & + & - & - & - \\ a_{11} & a_{12} & a_{13} & a_{11} & a_{12} \\ a_{21} & a_{22} & a_{23} & a_{21} & a_{22} \\ a_{31} & a_{32} & a_{33} & a_{31} & a_{32} \end{array}$$

**EXAMPLE 1**  Find the determinant of

$$A = \begin{bmatrix} 5 & 3 & -3 \\ -2 & 8 & 1 \\ 1 & -6 & 4 \end{bmatrix}$$

**SOLUTION**  We will find $\det(A)$ in two ways. First, the expansion along the first row gives us

$$\det(A) = 5 \begin{vmatrix} 8 & 1 \\ -6 & 4 \end{vmatrix} - 3 \begin{vmatrix} -2 & 1 \\ 1 & 4 \end{vmatrix} + (-3) \begin{vmatrix} -2 & 8 \\ 1 & -6 \end{vmatrix}$$
$$= 5 \cdot 38 - 3(-9) + (-3)(4) = 205$$

Second, the criss-cross diagram gives us

$$\det(A) = 5 \cdot 8 \cdot 4 + 3 \cdot 1 \cdot 1 + (-3)(-6)(-2)$$
$$- (-3)8 \cdot 1 - 5 \cdot 1(-6) - 3(-2)4$$
$$= 160 + 3 - 36 + 24 + 30 + 24 = 205 \quad \blacksquare\blacksquare$$

## COFACTOR EXPANSIONS

To extend the definition of determinant to $4 \times 4$ and larger matrices, it is advantageous to introduce some terminology and notation.

Let $A = [a_{ij}]$ be an $n \times n$ matrix. If we remove the $i$th row and $j$th column, which intersect in the entry $a_{ij}$, then the determinant of the remaining $n - 1 \times n - 1$ submatrix is called the **$(i, j)$-minor** of $A$. The $(i, j)$-minor is denoted by $\boldsymbol{M_{ij}}$.

For example, if

$$A = \begin{bmatrix} 5 & 3 & -3 \\ -2 & 8 & 1 \\ 1 & -6 & 4 \end{bmatrix}$$

then the $(2, 1)$-minor of $A$ is

$$M_{21} = \det \begin{bmatrix} 5 & 3 & -3 \\ -2 & 8 & 1 \\ 1 & -6 & 4 \end{bmatrix} = \det \begin{bmatrix} 3 & -3 \\ -6 & 4 \end{bmatrix} = -6$$

and the $(1, 3)$-minor of $A$ is

$$M_{13} = \det \begin{bmatrix} 5 & 3 & -3 \\ -2 & 8 & 1 \\ 1 & -6 & 4 \end{bmatrix} = \det \begin{bmatrix} -2 & 8 \\ 1 & -6 \end{bmatrix} = 4$$

There are nine possible minors for a $3 \times 3$ matrix, one corresponding to each entry. Similarly, there are 16 minors for a $4 \times 4$ matrix and $n^2$ minors for an $n \times n$ matrix.

Next we define the **$(i, j)$-cofactor** of $A$ associated with the entry $a_{ij}$, denoted by $A_{ij}$, to be

$$A_{ij} = (-1)^{i+j} M_{ij}$$

The cofactor $A_{ij}$ is sometimes called a "signed minor," since $M_{ij}$ is multiplied by $+1$ if $i + j$ is even and by $-1$ if $i + j$ is odd. The signs alternate as we proceed across a row or down a column, so that they can be displayed in a checkerboard array.

$$\begin{bmatrix} + & - & + & - & \cdots \\ - & + & - & + & \cdots \\ + & - & + & - & \cdots \\ \vdots & \vdots & \vdots & \vdots & \end{bmatrix}$$

For the matrix $A$ and the minors displayed above, we have the cofactors

$$A_{21} = (-1)^{2+1} M_{21} = (-1)(-6) = 6$$

and

$$A_{13} = (-1)^{1+3}M_{13} = (+1)(4) = 4$$

Thus to calculate a cofactor, we calculate the minor and adjust the sign appropriately.

The earlier definition of the determinant of a $3 \times 3$ matrix $A = [a_{ij}]$ can be stated in terms of the $2 \times 2$ cofactors for the entries in the first row. The definition states that

$$\det(A) = a_{11}A_{11} + a_{12}A_{12} + a_{13}A_{13}$$

We say that $\det(A)$ is given by the **cofactor expansion** across the first row. Note that determinants of $2 \times 2$ matrices were obtained from $1 \times 1$ cofactors in the same manner.

This pattern is used to extend the definition of determinant as follows.

### DEFINITION

The **determinant** of the $n \times n$ matrix $A = [a_{ij}]$ is defined for $n \geqslant 2$ by the cofactor expansion across the first row

$$\det(A) = a_{11}A_{11} + a_{12}A_{12} + \cdots + a_{1n}A_{1n}$$

where $A_{ij}$ is the cofactor for the entry $a_{ij}$.

We will not generally use the definition to calculate determinants of $4 \times 4$ or larger matrices in practice. However, to illustrate the pattern in the definition, we have the following example. Note that the calculation of the determinant of a $4 \times 4$ matrix entails the calculation of four cofactors that are determinants of $3 \times 3$ matrices.

*CAUTION*: There is no diagonal criss-cross scheme for calculating determinants of $4 \times 4$ or larger matrices as there was for $3 \times 3$ matrices.

**EXAMPLE 2** Compute the determinant of

$$A = \begin{bmatrix} 1 & -2 & 5 & 3 \\ -4 & 2 & -3 & -1 \\ 2 & -3 & -4 & 5 \\ -3 & 1 & -1 & 0 \end{bmatrix}$$

**SOLUTION** The cofactor expansion across the first row gives us

$$\det(A) = 1\begin{vmatrix} 2 & -3 & -1 \\ -3 & -4 & 5 \\ 1 & -1 & 0 \end{vmatrix} - (-2)\begin{vmatrix} -4 & -3 & -1 \\ 2 & -4 & 5 \\ -3 & -1 & 0 \end{vmatrix} + 5\begin{vmatrix} -4 & 2 & -1 \\ 2 & -3 & 5 \\ -3 & 1 & 0 \end{vmatrix}$$

$$- 3\begin{vmatrix} -4 & 2 & -3 \\ 2 & -3 & -4 \\ -3 & 1 & -1 \end{vmatrix}$$

$$= 1(-12) + 2(39) + 5(-3) - 3(21) = -12 \quad \blacksquare\blacksquare$$

To have an unambiguous definition, we have defined the determinant of a square matrix in terms of the cofactor expansion across the first row, as opposed to some other row or some column. It is a remarkable fact that a cofactor expansion across *any* row or down *any* column of $A$ will produce exactly the same value. This phenomenon is illustrated in the next example.

**EXAMPLE 3**  Find the cofactor expansion of

$$A = \begin{bmatrix} 5 & 3 & -3 \\ -2 & 8 & 1 \\ 1 & -6 & 4 \end{bmatrix}$$

(a) across the second row of $A$ and (b) down the first column of $A$.

**SOLUTION**  The matrix $A$ is that of Example 1 where we calculated $\det(A) = 205$.

(a) If we expand by cofactors across the second row of $A$, we get

$$\det(A) = a_{21}A_{21} + a_{22}A_{22} + a_{23}A_{23}$$

$$= (-2)(-1)^{2+1} \begin{vmatrix} 3 & -3 \\ -6 & 4 \end{vmatrix} + 8(-1)^{2+2} \begin{vmatrix} 5 & -3 \\ 1 & 4 \end{vmatrix}$$

$$+ 1(-1)^{2+3} \begin{vmatrix} 5 & 3 \\ 1 & -6 \end{vmatrix}$$

$$= 2(12 - 18) + 8(20 + 3) - 1(-30 - 3)$$

$$= -12 + 184 + 33 = 205$$

(b) If we expand by cofactors down the first column, we get

$$\det(A) = a_{11}A_{11} + a_{21}A_{21} + a_{31}A_{31}$$

$$= 5 \begin{vmatrix} 8 & 1 \\ -6 & 4 \end{vmatrix} - (-2) \begin{vmatrix} 3 & -3 \\ -6 & 4 \end{vmatrix} + 1 \begin{vmatrix} 3 & -3 \\ 8 & 1 \end{vmatrix}$$

$$= 5 \cdot 38 + 2(-6) + 1 \cdot 27 = 205 \quad \blacksquare\blacksquare$$

In general, we have the following theorem. It states that we get the same number no matter which row or column is chosen for the cofactor expansion. The proof, which involves showing that the same terms arise from every expansion, will be omitted.

**THEOREM 1**

If $A = [a_{ij}]$ is an $n \times n$ matrix where $n \geqslant 2$, then the cofactor expansion across any row or down any column has the value $\det(A)$. That is, we have for any row $i$

$$\det(A) = a_{i1}A_{i1} + a_{i2}A_{i2} + \cdots + a_{in}A_{in} \qquad \text{(cofactor expansion across row } i\text{)}$$

and for any column $j$

$$\det(A) = a_{1j}A_{1j} + a_{2j}A_{2j} + \cdots + a_{nj}A_{nj} \qquad \text{(cofactor expansion down column } j\text{)}$$

If a matrix has a row of zeros or a column of zeros, then that row or column can be chosen for the cofactor expansion. Since each term in the expansion will be zero, the determinant will be zero. Thus we have the following.

### COROLLARY

If $A$ has either a row of zeros or a column of zeros, then $\det(A) = 0$.

Recall that the transpose $A^t$ of a matrix $A$ is obtained by interchanging the rows and columns. Thus the first row of $A^t$ is the first column of $A$. Applying Theorem 1, we have the following.

### COROLLARY

If $A$ is a square matrix, then $\det(A^t) = \det(A)$.

## TRIANGULAR MATRICES

It is very easy to compute the determinant of certain types of matrices. For example, consider

$$A = \begin{bmatrix} 2 & 5 & 9 & 1 \\ 0 & 4 & -3 & 2 \\ 0 & 0 & -3 & 7 \\ 0 & 0 & 0 & 5 \end{bmatrix}$$

A square matrix in which all entries *below* the main diagonal are zero, such as this one, is called an **upper triangular** matrix. If the entries *above* the main diagonal are zero, then the matrix is called **lower triangular**. A matrix is **triangular** if it is either upper or lower triangular.

The determinant of the above matrix $A$ can be found by successive expansions down the first column of $A$ and the first column of each resulting cofactor as follows. Note that if an entry is 0, there is no need to compute its cofactor, since the product is automatically zero. We have

$$\det(A) = 2 \begin{vmatrix} 4 & -3 & 2 \\ 0 & -3 & 7 \\ 0 & 0 & 5 \end{vmatrix} = (2)(4) \begin{vmatrix} -3 & 7 \\ 0 & 5 \end{vmatrix} = (2)(4)(-3)(5) = -120$$

We see that $\det(A)$ is simply the product of the entries on the main diagonal.

The procedure works for any triangular matrix. Note that a lower triangular matrix is the transpose of an upper triangular matrix. We have the following result.

### THEOREM 2

The determinant of a triangular matrix is the product of the main diagonal entries. That is, we have

$$\det \begin{bmatrix} a_{11} & & \text{\Large *} \\ & \ddots & \\ \text{\Large 0} & & a_{nn} \end{bmatrix} = \det \begin{bmatrix} a_{11} & & \text{\Large 0} \\ & \ddots & \\ \text{\Large *} & & a_{nn} \end{bmatrix} = a_{11} \cdots a_{nn}$$

A square matrix in which every entry off the main diagonal is zero is called a **diagonal matrix**. Since a diagonal matrix is a special kind of triangular matrix, we can apply Theorem 2 to infer that its determinant is also the product of the diagonal entries.

**EXAMPLE 4**   Find the determinants of

$$A = \begin{bmatrix} -5 & 0 & 0 \\ 7 & 3 & 0 \\ 9 & 8 & -1 \end{bmatrix}, \quad B = \begin{bmatrix} -5 & 0 & 0 \\ 0 & 3 & 0 \\ 0 & 0 & -1 \end{bmatrix}$$

SOLUTION   Both $A$ and $B$ have the same diagonal entries. By Theorem 2 we have

$$\det(A) = \det(B) = (-5)(3)(-1) = 15 \quad \blacksquare\blacksquare$$

A very special diagonal matrix is the identity matrix $I$. Evidently, we have $\det(I) = 1$.

## DETERMINANTS AND ROW OPERATIONS

The definition of the determinant function in terms of cofactors is not a practical means of computing determinants if the matrix is $4 \times 4$ or larger. The number of arithmetic operations can be enormous. For example, the computation of the determinant of a $10 \times 10$ matrix by using cofactors can entail as many as 6,235,300 multiplications, as well as a substantial number of additions. Even the best electronic computer would be unable to find the determinant of a $100 \times 100$ matrix by this method in our lifetime, since more than 100! (100 factorial) multiplications may be required.

The calculation of determinants can be greatly simplified by using elementary row operations. The following theorem describes how the three row operations affect the value of the determinant function. The proof is omitted.

**THEOREM 3**

Let $A$ be a square matrix. Then the value of $\det(A)$ is affected by the elementary row operations as follows.

(i) If $A_1$ is obtained from $A$ by the interchange of two rows, then $\det(A_1) = -\det(A)$. That is, the sign of the determinant is changed.

(ii) If $A_2$ is obtained from $A$ by the multiplication of a row of $A$ by a constant $k$, then $\det(A_2) = k \cdot \det(A)$. That is, the determinant is multiplied by the constant.

(iii) If $A_3$ is obtained from $A$ by the addition of a multiple of one row to another row, then $\det(A_3) = \det(A)$. That is, the determinant is unchanged.

The next example illustrates the interaction of the determinant function and the elementary row operations.

**EXAMPLE 5** The determinant of the matrix

$$A = \begin{bmatrix} 1 & 2 & 3 \\ 0 & 1 & 2 \\ 2 & 4 & 8 \end{bmatrix}$$

is $\det(A) = 2$. Find the determinants of

$$A_1 = \begin{bmatrix} 1 & 2 & 3 \\ 2 & 4 & 8 \\ 0 & 1 & 2 \end{bmatrix}, \quad A_2 = \begin{bmatrix} 1 & 2 & 3 \\ 0 & 1 & 2 \\ 1 & 2 & 4 \end{bmatrix}, \quad A_3 = \begin{bmatrix} 1 & 2 & 3 \\ 0 & 1 & 2 \\ 0 & 0 & 2 \end{bmatrix}$$

**SOLUTION** Since $A_1$ is obtained from $A$ by interchanging row 2 and row 3 of $A$, we have by (*i*) of Theorem 3 that

$$\det(A_1) = -\det(A) = -2$$

The matrix $A_2$ is obtained from $A$ by multiplying row 3 of $A$ by $\frac{1}{2}$. Therefore by (*ii*) of Theorem 3 we have

$$\det(A_2) = \left(\frac{1}{2}\right)\det(A) = \left(\frac{1}{2}\right)2 = 1$$

If we add $-2$ times row 1 to row 3 of $A$, we get the matrix $A_3$. Therefore by (*iii*) of Theorem 3 we have

$$\det(A_3) = \det(A) = 2$$

Note that $A_3$ is in triangular form, so its determinant can be found easily by direct computation. ∎

If two rows of a matrix are related by a common factor, then the calculation of the determinant is easy. We simply apply (*iii*) of Theorem 3 as in the next example.

**EXAMPLE 6** Find $\det(A)$ when

$$A = \begin{bmatrix} 2 & 4 & 6 \\ 1 & 7 & -1 \\ 3 & 6 & 9 \end{bmatrix}$$

**SOLUTION** We observe that the first and third rows are proportional; in fact, row 1 is $\frac{2}{3}$ times row 3. Thus if we subtract $\frac{2}{3}$ times row 3 from row 1, we obtain a row of 0s. Therefore $\det(A) = 0$. ∎

The above technique will work on any matrix that has proportional rows, and it is the basis of the following consequence of Theorem 3.

*COROLLARY*

If the matrix $A$ has two rows that are proportional, then $\det(A) = 0$.

*NOTE*: It is possible to operate on the columns of a matrix in the same manner that elementary row operations operate on the rows. In effect, column operations can be viewed as row operations on the transpose of a matrix. That is, if one transposes, row operates, and transposes again, then the end result is the same as applying elementary column operations. Since transposing a matrix does not change the value of the determinant, column operations interact with the determinant function the same as row operations. Consequently, one can use column operations to simplify the computation of determinants as well as row operations.

A general rule of thumb is that the more zero entries there are in a matrix, the easier it is to compute the determinant. By adding appropriate multiples of a row to other rows, we can create zero entries without changing the value of the determinant, thereby simplifying the computation. Consider the following example.

**EXAMPLE 7**  Find the determinant of

$$A = \begin{bmatrix} 1 & 2 & -3 \\ 3 & 8 & -4 \\ 2 & 3 & -5 \end{bmatrix}$$

SOLUTION  We first use row 1 to create 0s in the first column. The row operations $R_2' = R_2 - 3R_1$ and $R_3' = R_3 - 2R_1$, which do not change the value of the determinant, convert $A$ to the matrix

$$\begin{bmatrix} 1 & 2 & -3 \\ 0 & 2 & 5 \\ 0 & -1 & 1 \end{bmatrix}$$

Expanding down the first column, we get

$$\det(A) = \begin{vmatrix} 2 & 5 \\ -1 & 1 \end{vmatrix} = 7 \quad \blacksquare$$

When computing determinants by hand, we should be alert to using combinations of row or column operations and cofactor expansions. Inspection and ingenuity can save labor, but there is no single approach that is best. We look for entries that can be used to generate zeros in a row or column, and there are usually several possibilities. One choice is made in the following example; the reader is invited to try another.

**EXAMPLE 8** Find the determinant of

$$A = \begin{bmatrix} -6 & 5 & 4 & 8 \\ -2 & 1 & 2 & 3 \\ 3 & -1 & -6 & -5 \\ -8 & 7 & 8 & 9 \end{bmatrix}$$

**SOLUTION** We observe that the entries in the third column are all multiples of 2. We eliminate the 4, −6, 8 in this column by adding appropriate multiples of the second row to get

$$\det(A) = \det \begin{bmatrix} -2 & 3 & 0 & 2 \\ -2 & 1 & 2 & 3 \\ -3 & 2 & 0 & 4 \\ 0 & 3 & 0 & -3 \end{bmatrix}$$

The effect is to reduce the size of the matrix. If we now expand by cofactors down the third column, we get

$$\det(A) = (-2)\det \begin{bmatrix} -2 & 3 & 2 \\ -3 & 2 & 4 \\ 0 & 3 & -3 \end{bmatrix}$$

We can now add column 3 to column 2 and then expand along the third row to get

$$\det(A) = (-2)\det \begin{bmatrix} -2 & 5 & 2 \\ -3 & 6 & 4 \\ 0 & 0 & -3 \end{bmatrix}$$

$$= (-2)(-3)\begin{vmatrix} -2 & 5 \\ -3 & 6 \end{vmatrix} = (-2)(-3)(3) = 18 \quad \blacksquare$$

# EXERCISES 3.4

In Exercises 1–8, compute the determinant of the given matrix.

1. $\begin{bmatrix} 5 & 4 \\ 6 & -2 \end{bmatrix}$  2. $\begin{bmatrix} 2 & -4 \\ -5 & 3 \end{bmatrix}$  3. $\begin{bmatrix} -1 & 7 \\ 3 & -8 \end{bmatrix}$  4. $\begin{bmatrix} -3 & -7 \\ 5 & 6 \end{bmatrix}$

5. $\begin{bmatrix} 2 & 4 & 1 \\ -2 & -1 & 3 \\ 6 & -4 & 5 \end{bmatrix}$  6. $\begin{bmatrix} -1 & -4 & -3 \\ -6 & -2 & -5 \\ -2 & -1 & -3 \end{bmatrix}$

7. $\begin{bmatrix} 5 & 1 & 7 \\ 3 & -2 & 2 \\ 4 & -4 & 6 \end{bmatrix}$  8. $\begin{bmatrix} 6 & 5 & 3 \\ 4 & 1 & 1 \\ 5 & 4 & 2 \end{bmatrix}$

In Exercises 9–12, find $M_{13}$, $A_{13}$, $M_{21}$, $A_{21}$, $M_{32}$, $A_{32}$ for the given matrices.

**9.**
$$\begin{bmatrix} 5 & 7 & -2 \\ 8 & 9 & 4 \\ -6 & 2 & -5 \end{bmatrix}$$

**10.**
$$\begin{bmatrix} 6 & 3 & 2 \\ 3 & 5 & -4 \\ 5 & 1 & -7 \end{bmatrix}$$

**11.**
$$\begin{bmatrix} 6 & 1 & 4 & 2 \\ 2 & -2 & 1 & -4 \\ -1 & 3 & -5 & -1 \\ 4 & -1 & 1 & 3 \end{bmatrix}$$

**12.**
$$\begin{bmatrix} 2 & 1 & 3 & 5 \\ -1 & 5 & 6 & 3 \\ 4 & 2 & 2 & 1 \\ -3 & -4 & 8 & -7 \end{bmatrix}$$

In Exercises 13–16, expand by cofactors (a) across the first row and (b) down the second column, and then (c) find the determinant of the given matrix.

**13.**
$$\begin{bmatrix} 6 & 4 & 5 \\ 7 & 2 & 1 \\ -5 & -3 & 8 \end{bmatrix}$$

**14.**
$$\begin{bmatrix} 2 & -6 & 1 \\ 5 & -5 & -3 \\ -2 & 3 & 4 \end{bmatrix}$$

**15.**
$$\begin{bmatrix} 5 & 1 & 2 & 4 \\ 3 & 3 & 6 & 2 \\ 1 & 2 & 1 & 4 \\ 3 & 5 & 6 & 3 \end{bmatrix}$$

**16.**
$$\begin{bmatrix} 4 & 6 & -2 & 3 \\ 1 & 5 & 0 & -1 \\ 2 & 4 & -3 & 0 \\ 0 & 3 & 1 & 5 \end{bmatrix}$$

In Exercises 17–20, find the determinant of the given matrix by appeal to Theorem 2.

**17.**
$$\begin{bmatrix} 9 & 5 & 7 & 42 \\ 0 & -3 & 5 & -17 \\ 0 & 0 & -2 & 7 \\ 0 & 0 & 0 & 5 \end{bmatrix}$$

**18.**
$$\begin{bmatrix} -5 & 4 & 18 & 3 \\ 0 & 2 & 51 & 7 \\ 0 & 0 & 6 & 22 \\ 0 & 0 & 0 & -1 \end{bmatrix}$$

**19.**
$$\begin{bmatrix} 4 & 0 & 0 & 0 \\ 16 & 5 & 0 & 0 \\ 2 & 8 & -6 & 0 \\ 47 & 3 & 9 & -2 \end{bmatrix}$$

**20.**
$$\begin{bmatrix} -2 & 0 & 0 & 0 \\ 5 & 3 & 0 & 0 \\ 19 & 23 & -4 & 0 \\ 16 & 4 & 61 & 7 \end{bmatrix}$$

In Exercises 21–22, find the determinant of the given matrix by using the known value of the determinants in Exercises 15–16 and an appeal to Theorem 3.

**21.**
$$\begin{bmatrix} 5 & 1 & 2 & 4 \\ 3 & 5 & 6 & 3 \\ 1 & 2 & 1 & 4 \\ 3 & 3 & 6 & 2 \end{bmatrix}$$

**22.**
$$\begin{bmatrix} 0 & 3 & 1 & 5 \\ 1 & 5 & 0 & -1 \\ 2 & 4 & -3 & 0 \\ 4 & 6 & -2 & 3 \end{bmatrix}$$

In Exercises 23–24, find the determinant of the given matrix by using the known value of the determinants in Exercises 7–8 and an appeal to Theorem 3.

**23.**
$$\begin{bmatrix} 5 & 1 & 7 \\ 9 & -6 & 6 \\ 4 & -4 & 6 \end{bmatrix}$$

**24.**
$$\begin{bmatrix} 6 & 5 & 3 \\ 4 & 1 & 1 \\ -10 & -8 & -4 \end{bmatrix}$$

In Exercises 25–28, compute the determinant of the given matrix by using row operations to find an upper triangular matrix.

**25.** $\begin{bmatrix} 5 & 1 & 2 \\ 3 & 5 & 2 \\ 2 & 4 & 6 \end{bmatrix}$  $R_2' = R_2 - \frac{3}{5} R_1$  **26.** $\begin{bmatrix} 3 & -7 & 11 \\ 1 & -2 & 3 \\ -2 & 8 & -16 \end{bmatrix}$

**27.** $\begin{bmatrix} 1 & 2 & -3 & 1 \\ 3 & 8 & -4 & 4 \\ 2 & 4 & -5 & 5 \\ 1 & 2 & -2 & -1 \end{bmatrix}$  **28.** $\begin{bmatrix} 2 & -1 & 3 & 4 \\ 6 & -4 & 10 & 7 \\ -4 & 2 & -3 & -5 \\ 4 & -3 & 7 & 6 \end{bmatrix}$

In Exercises 29–30, compute the determinant of the given matrix by means of row operations and cofactor expansion.

**29.** $\begin{bmatrix} 2 & 2 & -4 & 5 \\ 3 & 1 & 2 & -1 \\ 3 & -2 & -2 & 4 \\ -4 & 3 & 4 & -3 \end{bmatrix}$  **30.** $\begin{bmatrix} 4 & 5 & 2 & 3 \\ 2 & 3 & 4 & -1 \\ 3 & 5 & 2 & 1 \\ -2 & 5 & 6 & 2 \end{bmatrix}$

In Exercises 31–32, find the determinant of the given matrix by appeal to the corollary to Theorem 3.

**31.** $\begin{bmatrix} 4 & -6 & 3 & 7 & 2 \\ 1 & 5 & 2 & -1 & 4 \\ 6 & 2 & -6 & 8 & 3 \\ -8 & 12 & -6 & -14 & -4 \\ 5 & 5 & 3 & 4 & -2 \end{bmatrix}$  **32.** $\begin{bmatrix} 6 & 3 & 7 & 4 & 5 \\ -2 & 1 & 4 & 3 & 2 \\ 5 & 5 & 1 & 7 & 7 \\ 2 & 8 & -6 & -4 & 1 \\ -6 & 3 & 12 & 9 & 6 \end{bmatrix}$

In Exercises 33–34, suppose that $a$, $b$, $c$, $d$ are nonzero numbers and find the determinant of the given matrix.

**33.** $\begin{bmatrix} 0 & 0 & a \\ 0 & b & 0 \\ c & 0 & 0 \end{bmatrix}$  **34.** $\begin{bmatrix} 0 & 0 & 0 & a \\ 0 & 0 & b & 0 \\ 0 & c & 0 & 0 \\ d & 0 & 0 & 0 \end{bmatrix}$

In Exercises 35–36, find the value of $k$ such that the determinant of the given matrix is 0.

**35.** $\begin{bmatrix} 6 & k & 0 \\ 0 & 2 & -1 \\ k & 0 & 3 \end{bmatrix}$  **36.** $\begin{bmatrix} 1-k & 0 & 3 \\ 0 & 2-k & 1 \\ 1 & 2 & 4 \end{bmatrix}$

## 3.5 APPLICATIONS OF DETERMINANTS

*Cramer's Rule, Construction of the Inverse, Existence of the Inverse, Adjoint Matrices and Cramer's Rule*

In this section we apply the determinant function to two topics that were discussed earlier, namely, solving linear systems and finding the inverse of a matrix. We will consider linear systems that have equal numbers of equations and variables, that is, systems that have square coefficient matrices. In this case, if the determinant of the coefficient matrix is nonzero, then there is a determinantal formula for the solution called Cramer's Rule. We will describe Cramer's Rule at the beginning of the section, but its verification will be deferred to the end of the section.

The nonvanishing of the determinant of a square matrix also implies the existence of the inverse. We will actually construct the inverse out of determinants by means of a matrix called the adjoint. The connection between the adjoint matrix and Cramer's Rule is discussed at the end of the section. Thus the condition that a matrix have a nonzero determinant is related to both the uniqueness of solutions and invertibility.

## CRAMER'S RULE

We first describe Cramer's Rule for a system of two equations in two variables. Let us write the system

$$a_1 x_1 + b_1 x_2 = c_1$$
$$a_2 x_1 + b_2 x_2 = c_2$$

in matrix form $AX = B$ so that

$$A = \begin{bmatrix} a_1 & b_1 \\ a_2 & b_2 \end{bmatrix}, \quad B = \begin{bmatrix} c_1 \\ c_2 \end{bmatrix}$$

Either by direct algebraic manipulation (as in the analysis of Section 1.2 in Chapter 1) or by applying the formula for the inverse of $A$ (which was given in Section 3.2), we would find that the following situation emerges. If $a_1 b_2 - b_1 a_2 \neq 0$, then a solution exists and is unique, and it is given by

$$x_1 = \frac{c_1 b_2 - b_1 c_2}{a_1 b_2 - b_1 a_2}, \quad x_2 = \frac{a_1 c_2 - c_1 a_2}{a_1 b_2 - b_1 a_2}$$

We quickly recognize that the formulas can be expressed in terms of determinants. The denominators are both equal to $\det(A)$, and the numerators are related to $A$ as follows. If we let $A_1$ be the matrix obtained by replacing the first column of $A$ by $B$, then we get

$$\det(A_1) = \begin{vmatrix} c_1 & b_1 \\ c_2 & b_2 \end{vmatrix} = c_1 b_2 - b_1 c_2$$

which is the numerator for $x_1$. Similarly, if we replace the second column of $A$ by $B$ to get the matrix $A_2$, then we have

$$\det(A_2) = \begin{vmatrix} a_1 & c_1 \\ a_2 & c_2 \end{vmatrix} = a_1 c_2 - c_1 a_2$$

which is the numerator for $x_2$. Thus we can write the solution as

$$x_1 = \frac{\det(A_1)}{\det(A)}, \quad x_2 = \frac{\det(A_2)}{\det(A)}$$

These determinant formulas are referred to as Cramer's Rule for the case of two equations in two variables.

The following example illustrates Cramer's Rule for two variables.

**EXAMPLE 1** Use Cramer's Rule to solve the system

$$3x_1 + 2x_2 = 5$$
$$4x_1 + 5x_2 = 1$$

**SOLUTION** First we calculate the determinant of the coefficient matrix:

$$\det(A) = \det \begin{bmatrix} 3 & 2 \\ 4 & 5 \end{bmatrix} = 7$$

Since this is nonzero, we know that the solution exists and is unique. Then we calculate

$$\det(A_1) = \begin{vmatrix} 5 & 2 \\ 1 & 5 \end{vmatrix} = 23, \quad \det(A_2) = \begin{vmatrix} 3 & 5 \\ 4 & 1 \end{vmatrix} = -17$$

Hence by Cramer's Rule we obtain the solution $x_1 = \frac{23}{7}$, $x_2 = -\frac{17}{7}$. ■■

In general, consider the linear system

$$a_{11}x_1 + a_{12}x_2 + \cdots + a_{1n}x_n = b_1$$
$$a_{21}x_1 + a_{22}x_2 + \cdots + a_{2n}x_n = b_2$$
$$\vdots \qquad \vdots \qquad \vdots \qquad \vdots$$
$$a_{n1}x_1 + a_{n2}x_2 + \cdots + a_{nn}x_n = b_n$$

which can be written in matrix form as

$$AX = B$$

We define the matrix $A_j$ to be the matrix obtained by replacing the $j$th column of $A$ by the column $B$. That is, we define the matrix $A_j$ to be

$$A_j = \begin{bmatrix} a_{11} & \cdots & b_1 & \cdots & a_{1n} \\ a_{21} & \cdots & b_2 & \cdots & a_{2n} \\ \vdots & & \vdots & & \vdots \\ a_{n1} & \cdots & b_n & \cdots & a_{nn} \end{bmatrix}$$

$j$th column

Then we have the following theorem, which is known as Cramer's Rule. A derivation of Cramer's Rule is given at the end of the section.

**THEOREM 1** (*Cramer's Rule*)

If $A$ is an $n \times n$ matrix with $\det(A) \neq 0$, then the linear system

$$AX = B$$

has the unique solution $X = (x_j)$ given by

$$x_j = \frac{\det(A_j)}{\det(A)}, \quad j = 1, 2, \ldots, n$$

where $A_j$ is the matrix obtained by replacing the $j$th column of $A$ by $B$.

**EXAMPLE 2**   Use Cramer's Rule to find the value of $x_2$ only in the solution of the system

$$5x_1 + 7x_2 + 2x_3 = 1$$
$$2x_1 - 8x_2 - x_3 = 0$$
$$-3x_1 + 4x_2 + x_3 = -1$$

**SOLUTION**   The coefficient matrix $A$ has the determinant $\det(A) = -45$. To find the value of $x_2$, we need to calculate the determinant

$$\det(A_2) = \det \begin{bmatrix} 5 & 1 & 2 \\ 2 & 0 & -1 \\ -3 & -1 & 1 \end{bmatrix} = -8$$

Then according to Cramer's Rule, we have $x_2 = \frac{8}{45}$.  ∎

As a computational method for finding solutions, Cramer's Rule is inefficient except for small systems of equations, and elimination methods are generally preferable. Nevertheless, it does provide a formula for solutions that can be useful in certain situations. For instance, in solving a small system by hand where the determinant of the coefficient matrix is large, Cramer's Rule has the advantage of avoiding messy fractions that can arise in elimination methods. Also, if only the value of one variable is needed, as in the preceding example, then Cramer's Rule can be used to find it without solving the system completely.

The theoretical importance of formulas such as those in Theorem 1 is that it is often possible to deduce properties from a formula much more easily than from an algorithm. For example, if all the coefficients and constants in a system are integers and if $\det(A) = 1$ or $-1$, then we can deduce from Cramer's Rule that the solution will consist of integers—a fact that is not immediately apparent from the viewpoint of elimination procedures.

## CONSTRUCTION OF THE INVERSE

We will now describe a method for calculating the inverse of a square matrix, and at the same time we will obtain a condition that guarantees the existence of the inverse.

The construction of the inverse of a matrix $A = [a_{ij}]$ begins with the calculation of the cofactors $A_{ij}$ for all of the entries $a_{ij}$. We then define the **adjoint matrix** of $A$, written **adj($A$)**, as follows. The first *column* of adj($A$) consists of the cofactors of the first *row* of $A$, the second *column* of adj($A$) consists of the cofactors of the second *row* of $A$, and so on. Thus we calculate the cofactors by moving across the rows of $A$, but then we list them in columns to form the adjoint matrix.

In general, for the matrix $A = [a_{ij}]$ the adjoint matrix is

$$\text{adj}(A) = \begin{bmatrix} A_{11} & A_{21} & \cdots & A_{n1} \\ A_{12} & A_{22} & \cdots & A_{n2} \\ \vdots & \vdots & & \vdots \\ A_{1n} & A_{2n} & \cdots & A_{nn} \end{bmatrix}$$

Note that the $(i,j)$-entry of adj($A$) is the $(j,i)$-cofactor $A_{ji}$. In other words, the adjoint matrix is the transpose of the matrix obtained by replacing each $a_{ij}$ by its cofactor $A_{ij}$. That is, we have

$$\text{adj}(A) = [A_{ij}]^t$$

**EXAMPLE 3**  Find the adjoint matrix of

$$A = \begin{bmatrix} 1 & 5 & 7 \\ -2 & 3 & 1 \\ 2 & -1 & 4 \end{bmatrix}$$

**SOLUTION**  There are nine cofactors to be calculated. The cofactors corresponding to entries in the first *row* of $A$ are

$$A_{11} = \begin{vmatrix} 3 & 1 \\ -1 & 4 \end{vmatrix} = 13, \quad A_{12} = -\begin{vmatrix} -2 & 1 \\ 2 & 4 \end{vmatrix} = 10, \quad A_{13} = \begin{vmatrix} -2 & 3 \\ 2 & -1 \end{vmatrix} = -4$$

$$12 - (-1) = 13 \qquad -1(-8 - 2) = 10$$

These values form the first *column* of adj($A$). Thus far we have obtained

$$\text{adj}(A) = \begin{bmatrix} 13 & - & - \\ 10 & - & - \\ -4 & - & - \end{bmatrix}$$

After finding the other six cofactors, we obtain the adjoint matrix

$$\text{adj}(A) = \begin{bmatrix} 13 & -27 & -16 \\ 10 & -10 & -15 \\ -4 & 11 & 13 \end{bmatrix} \quad \blacksquare$$

If we multiply $A$ by its adjoint, then an interesting phenomenon occurs. For example, the matrix $A$ of Example 3 above has $\det(A) = 35$; and if we compute the product of $A$ and $\mathrm{adj}(A)$, we get

$$A \cdot \mathrm{adj}(A) = \begin{bmatrix} 1 & 5 & 7 \\ -2 & 3 & 1 \\ 2 & -1 & 4 \end{bmatrix} \begin{bmatrix} 13 & -27 & -16 \\ 10 & -10 & -15 \\ -4 & 11 & 13 \end{bmatrix}$$

$$= \begin{bmatrix} 35 & 0 & 0 \\ 0 & 35 & 0 \\ 0 & 0 & 35 \end{bmatrix} = 35 \cdot I$$

In general, if we multiply a matrix times its adjoint, we get

$$A \cdot \mathrm{adj}(A) = \begin{bmatrix} \det(A) & 0 & \ldots & 0 \\ 0 & \det(A) & \ldots & 0 \\ \vdots & \vdots & \ddots & \vdots \\ 0 & 0 & \ldots & \det(A) \end{bmatrix} = \det(A) \cdot I$$

The reasons for this result are discussed at the end of the section.

If it happens that $\det(A)$ is not zero, then we can divide this matrix equation by the number $\det(A)$ and so obtain

$$A \left[ \frac{1}{\det(A)} \mathrm{adj}(A) \right] = I$$

Thus we see that the expression in brackets must be the inverse matrix for $A$. Hence we have the following theorem concerning the inverse of $A$.

## THEOREM 2

If $A$ is a square matrix such that $D = \det(A) \neq 0$, then $A$ is invertible, and the inverse is given by

$$A^{-1} = \frac{1}{D} \cdot \mathrm{adj}(A)$$

The matrix $A$ in Example 3 is invertible, since $\det(A) = 35$, and the inverse $A^{-1}$ is obtained by multiplying the adjoint matrix found in that example by $\frac{1}{35}$. Here is another example.

**EXAMPLE 4**   Show that the matrix

$$B = \begin{bmatrix} 1 & -1 & -2 \\ 1 & 3 & 0 \\ 2 & 0 & -4 \end{bmatrix}$$

is invertible and find $B^{-1}$.

**SOLUTION** First we compute the cofactors for the entries in the first row and obtain $-12, 4, -6$. This gives us the first column of the adjoint matrix, and at the same time we can compute the determinant of $B$ by using the cofactor expansion across the first row. We have

$$\det(B) = -12 - 4 + 12 = -4$$

Since the determinant is not zero, we know that $B^{-1}$ exists. Next we compute the rest of the adjoint matrix and obtain

$$\text{adj}(B) = \begin{bmatrix} -12 & -4 & 6 \\ 4 & 0 & -2 \\ -6 & -2 & 4 \end{bmatrix}$$

Then according to Theorem 2, we have

$$B^{-1} = (-1/4) \cdot \text{adj}(B) = \begin{bmatrix} 3 & 1 & -3/2 \\ -1 & 0 & 1/2 \\ 3/2 & 1/2 & -1 \end{bmatrix}$$

The computations can be checked by forming the product $BB^{-1}$ and verifying that the result is the identity matrix $I$. This is left for the reader to carry out. ∎

As a general computational method for finding the inverse of a matrix, the use of the adjoint matrix is not very efficient except for small matrices. In general, the number of calculations is much greater than in the elimination methods given in Section 3.2. However, there is some advantage to using the adjoint matrix when computing $A^{-1}$ by hand if $\det(A)$ is large. Note that if the entries of $A$ are integers, then $A^{-1}$ will involve fractions with denominator $\det(A)$. On the other hand, if $\det(A) = 1$ or $-1$, then it follows from Theorem 2 that $A^{-1}$ will also have integer entries.

The formula for the inverse of a $2 \times 2$ matrix can be derived from Theorem 2 as follows. Suppose that

$$A = \begin{bmatrix} a & b \\ c & d \end{bmatrix}$$

is such that $D = \det(A) = ad - bc \neq 0$. The cofactors of $A$ are $A_{11} = d$, $A_{12} = -c$, $A_{21} = -b$, $A_{22} = a$, so that the adjoint matrix of $A$ is

$$\text{adj}(A) = \begin{bmatrix} d & -b \\ -c & a \end{bmatrix}$$

Hence by Theorem 2 the inverse is

$$A^{-1} = (1/D) \begin{bmatrix} d & -b \\ -c & a \end{bmatrix}$$

Thus we simply reverse the entries $a$ and $d$, change the signs of the entries $b$ and $c$, and divide by the determinant. This is the same formula that was given in Section 3.2.

**EXAMPLE 5**   Find the inverse of

$$A = \begin{bmatrix} 6 & 8 \\ 5 & 7 \end{bmatrix}$$

*42 − 40 = 2*

**SOLUTION**   First we find $\det(A) = 2$. Then by the above formula we have

$$A^{-1} = (1/2) \begin{bmatrix} 7 & -8 \\ -5 & 6 \end{bmatrix} = \begin{bmatrix} 7/2 & -4 \\ -5/2 & 3 \end{bmatrix} \; \blacksquare$$

## EXISTENCE OF THE INVERSE

We have seen that if $\det(A) \neq 0$, then $A$ is invertible. The converse is also valid, as we now show. We need the following theorem, whose proof we omit.

---
**THEOREM 3**

If $A$ and $B$ are $n \times n$ matrices, then

$$\det(AB) = \det(A)\det(B)$$

---

*NOTE*:   The fact that the determinant of the product is the product of the determinants may be quite surprising, since both matrix multiplication and determinants are rather complicated operations. However, it must be realized that there is no similar relation for matrix addition. In general, the determinant of a sum cannot be expressed in terms of the sum of the determinants.

We can now establish the following criterion for the invertibility of a square matrix.

---
**THEOREM 4**

A square matrix $A$ has an inverse if and only if $\det(A) \neq 0$. Moreover, if $A^{-1}$ exists, then

$$\det(A^{-1}) = \frac{1}{\det(A)}$$

---

***Proof.***   It has been shown that if $\det(A) \neq 0$, then $A^{-1}$ exists. To go in the other direction, assume that the inverse of $A$ exists. Then we have $AA^{-1} = I$; and if we apply Theorem 3, we get

$$\det(A)\det(A^{-1}) = \det(I) = 1$$

Since the product is nonzero, both factors $\det(A)$ and $\det(A^{-1})$ must be nonzero. Therefore we have $\det(A) \neq 0$, and division by $\det(A)$ gives us $\det(A^{-1}) = 1/\det(A)$. This proves the theorem.   $\blacksquare$

In certain situations, both applied and theoretical, it is more important to know whether a matrix is invertible or not than it is to compute the inverse explicitly. In these situations the determinant provides a very convenient test for invertibility as given in Theorem 4. Note also that $\det(A^{-1})$ can be found without actually finding the matrix $A^{-1}$.

**EXAMPLE 6**   For each of the following matrices, determine if the inverse exists; if so, find the determinant of the inverse.

$$A = \begin{bmatrix} 4 & 2 \\ 5 & 3 \end{bmatrix} \quad \text{and} \quad B = \begin{bmatrix} 4 & 6 \\ -6 & -9 \end{bmatrix}$$

**SOLUTION**   Since $\det(A) = 2$, the inverse of $A$ exists, and $\det(A^{-1}) = \frac{1}{2}$. However, since $\det(B) = 0$, the matrix $B$ does not have an inverse. ∎

The determinant thus provides a criterion for the existence of the inverse and a criterion for the uniqueness of solutions for systems that have a square coefficient matrix. We can restate Theorem 3 of Section 3.2 with determinants providing an additional criterion.

*THEOREM 5*

The following assertions are equivalent for an $n \times n$ matrix $A$.

(*i*)   $\det(A) \neq 0$.

(*ii*)   $A^{-1}$ exists.

(*iii*)   $AX = B$ has a unique solution for any $B$.

(*iv*)   The row rank of $A$ is $n$.

Since a homogeneous system $AX = O$ always has at least one solution, namely, the zero solution, we can deduce the following corollary.

*COROLLARY*

If $A$ is a square matrix, then the homogeneous system $AX = O$ has infinitely many solutions if and only if $\det(A) = 0$.

## ADJOINT MATRICES AND CRAMER'S RULE

We will now explain how the adjoint matrix leads to the inverse of a matrix and how this cofactor formula for the inverse gives rise to Cramer's Rule.

Let us examine the adjoint for the case of a general $3 \times 3$ matrix. We wish to calculate the product

$$A \cdot \text{adj}(A) = \begin{bmatrix} a_{11} & a_{12} & a_{13} \\ a_{21} & a_{22} & a_{23} \\ a_{31} & a_{32} & a_{33} \end{bmatrix} \begin{bmatrix} A_{11} & A_{21} & A_{31} \\ A_{12} & A_{22} & A_{32} \\ A_{13} & A_{23} & A_{33} \end{bmatrix}$$

First note that the $(1, 1)$-entry of the product, obtained by multiplying the first row of $A$ times the first column of $\text{adj}(A)$, is just the cofactor expansion of $\det(A)$ across the first row of $A$. That is, we have

$$a_{11}A_{11} + a_{12}A_{12} + a_{13}A_{13} = \det(A)$$

Similarly, the $(2, 2)$-entry of the product is the cofactor expansion of $\det(A)$ across the second row, and the $(3, 3)$-entry is the cofactor expansion across the third row. Thus we see that the diagonal entries of the product are all equal to $\det(A)$.

Let us now examine the nondiagonal entries of the product of $A$ and $\text{adj}(A)$. Consider the $(2, 1)$-entry of the product, which is given by

$$a_{21}A_{11} + a_{22}A_{12} + a_{23}A_{13}$$

To see that this sum must be zero, note that we can interpret the sum as being the cofactor expansion across the first row of the matrix

$$B = \begin{bmatrix} a_{21} & a_{22} & a_{23} \\ a_{21} & a_{22} & a_{23} \\ a_{31} & a_{32} & a_{33} \end{bmatrix}$$

where we have obtained $B$ by discarding the first row of $A$ and putting the second row in its place. Thus the first two rows of $B$ are the same. The first row cofactors of $B$ are $A_{11}$, $A_{12}$, $A_{13}$, the same as for the first row of $A$. But since $B$ has two identical rows, we have that $\det(B) = 0$. Hence we conclude that

$$a_{21}A_{11} + a_{22}A_{12} + a_{23}A_{13} = \det(B) = 0$$

The other nondiagonal entries of the product of $A$ and $\text{adj}(A)$ can be shown to be zero by the same device.

In summary, the multiplication of row $i$ of $A$ times column $i$ of $\text{adj}(A)$ is a cofactor expansion of $\det(A)$, but the multiplication of row $i$ times column $j$ of $\text{adj}(A)$ where $i \neq j$ is a cofactor expansion of a matrix with two identical rows and so is zero.

The preceding arguments can be extended to any $n \times n$ matrix. We can write the conclusion in a unified way as follows: The $(i, j)$-entry of $A \cdot \text{adj}(A)$ is given by

$$a_{i1}A_{j1} + a_{i2}A_{j2} + \cdots + a_{in}A_{jn} = \begin{cases} \det(A) & \text{if } i = j \\ 0 & \text{if } i \neq j \end{cases}$$

This is just another way of writing $A \cdot \text{adj}(A) = \det(A) \cdot I$. Thus if $\det(A) \neq 0$, then we divide both sides by $\det(A)$ and thereby obtain the formula for $A^{-1}$. This gives us Theorem 2.

***Derivation of Cramer's Rule.***  We now apply the formula for $A^{-1}$ to derive Cramer's Rule. Suppose that we have a system $AX = B$ where $\det(A) \neq 0$. Then $A^{-1}$ exists, and we can write the unique solution as

$$X = A^{-1}B$$

If we now express the inverse in terms of the adjoint matrix as in Theorem 2, then we can write the solution as

$$X = \begin{bmatrix} x_1 \\ \vdots \\ x_j \\ \vdots \\ x_n \end{bmatrix} = \frac{1}{\det(A)} \begin{bmatrix} A_{11} & \cdots & A_{i1} & \cdots & A_{n1} \\ \vdots & & \vdots & & \vdots \\ A_{1j} & \cdots & A_{ij} & \cdots & A_{nj} \\ \vdots & & \vdots & & \vdots \\ A_{1n} & \cdots & A_{in} & \cdots & A_{nn} \end{bmatrix} \begin{bmatrix} b_1 \\ \vdots \\ b_i \\ \vdots \\ b_n \end{bmatrix}$$

If we extract the $j$th entry from each side of this matrix equation, we get

$$x_j = \frac{1}{\det(A)}(A_{1j}b_1 + \cdots + A_{ij}b_i + \cdots + A_{nj}b_n)$$

The expression in parentheses can be interpreted as the cofactor expansion down the $j$th column of the matrix $A_j$ obtained by replacing the $j$th column of $A$ by the column $B$. Then the above expression for $x_j$ can be written as

$$x_j = \frac{\det(A_j)}{\det(A)}$$

Thus we have established Cramer's Rule.

# EXERCISES 3.5

Where applicable, use Cramer's Rule to solve the systems in Exercises 1–12.

**1.** $4x_1 + 2x_2 = 5$
$\quad 5x_1 - \ x_2 = 2$

**2.** $-3x_1 + 6x_2 = -4$
$\quad 2x_1 + 4x_2 = \ \ \ 7$

**3.** $6x - 4y = -3$
$\quad 5x + 7y = \ \ \ 2$

**4.** $-3x - 5y = 2$
$\quad \ \ 7x - 6y = 3$

**5.** $8x - 4y = -2$
$\quad -4x + 2y = \ \ \ 1$

**6.** $x + \ 5y = 2$
$\quad 3x + 15y = 6$

**7.** $\quad 4x_1 + 2x_2 - \ x_3 \ = \ \ \ 1$
$\quad -2x_1 + 5x_2 \qquad \ \ = \ \ \ 4$
$\qquad \qquad 6x_2 + 3x_3 \ = -2$

**8.** $\qquad \quad 4x_2 - 3x_3 = \ \ \ 5$
$\quad -6x_1 + 2x_2 + 4x_3 = \ \ \ 7$
$\quad \ \ \ 3x_1 - 2x_2 \qquad \ \ = -3$

**9.** $6x - 2y + 3z = 4$
$\quad 5x + 4y + 2z = 3$
$\quad 7x - \ y + \ z = 1$

**10.** $3x - 2y + 8z = 2$
$\quad \ -x + 4y + 5z = 6$
$\quad \ 2x - 3y + 6z = 1$

**11.** $3x_1 + 5x_2 - 6x_3 = 4$
$\quad 5x_1 + \ x_2 + 2x_3 = 5$
$\quad \ \ x_1 - 2x_2 + 4x_3 = 6$

**12.** $-2x_1 + \ x_2 + 5x_3 = -4$
$\quad \ \ 4x_1 + 5x_2 + 7x_3 = \ \ \ 2$
$\quad \ \ 3x_1 + 2x_2 + \ x_3 = -2$

In Exercises 13–16, find the adjoint of the given matrix. Then multiply the adjoint times the matrix.

**13.** $\begin{bmatrix} 6 & 2 \\ -3 & 8 \end{bmatrix}$
**14.** $\begin{bmatrix} -5 & 4 \\ 2 & 1 \end{bmatrix}$

**15.** $\begin{bmatrix} 6 & -2 & 1 \\ 3 & 2 & -3 \\ -1 & 4 & 5 \end{bmatrix}$
**16.** $\begin{bmatrix} 2 & -3 & 4 \\ -1 & 5 & -2 \\ 3 & 6 & 1 \end{bmatrix}$

In Exercises 17–24, use determinants to find the inverse of the given matrix if it exists.

**17.** $\begin{bmatrix} 4 & -2 \\ 7 & 9 \end{bmatrix}$
**18.** $\begin{bmatrix} -6 & 5 \\ 2 & 3 \end{bmatrix}$
**19.** $\begin{bmatrix} 4 & -8 \\ -2 & 4 \end{bmatrix}$
**20.** $\begin{bmatrix} -5 & 15 \\ 1 & -3 \end{bmatrix}$

**21.** $\begin{bmatrix} 2 & 7 & 4 \\ 1 & -1 & 3 \\ 5 & -2 & -3 \end{bmatrix}$
**22.** $\begin{bmatrix} 2 & 3 & -5 \\ 5 & -6 & -4 \\ 1 & -1 & -2 \end{bmatrix}$

**23.** $\begin{bmatrix} 4 & 6 & 7 \\ 1 & 2 & 5 \\ 6 & 10 & 17 \end{bmatrix}$
**24.** $\begin{bmatrix} 6 & 10 & 4 \\ 2 & 7 & 5 \\ -3 & -5 & -2 \end{bmatrix}$

In Exercises 25–26, find det($AB$) without finding $AB$.

**25.** $A = \begin{bmatrix} 2 & 5 & 3 \\ 3 & 2 & 1 \\ -5 & 4 & -2 \end{bmatrix}$, $B = \begin{bmatrix} 3 & 4 & -4 \\ 2 & 2 & -2 \\ -1 & -5 & -3 \end{bmatrix}$

**26.** $A = \begin{bmatrix} 5 & 3 & -6 \\ 2 & 1 & -2 \\ -3 & 4 & 5 \end{bmatrix}$, $B = \begin{bmatrix} 1 & 3 & 6 \\ -3 & 2 & -1 \\ 4 & -3 & 7 \end{bmatrix}$

In Exercises 27–32, use determinants to determine if the given matrix $A$ is invertible. If $A^{-1}$ exists, then find det($A^{-1}$) without finding $A^{-1}$.

**27.** $\begin{bmatrix} 2 & 8 \\ 3 & -7 \end{bmatrix}$
**28.** $\begin{bmatrix} -4 & 3 \\ 8 & -6 \end{bmatrix}$
**29.** $\begin{bmatrix} 5 & -2 \\ -10 & 4 \end{bmatrix}$
**30.** $\begin{bmatrix} 1 & 5 \\ -4 & 9 \end{bmatrix}$

**31.** $\begin{bmatrix} 2 & 5 & 5 \\ 1 & 3 & 2 \\ 0 & 4 & 1 \end{bmatrix}$
**32.** $\begin{bmatrix} 0 & -2 & -3 \\ 3 & 7 & 11 \\ 1 & 2 & 4 \end{bmatrix}$

In Exercises 33–40, use the determinant of the coefficient matrix to tell if the homogeneous system of equations has infinitely many solutions.

**33.** $3x + 2y = 0$
$4x - y = 0$

**34.** $4x - 6y = 0$
$-2x + 3y = 0$

**35.** $6x + 2y = 0$
$3x + y = 0$

**36.** $5x + y = 0$
$x + 4y = 0$

**37.** $2x + 4y - 2z = 0$
$x - y + 3z = 0$
$5x + 7y - z = 0$

**38.** $3x + 2y - z = 0$
$5x + 4y + 2z = 0$
$4x - 2y - 3z = 0$

**39.** $2x_1 + x_2 + 3x_3 = 0$
$5x_1 + 3x_2 - 2x_3 = 0$
$x_1 - 4x_2 + 2x_3 = 0$

**40.** $3x_1 - 3x_2 + 4x_3 = 0$
$2x_1 + 4x_2 - x_3 = 0$
$4x_1 - 10x_2 + 9x_3 = 0$

## 3.6 MARKOV ANALYSIS

*Markov Chains, Stable Vectors*

As another illustration of the use of matrix algebra, we will briefly outline some aspects of the method of mathematical modelling known as Markov analysis. Events that occur in stages over time in such a manner that the possible courses of action are the same at each stage can often be represented by a Markov chain, and future events can be estimated on the basis of past and current events.

The origins of Markov analysis lie in the study of particle motion in gases, published in 1906 by Andrei A. Markov (1856–1922). The method has since been applied in biology, sociology, and business as well as the physical sciences. Examples of successful applications in business include such things as estimations of customer movement between competing firms, customer loyalty to brand names, and accounts receivable relative to delinquent payments and bad debts. A forecast of possible future trends can be valuable in any area of managerial decision making.

### MARKOV CHAINS

We will introduce some of the basic notions of Markov analysis in the context of an example. Consider the situation of two firms that are competing in a community. Suppose that under aggressive management policies, the smaller company has been increasing its share of the market. A customer survey is conducted to determine the current market split, and the tendency for customers to switch firms. What inferences can be drawn for future years?

**EXAMPLE 1** A rural community is served by two competing seed companies, County Seed and Prairie Seed. Currently, County Seed has $c_0 = \frac{3}{5}$ of the total consumer market, and Prairie Seed has $p_0 = \frac{2}{5}$ of the total. However, because of product performance and management policies, County annually loses $\frac{2}{3}$ of its customers to Prairie, while Prairie loses $\frac{3}{7}$ of its customers to County during the same period. What share of the customers will each company have after one year?

**SOLUTION** Starting with the current market shares $c_0$ and $p_0$, we wish to determine the market shares $c_1$ and $p_1$ held by County and Prairie, respectively, after one year. Since County retains $\frac{1}{3}$ of its share $c_0$ and gains $\frac{3}{7}$ of Prairie's share $p_0$, we have

$$c_1 = \frac{1}{3}c_0 + \frac{3}{7}p_0$$

Similarly, Prairie 〜ts $\frac{2}{3}$ of County's share $c_0$ and retains $\frac{4}{7}$ of its share $p_0$, so that

$$p_1 = \frac{2}{3}c_0 + \frac{4}{7}p_0$$

In terms of matrices we have

$$\begin{bmatrix} c_1 \\ p_1 \end{bmatrix} = \begin{bmatrix} \frac{1}{3} & \frac{3}{7} \\ \frac{2}{3} & \frac{4}{7} \end{bmatrix} \begin{bmatrix} c_0 \\ p_0 \end{bmatrix}$$

If we insert the initial values $c_0 = \frac{3}{5}$ and $p_0 = \frac{2}{5}$, we get

$$c_1 = \frac{1}{3} \cdot \frac{3}{5} + \frac{3}{7} \cdot \frac{2}{5} = \frac{13}{35} = .3714$$

$$p_1 = \frac{2}{3} \cdot \frac{3}{5} + \frac{4}{7} \cdot \frac{2}{5} = \frac{22}{35} = .6286$$

The numbers $c_1$ and $p_1$ are the relative proportions of the total market held by County and Prairie, respectively, after one year. Note that $c_1 + p_1 = 1$. We see that after one year, County has lost, and Prairie has gained significantly. ∎

Suppose that we wish to examine the continuing effects of current management policies several years into the future. We can assume that the relative amount of customer movement between the two companies remains the same in subsequent years, regardless of the exact market positions in any particular year. Under this assumption we can apply the reasoning of Example 1 to find the market shares at the end of the second year, the third year, and so on.

**EXAMPLE 2**   Continue Example 1 to find each company's share of the market at the end of two years and at the end of three years. Assume that the rates of customer loss and retention are the same each year.

SOLUTION   Since it is assumed that the rate of customer turnover is the same each year, we can again use the matrix

$$T = \begin{bmatrix} C & P \\ 1/3 & 3/7 \\ 2/3 & 4/7 \end{bmatrix} \begin{matrix} \text{County} \\ \text{Prairie} \end{matrix}$$

If we apply $T$ to the customer distribution $c_1, p_1$ at the end of the first year, we can find the customer distribution $c_2, p_2$ at the end of the second year as follows:

$$\begin{bmatrix} c_2 \\ p_2 \end{bmatrix} = T \begin{bmatrix} c_1 \\ p_1 \end{bmatrix} = \begin{bmatrix} 1/3 & 3/7 \\ 2/3 & 4/7 \end{bmatrix} \begin{bmatrix} 13/35 \\ 22/35 \end{bmatrix} = \begin{bmatrix} .3932 \\ .6068 \end{bmatrix}$$

To find the customer distribution $c_3$, $p_3$ at the end of the third year, we compute

$$\begin{bmatrix} c_3 \\ p_3 \end{bmatrix} = T \begin{bmatrix} c_2 \\ p_2 \end{bmatrix} = \begin{bmatrix} 1/3 & 3/7 \\ 2/3 & 4/7 \end{bmatrix} \begin{bmatrix} .3932 \\ .6068 \end{bmatrix} = \begin{bmatrix} .3911 \\ .6089 \end{bmatrix}$$

We see that the changes after the first year are not very dramatic. The situation will stabilize a great deal. Although County Seed has a smaller share of the market than it did initially, it will not go out of business. ▌▌

The example we have been discussing is an example of a **Markov chain**. The key features are as follows. We have a process that occurs over fixed time intervals, and at each stage there are a finite number of possibilities, called **states**. It is assumed that the likelihood, or probability, of going from one state to another in any one time interval is the same at each stage. These are called the **transition probabilities**.

In the example the two states are represented by the two companies, since a customer goes either to County or to Prairie. The time interval in this case is one year. The probabilities are given in terms of market shares. We can interpret County's retaining 1/3 of its customers as meaning that the probability that a "random" customer will return to County is 1/3 and the probability that a random customer will go to the competition is 2/3. These are the transition probabilities for County. Similarly, Prairie had transition probabilities 4/7 and 3/7.

The matrix $T$ whose columns consist of the transition probabilities for each state is called the **transition matrix** of the Markov chain. Since each column represents movement from a particular state to all possible states, the sum of the column entries will be equal to 1. For instance, in the County versus Prairie example, each column exhibits customer turnover relative to one of the companies, and the column sums are 1. The term **stochastic matrix** is used for matrices whose entries are nonnegative and whose columns sum to 1.

A vector with nonnegative entries such that the sum of the entries is 1 is called a **distribution vector**. (The term "probability vector" is also used.) For example, the distribution vector

$$\begin{bmatrix} c_0 \\ p_0 \end{bmatrix} = \begin{bmatrix} 3/5 \\ 2/5 \end{bmatrix}$$

for County and Prairie shows the initial relative distribution of customers between the two companies.

If we are given an initial distribution vector $S_0$ for the states, then successive vectors are found by applying the transition matrix $T$. That is, we get $S_1 = TS_0$, $S_2 = TS_1$, and so on. For the County versus Prairie example we had

$$S_0 = \begin{bmatrix} c_0 \\ p_0 \end{bmatrix}, \quad S_1 = \begin{bmatrix} c_1 \\ p_1 \end{bmatrix} = TS_0, \quad S_2 = \begin{bmatrix} c_2 \\ p_2 \end{bmatrix} = TS_1$$

and so on.

Actually the chain of vectors can be expressed in terms of powers of $T$. Note that

$$S_2 = TS_1 = T(TS_0) = T^2S_0$$
$$S_3 = TS_2 = T(T^2S_0) = T^3S_0$$

In general, at the $n$th stage we have

$$S_n = T^nS_0$$

The matrix $T^n$ is the transition matrix for the stage after $n$ time periods have elapsed. We will now show that $T^n$ also has the property that its column sums are 1, that is, $T^n$ is again a stochastic matrix, and that the vector $S_n$ is again a distribution vector for any $n$.

### THEOREM 1

If $T$ is a stochastic matrix, then $T^n$ is again stochastic for any positive integer $n$. Also, if $S_0$ is a distribution vector, then $S_n = T^nS_0$ is a distribution vector for any $n$.

**Proof.**  The argument is general, but for notational simplicity we assume that $T$ is a $2 \times 2$ matrix. The column sums of the matrix $T$ can be found by premultiplying by a row of 1s. The fact that $T$ is stochastic is thus expressed by

$$[1 \quad 1]T = [1 \quad 1]$$

If we postmultiply both sides by $T$, then we get

$$[1 \quad 1]T^2 = [1 \quad 1]T = [1 \quad 1]$$

which shows that $T^2$ is stochastic. Repeated postmultiplication by $T$ shows that $T^n$ is stochastic for any $n$.

If $S_0$ is a distribution vector, then $S_n = T^nS_0$ has nonnegative entries and

$$[1 \quad 1]S_n = [1 \quad 1]T^nS_0 = [1 \quad 1]S_0 = [1]$$

Thus the entries of $S_n$ have sum 1, so that $S_n$ is again a distribution vector. This completes the proof.  ∎

**EXAMPLE 3**  Find $T^4$ and $S_4$ for

$$T = \begin{bmatrix} .2 & .7 \\ .8 & .3 \end{bmatrix}, \quad S_0 = \begin{bmatrix} .1 \\ .9 \end{bmatrix}$$

SOLUTION  For the stochastic matrix $T$ we have

$$T^2 = \begin{bmatrix} .60 & .35 \\ .40 & .65 \end{bmatrix}$$

and if we square $T^2$, we get

$$T^4 = \begin{bmatrix} .50 & .4375 \\ .50 & .5625 \end{bmatrix}$$

Note that $T^4$ has column sums equal to 1, so that it is a stochastic matrix. Also, we have

$$S_4 = T^4 S_0 = \begin{bmatrix} .44375 \\ .55625 \end{bmatrix}$$

and we see that $S_4$ is again a distribution vector. ∎

## STABLE VECTORS

Instead of merely projecting into the future for two or three years, it is often desirable to see what the long-range tendencies will be. To look farther ahead, we could continue to apply the transition matrix $T$, or we could calculate larger and larger powers of $T$. However, there is another way to proceed.

Suppose we have a Markov chain with transition matrix $T$. A distribution vector $S$ is called a **stable vector** (or a **steady state** vector) for $T$ if it satisfies $TS = S$. Thus if $T$ is applied to a stable vector, then no change occurs in the state distributions.

Since the requirement $TS = S$ can be written as $TS = IS$, where $I$ is the identity matrix, we can subtract to get $TS - IS = O$. If we use the distributive property for matrices, we obtain the condition

$$(T - I)S = O$$

Thus we have a homogeneous system with coefficient matrix $T - I$. It can be shown that $\det(T - I) = 0$ (see Exercises 27 and 28) so that by the Corollary to Theorem 5 of Section 3.5 we know that the system has a nonzero solution. These assertions are illustrated in the next example.

**EXAMPLE 4** Determine a stable vector for the County versus Prairie competition of Example 1.

SOLUTION We wish to see if there is a vector

$$S = \begin{bmatrix} c \\ p \end{bmatrix}, \quad c \geqslant 0, \quad p \geqslant 0, \quad c + p = 1$$

such that $(T - I)S = O$. The condition

$$\begin{bmatrix} -2/3 & 3/7 \\ 2/3 & -3/7 \end{bmatrix} \begin{bmatrix} c \\ p \end{bmatrix} = \begin{bmatrix} 0 \\ 0 \end{bmatrix}$$

gives us the homogeneous system

$$-\frac{2}{3}c + \frac{3}{7}p = 0$$

$$\frac{2}{3}c - \frac{3}{7}p = 0$$

One of the equations is redundant, since it is the negative of the other. Thus we have only the one equation

$$\frac{2}{3}c - \frac{3}{7}p = 0$$

However, since $S$ is a distribution vector, we also have the condition $c + p = 1$. Hence we seek a solution to the system

$$\frac{2}{3}c - \frac{3}{7}p = 0$$

$$c + \quad p = 1$$

The coefficient matrix has the nonzero determinant

$$\det \begin{bmatrix} 2/3 & -3/7 \\ 1 & 1 \end{bmatrix} = \frac{23}{21}$$

Therefore by Theorem 5 of the previous section, a unique solution exists. If we apply Cramer's Rule, we get

$$c = \frac{21}{23} \begin{vmatrix} 0 & -3/7 \\ 1 & 1 \end{vmatrix} = \frac{9}{23} = .3913$$

and

$$p = \frac{21}{23} \begin{vmatrix} 2/3 & 0 \\ 1 & 1 \end{vmatrix} = \frac{14}{23} = .6087$$

We infer (this will be discussed further following the example) that unless there is a change of product or management policy, County eventually will have about 39% and Prairie will have about 61% of the market. The market distribution is very close to this stable position after only three years, as we saw in Example 2.  ∎

The inference at the end of the preceding example was hastily made, since we have not yet shown that there is any connection between the initial distribution vector $S_0$ and the stable vector $S$. In other words, it is reasonable to ask if a stable vector can actually be reached by the chain $TS_0, T^2S_0, \ldots$. The numerical evidence that $T^3S_0$ was very close to the stable vector $S$ in the County versus Prairie example is convincing for that example. But what happens in general? The following extreme example shows that there may be no connection at all.

**EXAMPLE 5**   Consider

$$T = \begin{bmatrix} 0 & 1 \\ 1 & 0 \end{bmatrix} \quad \text{and} \quad S_0 = \begin{bmatrix} 1/4 \\ 3/4 \end{bmatrix}$$

Find the stable vector for $T$, and then find $TS_0, T^2S_0, \ldots$. Compare the results.

SOLUTION   We let the stable vector be denoted by

$$S = \begin{bmatrix} s_1 \\ s_2 \end{bmatrix}$$

and we solve the system

$$(T - I)S = O$$
$$s_1 + s_2 = 1$$

to obtain

$$s_1 = s_2 = \frac{1}{2}$$

We then observe that the powers of $T$ are $T^2 = I$, $T^3 = T$, $T^4 = I$, and so on. The powers of $T$ alternate between $T$ and $I$. Thus we get

$$TS_0 = \begin{bmatrix} 3/4 \\ 1/4 \end{bmatrix}, \quad T^2 S_0 = \begin{bmatrix} 1/4 \\ 3/4 \end{bmatrix}, \quad T^3 S_0 = \begin{bmatrix} 3/4 \\ 1/4 \end{bmatrix}, \quad \cdots$$

Hence the stable vector $S$ can never be reached from the initial distribution vector $S_0$ by repeatedly applying the transition matrix $T$. ▐▌

Fortunately, for most Markov chains there is a connection between the stable vector and the sequence of powers of $T$. The technical condition that assures a connection is as follows. A Markov chain is called **regular** if some power $T^n$ of the transition matrix $T$ has no zero entries. This condition is satisfied by a large class of Markov chains that arise in applications.

For regular Markov chains, it can be proved that stability will be approached regardless of the initial distribution; moreover, the stable vector can be found by taking powers of the transition matrix $T$. The rather remarkable connection between $T$ and the stable vector $S$ is as follows: If we form larger and larger powers $T^n$ of $T$, then each column of $T^n$ gets closer and closer to the stable vector $S$.

**EXAMPLE 6**   For the County versus Prairie transition matrix $T$, find $T^2$, $T^3$, $T^4$, $T^5$ to four decimal places. Compare the columns with the stable vector $S$ found in Example 4.

SOLUTION   Direct calculation gives us

$$T^2 = \begin{bmatrix} .3968 & .3878 \\ .6032 & .6122 \end{bmatrix}, \quad T^3 = \begin{bmatrix} .3908 & .3916 \\ .6092 & .6084 \end{bmatrix}$$

$$T^4 = \begin{bmatrix} .3914 & .3913 \\ .6086 & .6087 \end{bmatrix}, \quad T^5 = \begin{bmatrix} .3913 & .3913 \\ .6087 & .6087 \end{bmatrix}$$

Each of the columns of $T^5$ is equal to the stable vector $S$ for $T$, up to four decimal places. ▐▌

If we continued Example 6 and found higher powers of $T$, we would find that $T^n = T^5$ for $n > 5$, with four decimal place accuracy. In this case we call $T^5$

the **stable matrix** for the Markov chain. Note that this procedure not only determines the stable vector, but it also reveals the number of years needed to achieve stability up to the given decimal place accuracy.

An interesting conclusion can be deduced from the fact that powers of $T$ stabilize. We have

$$T^5 = \begin{bmatrix} c & c \\ p & p \end{bmatrix}$$

where the columns equal the stable vector for $T$. If we take *any* initial distribution vector

$$S_0 = \begin{bmatrix} a \\ b \end{bmatrix}, \qquad a + b = 1$$

then we get

$$T^5 S_0 = \begin{bmatrix} ac + bc \\ ap + bp \end{bmatrix} = \begin{bmatrix} (a + b)c \\ (a + b)p \end{bmatrix} = \begin{bmatrix} c \\ p \end{bmatrix}$$

Thus the same stable vector is reached *regardless* of the initial distribution. In other words, no matter what the market shares are at the beginning, after five years the company will reach a permanent market position. The reader can check this by taking different initial values for $c_0$ and $p_0$ (say, $c_0 = \frac{1}{8}$, $p_0 = \frac{7}{8}$) and seeing what happens in successive years.

The following theorem summarizes the salient aspects of regular Markov chains.

### THEOREM 2

A regular Markov chain with transition matrix $T$ will have a unique stable vector $S$. Successive powers of $T$ will approach the matrix whose columns are all equal to the vector $S$. If a fixed decimal place accuracy is prescribed, then $T^{n+1} = T^n$ for some $n$ so that $T^n$ is the stable matrix up to the prescribed accuracy. Furthermore, for any initial distribution vector $S_0$, we have $T^n S_0 = S$.

**EXAMPLE 7**   Fresh Rite (FR), Klean Kwik (KK), and Super Press (SP) cleaners compete for the local dry cleaning market. Each year FR loses 40% of its customers to KK and 20% to SP, while KK loses 30% to FR and 50% to SP, and SP loses 60% to FR and 10% to KK. Suppose that currently FR has 80%, KK has 10%, and SP has 10% of the market. Find the transition matrix, the relative proportions of the market that each holds after one and two years, the stable vector, and, by taking powers of the transition matrix, the stable matrix.

SOLUTION   The transition matrix, in decimals, is

$$
\begin{array}{ccc}
\text{FR} & \text{KK} & \text{SP}
\end{array}
$$
$$
T = \begin{bmatrix} .4 & .3 & .6 \\ .4 & .2 & .1 \\ .2 & .5 & .3 \end{bmatrix} \begin{array}{l} \text{FR} \\ \text{KK} \\ \text{SP} \end{array}
$$

Since 100% of each company's customers must be accounted for, each column sum equals 1.

The distributions after one year will be

$$\begin{bmatrix} .4 & .3 & .6 \\ .4 & .2 & .1 \\ .2 & .5 & .3 \end{bmatrix} \begin{bmatrix} .8 \\ .1 \\ .1 \end{bmatrix} = \begin{bmatrix} .41 \\ .35 \\ .24 \end{bmatrix}$$

That is, after one year FR will have 41% of the business, while KK will have 35% and SP will have 24%. Further, a second application of the transition matrix yields that the percentages after two years will be 41.3, 25.8, and 32.9 for FR, KK and SP, respectively, as the reader can verify.

Let $f$, $k$, and $s$ be the stable positions for FK, KK, and SP, respectively. Then the stable vector may be found by solving

$$(T - I)S = \begin{bmatrix} -.6 & .3 & .6 \\ .4 & -.8 & .1 \\ .2 & .5 & -.7 \end{bmatrix} \begin{bmatrix} f \\ k \\ s \end{bmatrix} = \begin{bmatrix} 0 \\ 0 \\ 0 \end{bmatrix}$$

together with the equation

$$f + k + s = 1$$

Since the third equation

$$.2f + .5k - .7s = 0$$

is the negative of the sum of the first two, it is redundant and may be deleted. Thus we must solve the system

$$\begin{bmatrix} -.6 & .3 & .6 \\ .4 & -.8 & .1 \\ 1 & 1 & 1 \end{bmatrix} \begin{bmatrix} f \\ k \\ s \end{bmatrix} = \begin{bmatrix} 0 \\ 0 \\ 1 \end{bmatrix}$$

Since the column of constants has mostly zeros, it is convenient to use Cramer's Rule. We obtain

$$f = \frac{.51}{1.17} = .4359, \quad k = \frac{.3}{1.17} = .2564, \quad s = \frac{.36}{1.17} = .3077$$

We can also find the stable vector by computing the stable matrix (again to four places). It is computationally convenient to proceed by squaring, since successive squaring yields large powers faster than repeatedly multiplying by $T$. Thus we find

$$\begin{aligned} T^2 &= T \cdot T \\ T^4 &= T^2 \cdot T^2 \\ T^8 &= T^4 \cdot T^4 \\ T^{16} &= T^8 \cdot T^8 \end{aligned}$$

The reader may show that

$$T^{16} = T^8 = \begin{bmatrix} .4359 & .4359 & .4359 \\ .2564 & .2564 & .2564 \\ .3077 & .3077 & .3077 \end{bmatrix}$$

is the stable matrix, and thus the stable vector, which is present in every column of the stable matrix, is reached somewhere between the fifth and eighth year from any starting position.  ■■

We close with a summary of two step-by-step procedures for a Markov analysis.

1. Find the transition matrix $T$ and the initial distribution vector $S_0$.

2. The distribution vector $S_i$ for the end of the $i$th time period can be found by successively computing

$$S_1 = TS_0, \quad S_2 = TS_1, \quad S_3 = TS_2, \quad \cdots$$

3. The stable vector, $S = (s_j)$, can be found by solving the system of equations

$$(T - I)S = O, \quad s_1 + \cdots + s_n = 1$$

for $s_1, \ldots, s_n$. Any one of the equations in the homogenous portion (equation constant 0) of the system of equations is redundant and may be discarded. Call the resulting system $AS = B$ where $A$ is the matrix $T - I$ with one row, say, the last, replaced by all 1s and $B$ is a column vector of 0s except for a 1 in the bottom position. The system $AS = B$ may be solved for the unique $S$ by

(a) Gaussian elimination

(b) Computation of $A^{-1}$; then $S = A^{-1}B$

(c) Cramer's Rule

4. The stable matrix is then the matrix with every column equal to $S$.

*Alternative Procedure.*   We may develop the same information by computing powers of $T$ to any required degree of accuracy.

2'. We find the distribution vector $S_n$ by finding $T^n$ and computing

$$S_n = T^n S_0$$

3'. The stable matrix is given by the first (or any higher) power of $T$ such that

$$T^{k+1} = T^k$$

4'. The stable vector $S$ is then approximated by any column of $T^k$.


# EXERCISES 3.6

In the exercises of this section, use rational fractions or decimals to four-place accuracy. A calculator would be helpful.

In Exercises 1–4, find the market split (a) after one time period and (b) after two time periods for the given transition matrix and the given initial market split for company A and company B.

**1.**
$$T = \begin{bmatrix} 3/4 & 3/8 \\ 1/4 & 5/8 \end{bmatrix} \begin{matrix} A \\ B \end{matrix} \quad \begin{matrix} A \text{ has } 40\% \\ B \text{ has } 60\% \end{matrix}$$

with column headers $A \quad B$

**2.**
$$T = \begin{bmatrix} 3/5 & 1/5 \\ 2/5 & 4/5 \end{bmatrix} \begin{matrix} A \\ B \end{matrix} \quad \begin{matrix} A \text{ has } 30\% \\ B \text{ has } 70\% \end{matrix}$$

with column headers $A \quad B$

**3.**
$$T = \begin{bmatrix} 2/3 & 2/5 \\ 1/3 & 3/5 \end{bmatrix} \begin{matrix} A \\ B \end{matrix} \quad \begin{matrix} A \text{ has } 90\% \\ B \text{ has } 10\% \end{matrix}$$

with column headers $A \quad B$

**4.**
$$T = \begin{bmatrix} 3/7 & 2/3 \\ 4/7 & 1/3 \end{bmatrix} \begin{matrix} A \\ B \end{matrix} \quad \begin{matrix} A \text{ has } 80\% \\ B \text{ has } 20\% \end{matrix}$$

with column headers $A \quad B$

In Exercises 5–12, find the transition matrix, the positions after the first and second time periods, the stable vector, and the stable matrix.

**5.** Sun City annually loses 35% of its residents to the suburbs, while the suburbs lose 45% of their residents to the city. Sun City currently has 65% of the population.

**6.** A transportation survey shows that 24% of the bus passengers will switch to personal auto each year while 43% of those driving an auto will switch to the bus. The bus line has 53% of the riders at the present time.

**7.** Freddie's Fries monthly picks up 59% of Hannah's Hashbrowns potato business, while Hannah's attracts 37% of Freddie's trade in the same period. Freddie has 73% of the business at this time.

**8.** Big Jack's Pancake House monthly picks up 44% of Satisfied Sadie's customers, while Sadie attracts 58% of Jack's clients in the same period. Sadie now has 52% of the business.

**9.** Jan's Copyshop monthly loses 1/6 of its customers to Paul's Dup-it, while Paul's loses 1/3 of its customers to Jan's in the same period. Jan's initially had 3/5 of the business.

**10.** Grabit Grocery monthly loses 2/7 of its customers to the Short Stop Market, while the Short Stop loses 1/7 of its customers to Grabit in the same period. Grabit initially had 2/3 of the business.

**11.** Demon (D), Lightning (L), and King (K) Motors vie for the nation's auto trade. Annually, D loses 8% of its customers to L and 6% to K, while L loses 12% to D and 4% to K, and K loses 3% to D and 14% to L. Initially, D has 43%, L has 22%, and K has 35% of the market.

**12.** General Refrigeration (GR), Hasseman (H), and Cold Box (CB) compete for the refrigerator market. GR annually loses 14% of its customers to H and 3% to CB, while H loses 11% to GR and 6% to CB, and CB loses 9% to GR and 7% to H. Initially, the market split is 37%, 29%, and 34% for GR, H, and CB, respectively.

In Exercises 13–18, determine if the given transition matrix is regular.

**13.** $\begin{bmatrix} .2 & .9 \\ .8 & .1 \end{bmatrix}$   **14.** $\begin{bmatrix} .3 & 0 \\ .7 & 1 \end{bmatrix}$   **15.** $\begin{bmatrix} 1 & .2 \\ 0 & .8 \end{bmatrix}$   **16.** $\begin{bmatrix} .4 & .5 \\ .6 & .5 \end{bmatrix}$

**17.** $\begin{bmatrix} .1 & .2 & .4 \\ .2 & .6 & 0 \\ .7 & .2 & .6 \end{bmatrix}$   **18.** $\begin{bmatrix} .3 & .5 & 0 \\ .4 & .1 & .2 \\ .3 & .4 & .8 \end{bmatrix}$

**19.** Find the year of stability in Exercise 5.

**20.** Find the year of stability in Exercise 6.

**21.** Find the month of stability in Exercise 7.

**22.** Find the month of stability in Exercise 8.

In Exercises 23–28, show that $\det(T - I) = 0$ for the given stochastic matrix $T$.

**23.** The matrix of Exercise 13.

**24.** The matrix of Exercise 16.

**25.** The matrix of Exercise 17.

**26.** The matrix of Exercise 18.

**27.** The matrix

$$T = \begin{bmatrix} t_{11} & t_{12} \\ t_{21} & t_{22} \end{bmatrix}$$

**28.** The matrix

$$T = \begin{bmatrix} t_{11} & t_{12} & t_{13} \\ t_{21} & t_{22} & t_{23} \\ t_{31} & t_{32} & t_{33} \end{bmatrix}$$

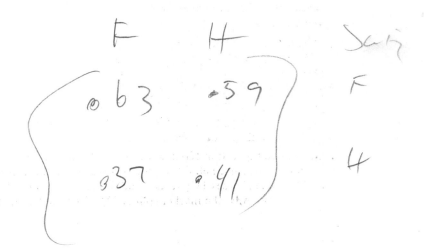

# 4

# Vector Spaces

Up to now we have developed systematic procedures and computational methods for solving systems of linear equations and finding values of linear functions subject to linear constraints. The procedures and computations, including the use of determinants, enabled us to examine a specific problem and either find the solution or determine that no solution exists. To progress beyond this point, to deepen our understanding of linear systems and the role of matrices, it is necessary to enlarge our view of linear problems and methods by introducing a structural perspective. The concept of vector space provides an enveloping structure in which the interplay of geometry and algebra is clarified and the different types of problems can be analyzed in a unified manner. The study of vector spaces and subspaces necessarily entails an increased degree of abstraction, but the resulting insights are well worth the effort to comprehend this viewpoint.

We have already used the term "vector" in the context of matrices, to refer to an ordered pair or ordered triple of numbers, such as the solution of a linear system, and we have thus regarded several numbers together as being a single entity. In Section 4.1 we will consider spaces of vectors and the operations of adding vectors and multiplying vectors by scalars, along with the geometric interpretations of these ideas. Combining the two operations on vectors leads to the notion of linear combination of vectors, and this is discussed in Section 4.2. In that section we will derive a vector criterion for a linear system to be consistent.

Sections 4.3 through 4.6 deal with the main concepts and the technical aspects of spaces of vectors and their relation to matrices and systems of equations. Applications to production problems and mixing problems are presented to illustrate the fact that the somewhat abstract concepts being discussed can provide insight into the solution of real problems.

In Section 4.7 we will examine the simplex algorithm of linear programming from the viewpoint of vectors. The ideas and methods of this chapter are applied to explain and extend the operations of the algorithm. The limited scope of the algorithm that was presented in Section 2.6 is broadened considerably so that a greater variety of linear optimization problems can be treated.

## 4.1   INTRODUCTION TO VECTORS

*Vectors, The Geometry of Vectors, The Magnitude of a Vector, Addition and Scalar Multiplication, Vector Equations of Lines*

In this section we introduce the vector space $R^n$ of all ordered $n$-tuples of numbers and define the two operations of addition and scalar multiplication on $R^n$. In the plane $R^2$ and space $R^3$, vectors and the operations can be interpreted geometrically; it is this interpretation that is emphasized in this section. The geometric point of view provides insight into the workings of vectors and will serve as a guide to higher dimensional spaces.

### VECTORS

A **vector** is an ordered $n$-tuple of numbers. Thus the couple $(5, 3)$, the triple $(1, -2, 7)$, and the 5-tuple $(3, 1, -5, 4, 1)$ are all vectors. We use boldface letters such as **u** and **v** to denote vectors. (For writing on paper or chalkboard it is convenient to put an arrow over the letter such as $\vec{u}$.) We will occasionally denote vectors as columns as well as rows, so that we have both

$$\mathbf{u} = (5, 3) \quad \text{and} \quad \mathbf{u} = \begin{bmatrix} 5 \\ 3 \end{bmatrix}$$

denoting the same vector. Each notation has its advantages, depending on the context.

Each number or entry in a vector is called a **component** of the vector. The key feature of a vector is the fact that the components are ordered, so that the positions of the components have special significance. For example, the vector $\mathbf{s} = (a, b, c)$ could represent the ingredients of a souffle, where $a$ is the number of eggs, $b$ is the number of cups of milk, and $c$ is the number of ounces of cheese. Thus $(2, 1, 3)$ would be a souffle with 2 eggs, 1 cup of milk, and 3 ounces of cheese. The order is important, since it would not be good to confuse the quantities of milk and cheese in a souffle.

If a company markets $n$ products and if $x_i$ denotes the number of units of the $i$th product manufactured in a specific time period, then the vector $(x_1, x_2, \ldots, x_n)$ is called a **production vector**. For example, if a company makes 143 stereos, 78 television sets, and 55 video recorders each week, then $(143, 78, 55)$ is the weekly production vector for the firm.

A generic vector can be written as $\mathbf{u} = (u_1, \ldots, u_n)$ or as $\mathbf{u} = (u_i)$ where $u_i$ is the $i$th component of **u**. As with matrices, two vectors are **equal** if they have the same components. Thus if $\mathbf{u} = (u_i)$ and $\mathbf{v} = (v_i)$, then $\mathbf{u} = \mathbf{v}$ if and only if they have the same number of components and $u_i = v_i$ for all $i$.

The operations of addition and scalar multiplication of vectors are defined in terms of components in the same way that they were for matrices. Thus addition of two vectors is defined by addition of components. To be more precise, if $\mathbf{u} = (u_1, \ldots, u_n)$ and $\mathbf{v} = (v_1, \ldots, v_n)$, then the **sum** of **u** and **v** is defined to be

$$\mathbf{u} + \mathbf{v} = (u_1 + v_1, \ldots, u_n + v_n)$$

Also the **scalar multiplication** of the vector **u** by a scalar $k$ is defined to be

$$k\mathbf{u} = (ku_1, \ldots, ku_n)$$

For example, if we have a souffle mix $\mathbf{s} = (2, 1, 3)$ in one bowl and a second mix $\mathbf{t} = (4, 1, 2)$ in another bowl, then combining the recipes will give us the souffle mix consisting of $2 + 4 = 6$ eggs, $1 + 1 = 2$ cups of milk, and $3 + 2 = 5$ ounces of cheese; that is, we have $\mathbf{s} + \mathbf{t} = (6, 2, 5)$. On the other hand, if the souffle vector **s** is doubled, then we get the new mixture $2\mathbf{s} = (4, 2, 6)$.

From the production point of view, let a plant produce 75 stoves, 55 refrigerators, and 60 dishwashers in January and 80 stoves, 50 refrigerators, and 70 dishwashers in February. Then we let $\mathbf{s} = (75, 55, 60)$ be the January production vector and $\mathbf{t} = (80, 50, 70)$ be the February production vector, and we find that the combined January-February production vector is $\mathbf{s} + \mathbf{t} = (155, 105, 130)$.

The collection of all vectors $\mathbf{u} = (u_1, \ldots, u_n)$ that have $n$ components will be denoted by $R^n$. It is understood that the elements of $R^n$ can be added together and multiplied by scalars in the manner defined above, so that we think of $R^n$ as a set of vectors along with these two operations. We refer to $R^n$ as a vector space, a notion that will be developed further as the chapter progresses.

There are a number of properties that hold for scalar multiplication and addition of vectors. As with matrices, they follow from properties of multiplication and addition of numbers. We list them here for reference. The symbol **0** denotes the zero vector whose components are all zero. (In the context of souffles, **0** would be the empty bowl.) There is no need to memorize this list of properties, since experience with numbers will lead to the correct manipulation of vector expressions.

---

### THEOREM 1

Let **u**, **v**, **w** be vectors in $R^n$, and let $a, b$ be scalars. Then:

$$\mathbf{u} + \mathbf{v} = \mathbf{v} + \mathbf{u} \qquad (\mathbf{u} + \mathbf{v}) + \mathbf{w} = \mathbf{u} + (\mathbf{v} + \mathbf{w})$$
$$a(b\mathbf{u}) = (ab)\mathbf{u} \qquad (a + b)\mathbf{u} = a\mathbf{u} + b\mathbf{u}$$
$$a(\mathbf{u} + \mathbf{v}) = a\mathbf{u} + a\mathbf{v}$$
$$\mathbf{u} + \mathbf{0} = \mathbf{u} \qquad 1 \cdot \mathbf{u} = \mathbf{u}$$
$$a \cdot \mathbf{0} = \mathbf{0} \qquad 0 \cdot \mathbf{u} = \mathbf{0}$$

Let $-\mathbf{u} = (-1) \cdot \mathbf{u}$; then $\mathbf{u} + (-\mathbf{u}) = \mathbf{0}$

If $a \cdot \mathbf{u} = \mathbf{0}$, then either $a = 0$ or $\mathbf{u} = \mathbf{0}$

---

**EXAMPLE 1** Given $\mathbf{u} = (4, 1, -3, 5)$ and $\mathbf{v} = (2, -2, 7, 3)$ in $R^4$, find the vectors $2\mathbf{u}$, $\mathbf{u} + \mathbf{v}$, and $\mathbf{u} - \mathbf{v}$.

SOLUTION We have $2\mathbf{u} = (8, 2, -6, 10)$ and $\mathbf{u} + \mathbf{v} = (6, -1, 4, 8)$. Also we find that $\mathbf{u} - \mathbf{v} = \mathbf{u} + (-1)\mathbf{v} = (2, 3, -10, 2)$. ∎

## THE GEOMETRY OF VECTORS

In the plane and in 3-space there is a useful and enlightening way to think about vectors as geometric entities. That is, we can view a vector in the plane as a directed line segment where the components of the vector are the displacements in the coordinate directions. Thus we have in the plane that

$$\mathbf{u} = (x\text{-displacement}, y\text{-displacement})$$

where we start with any **initial point** $P_1$ and move as specified by the components to a **terminal point** $P_2$. The vector is displayed as a directed line segment, or arrow, from $P_1$ to $P_2$, and we write $\mathbf{u} = \overrightarrow{P_1P_2}$.

If the initial point and terminal point have the coordinates $P_1(x_1, y_1)$ and $P_2(x_2, y_2)$, respectively, then the components $u_1$ and $u_2$ of the vector $\mathbf{u} = (u_1, u_2)$ are found by subtracting the coordinates of $P_1$ from the coordinates of $P_2$; that is, we have

$$u_1 = x_2 - x_1, \quad u_2 = y_2 - y_1$$

See Figure 4.1.

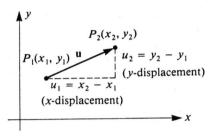

**FIGURE 4.1**               *The vector* $\mathbf{u} = \overrightarrow{P_1P_2}$

**EXAMPLE 2**   Let the vector $\mathbf{u} = (3, -2)$ have the initial point $P_1(2, 4)$. Find the terminal point $P_2$ so that $\mathbf{u} = \overrightarrow{P_1P_2}$. Draw the vector in the plane.

SOLUTION   The coordinates of $P_2(x_2, y_2)$ must satisfy the equations

$$3 = x_2 - 2, \quad -2 = y_2 - 4$$

Thus we solve for $x_2, y_2$ and get $x_2 = 5, y_2 = 2$, so that the terminal point is $P_2(5, 2)$. See Figure 4.2. ∎

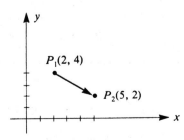

**FIGURE 4.2**               *The vector* $\mathbf{u} = (3, -2)$

In space a vector can be similarly represented by a directed line segment. Thus the vector **u** that is represented by the directed line segment with initial point $P_1(x_1, y_1, z_1)$ and terminal point $P_2(x_2, y_2, z_2)$ is given by

$$\mathbf{u} = \overrightarrow{P_1P_2} = (x_2 - x_1, y_2 - y_1, z_2 - z_1)$$

In higher dimensions we can conceptualize vectors in a geometrically analogous manner, but, of course, we are physically unable to create the representing line segments. Nevertheless, the geometric interpretation of vectors in two and three dimensions provides a valuable guide for our intuition in higher dimensions.

**EXAMPLE 3** Find the components of the vector $\mathbf{v} = \overrightarrow{P_1P_2}$ with initial point $P_1(2, 6, 4)$ and terminal point $P_2(4, 2, -2)$. Draw the vector in 3-space.

**SOLUTION** If we let $\mathbf{v} = (v_1, v_2, v_3)$, then we have

$$v_1 = 4 - 2 = 2, \quad v_2 = 2 - 6 = -4, \quad v_3 = -2 - 4 = -6$$

Thus the vector is $\mathbf{v} = (2, -4, -6)$. See Figure 4.3. ■■

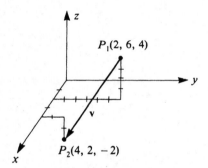

**FIGURE 4.3**

*The vector* $\mathbf{v} = (2, -4, -6)$

Since two vectors are equal if their components are equal, there are many different directed line segments that represent the same vector. Thus the vector $\overrightarrow{P_1P_2}$ from $P_1(1, 3)$ to $P_2(5, 4)$ equals the vector $\overrightarrow{Q_1Q_2}$ from $Q_1(3, 6)$ to $Q_2(7, 7)$, since $\overrightarrow{P_1P_2} = (4, 1) = \overrightarrow{Q_1Q_2}$. Figure 4.4 shows several other directed line segments that represent the same vector $\mathbf{u} = (4, 1)$ in the plane. Notice that all of the different directed line segments representing **u** have the same direction and the same length.

If the initial point of a vector is taken to be the origin $O$, then the components of the vector are identical to the coordinates of the terminal point $P$. In this case we call the vector $\overrightarrow{OP}$ a **position vector**. For example, for the point $P(2, 4, 5)$, we have the position vector $\overrightarrow{OP} = (2, 4, 5)$. See Figure 4.5. Thus each point in the plane or in 3-space can be identified as a vector. Consequently, the plane can be referred to as the vector space $R^2$ and 3-space can be regarded as the vector space $R^3$. Unless it is specifically stated otherwise or is clear from the context, a vector **u** in $R^n$ is understood to be a position vector.

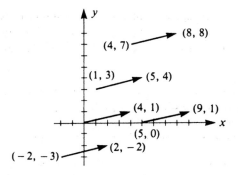

**FIGURE 4.4**                     *Vectors equal to* **u** = (4, 1)

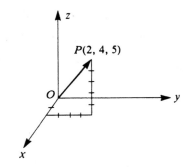

**FIGURE 4.5**              *The position vector* $\overrightarrow{OP}$ = (2, 4, 5)

## THE MAGNITUDE OF A VECTOR

The length of a directed line segment in the plane is easily found by applying the Pythagorean Theorem for right triangles. For example, the points $P_1(1, 2)$ and $P_2(8, 7)$ determine the right triangle shown in Figure 4.6. The components of $\overrightarrow{P_1P_2}$ = (7, 5) are the lengths of the legs of the triangle, and the directed line segment serves as hypotenuse. By the Pythagorean Theorem the hypotenuse has length $\sqrt{7^2 + 5^2} = \sqrt{74}$.

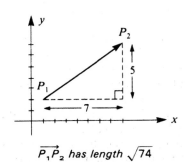

**FIGURE 4.6**                     $\overrightarrow{P_1P_2}$ *has length* $\sqrt{74}$

More generally, if $\mathbf{u} = (u_1, u_2)$ is a given vector in $R^2$, then the **magnitude** of $\mathbf{u}$, denoted by $|\mathbf{u}|$, is the length of any directed line segment in the plane that represents $\mathbf{u}$. Since we have a right triangle whose legs have the lengths $|u_1|$, $|u_2|$, the absolute value of the components, we see that the magnitude of $\mathbf{u}$ is given by

$$|\mathbf{u}| = \sqrt{u_1{}^2 + u_2{}^2}$$

A similar analysis applies to vectors in $R^3$. For example, given $\mathbf{u} = (3, 4, 10)$, we display it as a position vector and apply the Pythagorean Theorem twice. If we let $P(3, 4, 10)$, $Q(3, 4, 0)$ and the origin be the vertices of the right triangle, then we see first that $|\overrightarrow{OQ}| = \sqrt{3^2 + 4^2}$, and consequently we get

$$|\mathbf{u}| = |\overrightarrow{OP}| = \sqrt{(\sqrt{3^2 + 4^2})^2 + 10^2} = \sqrt{3^2 + 4^2 + 10^2} = 5\sqrt{5}$$

See Figure 4.7.

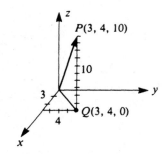

**FIGURE 4.7**     *The magnitude of $\mathbf{u}$ is $|\overrightarrow{OP}| = 5\sqrt{5}$*

In general, if $\mathbf{u} = (u_1, u_2, u_3)$ is a vector in $R^3$, then its magnitude is

$$|\mathbf{u}| = \sqrt{u_1{}^2 + u_2{}^2 + u_3{}^2}$$

The formulas for the magnitude of vectors in $R^2$ and $R^3$ serve as a guide for the definition of the magnitude of vectors in $R^n$. By extending the formulas in a natural way we define the **magnitude** of $\mathbf{u} = (u_1, \ldots, u_n)$ in $R^n$ to be

$$|\mathbf{u}| = \sqrt{u_1{}^2 + u_2{}^2 + \ldots + u_n{}^2}$$

**EXAMPLE 4**     Find the magnitude of the vector $\mathbf{u} = (1, 3, -4)$ in $R^3$ and the vector $\mathbf{v} = (1, 3, -4, 2, -1)$ in $R^5$.

SOLUTION     By the definition of the magnitude of a vector we have

$$|\mathbf{u}| = \sqrt{1^2 + 3^2 + (-4)^2} = \sqrt{26}$$

and

$$|\mathbf{v}| = \sqrt{1^2 + 3^2 + (-4)^2 + 2^2 + (-1)^2} = \sqrt{31} \quad \blacksquare$$

It should be noted that the magnitude of a vector is the same as the distance between its initial and terminal points. That is, the **distance** between two points $P_1$ and $P_2$ in $R^n$ is equal to the magnitude $|\mathbf{u}|$ of the vector $\mathbf{u} = \overrightarrow{P_1P_2}$. It is also equal to the magnitude of the vector $\overrightarrow{P_2P_1}$, since squaring eliminates the need for concern about minus signs. For example, to find the distance between $P_1(2, -1, 5)$ and $P_2(4, 2, 3)$, we find $\mathbf{u} = \overrightarrow{P_1P_2} = (2, 3, -2)$, and then we calculate $|\mathbf{u}| = \sqrt{4 + 9 + 4} = \sqrt{17}$.

## ADDITION AND SCALAR MULTIPLICATION

Addition of two vectors can be viewed geometrically in two different ways. One way is called the "parallelogram" method. If two nonzero vectors $\mathbf{u}$ and $\mathbf{v}$ in $R^2$ are given and if they are displayed as position vectors, then they are two sides of a parallelogram whose diagonal is the sum $\mathbf{u} + \mathbf{v}$. See Figure 4.8.

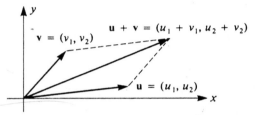

**FIGURE 4.8**    *The vector $\mathbf{u} + \mathbf{v}$ as a diagonal of a parallelogram*

**EXAMPLE 5**    The Dow-Jones average is at 970 in the twenty-fifth week of the year when the President's reassurances give it an upward thrust, which is judged to raise it by 30 points over two weeks. However, the latest unemployment figures give it a downward thrust, which is judged to lower it by 20 points over three weeks. Assume that the conflicting news causes indecision which in turn lengthens the time to five weeks. Find the resultant thrust and graph the situation as a parallelogram of vectors.

SOLUTION    If the average is plotted against time, then the upward thrust can be viewed as a vector $(2, 30)$ with initial point at $(25, 970)$, while the downward thrust is the vector $(3, -20)$ with the same initial point. The resultant thrust is represented by the vector $(2, 30) + (3, -20) = (5, 10)$. See Figure 4.9. ▮▮

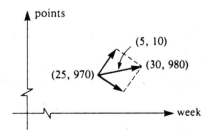

**FIGURE 4.9**    *The resultant thrust as a vector sum*

A second way to view addition of vectors is to place the vectors toe-to-tip. That is, we first display **u** as a position vector but then locate the initial point (the toe) of **v** at the terminal point (the tip) of **u**. See Figure 4.10. The same parallelogram as in Figure 4.8 appears, but now we think of **v** as starting where **u** leaves off.

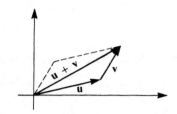

**FIGURE 4.10**        *The vector* **u** + **v**, *toe-to-tip addition*

The latter interpretation of addition is useful if more than two vectors are added. For example, in the sum **u** + **v** + **w**, we keep placing successive vectors in a toe-to-tip fashion, as in Figure 4.11. The same interpretation can be employed in three or more dimensions, but the pictures are difficult or impossible to draw.

**EXAMPLE 6**    Let **u** = (4, 1), **v** = (2, 2), **w** = (1, 2). Draw **u** + **v** + **w** toe-to-tip.

         **SOLUTION**    We sketch the vectors in Figure 4.11. ∎

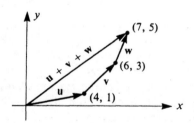

**FIGURE 4.11**        *The vector* **u** + **v** + **w**

It is often convenient to represent geometrically the difference **u** − **v** of two vectors **u** and **v**. Since it is true that

$$\mathbf{v} + (\mathbf{u} - \mathbf{v}) = \mathbf{u} + (\mathbf{v} - \mathbf{v}) = \mathbf{u}$$

then **u** − **v** must be the vector from the tip of **v** to the tip of **u** where **u** and **v** have the same initial point. See Figure 4.12(a). Alternatively, if we think of the parallelogram with sides **u** and −**v**, then **u** − **v** is the diagonal. See Figure 4.12(b).

Scalar multiplication has a natural geometric interpretation as a stretching or shrinking, depending on the size of the scalar. If $\mathbf{u} = (u_1, u_2)$ is a nonzero vector in $R^2$ and $k$ is a nonzero scalar, then $k\mathbf{u}$ has magnitude

$$|k\mathbf{u}| = \sqrt{(ku_1)^2 + (ku_2)^2} = |k| \cdot |\mathbf{u}|$$

Thus if $|k| > 1$, then **u** is stretched by a factor of $|k|$; if $0 < |k| < 1$, then **u** is shrunk

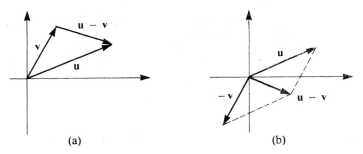

(a)                                              (b)

**FIGURE 4.12**                          *The vector* **u − v**

by a factor of $|k|$. Thus $k$ "changes the scale" of the vector **u** in the sense that its length is modified.

If $k$ is positive, the direction of $k\mathbf{u}$ is the same as that of **u**, but if $k < 0$, then the direction is reversed. For example, the vectors $2\mathbf{u}$ and $-2\mathbf{u}$ both have twice the magnitude of the vector **u**, but $2\mathbf{u}$ has the same direction as **u**, while $-2\mathbf{u}$ points in the opposite direction.

The preceding discussion extends to vectors in any dimension. Thus for any **u** in $R^n$, we have

$$|k\mathbf{u}| = |k||\mathbf{u}|$$

For example, if $\mathbf{v} = (3, 1, -2, 5)$ in $R^4$ and $k = -6$, then we have $|-6\mathbf{v}| = 6|\mathbf{v}| = 6\sqrt{39}$.

## VECTOR EQUATIONS OF LINES

Let $P_0(x_0, y_0)$ and $P_1(x_1, y_1)$ be two distinct points in the plane, and let $L$ be the line determined by the points. Then $L$ has the inclination of the vector $\mathbf{u} = \overrightarrow{P_0P_1}$ that has components $a = x_1 - x_0$, $b = y_1 - y_0$. We shall call $\mathbf{u} = (a, b)$ a **direction vector** for the line $L$. Thus $L$ is the line through $P_0$ that is parallel to **u**. See Figure 4.13 on the next page.

Note that the components of **u** are the run and the rise of the line, so that the slope of $L$ is the ratio of the components of **u**. That is, we have the following relationship.

$$\mathbf{u} = (x_1 - x_0, y_1 - y_0) = (a, b)$$
$$m = \frac{y_1 - y_0}{x_1 - x_0} = \frac{b}{a}$$

We can derive a vector equation for the line $L$ as follows. If $P(x, y)$ is a general point on the line $L$, then the vectors $\overrightarrow{P_0P}$ and $\mathbf{u} = \overrightarrow{P_0P_1}$ are parallel, so that there exists a scalar $t$ such that $\overrightarrow{P_0P} = t\mathbf{u}$. See Figure 4.13. If we express $\overrightarrow{P_0P}$ in terms of position vectors by writing $\overrightarrow{P_0P} = \overrightarrow{OP} - \overrightarrow{OP_0}$, then we obtain

$$\overrightarrow{OP} - \overrightarrow{OP_0} = t\mathbf{u}$$

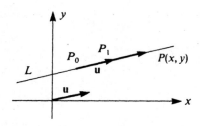

**FIGURE 4.13**            *The line through $P_0$ and parallel to* **u**

Putting $\overrightarrow{OP_0}$ on the other side of the equation, we get the vector equation for the line $L$:

$$\overrightarrow{OP} = \overrightarrow{OP_0} + t\mathbf{u}$$

where $t$ is any number. Thus we have

$$(x, y) = (x_0, y_0) + t(a, b)$$

We can interpret the vector equation as follows. To reach a point $P$ on the line, we first go from the origin to the point $P_0$ on the line via the position vector $\overrightarrow{OP_0}$, and then we move along the line an appropriate direction and distance as determined by $t\mathbf{u}$ to the point $P$. As $t$ varies over the set of all numbers, the point $P$ varies over all points of $L$. See Figure 4.14.

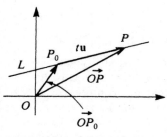

**FIGURE 4.14**            *The line $L$:* $\overrightarrow{OP} = \overrightarrow{OP_0} + t\mathbf{u}$

If we separate the vector equation for $L$ into component equations, we obtain the **parametric equations** of $L$:

$$x = x_0 + ta$$
$$y = y_0 + tb$$

where $t$, the parameter, is any number. In this form the coordinates of a point $P(x, y)$ on $L$ are given in terms of $t$.

**EXAMPLE 7**    Given $P_0(1, 3)$ and $P_1(4, 1)$ in the plane, find the vector equation and the parametric equations of the line through $P_0$ and $P_1$.

SOLUTION   We have $\mathbf{u} = \overrightarrow{P_0P_1} = (3, -2)$ so that the vector equation for $P(x, y)$ is

$$(x, y) = (1, 3) + t(3, -2)$$

Thus the parametric equations for the line are

$$x = 1 + 3t$$
$$y = 3 - 2t$$

Since only two equations occur, we can eliminate the parameter $t$ by substituting $t = (x - 1)/3$ from the first equation into the second equation; we get the equation $2x + 3y = 11$. We graph the line in Figure 4.15.  ∎

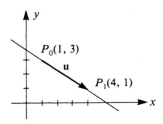

**FIGURE 4.15**                    *The line* $(x, y) = (1, 3) + t(3, -2)$

The advantage of vector equations for a line is that they have the same form in any dimension. The vector equation $\overrightarrow{OP} = \overrightarrow{OP_0} + t\mathbf{u}$ represents a line in any space $R^n$, the dimension being determined as soon as the point $P_0$ and vector $\mathbf{u}$ are specified. For example, if we take two points in 3-space instead of the plane, we will obtain a line in space.

If we have points $P_0(x_0, y_0, z_0)$ and $P_1(x_1, y_1, z_1)$ on the line $L$ in space, then we again define the direction vector $\mathbf{u} = \overrightarrow{P_0P_1} = (a, b, c)$ where $a = x_1 - x_0$, $b = y_1 - y_0$, $c = z_1 - z_0$. Proceeding exactly as before, we get the vector equation for a point $P(x, y, z)$ on the line to be

$$\overrightarrow{OP} = \overrightarrow{OP_0} + t\mathbf{u}$$

In terms of components we have

$$(x, y, z) = (x_0, y_0, z_0) + t(a, b, c)$$

which gives us the parametric equations

$$x = x_0 + ta$$
$$y = y_0 + tb$$
$$z = z_0 + tc$$

Unlike lines in the plane, the parameter cannot be eliminated to get a single equation. Recall that a single linear equation in $x$, $y$, $z$ determines a plane, not a line, in space. There is no analogue of slope for lines in space. To specify a direction of a line in 3-space requires three numbers, not two; consequently, a ratio of two numbers is inadequate.

**EXAMPLE 8**  Find the vector equation and the parametric equations of the line through the points $(1, 4, 2)$ and $(3, 5, -1)$.

**SOLUTION**  If we label the given points as $P_0$ and $P_1$, respectively, then we obtain the direction vector

$$\mathbf{u} = \overrightarrow{P_0 P_1} = (3 - 1, \, 5 - 4, \, -1 - 2) = (2, 1, -3).$$

Then the vector equation $\overrightarrow{OP} = \overrightarrow{OP_0} + t\mathbf{u}$ for $P(x, y, z)$ is

$$(x, y, z) = (1, 4, 2) + t(2, 1, -3)$$

which has the corresponding parametric equations

$$x = 1 + 2t$$
$$y = 4 + \ t$$
$$z = 2 - 3t$$

Setting $t = 0$ gives us the point $P_0(1, 4, 2)$, and the value $t = 1$ gives us the point $P_1(3, 5, -1)$. See Figure 4.16. Other points on the line are found by taking other values of $t$. For example, if $t = -1$, we get $(-1, 3, 5)$; and if $t = 2$, we get $(5, 6, -4)$. ∎

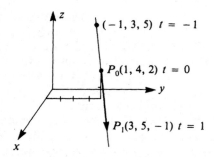

**FIGURE 4.16**          *The line through $P_0(1, 4, 2)$ and $P_1(3, 5, -1)$*

## EXERCISES 4.1

In Exercises 1–6, find $\mathbf{u} + \mathbf{v}$, $2\mathbf{u}$, $-3\mathbf{v}$.

**1.** $\mathbf{u} = (2, -3)$, $\mathbf{v} = (5, 1)$
**2.** $\mathbf{u} = (-4, 6)$, $\mathbf{v} = (7, 2)$
**3.** $\mathbf{u} = (-1, 3, 2)$, $\mathbf{v} = (2, 8, -3)$
**4.** $\mathbf{u} = (7, 4, -3)$, $\mathbf{v} = (-2, 5, 6)$
**5.** $\mathbf{u} = (-3, 4, -5, 2)$, $\mathbf{v} = (-1, 6, 7, -4)$
**6.** $\mathbf{u} = (7, -4, -3, 5)$, $\mathbf{v} = (-3, -5, 8, 2)$

In Exercises 7–8, find the production vectors for the day and evening shifts, and compute the production vector for the full day.

**7.** A plant produced 18 4-door sedans, 23 2-door sedans, and 10 station wagons on the day shift and 15 4-door sedans, 19 2-door sedans, and 6 station wagons on the evening shift.

**8.** A plant produced 56 quarter-ton trucks, 43 half-ton trucks, and 27 one-ton trucks on the day shift and 65 quarter-ton trucks, 57 half-ton trucks, and 44 one-ton trucks on the evening shift.

In Exercises 9–12, find $4(2\mathbf{u})$, $8\mathbf{u}$, $(3 + 5)\mathbf{u}$, $3\mathbf{u} + 5\mathbf{u}$.

**9.** $\mathbf{u} = (2, -4)$    **10.** $\mathbf{u} = (-5, 3)$    **11.** $\mathbf{u} = (8, -6, 1)$    **12.** $\mathbf{u} = (2, 4, -6)$

In Exercises 13–30, sketch the vector $\mathbf{u}$ with initial point $P_1$ and terminal point $P_2$. Find the missing point or vector.

**13.** $P_1(2, -5)$, $P_2(-4, 3)$    **14.** $P_1(-6, 3)$, $P_2(5, -1)$
**15.** $\mathbf{u} = (5, 4)$, $P_1(-2, -1)$    **16.** $\mathbf{u} = (6, 1)$, $P_1(-3, -5)$
**17.** $\mathbf{u} = (-2, -7)$, $P_2(6, 4)$    **18.** $\mathbf{u} = (5, 3)$, $P_2(8, 1)$
**19.** $P_1(2, 4)$, $P_2(-3, -5)$    **20.** $P_1(-6, -2)$, $P_2(5, 9)$
**21.** $\mathbf{u} = (-2, -3)$, $P_1(5, 7)$    **22.** $\mathbf{u} = (-4, -6)$, $P_1(9, 2)$
**23.** $\mathbf{u} = (4, 6)$, $P_2(-5, -2)$    **24.** $\mathbf{u} = (7, 4)$, $P_2(-1, -3)$
**25.** $\mathbf{u} = (-1, 3, 2)$, $P_1(2, 3, 1)$    **26.** $\mathbf{u} = (-3, 1, 5)$, $P_1(3, 2, -2)$
**27.** $P_1(1, 8, -2)$, $P_2(4, -2, 5)$    **28.** $P_1(-3, 4, 7)$, $P_2(6, -3, 5)$
**29.** $\mathbf{u} = (7, -2, -3)$, $P_2(5, -2, 4)$    **30.** $\mathbf{u} = (8, -4, 2)$, $P_2(3, 2, -5)$

In Exercises 31–34, sketch the given vector as a position vector.

**31.** $\mathbf{u} = (2, 5)$    **32.** $\mathbf{u} = (4, 6)$    **33.** $\mathbf{u} = (4, 5, 7)$    **34.** $\mathbf{u} = (1, 7, 4)$

In Exercises 35–40, find the magnitude of the given vector.

**35.** $\mathbf{u} = (-6, 3)$    **36.** $\mathbf{u} = (5, -4)$    **37.** $\mathbf{u} = (6, -1, 2)$    **38.** $\mathbf{u} = (-3, 8, 4)$
**39.** $\mathbf{u} = (-1, 3, 2, 1, -4)$    **40.** $\mathbf{u} = (4, 2, -3, 3, -1)$

In Exercises 41–46, find the distance between $P_1$ and $P_2$.

**41.** $P_1(-3, 6)$, $P_2(4, 10)$    **42.** $P_1(3, -7)$, $P_2(8, -5)$
**43.** $P_1(6, -5, 9)$, $P_2(9, 3, 4)$    **44.** $P_1(-3, 7, 2)$, $P_2(2, 1, 5)$
**45.** $P_1(1, 2, 7, 4, -3, -2)$   $P_2(-1, 2, 6, 5, -1, 1)$
**46.** $P_1(4, 8, -3, -1, 6, 5)$,   $P_2(6, 5, -1, 1, -3, 5)$

In Exercises 47–50, display $\mathbf{u} + \mathbf{v}$ as (a) the diagonal of a parallelogram and (b) toe-to-tip.

**47.** $\mathbf{u} = (-2, 6)$, $\mathbf{v} = (4, 2)$    **48.** $\mathbf{u} = (7, 3)$, $\mathbf{v} = (1, 6)$
**49.** $\mathbf{u} = (-4, -7)$, $\mathbf{v} = (3, -4)$    **50.** $\mathbf{u} = (3, -5)$, $\mathbf{v} = (4, 1)$

In Exercises 51–52, find the resultant thrust, and graph the situation as a parallelogram of vectors. (Put time on the horizontal axis.)

**51.** In week 23, sugar futures are at \$200/ton and are buoyed up by the news that saccharin has been banned pending further testing, but they are dragged down by the announcement that the formula for "Sweetenall" has been perfected. Analysts judge that the former announcement would cause prices to rise by \$25 over four weeks and that the latter would cause prices to fall by \$10 over one week.

**52.** In week 16 the common stock of the Consolidated Machine Screw Corporation sells for \$27/share and has received a boost from the news that a merger is being considered with National Amalgamated. However, it is adversely affected by the loss of an Air Force "Avenger" subcontract. Experts speculate that the former news will cause the stock to rise by 7 points over two weeks and that the latter news will cause it to fall by 3 points over three weeks.

In Exercises 53–54, display $\mathbf{u} + \mathbf{v} + \mathbf{w}$ toe-to-tip.

**53.** $\mathbf{u} = (4, -1)$, $\mathbf{v} = (2, 3)$, $\mathbf{w} = (1, 5)$      **54.** $\mathbf{u} = (2, -3)$, $\mathbf{v} = (5, 3)$, $\mathbf{w} = (2, 4)$

In Exercises 55–58, sketch $\mathbf{u}$, $\mathbf{v}$, and $\mathbf{u} - \mathbf{v}$. Let $\mathbf{u}$ and $\mathbf{v}$ be position vectors.

**55.** $\mathbf{u} = (8, 2)$, $\mathbf{v} = (4, -6)$      **56.** $\mathbf{u} = (-3, -5)$, $\mathbf{v} = (4, 1)$
**57.** $\mathbf{u} = (5, -2, 1)$, $\mathbf{v} = (-3, 6, 4)$      **58.** $\mathbf{u} = (7, -1, 3)$, $\mathbf{v} = (-2, 3, 5)$

In Exercises 59–60, sketch $\mathbf{u}$, $2\mathbf{u}$, $-3\mathbf{u}$, $(1/2)\mathbf{u}$.

**59.** $\mathbf{u} = (6, 2)$      **60.** $\mathbf{u} = (-2, 4)$

In Exercises 61–66, find the vector equation for the line through $P_0$ and parallel to $\mathbf{u}$.

**61.** $P_0(2, -7)$, $\mathbf{u} = (5, -3)$      **62.** $P_0(-4, 8)$, $\mathbf{u} = (-2, 9)$
**63.** $P_0(3, 5, -7)$, $\mathbf{u} = (-8, 4, 2)$      **64.** $P_0(8, -6, 3)$, $\mathbf{u} = (2, -5, 4)$
**65.** $P_0(6, 2, 8, -7, -3)$, $\mathbf{u} = (3, 5, -3, 6, 7)$
**66.** $P_0(4, -7, 2, -9, 1)$, $\mathbf{u} = (6, -4, 5, -7, 3)$

In Exercises 67–72, find a vector equation for the line through the given points.

**67.** $P_1(4, -5)$, $P_2(-6, 3)$      **68.** $P_1(7, 2)$, $P_2(-2, 4)$
**69.** $P_1(-2, 4, 1)$, $P_2(5, -5, 2)$      **70.** $P_1(8, -3, 4)$, $P_2(5, -5, -3)$
**71.** $P_1(4, 1, -3, -2)$, $P_2(6, 5, -4, 8)$      **72.** $P_1(2, -5, 7, -4)$, $P_2(5, 4, -3, -8)$

In Exercises 73–76, (a) sketch the line, (b) show the points for $t = 0$, $t = 1$, $t = -1$; and (c) write the parametric equations of the line.

**73.** $L$: $(4, 5) + t(3, -2)$      **74.** $L$: $(-6, 2) + t(-1, 4)$
**75.** $L$: $(3, 2, 1) + t(2, 3, 6)$      **76.** $L$: $(2, 4, 5) + t(1, -1, 3)$

In Exercises 77–78, find the vector equation of the line through $P_0$ and parallel to the line $L$.

**77.** $P_0(7, 3)$,   $L$: $3x + 5y = 15$      **78.** $P_0(5, 2)$,   $L$: $4x + 5y = 20$

## 4.2   LINEAR COMBINATIONS

*Linear Combinations of Vectors, Application, Linear Systems and Column Vectors*

The two basic operations on vectors are addition and scalar multiplication. By combining these operations we obtain what are called linear combinations of vectors. In this section we examine this idea of linear combinations in detail, since it will be the basis for much of the work in this chapter. We also introduce a new way of looking at systems of linear equations in terms of linear combinations of vectors and thereby set the stage for the analysis of linear systems that will be developed in subsequent sections.

## LINEAR COMBINATIONS OF VECTORS

If $\mathbf{u}_1$ and $\mathbf{u}_2$ are vectors in $R^n$ and if $c_1$ and $c_2$ are scalars, then $c_1\mathbf{u}_1 + c_2\mathbf{u}_2$ is again a vector in $R^n$. Thus the addition of scalar multiples of vectors produces another vector. This way of combining vectors need not be restricted to two vectors, since any finite number of vectors in $R^n$ can be multiplied by scalars and then added together. Since this type of activity occurs so often, there is a name for it.

### DEFINITION

If $\mathbf{u}_1, \mathbf{u}_2, \ldots, \mathbf{u}_k$ are vectors in $R^n$ and if $c_1, c_2, \ldots, c_k$ are scalars, then the vector

$$\mathbf{v} = c_1\mathbf{u}_1 + c_2\mathbf{u}_2 + \cdots + c_k\mathbf{u}_k$$

is called a **linear combination** of the vectors $\mathbf{u}_1, \mathbf{u}_2, \ldots, \mathbf{u}_k$.

For example, the vector $\mathbf{v} = (2, 9)$ is a linear combination of the vectors $\mathbf{u}_1 = (2, -3)$ and $\mathbf{u}_2 = (2, 1)$ because

$$\mathbf{v} = (2, 9) = -2(2, -3) + 3(2, 1) = -2\mathbf{u}_1 + 3\mathbf{u}_2$$

The geometric relationship is shown in Figure 4.17.

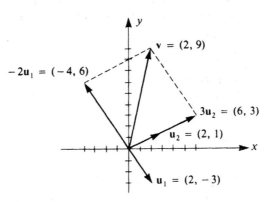

**FIGURE 4.17**      $\mathbf{v}$ *is a linear combination of* $\mathbf{u}_1$ *and* $\mathbf{u}_2$

**EXAMPLE 1**   Given the vectors $\mathbf{u}_1 = (1, 2, 5)$, $\mathbf{u}_2 = (2, 0, -1)$, $\mathbf{u}_3 = (-1, 3, 2)$ in $R^3$ and the scalars $c_1 = 2$, $c_2 = 4$, $c_3 = -3$, find the linear combination $\mathbf{v} = c_1\mathbf{u}_1 + c_2\mathbf{u}_2 + c_3\mathbf{u}_3$.

SOLUTION   We have

$$\begin{aligned}
\mathbf{v} &= 2(1, 2, 5) + 4(2, 0, -1) - 3(-1, 3, 2) \\
&= (2, 4, 10) + (8, 0, -4) + (3, -9, -6) \\
&= (2 + 8 + 3, \ 4 + 0 - 9, \ 10 - 4 - 6) \\
&= (13, -5, 0). \quad \blacksquare\blacksquare
\end{aligned}$$

A problem that arises frequently is that of finding scalars such that a particular vector can be expressed as a linear combination of other vectors. By considering the components of the vectors we can convert the problem to one of solving a system of linear equations. This concept is so critical that we give it special stress in the following statement.

*IMPORTANT*:   A vector equation is equivalent to a system of scalar equations, one equation for each component.

The following example illustrates the idea in $R^2$ where the geometric nature of the problem can also be seen.

**EXAMPLE 2**   Express the vector $\mathbf{v} = (7, 7)$ as a linear combination of $\mathbf{u}_1 = (-1, 2)$ and $\mathbf{u}_2 = (3, 1)$.

SOLUTION   We are asked to find scalars $c_1$ and $c_2$ such that $c_1\mathbf{u}_1 + c_2\mathbf{u}_2 = \mathbf{v}$. The geometry of the problem is shown in Figure 4.18; the scalars must be chosen so that $\mathbf{v}$ becomes the diagonal of a parallelogram with sides $c_1\mathbf{u}_1$ and $c_2\mathbf{u}_2$. To solve the problem algebraically, we express the vector equation in terms of components. This is most clearly seen if we write the vectors as columns. Doing so, we see that we need to find scalars $c_1, c_2$ such that

$$c_1\begin{bmatrix} -1 \\ 2 \end{bmatrix} + c_2\begin{bmatrix} 3 \\ 1 \end{bmatrix} = \begin{bmatrix} 7 \\ 7 \end{bmatrix}$$

Thus the vector equation is equivalent to the linear system

$$\begin{aligned}
-c_1 + 3c_2 &= 7 \qquad \text{first component} \\
2c_1 + c_2 &= 7 \qquad \text{second component}
\end{aligned}$$

We find the solution of the system to be (2, 3), so that we take $c_1 = 2, c_2 = 3$. Thus we can write $\mathbf{v}$ as the linear combination $\mathbf{v} = 2\mathbf{u}_1 + 3\mathbf{u}_2$.   $\blacksquare\blacksquare$

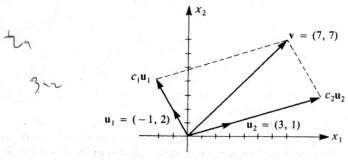

**FIGURE 4.18**                    *The linear combination* $\mathbf{v} = c_1\mathbf{u}_1 + c_2\mathbf{u}_2$

It is not always apparent that a particular vector can actually be written as a linear combination of the given vectors. If we have the vectors $\mathbf{u}_1, \ldots, \mathbf{u}_k$ on hand and another vector $\mathbf{v}$ is given to us, all in the same space $R^n$, then the problem is to determine if there exist scalars $c_1, \ldots, c_k$ such that $c_1\mathbf{u}_1 + \cdots + c_k\mathbf{u}_k = \mathbf{v}$. In some cases no such scalars can be found. By converting the problem to a system of linear equations, as in the preceding example, the question of existence becomes a question of whether or not the system of equations is consistent. If the system is in fact consistent, then the scalars can be found by solving the system. The technique is illustrated in the following example.

**EXAMPLE 3**  Determine if it is possible to express the vector $\mathbf{v} = (-1, 1, -7)$ as a linear combination of the vectors $\mathbf{u}_1 = (1, 2, 1)$ and $\mathbf{u}_2 = (2, 3, 4)$. If it is possible, write $\mathbf{v}$ explicitly as a linear combination of $\mathbf{u}_1$ and $\mathbf{u}_2$.

SOLUTION  We are asked to see if there exist scalars $c_1$, $c_2$ such that $\mathbf{v} = c_1\mathbf{u}_1 + c_2\mathbf{u}_2$. If we write the vectors as columns, then we have

$$c_1 \begin{bmatrix} 1 \\ 2 \\ 1 \end{bmatrix} + c_2 \begin{bmatrix} 2 \\ 3 \\ 4 \end{bmatrix} = \begin{bmatrix} -1 \\ 1 \\ -7 \end{bmatrix}$$

Thus we wish to determine if there exist solutions of the linear system

$$\begin{array}{ll} c_1 + 2c_2 = -1 & \text{first component} \\ 2c_1 + 3c_2 = 1 & \text{second component} \\ c_1 + 4c_2 = -7 & \text{third component} \end{array}$$

The vector $\mathbf{v}$ can be written as a linear combination of the vectors $\mathbf{u}_1$ and $\mathbf{u}_2$ if and only if the above system has a solution, that is, if it is consistent. The augmented matrix of the system is

$$\begin{bmatrix} 1 & 2 & | & -1 \\ 2 & 3 & | & 1 \\ 1 & 4 & | & -7 \end{bmatrix}$$

Note that the columns of the matrix are just the vectors $\mathbf{u}_1$, $\mathbf{u}_2$, and $\mathbf{v}$ in that order. By performing row operations we can put the matrix into the following row echelon form:

$$\begin{bmatrix} 1 & 2 & | & -1 \\ 0 & 1 & | & -3 \\ 0 & 0 & | & 0 \end{bmatrix}$$

We see from this matrix that the system is indeed consistent, and therefore we have answered the first question: Yes, $\mathbf{v}$ can be written as a linear combination of $\mathbf{u}_1$, $\mathbf{u}_2$.

To find explicit scalars that actually accomplish the task, we must proceed to solve the system. This is readily done by using back substitution on the last matrix, and we find that $c_1 = 5$, $c_2 = -3$. Hence we obtain $\mathbf{v} = 5\mathbf{u}_1 - 3\mathbf{u}_2$. ∎

The preceding example reveals the following technique for determining whether or not a vector $\mathbf{v}$ can be written as a linear combination of the vectors $\mathbf{u}_1, \mathbf{u}_2, \ldots, \mathbf{u}_k$.

1. Write the vectors as columns.
2. Form the matrix whose columns are the vectors $\mathbf{u}_1, \ldots, \mathbf{u}_k$ and $\mathbf{v}$ in that order. This is the augmented matrix for the system of equations corresponding to the vector equation

$$c_1\mathbf{u}_1 + \cdots + c_k\mathbf{u}_k = \mathbf{v}.$$

3. Use row operations to put the matrix into row echelon form.

An examination of the matrix in row echelon form then tells us if the linear combination in question is possible or not. If we have the augmented matrix of a consistent system, then the linear combination is possible, and the scalars are found by solving the system. On the other hand, if the corresponding system is inconsistent, then it is impossible to write $\mathbf{v}$ as a linear combination of the other vectors.

**EXAMPLE 4**  Determine if $\mathbf{v} = (1, -3, 2)$ can be written as a linear combination of $\mathbf{u}_1 = (1, 2, -1)$, $\mathbf{u}_2 = (3, 5, 2)$, $\mathbf{u}_3 = (4, 7, 1)$.

**SOLUTION**  The question of whether there exist scalars $c_1$, $c_2$, $c_3$ such that $c_1\mathbf{u}_1 + c_2\mathbf{u}_2 + c_3\mathbf{u}_3 = \mathbf{v}$ leads to a linear system whose augmented matrix has columns given by $\mathbf{u}_1, \mathbf{u}_2, \mathbf{u}_3, \mathbf{v}$ as shown below.

$$\begin{bmatrix} 1 & 3 & 4 & | & 1 \\ 2 & 5 & 7 & | & -3 \\ -1 & 2 & 1 & | & 2 \end{bmatrix}$$

We apply row operations to obtain the row echelon form

$$\begin{bmatrix} 1 & 3 & 4 & | & 1 \\ 0 & 1 & 1 & | & 4 \\ 0 & 0 & 0 & | & 1 \end{bmatrix}$$

We see from the last row that the system of equations is inconsistent, and therefore we conclude that the vector $\mathbf{v}$ *cannot* be written as a linear combination of the vectors $\mathbf{u}_1, \mathbf{u}_2, \mathbf{u}_3$. ∎

## APPLICATION

We now apply these ideas to a production example.

**EXAMPLE 5**  Eastbrook Quarries mines fine sand, coarse sand, and gravel at their Big Bend, Wydown Creek, and Orchard Road Quarries. The daily outputs for the quarries are 20 tons fine sand, 40 tons coarse sand, and 20 tons gravel at Big Bend; 60

tons fine sand, 60 tons coarse sand, and 30 tons gravel at Wydown Creek; and 30 tons fine sand, 40 tons coarse sand, and 20 tons gravel at Orchard Road. None of these locations is mined every day, and there are yearly fixed costs that can be reduced if one of the mines, say, Orchard Road, is closed. Is there some combination of outputs from the other two mines that will equal the output of the Orchard Road mine?

SOLUTION   Let the production vectors be $\mathbf{u}_1 = (20, 40, 20)$ for Big Bend, $\mathbf{u}_2 = (60, 60, 30)$ for Wydown Creek, and $\mathbf{v} = (30, 40, 20)$ for Orchard Road. Then we seek scalars $c_1$, $c_2$ such that

$$c_1 \mathbf{u}_1 + c_2 \mathbf{u}_2 = \mathbf{v}$$

or, equivalently, such that

$$c_1 \begin{bmatrix} 20 \\ 40 \\ 20 \end{bmatrix} + c_2 \begin{bmatrix} 60 \\ 60 \\ 30 \end{bmatrix} = \begin{bmatrix} 30 \\ 40 \\ 20 \end{bmatrix}$$

We reduce the augmented matrix

$$\begin{bmatrix} 20 & 60 & | & 30 \\ 40 & 60 & | & 40 \\ 20 & 30 & | & 20 \end{bmatrix}$$

to obtain

$$\begin{bmatrix} 1 & 0 & | & 1/2 \\ 0 & 1 & | & 1/3 \end{bmatrix}$$

Thus we have

$$\frac{1}{2} \mathbf{u}_1 + \frac{1}{3} \mathbf{u}_2 = \mathbf{v}$$

That is, the output of one day of operation at the Orchard Road mine can be obtained from the combination of $\frac{1}{2}$ day of operation at the Big Bend mine and $\frac{1}{3}$ day of operation at the Wydown Creek mine. ∎

## LINEAR SYSTEMS AND COLUMN VECTORS

From this point on, we will use the notation of vectors when dealing with linear systems of equations, and we will write $A\mathbf{x} = \mathbf{b}$ instead of $AX = B$ as we did earlier. Thus we have $\mathbf{x}$ instead of $X$ and $\mathbf{b}$ instead of $B$.

We wish to interpret the issue of consistency of a linear system in terms of linear combinations of vectors. This is done by thinking of each column of the matrix $A$ as a vector in its own right. We will refer to the columns of $A$ from this viewpoint as the **column vectors** of $A$. For example, the matrix

$$A = \begin{bmatrix} 1 & 2 & -1 \\ 2 & 7 & 4 \end{bmatrix}$$

will be viewed as consisting of the column vectors

$$\mathbf{a}_1 = \begin{bmatrix} 1 \\ 2 \end{bmatrix}, \quad \mathbf{a}_2 = \begin{bmatrix} 2 \\ 7 \end{bmatrix}, \quad \mathbf{a}_3 = \begin{bmatrix} -1 \\ 4 \end{bmatrix}$$

Now consider a system with coefficient matrix $A$ such as

$$x_1 + 2x_2 - x_3 = 5$$
$$2x_1 + 7x_2 + 4x_3 = 1$$

We observe that this system can be written in vector form as follows:

$$x_1 \begin{bmatrix} 1 \\ 2 \end{bmatrix} + x_2 \begin{bmatrix} 2 \\ 7 \end{bmatrix} + x_3 \begin{bmatrix} -1 \\ 4 \end{bmatrix} = \begin{bmatrix} 5 \\ 1 \end{bmatrix}$$

The components of the column vectors of $A$ are simply the coefficients of each of the system variables. If we let $\mathbf{b}$ denote the vector of constant terms, then we can write the system of equations as

$$x_1 \mathbf{a}_1 + x_2 \mathbf{a}_2 + x_3 \mathbf{a}_3 = \mathbf{b}$$

We see that the system has a solution $x_1 = c_1$, $x_2 = c_2$, $x_3 = c_3$ if and only if $\mathbf{b}$ can be written as the linear combination $\mathbf{b} = c_1 \mathbf{a}_1 + c_2 \mathbf{a}_2 + c_3 \mathbf{a}_3$ of the column vectors of $A$. Thus the question of whether the system $A\mathbf{x} = \mathbf{b}$ is consistent (has a solution) is equivalent to the question of whether $\mathbf{b}$ can be written as a linear combination of the column vectors of $A$.

The relation between solutions of linear systems and linear combinations of vectors is illustrated in the next example.

**EXAMPLE 6**   One solution of the system $A\mathbf{x} = \mathbf{b}$ where

$$A = \begin{bmatrix} 1 & 2 & -1 \\ 2 & 7 & 4 \end{bmatrix}, \quad \mathbf{b} = \begin{bmatrix} 5 \\ 1 \end{bmatrix}$$

is $\mathbf{x} = (16, -5, 1)$. Use this solution to write $\mathbf{b}$ as a linear combination of the columns of $A$.

SOLUTION   In the matrix notation of systems, we have

$$\begin{bmatrix} 1 & 2 & -1 \\ 2 & 7 & 4 \end{bmatrix} \begin{bmatrix} 16 \\ -5 \\ 1 \end{bmatrix} = \begin{bmatrix} 5 \\ 1 \end{bmatrix}$$

In vector form we would write

$$16 \begin{bmatrix} 1 \\ 2 \end{bmatrix} - 5 \begin{bmatrix} 2 \\ 7 \end{bmatrix} + \begin{bmatrix} -1 \\ 4 \end{bmatrix} = \begin{bmatrix} 5 \\ 1 \end{bmatrix}$$

Hence we have $\mathbf{b} = 16\mathbf{a}_1 - 5\mathbf{a}_2 + \mathbf{a}_3$.   ∎

The relationship between the consistency of a system and the ability to write one vector as a linear combination of other vectors is very important, and it anticipates work that will be done in later sections. Though it may seem to be just a simple rewriting of linear systems, it will prove to be a very significant step in the analysis of linear systems. We record the statement here as a theorem for emphasis.

**THEOREM 1**

The linear system $A\mathbf{x} = \mathbf{b}$ has a solution if and only if $\mathbf{b}$ can be written as a linear combination of the column vectors of $A$. Furthermore, the coefficients in the linear combination are the respective solution values.

The notation of the above discussion will be used throughout this chapter. Thus the vector obtained from the $j$th column of the coefficient matrix $A$ will always be denoted by $\mathbf{a}_j$.

We close with two examples. In the first the system has infinitely many solutions, and in the second the system is inconsistent.

**EXAMPLE 7**   Solve the system $A\mathbf{x} = \mathbf{b}$ where

$$A = \begin{bmatrix} 1 & 2 & 4 \\ 3 & 5 & 7 \\ -1 & -3 & -9 \end{bmatrix}, \quad \mathbf{b} = \begin{bmatrix} 2 \\ 9 \\ 1 \end{bmatrix}$$

and write $\mathbf{b}$ as a linear combination of the column vectors of $A$.

SOLUTION   The augmented matrix

$$\begin{bmatrix} 1 & 2 & 4 & | & 2 \\ 3 & 5 & 7 & | & 9 \\ -1 & -3 & -9 & | & 1 \end{bmatrix}$$

can be put into the following reduced echelon form

$$\begin{bmatrix} 1 & 0 & -6 & | & 8 \\ 0 & 1 & 5 & | & -3 \end{bmatrix}$$

If we introduce the parameter $t$, then we get the infinite set of solutions

$$x_1 = 6t + 8, \quad x_2 = -5t - 3, \quad x_3 = t$$

where $t$ is any arbitrary number.

To write $\mathbf{b}$ as a linear combination of the column vectors $\mathbf{a}_1, \mathbf{a}_2, \mathbf{a}_3$ of $A$, we may use a solution determined by any value of $t$. For instance, if we choose $t = 0$, we get $x_1 = 8$, $x_2 = -3$, $x_3 = 0$, so that

$$8\mathbf{a}_1 - 3\mathbf{a}_2 = \mathbf{b}$$

On the other hand, if we choose $t = -1$, then $x_1 = 2$, $x_2 = 2$, $x_3 = -1$, so that

$$2\mathbf{a}_1 + 2\mathbf{a}_2 - \mathbf{a}_3 = \mathbf{b}$$

The reader may verify that, in general,

$$(6t + 8)\mathbf{a}_1 + (-5t - 3)\mathbf{a}_2 + t\mathbf{a}_3 = \mathbf{b}$$

for any value of $t$. ∎

**EXAMPLE 8** Show that the system $A\mathbf{x} = \mathbf{b}$ where

$$A = \begin{bmatrix} 1 & 2 & 4 \\ 3 & 5 & 7 \\ -1 & -3 & -9 \end{bmatrix}, \quad \mathbf{b} = \begin{bmatrix} 3 \\ 5 \\ 2 \end{bmatrix}$$

is inconsistent, and thus demonstrate that $\mathbf{b}$ cannot be written as a linear combination of $\mathbf{a}_1, \mathbf{a}_2, \mathbf{a}_3$.

SOLUTION   The augmented matrix

$$\begin{bmatrix} 1 & 2 & 4 & 3 \\ 3 & 5 & 7 & 5 \\ -1 & -3 & -9 & 2 \end{bmatrix}$$

can be put into the form

$$\begin{bmatrix} 1 & 2 & 4 & 3 \\ 0 & 1 & 5 & 4 \\ 0 & 0 & 0 & 9 \end{bmatrix}$$

Thus the system is inconsistent, and no linear combination of $\mathbf{a}_1, \mathbf{a}_2$, and $\mathbf{a}_3$ will be equal to $\mathbf{b}$. ∎

# EXERCISES 4.2

In Exercises 1–6, let $\mathbf{u}_1 = (6, -5)$, $\mathbf{u}_2 = (-4, 2)$, $\mathbf{u}_3 = (7, 5)$, and find the indicated linear combination.

1. $\mathbf{v} = 2\mathbf{u}_1 + 3\mathbf{u}_2$ 
2. $\mathbf{v} = 3\mathbf{u}_1 - \mathbf{u}_2$
3. $\mathbf{v} = -2\mathbf{u}_1 + 4\mathbf{u}_3$ 
4. $\mathbf{v} = \mathbf{u}_1 - 3\mathbf{u}_3$
5. $\mathbf{v} = 2\mathbf{u}_1 - 2\mathbf{u}_2 + \mathbf{u}_3$ 
6. $\mathbf{v} = -3\mathbf{u}_1 + \mathbf{u}_2 + 3\mathbf{u}_3$

In Exercises 7–10, let $\mathbf{u}_1 = (4, -2, 1)$, $\mathbf{u}_2 = (6, 3, 2)$, $\mathbf{u}_3 = (-2, -1, 3)$, and find the indicated linear combination.

7. $\mathbf{v} = 4\mathbf{u}_1 - 2\mathbf{u}_2$ 
8. $\mathbf{v} = -6\mathbf{u}_1 + 3\mathbf{u}_2$
9. $\mathbf{v} = 2\mathbf{u}_1 + 3\mathbf{u}_2 - \mathbf{u}_3$ 
10. $\mathbf{v} = \mathbf{u}_1 - 3\mathbf{u}_2 + 4\mathbf{u}_3$

In Exercises 11–14, write $\mathbf{v}$ as a linear combination of $\mathbf{u}_1, \mathbf{u}_2$. Represent this linear combination graphically.

11. $\mathbf{v} = (8, 15/2)$,   $\mathbf{u}_1 = (1, 3)$,   $\mathbf{u}_2 = (4, 1)$
12. $\mathbf{v} = (2, 10)$,   $\mathbf{u}_1 = (-1, 2)$,   $\mathbf{u}_2 = (2, 3)$

13. $\mathbf{v} = (-5, 8)$,   $\mathbf{u}_1 = (1, 2)$,   $\mathbf{u}_2 = (-4, 1)$
14. $\mathbf{v} = (2, 4)$,   $\mathbf{u}_1 = (-1, 4)$,   $\mathbf{u}_2 = (3, -3)$

In Exercises 15–18, determine if it is possible to express $\mathbf{v}$ as a linear combination of $\mathbf{u}_1$ and $\mathbf{u}_2$. If it is possible, write $\mathbf{v}$ explicitly as a linear combination of $\mathbf{u}_1$ and $\mathbf{u}_2$.

15. $\mathbf{v} = (2, 3, -2)$,   $\mathbf{u}_1 = (2, 4, -4)$,   $\mathbf{u}_2 = (-2, -5, 6)$
16. $\mathbf{v} = (6, -4, 4)$,   $\mathbf{u}_1 = (-2, 2, 6)$,   $\mathbf{u}_2 = (4, -3, -8)$
17. $\mathbf{v} = (-6, 8, 3)$,   $\mathbf{u}_1 = (3, -3, -6)$,   $\mathbf{u}_2 = (6, -7, -3)$
18. $\mathbf{v} = (3, -4, 5)$,   $\mathbf{u}_1 = (-3, 6, -3)$,   $\mathbf{u}_2 = (6, -11, 7)$

19. The Energysaver Window Company manufactures casement, crank out, and double hung storm windows at their Cicero, Berwyn, and Skokie plants. The daily output for the three plants is 200 casement, 400 crank out, and 600 double hung windows at Cicero; 600 casement, 300 crank out, and 300 double hung windows at Berwyn; and 600 casement, 900 crank out, and 1300 double hung windows at Skokie. All plants are operating well below capacity, and the Skokie plant, though large, is old and inefficient, and the company would benefit from its closing. Is there some combination of outputs from the other two plants that will equal the output of the Skokie plant?

20. The Apske Paper Company produces onionskin, 60-pound paper, and 20-pound paper at their Huntington, Charleston, and Parkersburg mills. The daily outputs of the three mills are 3 tons of onionskin, 3 tons of 60-pound, and 6 tons of 20-pound paper at the Huntington mill; 6 tons of onionskin, 8 tons of 60-pound, and 10 tons of 20-pound paper at the Charleston mill; and 9 tons of onionskin, 10 tons of 60-pound, and 17 tons of 20-pound paper at the Parkersburg mill. The economy is in a recession, and the company would like to save management expenses by closing the Parkersburg mill. Is there some combination of outputs of the other two mills that will equal the output of the Parkersburg mill?

In Exercises 21–24, use the given information to find a solution to the system of equations $A\mathbf{x} = \mathbf{b}$.

21. $\mathbf{a}_1 = \begin{bmatrix} 5 \\ -2 \end{bmatrix}$,   $\mathbf{a}_2 = \begin{bmatrix} 4 \\ 7 \end{bmatrix}$,   $\mathbf{b} = \begin{bmatrix} 22 \\ -26 \end{bmatrix}$;   $6\mathbf{a}_1 - 2\mathbf{a}_2 = \mathbf{b}$

22. $\mathbf{a}_1 = \begin{bmatrix} -3 \\ 6 \end{bmatrix}$,   $\mathbf{a}_2 = \begin{bmatrix} 2 \\ -4 \end{bmatrix}$,   $\mathbf{b} = \begin{bmatrix} -1 \\ 2 \end{bmatrix}$;   $3\mathbf{a}_1 + 4\mathbf{a}_2 = \mathbf{b}$

23. $A = \begin{bmatrix} 3 & -4 & -2 \\ -2 & -1 & 1 \\ 1 & 2 & 3 \end{bmatrix}$,   $\mathbf{b} = \begin{bmatrix} 9 \\ -3 \\ 7 \end{bmatrix}$;   $3\mathbf{a}_1 - \mathbf{a}_2 + 2\mathbf{a}_3 = \mathbf{b}$

24. $A = \begin{bmatrix} -3 & 5 & -2 \\ -2 & 3 & -3 \\ 1 & 2 & -4 \end{bmatrix}$,   $\mathbf{b} = \begin{bmatrix} -17 \\ -7 \\ 4 \end{bmatrix}$;   $2\mathbf{a}_1 - 3\mathbf{a}_2 - 2\mathbf{a}_3 = \mathbf{b}$

In Exercises 25–30, find a solution of $A\mathbf{x} = \mathbf{b}$ and use it to determine a linear combination of the columns of $A$ that will equal $\mathbf{b}$.

**25.** $A = \begin{bmatrix} 2 & -6 \\ 4 & -11 \end{bmatrix}, \quad \mathbf{b} = \begin{bmatrix} 2 \\ 8 \end{bmatrix}$

**26.** $A = \begin{bmatrix} 3 & -6 \\ -6 & 11 \end{bmatrix}, \quad \mathbf{b} = \begin{bmatrix} -3 \\ 8 \end{bmatrix}$

**27.** $A = \begin{bmatrix} 2 & 4 & -5 \\ 5 & -4 & 2 \\ -1 & 2 & 3 \end{bmatrix}, \quad \mathbf{b} = \begin{bmatrix} 1 \\ 10 \\ 2 \end{bmatrix}$

**28.** $A = \begin{bmatrix} -4 & 3 & 3 \\ 1 & 3 & -6 \\ 5 & 2 & 3 \end{bmatrix}, \quad \mathbf{b} = \begin{bmatrix} -4 \\ 3 \\ 13 \end{bmatrix}$

**29.** $A = \begin{bmatrix} 1 & 3 & 4 \\ 3 & 10 & 5 \\ 2 & 7 & 1 \end{bmatrix}, \quad \mathbf{b} = \begin{bmatrix} 6 \\ 4 \\ -2 \end{bmatrix}$

**30.** $A = \begin{bmatrix} 1 & -2 & 3 \\ -2 & 5 & -9 \\ 3 & -7 & 12 \end{bmatrix}, \quad \mathbf{b} = \begin{bmatrix} 7 \\ -10 \\ 17 \end{bmatrix}$

## 4.3   SPANS OF VECTORS

*The Span of a Set of Vectors, Subspaces, The Null Space of a Matrix, The Column Space of a Matrix, Application*

There are special types of subsets of $R^n$ that are generated by taking linear combinations of a given set of vectors. Such a subset is called the subspace spanned by the given vectors. We will apply the concept of span to the analysis of linear systems by examining two subspaces that are related to a matrix. One is the null space of a matrix, which is the set of solutions of the associated homogeneous system of equations. The other is the column space of a matrix, which is related to consistency of systems. Some techniques for working with spans will be developed, and then we will apply the ideas to a production problem of combining materials in a proper manner.

### THE SPAN OF A SET OF VECTORS

If we start with a set $\{\mathbf{u}_1, \mathbf{u}_2, \ldots, \mathbf{u}_k\}$ of vectors in $R^n$, we can build new vectors by forming linear combinations and thereby creating a new set of vectors. The new set that is generated by taking all possible linear combinations of the given vectors is a useful concept that is called the span of the set of vectors.

---

**DEFINITION**

The **span** of a set of vectors $\{\mathbf{u}_1, \mathbf{u}_2, \ldots, \mathbf{u}_k\}$ in $R^n$ is the set of all vectors

$$c_1\mathbf{u}_1 + c_2\mathbf{u}_2 + \cdots + c_k\mathbf{u}_k$$

that are linear combinations of the given vectors, where $c_1, c_2, \ldots, c_k$ are arbitrary scalars.

---

To get an intuitive sense of the idea of a span of a set of vectors, we look at what happens in $R^3$ where we start with one, two, or three vectors. In this context we will always regard vectors as being position vectors (that is, based at the origin).

Suppose that we have a single nonzero vector $\mathbf{u}$ in $R^3$. Then the span consists of all multiples $t\mathbf{u}$ of $\mathbf{u}$ where $t$ is an arbitrary scalar. Thus we have the vector equation of a line, so that the resulting set is the line through the origin with direction vector $\mathbf{u}$. For example, if $\mathbf{u} = (1, 3, 2)$ and if we think of $t$ as a parameter, then the line has the parametric equations $x = t$, $y = 3t$, $z = 2t$. See Figure 4.19.

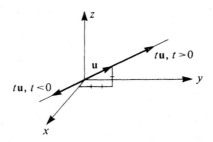

**FIGURE 4.19**              *The span of the vector* $\mathbf{u}$ *is the line* $\overrightarrow{OP} = t\mathbf{u}$

If we start with two nonzero vectors $\mathbf{u}_1$ and $\mathbf{u}_2$ in $R^3$, then their span is the set of all linear combinations $s\mathbf{u}_1 + t\mathbf{u}_2$ where $s, t$ are arbitrary scalars. In the special case that $\mathbf{u}_1$ and $\mathbf{u}_2$ are multiples of one another, then they are collinear (that is, they both lie on the same line through the origin), and we are back in the case of a single vector. However, if $\mathbf{u}_1$ and $\mathbf{u}_2$ are noncollinear (that is, not on the same line through the origin), then their span is the plane determined by the origin and the two terminal points of the vectors. See Figure 4.20. Note that any vector in the plane is either a multiple of one of the vectors or the diagonal of a parallelogram with sides $s\mathbf{u}_1$ and $t\mathbf{u}_2$ for appropriate scalars $s$ and $t$. We will provide techniques for finding an equation of the plane spanned by two vectors later in the section.

For the case of three vectors in $R^3$, the span may be all of $R^3$, as in the next example, or it may be a plane if one of the vectors lies in the span of the other two, or it may be a line if all three vectors are multiples of a single vector. The general issue of interdependence of vectors will be taken up in the next section.

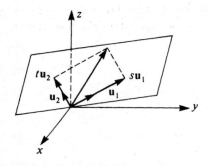

**FIGURE 4.20**                    *The span of noncollinear vectors* $\mathbf{u}_1$, $\mathbf{u}_2$

**EXAMPLE 1**    Determine the span in $R^3$ of the vectors

$$\mathbf{e}_1 = (1,0,0), \quad \mathbf{e}_2 = (0,1,0), \quad \mathbf{e}_3 = (0,0,1)$$

**SOLUTION**    Given any vector $\mathbf{u} = (a, b, c)$ in $R^3$, we can write

$$\mathbf{u} = (a,0,0) + (0,b,0) + (0,0,c)$$
$$= a\mathbf{e}_1 + b\mathbf{e}_2 + c\mathbf{e}_3$$

Hence any vector in $R^3$ can be written as a linear combination of $\mathbf{e}_1$, $\mathbf{e}_2$, $\mathbf{e}_3$, and we conclude that their span is all of $R^3$. See Figure 4.21. ∎

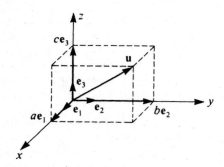

**FIGURE 4.21**                    *The span of* $\{\mathbf{e}_1, \mathbf{e}_2, \mathbf{e}_3\}$ *is* $R^3$

## SUBSPACES

The span of a set of vectors is generated by applying the two fundamental operations of addition and scalar multiplication to build linear combinations of the given vectors. If two vectors in the given span are added, then the sum is again a linear combination of the initial vectors, so that the sum is also in the span. Similarly, a scalar multiple of a vector in the span also stays in the span. These observations are illustrated in the next example.

**EXAMPLE 2**   The vectors $\mathbf{v}_1 = 3\mathbf{u}_1 - 4\mathbf{u}_2 + 2\mathbf{u}_3$ and $\mathbf{v}_2 = 5\mathbf{u}_1 - 7\mathbf{u}_3$ are in the span of $\{\mathbf{u}_1, \mathbf{u}_2, \mathbf{u}_3\}$. Show that the vectors $\mathbf{v}_1 + \mathbf{v}_2$ and $2\mathbf{v}_1$ are also in the span.

SOLUTION   If we add $\mathbf{v}_1$ and $\mathbf{v}_2$, we get

$$\begin{aligned}
\mathbf{v}_1 + \mathbf{v}_2 &= (3\mathbf{u}_1 - 4\mathbf{u}_2 + 2\mathbf{u}_3) + (5\mathbf{u}_1 - 7\mathbf{u}_3) \\
&= 8\mathbf{u}_1 - 4\mathbf{u}_2 - 5\mathbf{u}_3
\end{aligned}$$

Since $\mathbf{v}_1 + \mathbf{v}_2$ is a linear combination of $\mathbf{u}_1, \mathbf{u}_2, \mathbf{u}_3$, we see that $\mathbf{v}_1 + \mathbf{v}_2$ is in the span. Similarly, since

$$2\mathbf{v}_1 = 6\mathbf{u}_1 - 8\mathbf{u}_2 + 4\mathbf{u}_3$$

is a linear combination of $\mathbf{u}_1, \mathbf{u}_2, \mathbf{u}_3$, the vector $2\mathbf{v}_1$ is also in the span. ∎

Subsets of $R^n$ in which the operations of addition and scalar multiplication can be performed on vectors in the subset with the resulting vectors still belonging to the subset are called subspaces and they are defined as follows.

**DEFINITION**

A nonempty subset $S$ of $R^n$ is called a **subspace** if the following properties are satisfied: (1) If $\mathbf{u}$ and $\mathbf{v}$ are in $S$, then $\mathbf{u} + \mathbf{v}$ is in $S$, and (2) if $\mathbf{u}$ is in $S$ and if $c$ is any scalar, then $c\mathbf{u}$ is in $S$.

Properties 1 and 2 are often called **closure properties**. Property 1 states that a subspace is closed with respect to addition, since sums of vectors in $S$ are again in $S$. Property 2 states that $S$ is closed with respect to scalar multiplication, since scalar multiples of a vector in $S$ are again in $S$.

If the two properties are combined and applied to a finite number of vectors, then it follows that a subspace is closed under the formation of linear combinations. That is, *a linear combination of vectors in a subspace $S$ is also in $S$.* In particular, the scalar $c = 0$ can be used to multiply any vector $\mathbf{u}$ in a subspace with the result $c\mathbf{u} = \mathbf{0}$; thus we see that the zero vector $\mathbf{0}$ must belong to every subspace of $R^n$.

The significance of the idea of a subspace is that all the usual operations with vectors as described in Section 4.1 can be done within the subspace without leaving the subspace. Thus a subspace of $R^n$ is a "vector space" in its own right.

To gain a further sense of the idea of subspace, it is instructive to look at an example of a set of vectors that is *not* a subspace.

**EXAMPLE 3**   Show that the following set of vectors is *not* a subspace of $R^2$: the set of all $(x_1, x_2)$ such that $x_1 \geqslant 0$, $x_2 \geqslant 0$.

SOLUTION   This set is the first quadrant in the plane. Property 1 is satisfied, but property 2 is not. We note that the vector $(1, 1)$ satisfies the given condition that the components are nonnegative, but the scalar multiple $-(1, 1) =$

$(-1, -1)$ does not. Hence the set is not closed with respect to scalar multiplication, so that we do not have a subspace. See Figure 4.22.

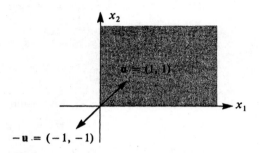

**FIGURE 4.22**                    *A subset of $R^2$ that is not a subspace*

The connection between spans and subspaces is given in the following theorem, which we state without proof.

### THEOREM 1

A nonempty subset $S$ of $R^n$ is a subspace if and only if it is the span of some finite set of vectors $\{\mathbf{u}_1, \ldots, \mathbf{u}_k\}$ in $R^n$.

Thus the concepts of span and subspace, which appear to be quite different at first, actually coincide for subsets of $R^n$. We shall often consider subspaces that are spanned by particular sets of vectors.

## THE NULL SPACE OF A MATRIX

An important subspace associated with a matrix is the following.

### DEFINITION

The **null space** of an $m \times n$ matrix $A$ is the set of all vectors $\mathbf{x}$ such that $A\mathbf{x} = \mathbf{0}$.

Thus the term null space is defined to be the set of solutions of the homogeneous system with coefficient matrix $A$. The relationship with spans is indicated in the following example.

**EXAMPLE 4**   Show that the null space of the matrix

$$A = \begin{bmatrix} 1 & -2 & 4 \\ -1 & 3 & -7 \end{bmatrix}$$

is the span of a single vector.

SOLUTION    We must solve the homogeneous system $A\mathbf{x} = \mathbf{0}$. Row operations on $A$ give us the reduced echelon form

$$\begin{bmatrix} 1 & 0 & -2 \\ 0 & 1 & -3 \end{bmatrix}$$

Therefore if we set $x_3 = t$, then we get $x_2 = 3t$, $x_1 = 2t$. Thus the solutions are given by

$$\begin{bmatrix} x_1 \\ x_2 \\ x_3 \end{bmatrix} = \begin{bmatrix} 2t \\ 3t \\ t \end{bmatrix} = t \begin{bmatrix} 2 \\ 3 \\ 1 \end{bmatrix}$$

Hence the solution set consists of all multiples of the vector $\mathbf{u} = (2, 3, 1)$. In other words, the null space of $A$ is the span of the vector $\mathbf{u}$. ∎

We recall from Section 2.3 that a homogeneous system either has the zero solution as its only solution or has infinitely many solutions, and in the latter case a parametric representation of the solution set is obtained by using the reduced echelon form of the coefficient matrix. Thus the null space of a matrix is either the zero vector alone or a set in which the vectors are given in terms of one or more parameters. The parametric representation can be written in the form of a linear combination of vectors where the parameters serve as the scalars in the linear combination.

Thus the null space of a matrix is in fact the span of a set of vectors in which the number of vectors generating the span is the same as the number of parameters. The following example illustrates how the null space of a matrix may need to be expressed as a span of more than one vector.

**EXAMPLE 5**    Express the null-space of the matrix $A$ as a span of vectors where

$$A = \begin{bmatrix} 1 & 2 & -1 & -3 \\ 2 & 4 & 1 & 0 \\ -1 & -2 & 0 & 1 \end{bmatrix}$$

SOLUTION    The null space consists of all solutions of the homogeneous system $A\mathbf{x} = \mathbf{0}$. The first step is to use row operations to put the augmented matrix into reduced echelon form. By pivoting on the entry 1 in the first row, we get the matrix

$$\left[\begin{array}{cccc|c} 1 & 2 & -1 & -3 & 0 \\ 0 & 0 & 3 & 6 & 0 \\ 0 & 0 & -1 & -2 & 0 \end{array}\right]$$

and then by pivoting on the 3 in the second row, we obtain the reduced echelon form

$$\left[\begin{array}{cccc|c} 1 & 2 & 0 & -1 & 0 \\ 0 & 0 & 1 & 2 & 0 \\ 0 & 0 & 0 & 0 & 0 \end{array}\right]$$

The nonleading variables are $x_2$ and $x_4$, and we set $x_2 = s$ and $x_4 = t$. Then we get $x_3 = -2t$ and $x_1 = -2s + t$, so that the null-space of $A$ consists of all vectors

$$\mathbf{x} = \begin{bmatrix} -2s + t \\ s \\ -2t \\ t \end{bmatrix}$$

where $s$ and $t$ are arbitrary.

We next wish to write these vectors as a linear combination of particular vectors. By splitting the above vector into a sum of two vectors, one for each parameter, we can write

$$\mathbf{x} = \begin{bmatrix} -2s \\ s \\ 0 \\ 0 \end{bmatrix} + \begin{bmatrix} t \\ 0 \\ -2t \\ t \end{bmatrix}$$

Then using $s$ and $t$ as scalar multiples, we get

$$\mathbf{x} = s\begin{bmatrix} -2 \\ 1 \\ 0 \\ 0 \end{bmatrix} + t\begin{bmatrix} 1 \\ 0 \\ -2 \\ 1 \end{bmatrix}$$

Thus the null space of $A$ is the span of the two vectors

$$\mathbf{u}_1 = \begin{bmatrix} -2 \\ 1 \\ 0 \\ 0 \end{bmatrix}, \quad \mathbf{u}_2 = \begin{bmatrix} 1 \\ 0 \\ -2 \\ 1 \end{bmatrix}$$

Note that $\mathbf{u}_1$ is obtained by setting $s = 1$, $t = 0$ and $\mathbf{u}_2$ is obtained by setting $s = 0$, $t = 1$. ∎

As the preceding example shows, the method for finding the null space of a matrix is essentially the same as the procedure for solving homogeneous systems, except that the parametric representation is rewritten so that the solutions are given as linear combinations of vectors with the parameters acting as scalar multiples. The number of vectors used to generate the **null space equals** the number of parameters, which is the same as **the number of columns minus** the number of leading 1s in the reduced echelon form of the matrix. In the preceding example all of the essential information about the solution set of $A\mathbf{x} = \mathbf{0}$ is provided by two key vectors; thus the amorphous idea of having infinitely many solutions is simplified to knowing that two particular vectors determine all solutions.

## THE COLUMN SPACE OF A MATRIX

If we are given a matrix $A$, we can apply the idea of span to the columns of $A$, where we regard each column as a vector. Thus we have the following definition.

**DEFINITION**

The **column space** of a matrix $A$ is defined to be the subspace spanned by the column vectors of $A$. That is, if $A$ has the column vectors $\mathbf{a}_1, \ldots, \mathbf{a}_k$, then the column space of $A$ is the set of all linear combinations $c_1\mathbf{a}_1 + \cdots + c_k\mathbf{a}_k$ where $c_1, \ldots, c_k$ are arbitrary scalars.

Example 1 dealt with the column vectors $\mathbf{e}_1, \mathbf{e}_2, \mathbf{e}_3$ of the $3 \times 3$ identity matrix $I_3$, and it was shown that the column space of $I_3$ was $R^3$. A similar argument shows that the column space of $I_n$, the $n \times n$ identity matrix, is $R^n$. However, as the next example shows, the column space of a general $n \times n$ matrix need not be all of $R^n$.

**EXAMPLE 6**    Describe the column space of the matrix

$$A = \begin{bmatrix} 1 & 0 & 1 \\ 0 & 1 & 1 \\ 1 & 1 & 2 \end{bmatrix}$$

SOLUTION    The column vectors of $A$ are

$$\mathbf{a}_1 = \begin{bmatrix} 1 \\ 0 \\ 1 \end{bmatrix}, \quad \mathbf{a}_2 = \begin{bmatrix} 0 \\ 1 \\ 1 \end{bmatrix}, \quad \mathbf{a}_3 = \begin{bmatrix} 1 \\ 1 \\ 2 \end{bmatrix}$$

We note that the third column is the sum of the first two columns, that is, we have $\mathbf{a}_3 = \mathbf{a}_1 + \mathbf{a}_2$. This means that there is a redundancy, since the third vector is not really needed to generate the column space. Any linear combination of the three vectors $\mathbf{a}_1, \mathbf{a}_2, \mathbf{a}_3$ can actually be written as a linear combination of the two vectors $\mathbf{a}_1, \mathbf{a}_2$. Therefore the column space of $A$ is the set of vectors in $R^3$ that can be written

$$\begin{aligned} \mathbf{v} &= c_1\mathbf{a}_1 + c_2\mathbf{a}_2 + c_3\mathbf{a}_3 \\ &= c_1\mathbf{a}_1 + c_2\mathbf{a}_2 + c_3(\mathbf{a}_1 + \mathbf{a}_2) \\ &= (c_1 + c_3)\mathbf{a}_1 + (c_2 + c_3)\mathbf{a}_2 \end{aligned}$$

Thus the span of $\{\mathbf{a}_1, \mathbf{a}_2, \mathbf{a}_3\}$ is the same as the span of $\{\mathbf{a}_1, \mathbf{a}_2\}$, so that the column space of $A$ is the plane in $R^3$ determined by the vectors $\mathbf{a}_1$ and $\mathbf{a}_2$. A portion of the plane that lies in the first octant is shown in Figure 4.23. ∎

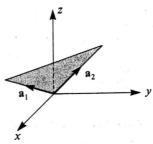

**FIGURE 4.23**    *The span of $\mathbf{a}_1 = (1, 0, 1)$ and $\mathbf{a}_2 = (0, 1, 1)$*

The relationship between the column space of a matrix $A$ and the solvability of linear systems $A\mathbf{x} = \mathbf{b}$ was given in Theorem 1 of the preceding section. It stated that the system is consistent if and only if $\mathbf{b}$ can be written as a linear combination of the column vectors of $A$. We can restate that criterion in terms of column spaces as follows.

### THEOREM 2

The linear system $A\mathbf{x} = \mathbf{b}$ is consistent if and only if $\mathbf{b}$ is in the column space of $A$.

Thus the set of all vectors $\mathbf{b}$ for which $A\mathbf{x} = \mathbf{b}$ has a solution is the same as the subspace spanned by the columns of $A$. This result can be used to describe spans of vectors in terms of equations. The method is illustrated in the next example, in which an equation of the plane spanned by two noncollinear vectors in $R^3$ is found.

**EXAMPLE 7** Describe the span of the vectors $\mathbf{a}_1 = (1, 1, 4)$ and $\mathbf{a}_2 = (1, 2, 3)$ in $R^3$.

SOLUTION   We wish to find an equation in the components of a general vector $\mathbf{b} = (x, y, z)$ such that $\mathbf{b}$ lies in the span of $\mathbf{a}_1$ and $\mathbf{a}_2$. If we let $A$ be the matrix whose columns are $\mathbf{a}_1$ and $\mathbf{a}_2$, then by Theorem 2 we know that $\mathbf{b}$ is a linear combination of $\mathbf{a}_1$ and $\mathbf{a}_2$ if and only if the system $A\mathbf{x} = \mathbf{b}$ is consistent. The augmented matrix for this system is the matrix

$$\begin{bmatrix} 1 & 1 & x \\ 1 & 2 & y \\ 4 & 3 & z \end{bmatrix}$$

Performing row operations as usual, we get the matrices

$$\begin{bmatrix} 1 & 1 & x \\ 0 & 1 & y - x \\ 0 & -1 & z - 4x \end{bmatrix}$$

$$\begin{bmatrix} 1 & 1 & x \\ 0 & 1 & y - x \\ 0 & 0 & z + y - 5x \end{bmatrix}$$

From the last row we see that the system is consistent if and only if $z + y - 5x = 0$. Hence by Theorem 2 the vector $\mathbf{b}$ lies in the span of $\mathbf{a}_1$ and $\mathbf{a}_2$ if and only if the components of $\mathbf{b}$ satisfy the equation $5x - y - z = 0$, which is the equation of a plane through the origin. The plane is shown in Figure 4.24. ∎

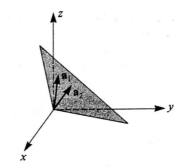

**FIGURE 4.24**                    *The span of* **a**$_1$ = (1,1,4) *and* **a**$_2$ = (1,2,3)

The method of the preceding example can be carried further. We can actually use reduced echelon form to find the scalars needed to express vectors as linear combinations of the column vectors. These scalars are just the solutions of the corresponding system of equations. The technique is illustrated in the next example.

**EXAMPLE 8**    Describe the span of the vectors $\mathbf{a}_1 = (1, 0, 1)$, $\mathbf{a}_2 = (1, 1, 3)$, $\mathbf{a}_3 = (2, 3, 8)$. Write each vector in the span as a linear combination of the given vectors.

**SOLUTION**    We wish to find all vectors $\mathbf{b} = (x, y, z)$ such that $r\mathbf{a}_1 + s\mathbf{a}_2 + t\mathbf{a}_3 = \mathbf{b}$, that is,

$$r\begin{bmatrix} 1 \\ 0 \\ 1 \end{bmatrix} + s\begin{bmatrix} 1 \\ 1 \\ 3 \end{bmatrix} + t\begin{bmatrix} 2 \\ 3 \\ 8 \end{bmatrix} = \begin{bmatrix} x \\ y \\ z \end{bmatrix}$$

We operate on the augmented matrix to obtain the reduced echelon form.

$$\begin{bmatrix} 1 & 1 & 2 & | & x \\ 0 & 1 & 3 & | & y \\ 1 & 3 & 8 & | & z \end{bmatrix}$$

$$\begin{bmatrix} 1 & 1 & 2 & | & x \\ 0 & 1 & 3 & | & y \\ 0 & 2 & 6 & | & z - x \end{bmatrix}$$

$$\begin{bmatrix} 1 & 0 & -1 & | & x - y \\ 0 & 1 & 3 & | & y \\ 0 & 0 & 0 & | & z - x - 2y \end{bmatrix}$$

The bottom row gives us the condition that **b** belongs to the span if $x + 2y - z = 0$. Otherwise there is no solution.

If the condition is satisfied, then we may let $t = 0$ and thus obtain from the first two rows that the needed scalars are

$$r = x - y, \qquad s = y$$

That is, we have

$$\mathbf{b} = (x - y)\begin{bmatrix} 1 \\ 0 \\ 1 \end{bmatrix} + y\begin{bmatrix} 1 \\ 1 \\ 3 \end{bmatrix}$$

$$= (x - y)\mathbf{a}_1 + y\mathbf{a}_2$$

For example, the vector $\mathbf{b} = (5, -2, 1)$ belongs to the span, and we get $r = 7$, $s = -2$, so that $\mathbf{b} = 7\mathbf{a}_1 - 2\mathbf{a}_2$. ∎

**EXAMPLE 9**  Describe the span of $\mathbf{a}_1 = (1, 0, 1)$, $\mathbf{a}_2 = (1, 1, 3)$, $\mathbf{a}_3 = (2, 3, 7)$.

SOLUTION  In this case the matrix with column vectors $\mathbf{a}_1$, $\mathbf{a}_2$, $\mathbf{a}_3$ augmented with $\mathbf{b} = (x, y, z)$ can be reduced to

$$\begin{bmatrix} 1 & 0 & 0 & \bigm| & 2x + y - z \\ 0 & 1 & 0 & \bigm| & -3x - 5y + 3z \\ 0 & 0 & 1 & \bigm| & x + 2y - z \end{bmatrix}$$

Therefore the span is all of $R^3$, and we have for any $\mathbf{b}$ that

$$\mathbf{b} = (2x + y - z)\mathbf{a}_1 - (3x + 5y - 3z)\mathbf{a}_2 + (x + 2y - z)\mathbf{a}_3$$

For example, the vector $\mathbf{b} = (2, -2, 3)$ can be written

$$\mathbf{b} = -\mathbf{a}_1 + 13\mathbf{a}_2 - 5\mathbf{a}_3 \qquad ∎$$

## APPLICATION

We now investigate some of these concepts in terms of a mixture problem.

**EXAMPLE 10**  Rustfree Products Inc. manufactures kitchen sinks from a steel alloy that is 76% iron, 16% nickel, and 8% chromium and counter tops from an alloy that is 70% iron, 20% nickel, and 10% chromium. They have located two supplies of scrap metal and can save substantially on the production costs if their products can be blended from these scraps. One scrap mixture contains 80% iron, 15% nickel, and 5% chromium, and the other scrap mixture contains 60% iron, 20% nickel, and 20% chromium. Determine if the products can be manufactured from a blend of these scrap mixtures; if so, find the blend. These supply sources appear to be of reasonably long duration, and the company is considering the manufacture of other products from them. Find the relationship between the percentages of metals that must be satisfied for a product to be blended from these scrap mixtures.

SOLUTION  We let the first scrap mixture be represented by the vector $\mathbf{a}_1 = (80, 15, 5)$ and the second by $\mathbf{a}_2 = (60, 20, 20)$. Then let the products be represented by $\mathbf{u}_1 = (76, 16, 8)$ for kitchen sinks and $\mathbf{u}_2 = (70, 20, 10)$ for counter tops. First of all we want to know if $\mathbf{u}_1$ and $\mathbf{u}_2$ lie in the span of $\mathbf{a}_1$ and $\mathbf{a}_2$. That is, if $A$ is the matrix with columns $\mathbf{a}_1$, $\mathbf{a}_2$, do the vectors $\mathbf{u}_1$ and $\mathbf{u}_2$ lie in the column space of $A$? There are two systems of equations to solve, and we will treat them in the same augmented matrix (see multisystems in Section 2.3).

We start with the augmented matrix

$$\begin{bmatrix} 80 & 60 & | & 76 & 70 \\ 15 & 20 & | & 16 & 20 \\ 5 & 20 & | & 8 & 10 \end{bmatrix}$$

and row operate to obtain

$$\begin{bmatrix} 1 & 0 & | & 4/5 & 1 \\ 0 & 1 & | & 1/5 & 1/4 \\ 0 & 0 & | & 0 & -25 \end{bmatrix}$$

We see from the solution to the first system that kitchen sinks can be blended from a mixture that is 80% scrap type 1 and 20% scrap type 2. However, the second system is inconsistent, as revealed by the bottom row; therefore counter tops cannot be blended from the available scrap.

To treat the general problem, that of producing new products from cheap materials, let the product vector be $\mathbf{v} = (x, y, z)$, where $x + y + z = 100$. Then, as before, we row operate on the augmented matrix

$$\begin{bmatrix} 80 & 60 & | & x \\ 15 & 20 & | & y \\ 5 & 20 & | & z \end{bmatrix}$$

to obtain the matrix

$$\begin{bmatrix} 1 & 0 & | & z/5 + (1/10)(y - 3x) \\ 0 & 1 & | & (-1/40)(y - 3z) \\ 0 & 0 & | & (x - 16z) - (13/2)(y - 3z) \end{bmatrix}$$

Thus $x, y, z$ must be related by

$$(x - 16z) - \frac{13}{2}(y - 3z) = 0$$

Since we also have the equation

$$x + y + z = 100$$

we can eliminate $x$ to obtain the relation

$$3y - z = 40$$

Therefore a product can be blended from the scrap if three times the percentage of nickel minus the percentage of chromium equals 40. Of course, any combination must be in terms of nonnegative multiples of the scrap in order to be feasible. We will address this issue with the simplex machinery in Section 4.7. ∎

## EXERCISES 4.3

In Exercises 1–4, demonstrate that the given vector $\mathbf{b}$ is in the span of $\{\mathbf{e}_1 = (1, 0, 0),$ $\mathbf{e}_2 = (0, 1, 0), \mathbf{e}_3 = (0, 0, 1)\}$ by writing $\mathbf{b}$ as a linear combination of $\mathbf{e}_1, \mathbf{e}_2, \mathbf{e}_3$.

1. $\mathbf{b} = (4, 2, -3)$
2. $\mathbf{b} = (-5, 1, 7)$
3. $\mathbf{b} = (-6, -8, 2)$
4. $\mathbf{b} = (3, -5, -9)$

In Exercises 5–8, $\mathbf{v}_1$ and $\mathbf{v}_2$ are in the span of $\mathbf{u}_1, \mathbf{u}_2, \mathbf{u}_3$. Show that $\mathbf{v}_1 + \mathbf{v}_2$, $3\mathbf{v}_1$, and $2\mathbf{v}_1 - 4\mathbf{v}_2$ are also in the span of $\mathbf{u}_1, \mathbf{u}_2, \mathbf{u}_3$.

5. $\mathbf{v}_1 = 4\mathbf{u}_1 - 5\mathbf{u}_2 + \mathbf{u}_3$
   $\mathbf{v}_2 = 6\mathbf{u}_1 + 2\mathbf{u}_2 - 7\mathbf{u}_3$

6. $\mathbf{v}_1 = \phantom{-}7\mathbf{u}_1 - 6\mathbf{u}_2 + 2\mathbf{u}_3$
   $\mathbf{v}_2 = -5\mathbf{u}_1 + 3\mathbf{u}_2 + 4\mathbf{u}_3$

7. $\mathbf{v}_1 = -8\mathbf{u}_1 + 2\mathbf{u}_2 - 6\mathbf{u}_3$
   $\mathbf{v}_2 = -4\mathbf{u}_1 + 3\mathbf{u}_2 + 5\mathbf{u}_3$

8. $\mathbf{v}_1 = -2\mathbf{u}_1 + 4\mathbf{u}_2 + 5\mathbf{u}_3$
   $\mathbf{v}_2 = \phantom{-}6\mathbf{u}_1 - 9\mathbf{u}_2 + 7\mathbf{u}_3$

In Exercises 9–16, indicate whether or not the subset of points, $P(x, y, z)$, described by the given relations on $x$, $y$, $z$ is a subspace of $R^3$. Indicate why or why not.

9. $x = 4t$, $y = -2t$, $z = t$
10. $x = -7t$, $y = t$, $z = 8t$
11. $x = -3t + 2$, $y = t$, $z = 5t$
12. $x = t$, $y = 2t - 1$, $z = t$
13. $4x + 3y - z = 2$
14. $2x + 5y - z = 0$
15. $8x - y + 2z = 0$
16. $5x - 3y - 3z = 3$

In Exercises 17–24, find the null space of the given matrix, $A$. If the null space is more than the zero vector alone, describe it as the span of a set of vectors.

17. $\begin{bmatrix} 3 & -9 & -3 \\ 6 & -20 & -10 \end{bmatrix}$

18. $\begin{bmatrix} 3 & 6 & 12 \\ -3 & -4 & -10 \end{bmatrix}$

19. $\begin{bmatrix} 2 & -4 & 6 \\ -4 & 8 & -10 \end{bmatrix}$

20. $\begin{bmatrix} -4 & -8 & 12 \\ 8 & 16 & -20 \end{bmatrix}$

21. $\begin{bmatrix} 5 & -5 & 10 \\ 10 & -11 & 22 \\ -5 & 7 & -15 \end{bmatrix}$

22. $\begin{bmatrix} 4 & -8 & -4 \\ -8 & 15 & 10 \\ 4 & -10 & 1 \end{bmatrix}$

23. $\begin{bmatrix} 1 & 4 & 2 & -3 \\ -2 & -9 & 8 & 1 \\ 1 & 3 & 14 & -8 \end{bmatrix}$

24. $\begin{bmatrix} 1 & -5 & 4 & -2 \\ -3 & 14 & -15 & 10 \\ -2 & 8 & -14 & 12 \end{bmatrix}$

In Exercises 25–28, determine whether or not $\mathbf{u}$ or $\mathbf{v}$ is in the column space of $A$. If a vector is in the column space of $A$, write the vector as a linear combination of the columns of $A$.

25. $A = \begin{bmatrix} 2 & -6 & -2 \\ -2 & 8 & 4 \\ -4 & 12 & 4 \end{bmatrix}$ $\quad \mathbf{u} = (4, 2, 1)$
    $\mathbf{v} = (-2, -2, 4)$

$V = 8x_2$

**26.** $A = \begin{bmatrix} 3 & 6 & -3 \\ 3 & 3 & -3 \\ -6 & -12 & 6 \end{bmatrix}$   $\mathbf{u} = (-3, 6, 6)$
$\mathbf{v} = (6, 6, -3)$

**27.** $A = \begin{bmatrix} 2 & -2 & 4 \\ -2 & 4 & -2 \\ 4 & 0 & 12 \end{bmatrix}$   $\mathbf{u} = (7, -12, 4)$
$\mathbf{v} = (-2, 6, 2)$   $X$

**28.** $A = \begin{bmatrix} -3 & -3 & 3 \\ 6 & 8 & -4 \\ 0 & 2 & 2 \end{bmatrix}$   $\mathbf{u} = (3, 1, 7)$
$\mathbf{v} = (1, 2, 6)$

$8x = -22 + y$

$x = -\frac{1}{4}, 2 + \frac{1}{8}y$

In Exercises 29–32, find the equation relating $x, y, z$ for any vector $\mathbf{b} = (x, y, z)$ in the span of the vectors $\mathbf{u}_1, \mathbf{u}_2$.

**29.** $\mathbf{u}_1 = (1, 2, -2),\quad \mathbf{u}_2 = (2, 7, -5)$   **30.** $\mathbf{u}_1 = (-1, -3, 1),\quad \mathbf{u}_2 = (4, 11, 6)$

**31.** $\mathbf{u}_1 = (2, -2, 4),\quad \mathbf{u}_2 = (-4, 5, -7)$   **32.** $\mathbf{u}_1 = (-3, 3, 6),\quad \mathbf{u}_2 = (-6, 7, 8)$

In Exercises 33–38, describe the span of the given vectors in terms of the coefficients $x, y, z$ of a general vector $\mathbf{b} = (x, y, z)$ in the span. Write $\mathbf{b}$ as a linear combination of the given vectors.

**33.** $\mathbf{a}_1 = (1, 2, -3),\quad \mathbf{a}_2 = (2, 5, 3),\quad \mathbf{a}_3 = (1, 1, -12)$

**34.** $\mathbf{a}_1 = (2, 4, -2),\quad \mathbf{a}_2 = (4, 7, 1),\quad \mathbf{a}_3 = (2, 2, 8)$

**35.** $\mathbf{a}_1 = (3, -6, 3),\quad \mathbf{a}_2 = (-3, 5, 6),\quad \mathbf{a}_3 = (3, -7, 12)$

**36.** $\mathbf{a}_1 = (1, 3, -2),\quad \mathbf{a}_2 = (5, 16, -6),\quad \mathbf{a}_3 = (2, 5, -8)$

**37.** $\mathbf{a}_1 = (1, 3, -1),\quad \mathbf{a}_2 = (1, 3, 0),\quad \mathbf{a}_3 = (-2, -7, 3)$

**38.** $\mathbf{a}_1 = (1, -2, -1),\quad \mathbf{a}_2 = (1, -1, 0),\quad \mathbf{a}_3 = (-2, 6, 5)$

Solve Exercises 39–40 by formulating the problem in terms of determining if certain vectors are, or are not, in the column space of some matrix.

**39.** The Peoria Bottle Company manufactures two bottle types from mixtures of recycled white, brown, and green glass. The first bottle type is made from 74% white glass, 22% brown glass, and 4% green glass; the second type is made from 81% white glass, 13% brown glass, and 6% green glass. Scout troops in the North End and on the West Side have bottle collection days, and the bottles collected in the North End are consistently in the mixture 92% white glass, 6% brown glass, and 2% green glass, while the bottles collected on the West Side are consistently in the mixture 70% white glass, 20% brown glass, and 10% green glass. Determine if the products can be blended from these glass sources; if so, find the blend. The company is considering the manufacture of other types of bottles. Find the relationship between the percentages of glass that must be satisfied for a product to be blended from these sources.

**40.** The Chippawa Pulp Company produces two specialty papers from a blend of white, black, and Scotch pines. The first paper is composed of 73% white pine, 20% black pine, and 7% Scotch pine; the second paper is composed of

60% white pine, 32% black pine, and 8% Scotch pine. The company has options on two large tracts of land, and the pine mixture on the first tract is 84% white, 12% black, and 4% Scotch, while the mixture on the second tract is 40% white, 44% black, and 16% Scotch. Determine if the papers can be manufactured from a blend of pulp from these two tracts; if so, find the blend. The company is considering the production of other types of paper. Find the relationship that must exist between the percentages of pines in the pulp composition in order for a paper to be manufactured from a blend of lumber from these two tracts.

## 4.4 LINEAR DEPENDENCE AND INDEPENDENCE

*Linear Dependence, Linear Independence, Application*

In this section we introduce the very important notion of linear independence of a set of vectors. The fundamental idea is fairly simple. In generating linear combinations of vectors, we wish to avoid redundancies by using the fewest possible vectors in the initial set; thus these vectors should not be related to or dependent upon one another. We will formulate these ideas in precise language and then develop procedures for working with them. At the end of the section the practical role of the idea of linear independence will be illustrated in a production model.

### LINEAR DEPENDENCE

Many different sets of vectors can be chosen to span a given subspace, but it is desirable to use the smallest possible number of vectors. A set of vectors that is used to span a subspace should be free of internal relationships and dependencies so that each vector acts as an independent agent in the formation of linear combinations. In fact, if superfluous vectors are present, they could create possible confusion in the formation of linear combinations.

For example, consider the vectors

$$\mathbf{u}_1 = (1, 2), \quad \mathbf{u}_2 = (2, 1), \quad \mathbf{u}_3 = (3, 3)$$

in $R^2$. See Figure 4.25. Any of these vectors can be written in terms of the other two. Indeed, we have

$$\mathbf{u}_1 = \mathbf{u}_3 - \mathbf{u}_2, \quad \mathbf{u}_2 = \mathbf{u}_3 - \mathbf{u}_1, \quad \mathbf{u}_3 = \mathbf{u}_1 + \mathbf{u}_2$$

Other vectors can be written in terms of these three vectors in a variety of ways. For instance, the vector $\mathbf{v} = (7, 8)$ can be written as a linear combination of the vectors in the following ways:

$$\mathbf{v} = 2\mathbf{u}_1 + \mathbf{u}_2 + \mathbf{u}_3 = 3\mathbf{u}_1 + 2\mathbf{u}_2 = \mathbf{u}_1 + 2\mathbf{u}_3 = -\mathbf{u}_2 + 3\mathbf{u}_3$$

One of the vectors could be discarded and we would still be left with the same span, namely, all of $R^2$. This is an example of vectors being dependent on one another.

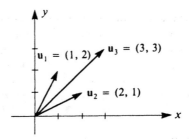

**FIGURE 4.25** *A dependent set of vectors in $R^2$*

The precise formulation we need is given in the following definition.

### DEFINITION

The set of $k$ (where $k \geq 2$) vectors $\mathbf{u}_1, \ldots, \mathbf{u}_k$ in $R^n$ is said to be **linearly dependent** if one or more of the vectors can be written as a linear combination of the other vectors. The set of vectors is called **linearly independent** if it is not linearly dependent. A set $\{\mathbf{u}\}$ that consists of a single vector $\mathbf{u}$ is called linearly dependent if and only if $\mathbf{u}$ is the zero vector.

The vectors $\mathbf{u}_1, \mathbf{u}_2, \mathbf{u}_3$ given above are linearly dependent, or more simply, dependent, because any one of the three vectors can be written as a linear combination of the other two. In general, it is not feasible to test a set of vectors for linear dependence or independence by conducting a search to see which vectors, if any, can be written as a linear combination of the other vectors. A more convenient criterion is needed so that no individual vector plays a distinguished role. The following theorem provides a criterion for linear dependence that can be applied in a straightforward manner.

### THEOREM 1    (Dependence Criterion)

The vectors $\mathbf{u}_1, \ldots, \mathbf{u}_k$ in $R^n$ are linearly dependent if and only if there exist scalars $c_1, c_2, \ldots, c_k$, with at least one of the scalars *not* zero, such that

$$(*) \qquad c_1\mathbf{u}_1 + c_2\mathbf{u}_2 + \cdots + c_k\mathbf{u}_k = \mathbf{0}$$

An equation of the type (*) in which some of the scalars are nonzero is called a **dependency equation**. The condition that at least one scalar is nonzero is essential to have linear dependence. Note that if $c_j \neq 0$, then $\mathbf{u}_j$ can be written as a linear combination of the other vectors. For example, if we have the dependency equation $\mathbf{u}_1 + \mathbf{u}_2 - \mathbf{u}_3 = \mathbf{0}$, then since each $\mathbf{u}_j$ has a nonzero coefficient, we can write any one of the vectors in terms of the other two, as was done above. Conversely, if one vector is written as a linear combination of the others, it can be moved across the equality sign to give us a dependency equation. For example, the equality $u_3 = u_1 + u_2$ can be rewritten as the dependency equation $u_1 + u_2 - u_3 = 0$.

The case of two vectors is easy to handle, since two vectors are linearly dependent if and only if each is a multiple of the other, that is, they are collinear. In this event a dependency equation is quickly obtained.

**EXAMPLE 1**   Show that the vectors $u_1 = (-6, 2)$ and $u_2 = (9, -3)$ are linearly dependent.

**SOLUTION**   We observe that $u_1$ and $u_2$ are multiples of the same vector $v = (3, -1)$. That is, we have

$$u_1 = -2(3, -1), \quad u_2 = 3(3, -1)$$

Therefore we have $u_2 = -\frac{3}{2}u_1$. If we multiply by 2 and move the terms to the same side of the equality, we get the dependency equation $3u_1 + 2u_2 = 0$. Thus the vectors are linearly dependent. See Figure 4.26.  ▌▌

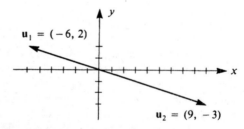

**FIGURE 4.26**                    *The vectors $u_1$ and $u_2$ are linearly dependent*

The linear dependence of three vectors in $R^3$ has a similar geometric interpretation. If the span of the three vectors is a plane, then one of the vectors will be a linear combination of the other two. We encountered examples of this type in the preceding section, though the formal term "linear dependence" was not used. To handle these and more general situations, we need to develop a systematic procedure for determining if a set of vectors is dependent or not in terms of homogeneous systems. This will be done shortly.

## LINEAR INDEPENDENCE

Linear independence is the opposite of linear dependence. A set of two or more vectors is linearly independent if none of the vectors can be written as a linear combination of the others. The following criterion for linear independence is obtained by negating the dependence criterion of Theorem 1.

### THEOREM 2    (*Independence Criterion*)

The vectors $\mathbf{u}_1, \mathbf{u}_2, \ldots, \mathbf{u}_k$ in $R^n$ are linearly independent if and only if the scalars that satisfy

$$(*) \qquad c_1\mathbf{u}_1 + c_2\mathbf{u}_2 + \cdots + c_k\mathbf{u}_k = \mathbf{0}$$

are $c_1 = 0,\ c_2 = 0,\ \ldots,\ c_k = 0$.

---

The criteria for linear dependence and independence can be formulated in terms of whether or not a homogeneous system of equations has nonzero solutions or only the zero solution. If we write the vectors $\mathbf{u}_1, \ldots, \mathbf{u}_k$ as columns, then the vector equation $(*)$ that determines dependence or independence corresponds to a homogeneous system of equations in the unknowns $c_1, \ldots, c_k$ whose coefficient matrix $U = [\mathbf{u}_1, \ldots, \mathbf{u}_k]$ has columns equal to the given vectors. The question of whether some scalars in the linear combination are nonzero becomes the question of whether or not the system has nonzero solutions.

The following example develops this approach for testing linear dependence and independence.

**EXAMPLE 2**  Determine if the vectors $\mathbf{u}_1 = (1, 2, -2, -1)$, $\mathbf{u}_2 = (2, 1, -1, -2)$, and $\mathbf{u}_3 = (1, -4, 4, -1)$ are linearly dependent or independent. If they are dependent, find a dependency equation, and then write one of the vectors as a linear combination of the others.

SOLUTION  Writing the vectors as columns, we must determine if the vector equation

$$c_1 \begin{bmatrix} 1 \\ 2 \\ -2 \\ -1 \end{bmatrix} + c_2 \begin{bmatrix} 2 \\ 1 \\ -1 \\ -2 \end{bmatrix} + c_3 \begin{bmatrix} 1 \\ -4 \\ 4 \\ -1 \end{bmatrix} = \begin{bmatrix} 0 \\ 0 \\ 0 \\ 0 \end{bmatrix}$$

has a solution $(c_1, c_2, c_3)$ other than the zero solution $(0, 0, 0)$. By equating components we obtain the homogeneous system

$$\begin{aligned} c_1 + 2c_2 + c_3 &= 0 \\ 2c_1 + c_2 - 4c_3 &= 0 \\ -2c_1 - c_2 + 4c_3 &= 0 \\ -c_1 - 2c_2 - c_3 &= 0 \end{aligned}$$

The system has the coefficient matrix $U$ whose columns are the given vectors:

$$U = \begin{bmatrix} 1 & 2 & 1 \\ 2 & 1 & -4 \\ -2 & -1 & 4 \\ -1 & -2 & -1 \end{bmatrix}$$

To determine if the system has nonzero solutions, we apply a sequence of row operations to put the matrix into row echelon form. Since the rightmost column of the augmented matrix would be all 0s for a homogeneous system, we will not explicitly display it. We get the row echelon form

$$E = \begin{bmatrix} 1 & 2 & 1 \\ 0 & 1 & 2 \\ 0 & 0 & 0 \\ 0 & 0 & 0 \end{bmatrix}$$

At this stage, since only two of the three columns of $E$ have leading 1s, we know that nonzero solutions exist, and hence we can conclude that the vectors are linearly dependent without further work.

However, since a dependency equation is requested, we must proceed further. The next step is to move to the reduced echelon form

$$\begin{bmatrix} 1 & 0 & -3 \\ 0 & 1 & 2 \end{bmatrix}$$

where the rows of 0s have been deleted. From this we obtain the solutions $c_1 = 3t$, $c_2 = -2t$, $c_3 = t$. Since only one particular solution is needed, we may set $t = 1$ and get $c_1 = 3$, $c_2 = -2$, $c_3 = 1$. This solution gives us the dependency equation

$$3\mathbf{u}_1 - 2\mathbf{u}_2 + \mathbf{u}_3 = \mathbf{0}$$

Thus we can write either

$$\mathbf{u}_1 = \frac{2}{3}\mathbf{u}_2 - \frac{1}{3}\mathbf{u}_3$$

or

$$\mathbf{u}_2 = \frac{3}{2}\mathbf{u}_1 + \frac{1}{2}\mathbf{u}_3$$

or

$$\mathbf{u}_3 = -3\mathbf{u}_1 + 2\mathbf{u}_2 \quad \blacksquare$$

The steps in the preceding example can be identified to formulate a general procedure for testing whether a set of vectors is linearly independent or dependent. The criteria of Theorems 1 and 2 are restated as follows.

### Independence/Dependence Test for $\mathbf{u}_1, \ldots, \mathbf{u}_k$

1. Form the matrix $U = [\mathbf{u}_1, \ldots, \mathbf{u}_k]$ whose columns are the given vectors. Then the vector equation

$$c_1\mathbf{u}_1 + \cdots + c_k\mathbf{u}_k = \mathbf{0}$$

corresponds to the homogeneous system

$$U \begin{bmatrix} c_1 \\ \vdots \\ c_k \end{bmatrix} = \mathbf{0}$$

2. Row reduce $U$ to a row echelon from $E$. Determine those columns of $E$ that contain a leading 1.

3. If each column of $E$ has a leading 1, then the vectors are linearly independent. In this case the homogeneous system has only the zero solution.

4. If some columns of $E$ do not have leading 1s, then the vectors are linearly dependent. If a dependency equation is needed, then go to reduced echelon form and find a solution to the homogeneous system.

Note that the number of leading 1s in $E$ is the same as the number of nonzero rows in $E$, that is, the row rank of $U$. Thus if the row rank of $U$ is the same as the number of vectors, then the vectors are linearly independent. Otherwise, if the row rank is less than the number of vectors, then the vectors are linearly dependent.

The procedure is illustrated in the following examples.

**EXAMPLE 3**   Determine if the vectors $\mathbf{u}_1 = (1, 0, 1, 1)$, $\mathbf{u}_2 = (1, 1, -1, 2)$, $\mathbf{u}_3 = (1, 2, -2, 3)$ in $R^4$ are linearly dependent or independent.

SOLUTION   We write the vectors as columns and form the matrix

$$U = \begin{bmatrix} 1 & 1 & 1 \\ 0 & 1 & 2 \\ 1 & -1 & -2 \\ 1 & 2 & 3 \end{bmatrix}$$

Then we row operate to obtain the row echelon form

$$E = \begin{bmatrix} 1 & 1 & 1 \\ 0 & 1 & 2 \\ 0 & 0 & 1 \\ 0 & 0 & 0 \end{bmatrix}$$

Since every column has a leading 1, we conclude that the vectors are linearly independent. ∎

**EXAMPLE 4**   Show that the vectors $\mathbf{u}_1 = (1, 0, 0)$, $\mathbf{u}_2 = (a, 1, 0)$, $\mathbf{u}_3 = (b, c, 1)$ in $R^3$ are linearly independent, where $a, b, c$ are arbitrary numbers.

SOLUTION   The matrix $U$ corresponding to the vectors is

$$U = \begin{bmatrix} 1 & a & b \\ 0 & 1 & c \\ 0 & 0 & 1 \end{bmatrix}$$

The matrix $U$ is already in echelon form, and there are three leading 1s. Hence we deduce that the vectors $\mathbf{u}_1$, $\mathbf{u}_2$, $\mathbf{u}_3$ are linearly independent. ∎

We have seen earlier that a homogeneous system with more variables than equations will possess infinitely many solutions. (See Theorem 3 of Section 2.3.) In other terms, if $U$ has more columns than rows, then $U\mathbf{x} = \mathbf{0}$ has nonzero solutions. Thus we have the following theorem.

### THEOREM 3

Let $\mathbf{u}_1, \ldots, \mathbf{u}_k$ be vectors in $R^n$. If $k > n$, then the vectors are linearly dependent.

Thus if the number of vectors under consideration exceeds the number of components in each vector, then they are automatically linearly dependent. For example, we see that any set of three vectors in $R^2$—$(4, 2)$, $(-3, 1)$, $(5, -2)$, for example—must be linearly dependent. Similarly, a set of four or more vectors in $R^3$ is linearly dependent.

In the special case that $U$ is a square matrix, then there are alternative methods of determining if the column vectors of $U$ are linearly dependent or independent. If it happens that $U$ is an invertible matrix, then the homogeneous system has a unique solution, which implies that the zero solution is the only solution, and therefore the columns are linearly independent. On the other hand, if $U$ is not invertible, then nonzero solutions exist so that the columns are linearly dependent. (See Theorem 3 of Section 2 in Chapter 3.) Thus if $U$ is square, then the invertibility of $U$ is equivalent to the linear independence of the column vectors.

Since a square matrix $U$ is invertible if and only if $\det(U) \neq 0$, it follows that the column vectors of $U$ are linearly independent if $\det(U) \neq 0$ and linearly dependent if $\det(U) = 0$. In summary, we have the following theorem.

### THEOREM 4

Let $U$ be an $n \times n$ matrix. Then the following statements are all equivalent.
 (*i*) The columns of $U$ are linearly independent.
 (*ii*) The matrix $U$ is invertible.
 (*iii*) The determinant of $U$ is not zero.

Attempting to invert a matrix is not a practical test for independence, since the computations can be lengthy. On the other hand, the determinant can provide a convenient test if the matrix is not large.

**EXAMPLE 5** Determine if the vectors

$$\mathbf{u}_1 = (1, 2, 1), \quad \mathbf{u}_2 = (3, 1, 2), \quad \mathbf{u}_3 = (2, 5, 1)$$

are linearly independent or not.

**SOLUTION** The matrix whose columns are the given vectors is

$$U = \begin{bmatrix} 1 & 3 & 2 \\ 2 & 1 & 5 \\ 1 & 2 & 1 \end{bmatrix}$$

Since the determinant of this square matrix is $\det(U) = 6$, we conclude that the vectors $\mathbf{u}_1, \mathbf{u}_2, \mathbf{u}_3$ are linearly independent. ▮▮

### APPLICATION

We now apply the concepts of linear independence and linear dependence to a production model.

**EXAMPLE 6**    The ACDC Motor Company manufactures 2-hp, 1-hp, and $\frac{1}{2}$-hp 400-cycle motors on four assembly lines in their Southwood plant. The hourly production for the four lines is given in the following table:

|         | Line 1 | Line 2 | Line 3 | Line 4 |
|---------|--------|--------|--------|--------|
| 2-hp    | 1      | 3      | 3      | 2      |
| 1-hp    | 2      | 5      | 5      | 3      |
| $\frac{1}{2}$-hp | 4 | 8 | 9 | 7 |

The plant is wholly dedicated to meet the exact requirements of a military contract which is for 82 2-hp, 137 1-hp, and 259 $\frac{1}{2}$-hp motors per day. This demand is currently met by 10 hours on line 1, 6 hours on line 2, 12 hours on line 3, and 9 hours on line 4. If possible, the company would like to close one of the lines and shift the production to the other lines. Determine if this is possible; if so, what are the other feasible production schedules?

SOLUTION    Let the production vectors for the four lines be $\mathbf{u}_1 = (1, 2, 4)$, $\mathbf{u}_2 = (3, 5, 8)$, $\mathbf{u}_3 = (3, 5, 9)$, $\mathbf{u}_4 = (2, 3, 7)$, respectively, and let the production demand vector be $\mathbf{b} = (82, 137, 259)$. Then we are given the solution

$$10\mathbf{u}_1 + 6\mathbf{u}_2 + 12\mathbf{u}_3 + 9\mathbf{u}_4 = \mathbf{b}$$

and we are asked if it is possible to eliminate one of the vectors from the solution.

First we examine the question of linear independence or dependence of the lines. Since we have four vectors in $R^3$, we know from Theorem 3 that they must be linearly dependent. To find a dependency equation, we solve the system $U\mathbf{c} = \mathbf{0}$ where $U$ has the columns $\mathbf{u}_1$, $\mathbf{u}_2$, $\mathbf{u}_3$, $\mathbf{u}_4$ and $\mathbf{c} = (c_j)$ is a vector of coefficients. The matrix $U$ may be row reduced to

$$\begin{bmatrix} 1 & 0 & 0 & -1 \\ 0 & 1 & 0 & -2 \\ 0 & 0 & 1 & 3 \end{bmatrix}$$

so that the solutions are of the form $(t, 2t, -3t, t)$, where $t$ is any number. Let $t = 1$; then the dependency equation is

$$\mathbf{u}_1 + 2\mathbf{u}_2 - 3\mathbf{u}_3 + \mathbf{u}_4 = \mathbf{0}$$

Since all vectors appear with a nonzero coefficient, the output of any of the lines can be obtained by a linear combination of the other lines.

The possibilities are:

1. $\mathbf{u}_1 = -2\mathbf{u}_2 + 3\mathbf{u}_3 - \mathbf{u}_4$

2. $\mathbf{u}_2 = -\frac{1}{2}\mathbf{u}_1 + \frac{3}{2}\mathbf{u}_3 - \frac{1}{2}\mathbf{u}_4$

3. $\mathbf{u}_3 = \frac{1}{3}\mathbf{u}_1 + \frac{2}{3}\mathbf{u}_2 + \frac{1}{3}\mathbf{u}_4$

4. $\mathbf{u}_4 = -\mathbf{u}_1 - 2\mathbf{u}_2 + 3\mathbf{u}_3$

Three of these equations have negative coefficients. These must be interpreted as closing an assembly line for a period of time. We examine the possibilities.

1. One hour on line 1 is equivalent to closing line 2 for 2 hours, running line 3 for 3 extra hours, and closing line 4 for 1 hour. On substituting into the current schedule we obtain

$$10(-2\mathbf{u}_2 + 3\mathbf{u}_3 - \mathbf{u}_4) + 6\mathbf{u}_2 + 12\mathbf{u}_3 + 9\mathbf{u}_4 = \mathbf{b}$$

or

$$-14\mathbf{u}_2 + 42\mathbf{u}_3 - \mathbf{u}_4 = \mathbf{b}$$

Thus line 2 must be run for $-14$ hours, line 3 for 42 hours, and line 4 for $-1$ hour a day. None of this is feasible.

2. One hour on line 2 is equivalent to closing line 1 for $\frac{1}{2}$ hour, running line 2 for $\frac{3}{2}$ hours extra, and closing line 4 for $\frac{1}{2}$ hour. On substituting into the original schedule we obtain

$$10\mathbf{u}_1 + 6\left(-\frac{1}{2}\mathbf{u}_1 + \frac{3}{2}\mathbf{u}_3 - \frac{1}{2}\mathbf{u}_4\right) + 12\mathbf{u}_3 + 9\mathbf{u}_4 = \mathbf{b}$$

or

$$7\mathbf{u}_1 + 21\mathbf{u}_3 + 6\mathbf{u}_4 = \mathbf{b}$$

This is a feasible schedule. It is somewhat unbalanced, since two lines run for less than one shift while the third runs for almost three shifts. Management may or may not find this attractive.

3. One hour on line 3 is equivalent to $\frac{1}{3}$ hour on line 1 plus $\frac{2}{3}$ hour on line 2 plus $\frac{1}{3}$ hour on line 4. This is the only possibility in which the solution is guaranteed to stay nonnegative. However, it could happen that a line would be run for more than 24 hours. We substitute into the original schedule to obtain

$$10\mathbf{u}_1 + 6\mathbf{u}_2 + 12\left(\frac{1}{3}\mathbf{u}_1 + \frac{2}{3}\mathbf{u}_2 + \frac{1}{3}\mathbf{u}_4\right) + 9\mathbf{u}_4 = \mathbf{b}$$

or

$$14\mathbf{u}_1 + 14\mathbf{u}_2 + 13\mathbf{u}_4 = \mathbf{b}$$

Here we have a balanced, feasible schedule. Lines 1 and 2 run for 14 hours each, while line 4 runs for 13 hours.

4. One hour on line 4 is equivalent to closing line 1 for 1 hour, closing line 2 for 2 hours, and running line 3 for 3 extra hours. We substitute into the original schedule to obtain

$$10\mathbf{u}_1 + 6\mathbf{u}_2 + 12\mathbf{u}_3 + 9(-\mathbf{u}_1 - 2\mathbf{u}_2 + 3\mathbf{u}_3) = \mathbf{b}$$

or

$$\mathbf{u}_1 - 12\mathbf{u}_2 + 39\mathbf{u}_3 = \mathbf{b}$$

In this case the new schedule is not feasible, since line 2 is run a negative amount and line 3 is run more hours than there are in a day.

Thus management can choose the unbalanced schedule given by (2) or the balanced schedule given by (3).

The issue of feasibility, which we have treated here in a somewhat ad hoc manner, is easily dealt with by the simplex machinery, as we will see in Section 4.7. ∎

## EXERCISES 4.4

In Exercises 1–6, use the given dependency equation to write one of the vectors as a linear combination of the others.

**1.** $2(1, 0, -4) - 3(2, -1, 1) + (4, -3, 11) = (0, 0, 0)$

**2.** $(6, 2, -8) + 4(-1, 3, 3) + 2(-1, -7, -2) = (0, 0, 0)$

**3.** $-(2, 1, 0, -3) + 2(2, 3, 1, -1) + 3(-1, -3, 2, 4) + (1, 4, -8, -5) = \mathbf{0}$

**4.** $3(-1, 2, -2, 1) + 2(2, -3, 1, -4) - 4(1, 2, -2, -2) + (3, 8, -4, -3) = \mathbf{0}$

**5.** $3\mathbf{u}_1 + 2\mathbf{u}_2 + \mathbf{u}_3 - 5\mathbf{u}_4 = \mathbf{0}$

**6.** $-4\mathbf{u}_1 - \mathbf{u}_2 + 5\mathbf{u}_3 + 7\mathbf{u}_4 = \mathbf{0}$

In Exercises 7–12, show that the given vectors are linearly dependent, find a dependency equation, and then write one of the vectors as a linear combination of the others.

**7.** $(1, 4), (2, -4), (-2, 7)$  **8.** $(1, -3), (6, 2), (2, 4)$

**9.** $(2, 3, -5), (-4, -1, 3), (-8, 3, -1)$  **10.** $(3, -2, 4), (6, -3, 5), (-6, 0, 4)$

**11.** $(-2, 5, 1, -3), (4, -2, 3, -4), (2, 11, 9, -17), (8, 4, 11, -18)$

**12.** $(-3, 2, 4, -3), (3, -1, 1, 2), (-6, 6, 18, -8), (12, -5, -1, 9)$

In Exercises 13–22, show that the given vectors are linearly independent.

**13.** $(7, 6, 4), (8, 2, 0), (-5, 0, 0)$  **14.** $(-9, 2, 6), (7, 4, 0), (8, 0, 0)$

In Exercises 15–16, let $a, c, f$ be any nonzero numbers and $b, d, e$ any numbers.

**15.** $(a, 0, 0), (b, c, 0), (d, e, f)$  **16.** $(0, 0, a), (0, c, b), (f, e, d)$

17. $(-2, 3), (4, 5)$

18. $(3, -1), (9, 2)$

19. $(1, -3, 5), (2, -5, 8), (-2, 4, 5)$

20. $(-1, 3, -4), (5, -12, 15), (-2, 3, 5)$

21. $(2, 3, -5, -2), (4, -4, -11, -2), (-4, -2, 6, 5)$

22. $(3, 5, 6, 4), (-3, -2, 4, -5), (6, 9, 7, 2)$

In Exercises 23–28, determine if the given vectors are linearly independent or dependent. If they are linearly dependent, then find a dependency equation.

23. $(-5, 4, -1), (-5, 3, 1), (4, -2, 1)$

24. $(1, -1, -3), (-3, 2, 7), (1, 0, -2)$

25. $(2, -2, 3), (-4, 5, -1), (4, -3, 11)$

26. $(3, -5, 3), (6, -2, 7), (9, 1, 11)$

27. $(1, -2, 1), (1, -1, 0), (-2, 6, 5)$

28. $(1, -1, 2), (-1, 2, 3), (1, -2, 4)$

In Exercises 29–38, apply Theorem 3 or 4 to establish linear dependence or independence of the given set of vectors.

29. $(6, 1), (5, 2)$

30. $(-2, 5), (6, -15)$

31. $(8, 3), (-16, -6)$

32. $(-9, 1), (5, -2)$

33. $(8, 1), (6, -3), (4, 5)$

34. $(2, -4), (7, 3), (5, -1)$

35. $(3, 1, 0), (2, -2, 1), (3, 0, 2)$

36. $(2, 0, 5), (4, -1, 3), (0, 5, -4)$

37. $(4, 1, 5), (6, 8, -2), (9, -9, 3), (1, -7, 4)$

38. $(8, 1, 9), (2, -5, 4), (3, -3, 7), (8, 2, -2)$

In Exercises 39–42, find a value of $k$ such that the given vectors are linearly dependent.

39. $(1, 0, 1), (0, 1, 3), (2, k, -1)$

40. $(-1, 1, 3), (2, -3, 4), (3, k, 1)$

41. $(0, 2, 1), (-1, 1, k), (1, k, 3)$

42. $(1, k, -2), (0, 2, -1), (4, 4, k)$

In Exercises 43–44 a company meets its production schedule by operating four plants. Determine if it is possible to close one of the plants and meet the production demands with only three. If so, what are the feasible production schedules?

43. Zephyr Shoe manufactures spikes, training flats, and running flats in four plants. The daily production (in 100s) for the four plants is given in the following table:

| (100) | Plant 1 | Plant 2 | Plant 3 | Plant 4 |
|---|---|---|---|---|
| Spikes | 1 | 2 | 2 | 1 |
| Training flats | 3 | 7 | 5 | 0 |
| Running flats | 5 | 8 | 11 | 10 |

The company has contracted to provide 1800 spikes, 5100 training flats, and 9300 running flats per week to a national retailing organization. This demand is currently met by 6 days at plant one, 4 days at plant two, 1 day at plant three, and 2 days at plant four.

**44.** The Kirkwood Apparel Company manufactures knitted sweaters, hats, and gloves in each of four plants. The daily production (in 100s) for the four plants is given in the following table:

| (100) | Plant 1 | Plant 2 | Plant 3 | Plant 4 |
|---|---|---|---|---|
| Sweaters | 1 | 4 | 3 | 7 |
| Hats | 2 | 7 | 8 | 8 |
| Gloves | 3 | 10 | 12 | 11 |

The company has contracted to provide 4700 sweaters, 8600 hats, and 12,500 gloves per week to the Navy. This demand is currently met by 5 days at plant one, 4 days at plant two, 4 days at plant three, and 2 days at plant four.

## 4.5  BASES AND BASIS SELECTION

*Basis Vectors, Pivots and Vector Replacement, Basis Selection, Application*

In this section we will begin to tie together the concepts that were introduced in the previous sections. Suppose we have a subspace $S$ of $R^n$, which may be all of $R^n$ or the column space or the null-space of a matrix, for example. The idea of a spanning set can be applied so that each vector in $S$ can be written as a linear combination of a fixed set of vectors. The idea of linear independence is important, since it is desirable that the set of spanning vectors does not contain extraneous vectors and thereby produce redundancies. Putting these ideas together, we seek a set of linearly independent vectors that span $S$. A set of vectors with these two properties is called a "basis" for $S$. In a sense, the study of the subspace $S$ is reduced to the study of these basis vectors, since knowledge of the basis vectors can be extrapolated to gain information about all of $S$. Thus the notion of basis is fundamental in linear algebra.

If a spanning set of vectors happens to be linearly dependent, then we are faced with the problem of selecting vectors from the set in such a way that the chosen vectors are independent and still span the same space. In other words, we wish to select a basis from the given spanning set. We will develop a method of vector replacement that is based on the operation of pivoting and then use it to select basis vectors from a given set. This method will also be put to use in Section 4.7 on the vector formulation of the simplex method of solving linear programs.

## BASIS VECTORS

When the concepts of span and linear independence are combined, we obtain the following definition.

---

**DEFINITION**

Let $S$ be a subspace of $R^n$. The set $\{\mathbf{u}_1, \ldots, \mathbf{u}_k\}$ of vectors in $S$ is called a **basis** for $S$ if both

(i) the vectors $\mathbf{u}_1, \ldots, \mathbf{u}_k$ are linearly independent and
(ii) $S$ is spanned by $\mathbf{u}_1, \ldots, \mathbf{u}_k$.

Each vector in a basis is called a **basis vector**.

---

Thus a basis is a spanning set of linearly independent vectors. For the vector space $R^n$ we will use the term **standard basis vectors** to refer to the vectors

$$\mathbf{e}_1 = \begin{bmatrix} 1 \\ 0 \\ \vdots \\ 0 \end{bmatrix}, \quad \mathbf{e}_2 = \begin{bmatrix} 0 \\ 1 \\ \vdots \\ 0 \end{bmatrix}, \quad \ldots, \quad \mathbf{e}_n = \begin{bmatrix} 0 \\ 0 \\ \vdots \\ 1 \end{bmatrix}$$

These vectors are the columns of the identity matrix $I_n$. Since they are linearly independent and since each vector $\mathbf{x} = (x_1, \ldots, x_n)$ in $R^n$ can be written

$$\mathbf{x} = x_1\mathbf{e}_1 + \cdots + x_n\mathbf{e}_n$$

the set $\{\mathbf{e}_1, \ldots, \mathbf{e}_n\}$ has the two properties required to be a basis for $R^n$.

In the following example we find a basis for a plane through the origin in $R^3$.

**EXAMPLE 1** The set $S$ of vectors $\mathbf{v} = (x, y, z)$ in $R^3$ such that $x - 2y - z = 0$ is a subspace of $R^3$. Find a basis for $S$.

SOLUTION   If we let $y = s$ and $z = t$, then we have $x = 2s + t$ so that each vector $\mathbf{v}$ in $S$ can be written

$$\mathbf{v} = \begin{bmatrix} x \\ y \\ z \end{bmatrix} = \begin{bmatrix} 2s + t \\ s \\ t \end{bmatrix} = s \begin{bmatrix} 2 \\ 1 \\ 0 \end{bmatrix} + t \begin{bmatrix} 1 \\ 0 \\ 1 \end{bmatrix}$$

Therefore if we let $\mathbf{u}_1 = (2, 1, 0)$ and $\mathbf{u}_2 = (1, 0, 1)$, then $\mathbf{v} = s\mathbf{u}_1 + t\mathbf{u}_2$ so that $S$ is the span of $\mathbf{u}_1$ and $\mathbf{u}_2$. (Note that $\mathbf{u}_1$ and $\mathbf{u}_2$ can be obtained by setting $s = 1$, $t = 0$ and $s = 0$, $t = 1$, respectively.) Furthermore, the vectors $\mathbf{u}_1$, $\mathbf{u}_2$ are linearly independent, which we leave to the reader to verify. Hence the vectors $\mathbf{u}_1$, $\mathbf{u}_2$ form a basis for $S$. (See Figure 4.27.) ▮▮

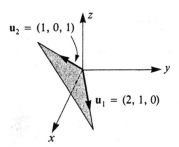

**FIGURE 4.27**                    *The plane $x - 2y - z = 0$*

Many different bases can be selected for the same space. In the following example we have another basis for $R^3$.

**EXAMPLE 2**   Show that the vectors $\mathbf{u}_1 = (1, 0, 1)$, $\mathbf{u}_2 = (0, 1, 1)$, $\mathbf{u}_3 = (1, 1, 0)$ are a basis for $R^3$. Then write $\mathbf{b} = (2, -2, 4)$ as a linear combination of $\mathbf{u}_1, \mathbf{u}_2, \mathbf{u}_3$.

**SOLUTION**   To show that the vectors are linearly independent, we can show that the matrix

$$U = \begin{bmatrix} 1 & 0 & 1 \\ 0 & 1 & 1 \\ 1 & 1 & 0 \end{bmatrix}$$

has the nonzero determinant $\det(U) = -2$, so that the matrix $U$ is invertible. Then the invertibility of $U$ implies that its column vectors are linearly independent by Theorem 4 of the preceding section.

To see that the columns of $U$ span all of $R^3$, note that since $U$ is invertible the system $U\mathbf{x} = \mathbf{b}$ has a solution for any choice of $\mathbf{b}$ in $R^3$, namely, $\mathbf{x} = U^{-1}\mathbf{b}$. In this example we find the inverse

$$U^{-1} = \frac{1}{2} \begin{bmatrix} 1 & -1 & 1 \\ -1 & 1 & 1 \\ 1 & 1 & -1 \end{bmatrix}$$

Then, for any specific $\mathbf{b}$, say, $\mathbf{b} = (2, -2, 4)$, we have $\mathbf{x} = U^{-1}\mathbf{b} = (4, 0, -2)$. Thus $\mathbf{b} = 4\mathbf{u}_1 - 2\mathbf{u}_3$. Since $\mathbf{u}_1, \mathbf{u}_2, \mathbf{u}_3$ are linearly independent and span $R^3$, we conclude that they are a basis for $R^3$.   ∎

We noted in the above example that the invertibility of a matrix is related to both spans and linear independence. In general, the column vectors of an invertible $n \times n$ matrix will form a basis for $R^n$. We have the following theorem.

*THEOREM 1*

The column vectors of an $n \times n$ matrix form a basis for $R^n$ if and only if the matrix is invertible.

One important consequence of having a basis for a subspace $S$ is that any vector $\mathbf{v}$ in $S$ has a *unique* representation as a linear combination of the basis vectors. This uniqueness is a consequence of the linear independence of the basis vectors. We have the following theorem.

### THEOREM 2

Let $\{\mathbf{u}_1, \ldots, \mathbf{u}_k\}$ be a basis for the subspace $S$ of $R^n$. Then for any $\mathbf{v}$ in $S$, there are unique scalars $c_1, \ldots, c_k$ such that $\mathbf{v} = c_1\mathbf{u}_1 + \cdots + c_k\mathbf{u}_k$.

**Proof.** Since a basis spans $S$, we know that each $\mathbf{v}$ in $S$ can be written as a linear combination of the basis vectors. Suppose $\mathbf{v}$ can be written as

$$\mathbf{v} = c_1\mathbf{u}_1 + \cdots + c_k\mathbf{u}_k$$

and also as

$$\mathbf{v} = d_1\mathbf{u}_1 + \cdots + d_k\mathbf{u}_k$$

If we subtract, we get

$$(c_1 - d_1)\mathbf{u}_1 + \cdots + (c_k - d_k)\mathbf{u}_k = \mathbf{v} - \mathbf{v} = \mathbf{0}$$

Since $\mathbf{u}_1, \ldots, \mathbf{u}_k$ are linearly independent, we have $c_1 - d_1 = 0, \ldots, c_k - d_k = 0$ and hence $c_1 = d_1, \ldots, c_k = d_k$. Thus the scalars used to obtain $\mathbf{v}$ are uniquely determined. ∎

## PIVOTS AND VECTOR REPLACEMENT

Pivot operations have been used in Gauss-Jordan elimination and the simplex algorithm in linear programming. We now show how pivoting can be interpreted in terms of vector replacement. We will then use pivoting as a method of deriving linear relationships between vectors and as a method of selecting a basis from a given set of vectors.

Consider the matrix

$$A = \begin{bmatrix} 1 & 1 & 5 \\ 1 & -1 & 3 \end{bmatrix}$$

Each column can be written in terms of the standard basis vectors $\mathbf{e}_1 = (1, 0)$ and $\mathbf{e}_2 = (0, 1)$ as follows:

$$\mathbf{a}_1 = (1, 1) = (1, 0) + (0, 1) = \mathbf{e}_1 + \mathbf{e}_2$$
$$\mathbf{a}_2 = (1, -1) = (1, 0) + (0, -1) = (1, 0) - (0, 1) = \mathbf{e}_1 - \mathbf{e}_2$$
$$\mathbf{a}_3 = (5, 3) = (5, 0) + (0, 3) = 5(1, 0) + 3(0, 1) = 5\mathbf{e}_1 + 3\mathbf{e}_2$$

These relationships can be displayed by labeling the columns of the matrix with

$\mathbf{a}_1, \mathbf{a}_2, \mathbf{a}_3$ and labeling the rows with $\mathbf{e}_1, \mathbf{e}_2$ as shown below

$$\begin{array}{c} \quad \mathbf{a}_1 \quad \mathbf{a}_2 \quad \mathbf{a}_3 \\ \begin{array}{c} \mathbf{e}_1 \\ \mathbf{e}_2 \end{array} \begin{bmatrix} 1 & 1 & 5 \\ 1 & -1 & 3 \end{bmatrix} \end{array}$$

We call this labeled matrix a **dependency table**, since it displays how each vector $\mathbf{a}_1, \mathbf{a}_2, \mathbf{a}_3$ on the top can be written as a linear combination of the vectors $\mathbf{e}_1, \mathbf{e}_2$ listed on the left-hand side.

Let us now perform a pivot operation on the corner entry 1 in the $\mathbf{a}_1$ column and the $\mathbf{e}_1$ row. The result of this pivot is the following dependency table, where the vector $\mathbf{e}_1$ has been replaced by the vector $\mathbf{a}_1$.

$$\begin{array}{c} \quad \mathbf{a}_1 \quad \mathbf{a}_2 \quad \mathbf{a}_3 \\ \begin{array}{c} \mathbf{a}_1 \\ \mathbf{e}_2 \end{array} \begin{bmatrix} 1 & 1 & 5 \\ 0 & -2 & -2 \end{bmatrix} \end{array}$$

The columns now tell us how the vectors above the columns can be written as linear combinations of the vectors $\mathbf{a}_1, \mathbf{e}_2$ on the side. That is, we have the dependency relations:

column 1:  $\mathbf{a}_1 = \mathbf{a}_1$
column 2:  $\mathbf{a}_2 = \mathbf{a}_1 - 2\mathbf{e}_2$
column 3:  $\mathbf{a}_3 = 5\mathbf{a}_1 - 2\mathbf{e}_2$

If we now pivot on the entry $-2$ in the $\mathbf{a}_2$ column and $\mathbf{e}_2$ row, we obtain

$$\begin{array}{c} \quad \mathbf{a}_1 \quad \mathbf{a}_2 \quad \mathbf{a}_3 \\ \begin{array}{c} \mathbf{a}_1 \\ \mathbf{a}_2 \end{array} \begin{bmatrix} 1 & 0 & 4 \\ 0 & 1 & 1 \end{bmatrix} \end{array}$$

We interpret the columns to mean that

column 1:  $\mathbf{a}_1 = \mathbf{a}_1$
column 2:  $\mathbf{a}_2 = \mathbf{a}_2$
column 3:  $\mathbf{a}_3 = 4\mathbf{a}_1 + \mathbf{a}_2$

Thus we may conclude that $\mathbf{a}_1, \mathbf{a}_2$ are linearly independent and that $\mathbf{a}_3 = 4\mathbf{a}_1 + \mathbf{a}_2$.

Each pivot operation corresponds to a vector replacement in the dependency table. In general, if we have an $n \times k$ matrix with column vectors $\mathbf{a}_1, \dots, \mathbf{a}_k$, and if the vectors $\mathbf{e}_1, \dots, \mathbf{e}_n$ are listed on the left-hand side, then we can pivot at any nonzero entry. The effect of pivoting at the $(i, j)$-entry is to replace the vector $\mathbf{e}_i$ on the side of the matrix by the vector $\mathbf{a}_j$, as indicated in the following diagrams.

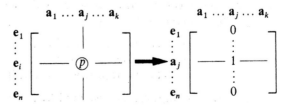

The columns of the new table contain the scalars that are required to write each $\mathbf{a}_1, \ldots, \mathbf{a}_k$ as a linear combination of the vectors $\mathbf{e}_1, \ldots, \mathbf{a}_j, \ldots, \mathbf{e}_n$ listed on the side. The key properties of this procedure are summarized as follows.

**Vector Replacement Procedure.**   Suppose that a pivot is made on the entry in row $i$ and column $j$ of a dependency table so that the vector that heads column $j$ replaces the vector that heads row $i$. Then the vectors listed on the left-hand side of the table always form a basis for $R^n$, and each column contains the unique scalars required to write the vector that heads the column as a linear combination of these basis vectors.

The pivot operations and corresponding vector replacements can be continued until the independent vectors are identified and the dependency relations of the other vectors are revealed. To illustrate the procedure, we will first solve a system $A\mathbf{x} = \mathbf{b}$ by expressing the vector $\mathbf{b}$ as a linear combination of the column vectors of $A$. Note how the pivot operations are employed as in Gauss-Jordan elimination, but now each pivot is interpreted as a vector replacement.

**EXAMPLE 3**   Solve the system of equations $A\mathbf{x} = \mathbf{b}$ by writing the vector $\mathbf{b} = (4, -5, 5)$ as a linear combination of $\mathbf{a}_1 = (2, 1, 3)$ and $\mathbf{a}_2 = (1, 4, 2)$, the column vectors of $A$.

**SOLUTION**   We write the augmented matrix as a dependency table and circle the first pivot entry.

$$
\begin{array}{c}
\mathbf{a}_1 \quad \mathbf{a}_2 \qquad \mathbf{b} \\
\begin{array}{c} \mathbf{e}_1 \\ \mathbf{e}_2 \\ \mathbf{e}_3 \end{array}
\left[
\begin{array}{cc|c}
2 & 1 & 4 \\
\textcircled{1} & 4 & -5 \\
3 & 2 & 5
\end{array}
\right]
\end{array}
$$

This particular pivot entry was chosen for numerical convenience. Any entry in the first two columns could have been chosen, but the third column must be excluded in this problem, since we are trying to write the third column as a linear combination of the first two columns.

After pivoting we obtain the following table, in which $\mathbf{e}_2$ has been replaced by $\mathbf{a}_1$. We have circled the next pivot, and to the right we have written the relations dictated by the columns.

$$
\begin{array}{c}
\mathbf{a}_1 \qquad \mathbf{a}_2 \qquad \mathbf{b} \\
\begin{array}{c} \mathbf{e}_1 \\ \mathbf{a}_1 \\ \mathbf{e}_3 \end{array}
\left[
\begin{array}{cc|c}
0 & \textcircled{-7} & 14 \\
1 & 4 & -5 \\
0 & -10 & 20
\end{array}
\right]
\end{array}
\qquad
\begin{array}{l}
\mathbf{a}_1 = \mathbf{a}_1 \\
\mathbf{a}_2 = -7\mathbf{e}_1 + 4\mathbf{a}_1 - 10\mathbf{e}_3 \\
\mathbf{b} = 14\mathbf{e}_1 - 5\mathbf{a}_1 + 20\mathbf{e}_3
\end{array}
$$

There are two possible choices for the pivot in the second column (first or third rows), and either will serve the purpose. We have chosen the entry in the first row as indicated by the circle. This choice of pivot leads to the following table, in which $e_1$ has been replaced by $a_2$. The dependency relations are written to the right.

$$
\begin{array}{c}
\phantom{a_2} \\
a_2 \\
a_1 \\
e_3
\end{array}
\begin{array}{cc}
a_1 & a_2 \\
\end{array}
\left[
\begin{array}{cc|c}
0 & 1 & -2 \\
1 & 0 & 3 \\
0 & 0 & 0
\end{array}
\right]
\qquad
\begin{array}{l}
a_1 = a_1 \\
a_2 = a_2 \\
b \ = -2a_2 + 3a_1
\end{array}
$$

Hence we have found that **b** can be written as the linear combination $b = -2a_2 + 3a_1$. The solution is $x_2 = -2$, $x_1 = 3$. ∎

## BASIS SELECTION

We now apply the method of vector replacement by means of pivots to solve the problem of selecting linearly independent vectors from a set of vectors. As we saw earlier, the column vectors of a matrix may not be linearly independent, and thus they need not constitute a basis for the column space. We would like to select a basis for the column space from the given column vectors and at the same time display the dependency of the remaining vectors on the selected vectors. This is accomplished by performing a sequence of pivots.

**EXAMPLE 4**    Select a basis for the column space of the matrix

$$
A = \begin{bmatrix}
0 & 2 & 4 & -2 \\
2 & -1 & 0 & 5 \\
1 & -2 & -3 & 4
\end{bmatrix}
$$

and write the remaining column vectors as linear combinations of the chosen basis vectors.

SOLUTION    We begin by labeling the matrix and selecting a nonzero entry as a pivot.

$$
\begin{array}{c}
\phantom{e_1} \\
e_1 \\
e_2 \\
e_3
\end{array}
\begin{array}{cccc}
a_1 & a_2 & a_3 & a_4
\end{array}
\left[
\begin{array}{cccc}
0 & 2 & 4 & -2 \\
2 & -1 & 0 & 5 \\
① & -2 & -3 & 4
\end{array}
\right]
$$

After pivoting on the circled entry we obtain the following matrix, in which $a_1$ has replaced $e_3$ on the side.

$$
\begin{array}{c}
\phantom{e_1} \\
e_1 \\
e_2 \\
a_1
\end{array}
\begin{array}{cccc}
a_1 & a_2 & a_3 & a_4
\end{array}
\left[
\begin{array}{cccc}
0 & ② & 4 & -2 \\
0 & 3 & 6 & -3 \\
1 & -2 & -3 & 4
\end{array}
\right]
$$

Pivoting on the circled entry leads to the following table with $\mathbf{e}_1$ replaced by $\mathbf{a}_2$:

$$
\begin{array}{c}
\\
\mathbf{a}_2 \\
\mathbf{e}_2 \\
\mathbf{a}_1
\end{array}
\begin{array}{c}
\mathbf{a}_1 \quad \mathbf{a}_2 \quad \mathbf{a}_3 \quad \mathbf{a}_4 \\
\left[\begin{array}{cccc}
0 & 1 & 2 & -1 \\
0 & 0 & 0 & 0 \\
1 & 0 & 1 & 2
\end{array}\right]
\end{array}
$$

In this table the first two columns (the pivot columns) indicate that $\mathbf{a}_1$ and $\mathbf{a}_2$ are linearly independent, and the third and fourth columns reveal that

$$\mathbf{a}_3 = 2\mathbf{a}_2 + \mathbf{a}_1 \quad \text{and} \quad \mathbf{a}_4 = -\mathbf{a}_2 + 2\mathbf{a}_1$$

Hence the vectors $\mathbf{a}_1, \mathbf{a}_2$ are a basis for the column space of $A$, and $\mathbf{a}_3, \mathbf{a}_4$ are given as linear combinations of $\mathbf{a}_1, \mathbf{a}_2$.

It should be noted that other choices of basis vectors are possible. For example, in the second matrix we could have chosen the entry $-3$ in the second row and fourth column as pivot and thereby obtained

$$
\begin{array}{c}
\\
\mathbf{e}_1 \\
\mathbf{a}_4 \\
\mathbf{a}_1
\end{array}
\begin{array}{c}
\mathbf{a}_1 \quad \mathbf{a}_2 \quad \mathbf{a}_3 \quad \mathbf{a}_4 \\
\left[\begin{array}{cccc}
0 & 0 & 0 & 0 \\
0 & -1 & -2 & 1 \\
1 & 2 & 5 & 0
\end{array}\right]
\end{array}
$$

In this case we would select $\mathbf{a}_4, \mathbf{a}_1$ as basis vectors and obtain the relations

$$\mathbf{a}_2 = -\mathbf{a}_4 + 2\mathbf{a}_1 \quad \text{and} \quad \mathbf{a}_3 = -2\mathbf{a}_4 + 5\mathbf{a}_1 \quad \blacksquare$$

As was pointed out in the above example, the choice of basis vectors is not unique. The procedure can be made more systematic by proceeding as in Gauss-Jordan elimination until a reduced echelon form is obtained, but this is not essential. In any case the basis vectors correspond to the chosen pivot columns, and the process stops when pivots are no longer available. Each pivot entry must be nonzero, and it must not lie in the row or column of a previous pivot. We illustrate the procedure with one more example.

**EXAMPLE 5**   Select a basis for the span of the vectors $\mathbf{u}_1 = (1, 2, 1)$, $\mathbf{u}_2 = (2, 4, 2)$, $\mathbf{u}_3 = (1, 1, 1)$, $\mathbf{u}_4 = (2, 7, 7)$, $\mathbf{u}_5 = (1, 6, 11)$, and write the remaining vectors as linear combinations of the selected basis vectors.

**SOLUTION**   Writing the vectors as column vectors, we obtain the following sequence of dependency tables, where the pivots are circled:

$$
\begin{array}{c}
\\
\mathbf{e}_1 \\
\mathbf{e}_2 \\
\mathbf{e}_3
\end{array}
\begin{array}{c}
\mathbf{u}_1 \quad \mathbf{u}_2 \quad \mathbf{u}_3 \quad \mathbf{u}_4 \quad \mathbf{u}_5 \\
\left[\begin{array}{ccccc}
① & 2 & 1 & 2 & 1 \\
2 & 4 & 1 & 7 & 6 \\
1 & 2 & 1 & 7 & 11
\end{array}\right]
\end{array}
$$

$$
\begin{array}{c}
\begin{array}{ccccc} \mathbf{u}_1 & \mathbf{u}_2 & \mathbf{u}_3 & \mathbf{u}_4 & \mathbf{u}_5 \end{array} \\
\begin{array}{c} \mathbf{u}_1 \\ \mathbf{e}_2 \\ \mathbf{e}_3 \end{array}
\left[ \begin{array}{ccccc}
1 & 2 & 1 & 2 & 1 \\
0 & 0 & \boxed{-1} & 3 & 4 \\
0 & 0 & 0 & 5 & 10
\end{array} \right]
\end{array}
$$

$$
\begin{array}{c}
\begin{array}{ccccc} \mathbf{u}_1 & \mathbf{u}_2 & \mathbf{u}_3 & \mathbf{u}_4 & \mathbf{u}_5 \end{array} \\
\begin{array}{c} \mathbf{u}_1 \\ \mathbf{u}_3 \\ \mathbf{e}_3 \end{array}
\left[ \begin{array}{ccccc}
1 & 2 & 0 & 5 & 5 \\
0 & 0 & 1 & -3 & -4 \\
0 & 0 & 0 & \boxed{5} & 10
\end{array} \right]
\end{array}
$$

$$
\begin{array}{c}
\begin{array}{ccccc} \mathbf{u}_1 & \mathbf{u}_2 & \mathbf{u}_3 & \mathbf{u}_4 & \mathbf{u}_5 \end{array} \\
\begin{array}{c} \mathbf{u}_1 \\ \mathbf{u}_3 \\ \mathbf{u}_4 \end{array}
\left[ \begin{array}{ccccc}
1 & 2 & 0 & 0 & -5 \\
0 & 0 & 1 & 0 & 2 \\
0 & 0 & 0 & 1 & 2
\end{array} \right]
\end{array}
$$

The pivot columns determine the basis vectors $\mathbf{u}_1$, $\mathbf{u}_3$, $\mathbf{u}_4$ (which are listed on the side of the matrix), and the other columns give us the linear combinations

$$\mathbf{u}_2 = 2\mathbf{u}_1 \quad \text{and} \quad \mathbf{u}_5 = -5\mathbf{u}_1 + 2\mathbf{u}_3 + 2\mathbf{u}_4 \quad \blacksquare$$

## APPLICATION

The ability to write a vector as a linear combination of a set of basic vectors has an interesting and valuable interpretation in mixture problems. We illustrate this with an example of a diet problem.

**EXAMPLE 6**  Let the foods spaghetti, eggs, beans, and asparagus contain the nutrients food energy (calories), protein, and iron. Specifically, let 1 cup of spaghetti contain 170 calories, 5 grams of protein, and 2 milligrams of iron; let 1 egg contain 85 calories, 6 grams of protein, and 1 milligram of iron; let 1 cup of beans contain 200 calories, 16 grams of protein, and 5 milligrams of iron; and let 1 bunch of asparagus contain 10 calories, 3 grams of protein, and 1 milligram of iron. (a) Find a basic set of foods; (b) determine the formula for making the other food synthetically from this basic set; and (c) if spaghetti costs 15¢ per cup, eggs cost 6¢ each, beans cost 20¢ per cup, and asparagus costs 10¢ per bunch, then determine the cost of the synthetic food and compare it with the cost of the true food.

**SOLUTION**   We represent each of the foods in a "nutrient space" with the vector $\mathbf{x} = (x_1, x_2, x_3)$ where $x_1$ is the number of calories of food energy, $x_2$ is the number of grams of protein, and $x_3$ is the number of milligrams of iron in the indicated quantity of the food. Thus we have $\mathbf{a}_1 = (170, 5, 2)$ for spaghetti, $\mathbf{a}_2 = (85, 6, 1)$ for eggs, $\mathbf{a}_3 = (200, 16, 5)$ for beans, and $\mathbf{a}_4 = (10, 3, 1)$ for asparagus. We use the "pure" nutrients $\mathbf{e}_1 = (1, 0, 0)$ (1 calorie), $\mathbf{e}_2 = (0, 1, 0)$ (1 gram of protein), and $\mathbf{e}_3 = (0, 0, 1)$ (1 milligram of iron) to make up the foods. That is, we form the initial dependency table for $\mathbf{a}_1$, $\mathbf{a}_2$, $\mathbf{a}_3$, $\mathbf{a}_4$ with $\mathbf{e}_1$, $\mathbf{e}_2$, $\mathbf{e}_3$ as the basis.

$$
\begin{array}{c}
\phantom{e_1}\;\; \mathbf{a}_1 \quad \mathbf{a}_2 \quad \mathbf{a}_3 \quad \mathbf{a}_4 \\
\begin{array}{c} e_1 \\ e_2 \\ e_3 \end{array}
\left[
\begin{array}{cccc}
170 & 85 & 200 & 10 \\
5 & 6 & 16 & 3 \\
2 & 1 & 5 & \textcircled{1}
\end{array}
\right]
\end{array}
$$

We now want to pivot three foods into the basis. For ease in pivoting we select the 1 in the $\mathbf{a}_4$ (asparagus) column, and we obtain the table

$$
\begin{array}{c}
\phantom{e_1}\;\; \mathbf{a}_1 \quad \mathbf{a}_2 \quad \mathbf{a}_3 \quad \mathbf{a}_4 \\
\begin{array}{c} e_1 \\ e_2 \\ \mathbf{a}_4 \end{array}
\left[
\begin{array}{cccc}
150 & \textcircled{75} & 150 & 0 \\
-1 & 3 & 1 & 0 \\
2 & 1 & 5 & 1
\end{array}
\right]
\end{array}
$$

This table shows how to construct nutritionally the first three foods from pure food energy, pure protein, and asparagus. Any nonzero entry in the first two rows can now be used for a pivot. We choose the 75 in the $\mathbf{a}_2$ (eggs) column to obtain the table

$$
\begin{array}{c}
\phantom{e_1}\;\; \mathbf{a}_1 \quad \mathbf{a}_2 \quad \mathbf{a}_3 \quad \mathbf{a}_4 \\
\begin{array}{c} \mathbf{a}_2 \\ e_2 \\ \mathbf{a}_4 \end{array}
\left[
\begin{array}{cccc}
2 & 1 & 2 & 0 \\
\textcircled{-7} & 0 & -5 & 0 \\
0 & 0 & 3 & 1
\end{array}
\right]
\end{array}
$$

Here we have spaghetti and beans described as combinations of eggs, pure protein, and asparagus. For the last pivot we may take the $-7$ in the $\mathbf{a}_1$ (spaghetti) column or the $-5$ in the $\mathbf{a}_3$ (beans) column. We take the $-7$ as the pivot and find

$$
\begin{array}{c}
\phantom{e_1}\;\; \mathbf{a}_1 \quad \mathbf{a}_2 \quad \mathbf{a}_3 \quad \mathbf{a}_4 \\
\begin{array}{c} \mathbf{a}_2 \\ \mathbf{a}_1 \\ \mathbf{a}_4 \end{array}
\left[
\begin{array}{cccc}
0 & 1 & 4/7 & 0 \\
1 & 0 & 5/7 & 0 \\
0 & 0 & 3 & 1
\end{array}
\right]
\end{array}
$$

Now we have $\mathbf{a}_2, \mathbf{a}_1, \mathbf{a}_4$ forming a basis. That is, eggs, spaghetti, and asparagus form a basic set of foods. Moreover, we have

$$
\mathbf{a}_3 = \frac{4}{7}\mathbf{a}_2 + \frac{5}{7}\mathbf{a}_1 + 3\mathbf{a}_4
$$

Therefore from a food energy, protein, and iron point of view, we can manufacture a cup of beans from $\frac{4}{7}$ of an egg, $\frac{5}{7}$ cup of spaghetti, and 3 bunches of asparagus. Thus we may think of this linear combination as the formula for synthetic beans.

Finally, we can compute the cost of synthetic beans from this same formula. We obtain

$$
6\frac{4}{7} + 15\frac{5}{7} + 10(3) = 44\frac{1}{7}\,\text{¢ per cup}
$$

Since this is considerably more than the 20¢ per cup that real beans cost, we can see that any basic diet could be made cheaper by reducing the amounts of the basic foods (in the proportions described by the formula) and adding real beans. ∎

The notion of computing the cost of a synthetic substance in terms of the basic substances and making a replacement if the real substance is cheaper is at the heart of rule 1 of the simplex method. We will return to this issue when we discuss the minimization form of the algorithm in Section 4.7.

## EXERCISES 4.5

In Exercises 1–10, write the given vector in terms of the standard basis vectors.

**1.** $(8, 3)$      **2.** $(5, 2)$      **3.** $(-6, 4)$      **4.** $(7, -2)$
**5.** $(4, -2, 8)$      **6.** $(9, 5, -3)$      **7.** $(5, -2, 0)$      **8.** $(0, 3, -2)$
**9.** $(6, 4, 9, -1)$      **10.** $(8, 5, -4, 7)$

In Exercises 11–14, find a basis for the given subspace of $R^3$.

**11.** The plane $4x + y + 3z = 0$      **12.** The plane $6x + 5y + 2z = 0$
**13.** The plane $2x + y - 3z = 0$      **14.** The plane $3x - 5y + 4z = 0$

In Exercises 15–18, show that the vectors $\mathbf{u}_1$, $\mathbf{u}_2$ are a basis for $R^2$. Write the vector $\mathbf{b}$ as a linear combination of $\mathbf{u}_1$, $\mathbf{u}_2$.

**15.** $\mathbf{u}_1 = (2, 5)$,   $\mathbf{u}_2 = (4, 3)$,   $\mathbf{b} = (7, -1)$
**16.** $\mathbf{u}_1 = (-3, 2)$,   $\mathbf{u}_2 = (3, 7)$,   $\mathbf{b} = (-2, 6)$
**17.** $\mathbf{u}_1 = (1, 4)$,   $\mathbf{u}_2 = (-2, 5)$,   $\mathbf{b} = (b_1, b_2)$
**18.** $\mathbf{u}_1 = (3, -1)$,   $\mathbf{u}_2 = (5, 4)$,   $\mathbf{b} = (b_1, b_2)$

In Exercises 19–20, show that the given vectors $\mathbf{u}_1$, $\mathbf{u}_2$, $\mathbf{u}_3$ are a basis for $R^3$. Write the vector $\mathbf{b}$ as a linear combination of $\mathbf{u}_1$, $\mathbf{u}_2$, $\mathbf{u}_3$.

**19.** $\mathbf{u}_1 = (2, 3, -4)$,   $\mathbf{u}_2 = (4, 8, -5)$,   $\mathbf{u}_3 = (-2, -5, 0)$,   $\mathbf{b} = (8, 6, 3)$
**20.** $\mathbf{u}_1 = (-2, 4, 3)$,   $\mathbf{u}_2 = (2, -5, -1)$,   $\mathbf{u}_3 = (6, -8, -15)$,   $\mathbf{b} = (-4, 9, 6)$

In Exercises 21–24, show that the given set of vectors is not a basis for $R^2$.

**21.** $(5, -1), (-10, 2)$            **22.** $(8, 1), (-24, -3)$
**23.** $(2, -3), (8, -12)$            **24.** $(-1, 4), (-4, 16)$

In Exercises 25–28, show that the given set of vectors is not a basis for $R^3$.

**25.** $(1, 4, -2), (-2, -7, 4), (-4, -13, 8)$
**26.** $(2, -2, 5), (6, 3, -1), (18, 0, 13)$
**27.** $(1, 1, 1), (1, 1, 0)$            **28.** $(1, 0, 1), (0, 1, 0)$

In Exercises 29–30, let $\mathbf{u}_1$, $\mathbf{u}_2$, $\mathbf{u}_3$ be a basis for $R^3$ and find the value of $k$.

**29.** $8\mathbf{u}_1 + 2\mathbf{u}_2 - 3\mathbf{u}_3 = (7 + k)\mathbf{u}_1 + (3 - k)\mathbf{u}_2 - (2 + k)\mathbf{u}_3$

**30.** $4\mathbf{u}_1 - 6\mathbf{u}_2 - 2\mathbf{u}_3 = (2k)\mathbf{u}_1 - (3k)\mathbf{u}_2 - k\mathbf{u}_3$

In Exercises 31–34, display the given matrix, $A$, as a dependency table for the columns of $A$ in terms of the standard basis. Use Gauss-Jordan pivoting to replace the standard basis vectors with columns of $A$ in the dependency table. Write $\mathbf{a}_5$ as a linear combination of the vectors in the column basis.

**31.** $\begin{bmatrix} -2 & 4 & 6 & 2 & -4 \\ 2 & -6 & -10 & -4 & 8 \end{bmatrix}$
    **32.** $\begin{bmatrix} 3 & -9 & 6 & -3 & -6 \\ -3 & 6 & -12 & 6 & 9 \end{bmatrix}$

**33.** $\begin{bmatrix} 1 & -3 & -1 & 4 & -2 \\ -2 & 6 & 3 & -10 & 6 \\ 2 & -6 & 2 & 2 & -8 \end{bmatrix}$
    **34.** $\begin{bmatrix} -1 & 3 & -3 & 2 & 3 \\ 3 & -10 & 9 & -4 & -4 \\ -3 & 11 & -9 & 3 & 3 \end{bmatrix}$

In Exercises 35–40, use the vectors $\mathbf{a}_1$, $\mathbf{a}_2$, ... to form the matrix $A$. Then use dependency tables to solve the system of equations $A\mathbf{x} = \mathbf{b}$ by writing $\mathbf{b}$ as a linear combination of columns of $A$.

**35.** $\mathbf{a}_1 = (2, 3)$, $\mathbf{a}_2 = (6, -5)$, $\mathbf{b} = (-14, 7)$

**36.** $\mathbf{a}_1 = (-3, -6)$, $\mathbf{a}_2 = (9, 20)$, $\mathbf{b} = (21, 44)$

**37.** $\mathbf{a}_1 = (-2, 5)$, $\mathbf{a}_2 = (4, -10)$, $\mathbf{a}_3 = (-6, 17)$, $\mathbf{b} = (14, -41)$

**38.** $\mathbf{a}_1 = (3, -3)$, $\mathbf{a}_2 = (6, -6)$, $\mathbf{a}_3 = (-12, 15)$, $\mathbf{b} = (6, -3)$

**39.** $\mathbf{a}_1 = (1, -3, -4)$, $\mathbf{a}_2 = (4, 6, 5)$, $\mathbf{b} = (-1, -15, -17)$

**40.** $\mathbf{a}_1 = (-1, 2, -3)$, $\mathbf{a}_2 = (6, -10, 15)$, $\mathbf{b} = (8, -12, 18)$

In Exercises 41–46, use dependency tables to select a basis for the column space of the given matrix and write the remaining column vectors as a linear combination of the basic columns.

**41.** $\begin{bmatrix} 1 & -3 & -1 \\ 6 & -15 & -12 \end{bmatrix}$
    **42.** $\begin{bmatrix} -1 & 4 & 4 \\ 3 & -10 & -6 \end{bmatrix}$

**43.** $\begin{bmatrix} 2 & -6 & 8 & -4 \\ -4 & 12 & -10 & -4 \end{bmatrix}$
    **44.** $\begin{bmatrix} -3 & 6 & 9 & 6 \\ 5 & -10 & -2 & 16 \end{bmatrix}$

**45.** $\begin{bmatrix} 1 & 2 & -1 & 2 & -1 \\ 5 & 11 & -7 & 9 & -9 \\ -2 & 3 & -12 & -12 & -28 \end{bmatrix}$
    **46.** $\begin{bmatrix} -1 & 3 & 3 & 2 & -1 \\ -4 & 11 & 10 & 7 & -3 \\ 3 & -5 & -1 & 0 & -7 \end{bmatrix}$

**47.** Let the foods oat squares, dry milk, dry potatoes, and noodles contain the nutrients calories, protein, and carbohydrates. Specifically, let one ounce of oat squares contain 120 calories, 6 grams of protein, and 20 grams of carbohydrates; let one ounce of dry milk contain 100 calories, 10 grams of protein, and 20 grams of carbohydrates; let one ounce of dry potatoes contain 100 calories, 2 grams of protein, and 20 grams of carbohydrates; and let one ounce of noodles contain 110 calories, 4 grams of protein, and 20 grams of carbohydrates. Describe the nutritional makeup of the four foods as vectors, and use dependency tables to express noodles in terms of the basic set of foods: oat squares, dry milk, and dry potatoes. Let oat squares cost 7 cents per ounce, dry milk cost 6 cents per ounce, dry potatoes cost 5 cents per ounce, and noodles cost 3 cents per ounce. Find the cost of synthetic noodles and compare it with the cost of real noodles.

**48.** Let the foods cottage cheese, cultured milk, American cheese, and yoghurt contain the nutrients calories, protein, and lysine. Specifically, let one ounce of cottage cheese contain 25 calories, 4 grams of protein, and 300 milligrams lysine; let one ounce of cultured milk contain 60 calories, 1 gram of protein, and 60 milligrams lysine; let one ounce of American cheese contain 110 calories, 7 grams of protein, and 510 milligrams lysine; and let one ounce of yoghurt contain 15 calories, 1 gram of protein, and 90 milligrams lysine. Describe the nutritional makeup of the four foods as vectors, and use dependency tables to express American cheese in terms of the basic set of foods: cottage cheese, cultured milk, and yoghurt. Let cottage cheese cost 7 cents per ounce, cultured milk cost 4 cents per ounce, American cheese cost 19 cents per ounce, and yoghurt cost 7 cents per ounce. Find the cost of synthetic American cheese and compare it with the cost of real American cheese.

## 4.6   DIMENSION AND RANK

*Dimension, The Rank of a Matrix, The Nullity of a Matrix, Nonhomogeneous Systems*

In this section we define the dimension of a subspace $S$ of $R^n$ to be the number of vectors in a basis for $S$. This is an algebraic concept of dimension that coincides with our geometric sense of dimension in the plane and in space, and it also provides us with a technical notion of dimension in the spaces $R^n$ with $n \geqslant 4$, where our inability to draw pictures hampers our geometric intuition.

We will define the rank of a matrix in terms of dimension, but the dimensional definition of rank assigns the same number to a matrix as the previous notion of row rank that was introduced in Chapter 2, so that there is no disparity between the different approaches. A second number associated with a matrix is called its nullity, which is the dimension of its null-space, and we will relate the nullity of a matrix to its rank in the important rank-plus-nullity theorem. We will then apply these concepts to the analysis of systems of linear equations.

### DIMENSION

Even though it is possible to have many different sets of basis vectors for a given subspace $S$ of $R^n$, it can be proved that every basis must have the same number of vectors. This fact is quite reasonable on geometric and intuitive grounds, but the formal proof is somewhat technical and will be omitted.

### THEOREM 1

Let $S$ be a subspace of $R^n$. Then every basis for $S$ has the same number of vectors.

The number of vectors in a basis for a space $S$ is called the **dimension** of $S$. For example, since the standard basis for $R^n$ consists of the $n$ vectors $\mathbf{e}_1, \ldots, \mathbf{e}_n$, the space $R^n$ is $n$-dimensional. By Theorem 1 any other basis for $R^n$ must also consist of $n$ vectors. The subspace consisting of the zero vector alone is a special case, and its dimension is defined to be zero.

The space $R^3$ has dimension three, which agrees with our geometric viewpoint. The subspaces of $R^3$ that are spanned by one nonzero vector are lines through the origin, and they are 1-dimensional. Planes through the origin are spanned by two linearly independent vectors, and they are 2-dimensional. If we have three linearly independent vectors in $R^3$, then their span must be all of $R^3$, since $R^3$ is known to be 3-dimensional. Thus we have classified all the types of subspaces in $R^3$.

In general, if a subspace of $R^n$ is known to have dimension $k$, then it can be proved that a set of $k$ vectors in $S$ will be a basis for $S$ if *either* the vectors are linearly independent *or* they span $S$. Thus knowledge of the dimension means that only one of two properties of a basis need be established, the other property being a consequence of the dimension. We state this useful fact as a theorem; its proof will be omitted.

### THEOREM 2

Let $S$ be a $k$-dimensional subspace of $R^n$. If a set of $k$ vectors in $S$ either spans $S$ or is linearly independent, then it is a basis for $S$.

**EXAMPLE 1**    Find a basis for the subspace $S$ of $R^3$ that is the plane with equation $x - 2y - 3z = 0$.

**SOLUTION**    Since $S$ is 2-dimensional, we need to find two linearly independent vectors in $S$. Many choices are possible, but the following technique is easy and direct. We set $y = 1$, $z = 0$ and solve for $x$; we get $x = 2$, so that $\mathbf{u}_1 = (2, 1, 0)$ is in $S$. Similarly, we set $y = 0$, $z = 1$ and solve for $x$; we get $x = 3$, so that $\mathbf{u}_2 = (3, 0, 1)$ is in $S$. The vectors $\mathbf{u}_1$ and $\mathbf{u}_2$ are linearly independent because of the location of the components 0 and 1. That is, we note that the second component of the equation

$$c_1 \begin{bmatrix} 2 \\ 1 \\ 0 \end{bmatrix} + c_2 \begin{bmatrix} 3 \\ 0 \\ 1 \end{bmatrix} = \begin{bmatrix} 0 \\ 0 \\ 0 \end{bmatrix}$$

gives us $c_1 = 0$ and the third component gives us $c_2 = 0$. Hence the vectors

$\mathbf{u}_1, \mathbf{u}_2$ are linearly independent, and therefore by Theorem 2 they form a basis for $S$. ∎

## THE RANK OF A MATRIX

We have previously defined the row rank of a matrix to be the number of nonzero rows in the reduced echelon form of the matrix. Let the space spanned by the row vectors of a matrix be called the **row space** of the matrix. Then it can be shown that the row rank is the same as the dimension of the row space. (In fact, the nonzero rows of the reduced echelon form of the matrix constitute a basis for the row space of the matrix. See Exercises 9–14.) We now define the **column rank** of a matrix to be the dimension of the column space of the matrix. Thus it appears that we have two different notions of rank for a matrix. However, the following important theorem states that these two notions of rank are actually the same.

**THEOREM 3**

The row ra           matrix are equal.

The proc                , but the reasons behind it are indicated
by the followi                 le procedure leads to both the row rank
and the colu

**EXAMPLE 2**   Show that the row rank are equal for the matrix

$$A = \begin{bmatrix} ① & -3 & 1 & 2 & 1 \\ -2 & 6 & 0 & -4 & 2 \\ 1 & -3 & 2 & 3 & 1 \end{bmatrix}$$

SOLUTION   We put the matrix into reduced echelon form by using a sequence of pivots. We obtain the following matrices, where the pivots have been circled.

$$\begin{bmatrix} 1 & -3 & 1 & 2 & 1 \\ 0 & 0 & ② & 0 & 4 \\ 0 & 0 & 1 & 1 & 0 \end{bmatrix}$$

$$\begin{bmatrix} 1 & -3 & 0 & 2 & -1 \\ 0 & 0 & 1 & 0 & 2 \\ 0 & 0 & 0 & ① & -2 \end{bmatrix}$$

$$E = \begin{bmatrix} 1 & -3 & 0 & 0 & 3 \\ 0 & 0 & 1 & 0 & 2 \\ 0 & 0 & 0 & 1 & -2 \end{bmatrix}$$

There are three nonzero rows in the reduced echelon matrix $E$, so that the row rank of $A$ is 3. According to the vector replacement procedure, the pivot columns determine a basis for the column space.  (The pivot columns contain the leading 1s for the nonzero rows.)  Since there are three pivot columns, the column rank is also 3.  Hence the row rank and the column rank are the same.  ∎

The **rank** of a matrix refers to either its row rank or its column rank.  Either number may be used, since they are equal.

## THE NULLITY OF A MATRIX

The **nullity** of a matrix is defined to be the dimension of the null space of the matrix.  That is, the set of solutions of the homogeneous system $A\mathbf{x} = \mathbf{0}$ is a subspace, and the dimension of this subspace is the nullity of $A$.

The rank and the nullity of a matrix are related in an important way.  The following theorem is a restatement of Theorem 2 in Section 2.3 of Chapter 2.

### THEOREM 4

Let $A$ be a matrix with $n$ columns.  Then

$$\text{rank} + \text{nullity} = n$$

That is, the rank of $A$ plus the nullity of $A$ equals the number of columns of $A$.

The result of the theorem is obtained in a natural way when a matrix $A$ is put into reduced echelon form by a sequence of pivots.  The pivot columns correspond to the basis vectors for the column space of $A$, and the nonpivot columns correspond to the nonleading variables that are used as parameters to determine a basis for the null space of $A$.  Consider the following example.

**EXAMPLE 3**   Find the rank and the nullity of the matrix

$$A = \begin{bmatrix} 1 & -2 & -1 & 2 & 8 \\ 1 & -2 & 0 & 1 & 5 \\ 2 & -4 & 0 & 3 & 12 \\ -2 & 4 & 1 & -1 & -9 \end{bmatrix}$$

**SOLUTION**   A sequence of pivots puts $A$ into the reduced echelon form

$$E = \begin{bmatrix} 1 & -2 & 0 & 0 & 3 \\ 0 & 0 & 1 & 0 & -1 \\ 0 & 0 & 0 & 1 & 2 \\ 0 & 0 & 0 & 0 & 0 \end{bmatrix}$$

The rank of $A$ is 3, which can be seen by noting that $E$ has three nonzero rows or by noting that there are three pivot columns so that the column rank of $A$ is 3.  According to Theorem 4, the nullity of $A$ is $5 - 3 = 2$.

Let us also determine the nullity of $A$ directly by finding a basis for the null-space of $A$.  We introduce the parameters $s, t$ for the variables of the nonpivot columns. Specifically, let $x_2 = s$, $x_5 = t$. Then the solutions of the homogeneous system $Ax = 0$, which is equivalent to the system $Ex = 0$, is found to be

$$x = s \begin{bmatrix} 2 \\ 1 \\ 0 \\ 0 \\ 0 \end{bmatrix} + t \begin{bmatrix} -3 \\ 0 \\ 1 \\ -2 \\ 1 \end{bmatrix}$$

Since a basis for the null-space of $A$ consists of two vectors, we conclude that the nullity of $A$ is 2. Adding the rank and the nullity of $A$, we get $3 + 2 = 5$, which is the number of columns of $A$. Thus we have verified Theorem 4 for this matrix.  ▪▪

The rank-plus-nullity theorem provides insights into the structure of the solution sets of linear systems. For homogeneous systems, if we know the rank of the coefficient matrix, then we know the dimension of the solution space. This is much more precise information than just knowing that there are infinitely many solutions.

**EXAMPLE 4**   Suppose we know that the rank of a $5 \times 7$ matrix $A$ is $r = 4$. Find the dimension of the solution space of the homogeneous system $Ax = 0$.

SOLUTION   We are asked to find the nullity of $A$. Since $A$ has seven columns and since the rank is 4, we apply Theorem 4 to deduce that the nullity of $A$ is $7 - 4 = 3$.  ▪▪

## NONHOMOGENEOUS SYSTEMS

The preceding results can also be used to obtain insight into the structure of the solution sets of nonhomogeneous systems, even though these solution sets do not contain the origin and therefore are not subspaces. There is a relationship between the solution set of a nonhomogeneous system $Ax = b$ and the associated homogeneous system $Ax = 0$. The relationship is revealed in the following example.

**EXAMPLE 5**   Solve the system $Ax = b$ where

$$A = \begin{bmatrix} 1 & -2 & 4 \\ -1 & 3 & -7 \\ -2 & 3 & -5 \end{bmatrix}, \quad b = \begin{bmatrix} -1 \\ 2 \\ 1 \end{bmatrix}$$

SOLUTION   The augmented matrix $[A|b]$ has the reduced echelon form

$$\begin{bmatrix} 1 & 0 & -2 & | & 1 \\ 0 & 1 & -3 & | & 1 \\ 0 & 0 & 0 & | & 0 \end{bmatrix}$$

If we set $x_3 = t$, we get the solution

$$\mathbf{x} = \begin{bmatrix} 1 + 2t \\ 1 + 3t \\ t \end{bmatrix}$$

which can be written in the form

$$\mathbf{x} = \begin{bmatrix} 1 \\ 1 \\ 0 \end{bmatrix} + t \begin{bmatrix} 2 \\ 3 \\ 1 \end{bmatrix}$$

Note that the second vector $\mathbf{v} = t(2, 3, 1)$ is in the null-space of $A$, that is, $A\mathbf{v} = \mathbf{0}$. The first vector $\mathbf{u} = (1, 1, 0)$ satisfies $A\mathbf{u} = \mathbf{b}$. Hence we have

$$A\mathbf{x} = A(\mathbf{u} + \mathbf{v}) = A\mathbf{u} + A\mathbf{v} = \mathbf{b} + \mathbf{0} = \mathbf{b}$$

Therefore the solution vector comes in two parts. The first part $\mathbf{u}$ yields the vector $\mathbf{b}$, and the second part $\mathbf{v}$ yields $A\mathbf{v} = \mathbf{0}$.  ∎

In general, the solution set of a consistent nonhomogeneous system $A\mathbf{x} = \mathbf{b}$ can be split into parts. If $\mathbf{u}$ is a particular vector such that $A\mathbf{u} = \mathbf{b}$, and if $\mathbf{v}$ is any vector satisfying $A\mathbf{v} = \mathbf{0}$, then the vector $\mathbf{u} + \mathbf{v}$ also gives us $A(\mathbf{u} + \mathbf{v}) = \mathbf{b}$. Moreover, it can be shown that the converse is also true: every solution of $A\mathbf{x} = \mathbf{b}$ can be written in this way. Thus if a particular solution $\mathbf{u}$ of the nonhomogeneous system $A\mathbf{x} = \mathbf{b}$ is known, then we add to $\mathbf{u}$ the solutions of the associated homogeneous system $A\mathbf{x} = \mathbf{0}$ and obtain the general solution set of $A\mathbf{x} = \mathbf{b}$. We state this information as a theorem; the proof is omitted.

### THEOREM 5

The general solution of $A\mathbf{x} = \mathbf{b}$ is found by adding a particular solution of $A\mathbf{x} = \mathbf{b}$ to the general solution of $A\mathbf{x} = \mathbf{0}$.

**EXAMPLE 6**   Let

$$A = \begin{bmatrix} 1 & 0 & 2 & -1 \\ 2 & 1 & 3 & 1 \end{bmatrix}, \quad \mathbf{b} = \begin{bmatrix} 1 \\ 3 \end{bmatrix}$$

Given that the vector $\mathbf{u} = (1, 1, 0, 0)$ satisfies $A\mathbf{u} = \mathbf{b}$, find the general solution of the nonhomogeneous system $A\mathbf{x} = \mathbf{b}$.

**SOLUTION**   We need only solve the homogeneous system $A\mathbf{x} = \mathbf{0}$ and add the solutions to $\mathbf{u}$. We find that $A$ has the reduced echelon form

$$\begin{bmatrix} 1 & 0 & 2 & -1 \\ 0 & 1 & -1 & 3 \end{bmatrix}$$

and thus the null-space of $A$ consists of the vectors

$$\mathbf{v} = s \begin{bmatrix} -2 \\ 1 \\ 1 \\ 0 \end{bmatrix} + t \begin{bmatrix} 1 \\ -3 \\ 0 \\ 1 \end{bmatrix}$$

Therefore the solution set of the nonhomogeneous system $A\mathbf{x} = \mathbf{b}$ is given by

$$\mathbf{x} = \mathbf{u} + \mathbf{v} = \begin{bmatrix} 1 \\ 1 \\ 0 \\ 0 \end{bmatrix} + s \begin{bmatrix} -2 \\ 1 \\ 1 \\ 0 \end{bmatrix} + t \begin{bmatrix} 1 \\ -3 \\ 0 \\ 1 \end{bmatrix} \quad \blacksquare$$

## EXERCISES 4.6

In Exercises 1–4, state whether or not the given vectors are a basis for $R^2$. Give reasons.

**1.** $(5, 3), (-4, 7)$                     **2.** $(19, 7), (4, 9)$

**3.** $(5, -8), (-15, 24)$            **4.** $(9, -3), (-3, 1)$

In Exercises 5–8, find a basis for the given space.

**5.** The line $2x - 5y = 0$              **6.** The line $3x + 7y = 0$

**7.** The plane $4x - 2y + 7z = 0$      **8.** The plane $-5x + 3y + 6z = 0$

In Exercises 9–10 the matrix $B$ is obtained from $A$ by means of the given row operations. Let the rows of $A$ be designated by $\mathbf{u}_1, \mathbf{u}_2, \mathbf{u}_3$ and the rows of $B$ by $\mathbf{v}_1, \mathbf{v}_2, \mathbf{v}_3$. Use the information about the row operations to write $\mathbf{v}_1, \mathbf{v}_2, \mathbf{v}_3$ as linear combinations of $\mathbf{u}_1, \mathbf{u}_2, \mathbf{u}_3$. Use this same information in the reverse order to write $\mathbf{u}_1, \mathbf{u}_2, \mathbf{u}_3$ as linear combinations of $\mathbf{v}_1, \mathbf{v}_2, \mathbf{v}_3$.

**9.**
$$A = \begin{bmatrix} 0 & 5 & 1 \\ 2 & -4 & 6 \\ 4 & -5 & 8 \end{bmatrix} \quad \begin{matrix} R_1 \leftrightarrow R_2 \\ R_1' = 1/2R_1 \\ R_3' = R_3 - 4R_1 \end{matrix} \quad \begin{bmatrix} 1 & -2 & 3 \\ 0 & 5 & 1 \\ 0 & 3 & -4 \end{bmatrix} = B$$

**10.**
$$A = \begin{bmatrix} 6 & 8 & -10 \\ 0 & 5 & 2 \\ 3 & 6 & -9 \end{bmatrix} \quad \begin{matrix} R_1 \leftrightarrow R_3 \\ R_1' = 1/3R_1 \\ R_3' = R_3 - 6R_1 \end{matrix} \quad \begin{bmatrix} 1 & 2 & -3 \\ 0 & 5 & 2 \\ 0 & -4 & 8 \end{bmatrix} = B$$

In Exercises 11–12, write the vectors $\mathbf{w}_1, \mathbf{w}_2$ as linear combinations of $\mathbf{v}_1, \mathbf{v}_2$.

**11.** $\mathbf{w}_1 = 4\mathbf{u}_1 + 5\mathbf{u}_2, \quad \mathbf{w}_2 = -6\mathbf{u}_1 + 3\mathbf{u}_2$
$\quad\; \mathbf{u}_1 = 2\mathbf{v}_1 - 3\mathbf{v}_2, \quad \mathbf{u}_2 = \quad 6\mathbf{v}_1 + 5\mathbf{v}_2$

**12.** $\mathbf{w}_1 = -6\mathbf{u}_1 + 3\mathbf{u}_2, \quad \mathbf{w}_2 = \mathbf{u}_1 + 4\mathbf{u}_2$
$\quad\; \mathbf{u}_1 = -2\mathbf{v}_1 + 4\mathbf{v}_2, \quad \mathbf{u}_2 = 3\mathbf{v}_1 + 5\mathbf{v}_2$

13. Let the matrix $A$ be row reduced to obtain the matrix $E$. Argue that the rows of $E$ can be written as linear combinations of the rows of $A$ and that the rows of $A$ can be written as linear combinations of the nonzero rows of $E$.

14. Let $E$ be the reduced echelon form of the matrix $A$. Argue that the nonzero rows of $E$ are a basis for the row space of $A$.

In Exercises 15–18, find the rank and the nullity of the given matrix $A$. Find a basis for the null-space of $A$.

15. $\begin{bmatrix} 5 & 10 & -5 \\ 3 & 7 & -2 \\ 2 & 7 & 1 \end{bmatrix}$

16. $\begin{bmatrix} 3 & -3 & -9 \\ 2 & 3 & 14 \\ 6 & -5 & -14 \end{bmatrix}$

17. $\begin{bmatrix} 1 & -2 & 3 & -2 \\ 3 & -6 & 9 & -6 \\ -4 & 8 & -10 & 4 \\ 2 & -4 & 10 & -12 \end{bmatrix}$

18. $\begin{bmatrix} -1 & 3 & 2 & -5 \\ 4 & -12 & -8 & 20 \\ 3 & -9 & -7 & 16 \\ -2 & 6 & 9 & -15 \end{bmatrix}$

In Exercises 19–22, use the information about the matrix $A$ obtained in Exercises 15–18, respectively, together with the particular solution $x_0$ to find the general solution of the system of equations $Ax = b$.

19. $x_0 = (2, -2, 1)$, $b = (-15, -10, -9)$

20. $x_0 = (4, 2, 1)$, $b = (-3, 28, 0)$

21. $x_0 = (5, 2, -1, -2)$, $b = (2, 6, -2, 16)$

22. $x_0 = (2, 1, 3, -1)$, $b = (12, -48, -40, 44)$

## 4.7 THE GENERALIZED SIMPLEX ALGORITHM

*Review of Maximization, Minimization, The Simplex Constraints as a Dependency Table, The Artificial Program, Application, The Two-Phase Method, Production at Minimum Cost*

In Section 2.6 we introduced the simplex rules for maximization programs and treated the linear program that maximized revenue subject to available resources. This choice was made because of the ease in getting the simplex algorithm started. We will now expand our ability to solve linear programs by treating the minimization form of the algorithm and by using this form on what is called the "artificial program" to find nonnegative solutions to systems of equations. We will see that arbitrary linear programs can be solved by a "two-phase" scheme in which the artificial program is first used to find a basic feasible solution, which is then used as a starting point to find the optimum (maximum or minimum) of the true objective function. Finally, the two-phase method is used to solve a linear program to meet a given production demand at minimum cost. Vector methods are introduced into the algorithm, and they are used to check on the accuracy of the entries in the simplex table as well as to analyze the results in the applications.

## REVIEW OF MAXIMIZATION

Let us first review the simplex algorithm for the standard maximum program and isolate the features that were necessary in order to operate the procedure. To be specific, let us consider the program

$$\text{Maximize} \quad z = -3x_1 + 2x_2$$
$$\text{subject to} \quad 6x_1 + 2x_2 \leqslant 4$$
$$5x_1 + 4x_2 \leqslant 12$$
$$3x_1 - 4x_2 \leqslant 1$$
$$x_1 \geqslant 0, \quad x_2 \geqslant 0$$

In order to solve this program we add nonnegative slack variables $x_3$, $x_4$, $x_5$ to the constraints and treat the system of equations

$$z + 3x_1 - 2x_2 \qquad\qquad = 0$$
$$6x_1 + 2x_2 + x_3 \qquad = 4$$
$$5x_1 + 4x_2 \qquad + x_4 \quad = 12$$
$$3x_1 - 4x_2 \qquad\qquad x_5 = 1$$

where the only solutions of interest are those in which the constraint variables $x_1$, $x_2$, $x_3$, $x_4$, $x_5$ are nonnegative. The augmented matrix of this system is

$$\begin{bmatrix} 1 & 3 & -2 & 0 & 0 & 0 & 0 \\ 0 & 6 & ② & 1 & 0 & 0 & 4 \\ 0 & 5 & 4 & 0 & 1 & 0 & 12 \\ 0 & 3 & -4 & 0 & 0 & 1 & 1 \end{bmatrix}$$

This augmented matrix is called the initial simplex table. (Refer to the subsection *"Simplex Tables and Basic Feasible Solutions"* of Section 2.6.) The special features that make this matrix a simplex table are

1. The first column has a 1 in the top row and 0 elsewhere.
2. In each row other than the top row there is a 1 with 0s elsewhere in the same column.

This second feature may be stated in vector terms as

2ʹ. The standard basis vectors $e_1$, $e_2$, $e_3$ appear among the columns of the constraint system with a 0 entry above them in the top row.

We say that a variable is basic if it corresponds to a column with a 1 in a row of the constraint system and 0 elsewhere in the column. Thus the columns with the standard basis vectors in the constraint system portion of the table correspond to the basic variables. The remaining constraint variables are called nonbasic, and the basic solution of the simplex table is obtained by setting the nonbasic variables equal to 0 and determining the value for the basic variables from the equation constants.

In the above table, $x_1$, $x_2$ are nonbasic and $x_3$, $x_4$, $x_5$ are basic. Thus the basic solution of the table is $x_1 = x_2 = 0, x_3 = 4, x_4 = 12, x_5 = 1$, and the objective function value $z = 0$ is obtained from the upper right-hand entry in the table. Since all of the constraint variables have nonnegative values in this solution, we say that it is feasible. The values for the basic variables always come from the rightmost column, and therefore we say that a simplex table is feasible when the entries in the constraint rows of this column are nonnegative. Thus the third essential feature in the initial simplex table is:

3. The entries in the rightmost column of the constraint rows are nonnegative.

Now, the simplex maximization rule 1 dictates that a negative entry be found in the top row of a constraint variable column, in this case the $-2$ in the $x_2$ column. Then by rule 2 the quotients $\frac{4}{2} < \frac{12}{4}$ indicate that the 2 is the pivot. We obtain the following simplex table.

$$\begin{bmatrix} 1 & 9 & 0 & 1 & 0 & 0 & 4 \\ \hline 0 & 3 & 1 & 1/2 & 0 & 0 & 2 \\ 0 & -7 & 0 & -2 & 1 & 0 & 4 \\ 0 & 15 & 0 & 2 & 0 & 1 & 9 \end{bmatrix}$$

The basic variables are now $x_2$, $x_4$, $x_5$, and the nonbasic variables are $x_1$, $x_3$. Thus we set $x_1 = x_3 = 0$ and find that $x_2 = 2$, $x_4 = 4$, $x_5 = 9$ with value $z = 4$. We see that the simplex maximization rules led us from a feasible simplex table to another feasible simplex table with an improved objective function value. The improvement in the objective function value was brought about by the selection of a pivot column with a negative entry at the top and a positive pivot, while the positive pivot together with the quotient comparison of rule 2 resulted in another feasible table. Since there are no negative entries in the top row of a constraint variable column, the current basic feasible solution is maximal.

The essential properties of the standard maximum program that produced an initial simplex table were

1. All the constraints were "$\leqslant$".
2. Each constraint had a nonnegative constant to the right of the inequality.

Thus when the program was converted to an equation format through the addition of slack variables, we had the standard basis vectors present among the columns of the constraint system, and since the slack variables did not appear in the objective function, the augmented matrix of the system was a simplex table. We will see that the simplex algorithm is not restricted to standard maximum programs, but merely to those programs for which an initial simplex table is present.

## MINIMIZATION

The simplex rules for minimization are very similar to those for maximization. We start with a feasible simplex table, and since we wish to decrease the objective function value on each pivot rather than increase it, we look for a positive value instead of a negative value in the top row of a constraint variable column in order to find a pivot column. From there on, the procedure is exactly the same as with maximization.

### The simplex algorithm for minimum programs

**Step 1.**   Given a feasible simplex table, select a *positive* entry in a constraint variable column of the top row of the table. This entry determines the pivot column.

**Step 2.**   Look at the quotients obtained by dividing each positive entry below the top row of the pivot column into the corresponding entry of the last column. Select the entry that produces the smallest quotient. In case of a tie, choose either. This determines the pivot row.

**Step 3.**   Use the entry found in Step 2 as the pivot. (Multiply the row to make the entry 1 and then use row operations to get 0s above and below the pivot location.)

**Stopping rule.**   Repeat steps 1–3 until the top row has no positive entries in a constraint variable column. This is the final simplex table.

**Minimum value.**   The minimum value of $z$ subject to the constraints will be the last entry in the top row of the final simplex table.

We now demonstrate the procedure with an example of a minimization program where the constraints are "$\leqslant$" and the equation constants are non-negative. Thus there will be an initial feasible simplex table present.

**EXAMPLE 1**   Use the simplex algorithm to solve the linear program

$$\text{Minimize} \quad z = 4x_1 - 10x_2 + 6x_3$$
$$\text{subject to} \quad -10x_1 + 4x_2 + 8x_3 \leqslant 20$$
$$-2x_1 + 2x_2 + 4x_3 \leqslant 6$$
$$4x_1 - 2x_3 + 2x_3 \leqslant 4$$
$$x_1 \geqslant 0, \quad x_2 \geqslant 0, \quad x_3 \geqslant 0$$

**SOLUTION**   As in Section 2.6 of Chapter 2, we write the system

$$
\begin{aligned}
z - 4x_1 + 10x_2 - 6x_3 &&&= 0 \\
-10x_1 + 4x_2 + 8x_3 + x_4 &&&= 20 \\
-2x_1 + 2x_2 + 4x_3 &+ x_5 &&= 6 \\
4x_1 - 2x_2 + 2x_3 && + x_6 &= 4
\end{aligned}
$$

where the variables $x_4 \geqslant 0$, $x_5 \geqslant 0$, $x_6 \geqslant 0$ are slack variables. Next we form the initial simplex table

$$
\begin{bmatrix}
1 & -4 & 10 & -6 & 0 & 0 & 0 & 0 \\
\hline
0 & -10 & 4 & 8 & 1 & 0 & 0 & 20 \\
0 & -2 & ② & 4 & 0 & 1 & 0 & 6 \\
0 & 4 & -2 & 2 & 0 & 0 & 1 & 4
\end{bmatrix}
$$

The initial basic feasible solution is $x_4 = 20$, $x_5 = 6$, $x_6 = 4$, $x_1 = x_2 = x_3 = 0$ with $z = 0$. The only possible pivot column is column 3, which has a 10 as the top entry. (The $z$ column is never the pivot column.) Since $20/4 > 6/2$, we choose the 2 in the third row as the pivot. The new table is

$$
\begin{bmatrix}
1 & 6 & 0 & -26 & 0 & -5 & 0 & -30 \\
\hline
0 & -6 & 0 & 0 & 1 & -2 & 0 & 8 \\
0 & -1 & 1 & 2 & 0 & 1/2 & 0 & 3 \\
0 & \textcircled{2} & 0 & 6 & 0 & 1 & 1 & 10
\end{bmatrix}
$$

The new basic feasible solution is $x_2 = 3$, $x_4 = 8$, $x_6 = 10$, $x_1 = x_3 = x_5 = 0$, with $z = -30$. This is a decrease from the value 0 given by the initial solution. There is a 6 in the top row of column 2. Thus we choose column 2 as the pivot column. The only positive entry below the top row in this column is the 2 in row 4, and we take this as the pivot. We obtain the table

$$
\begin{bmatrix}
1 & 0 & 0 & -44 & 0 & -8 & -3 & -60 \\
\hline
0 & 0 & 0 & 18 & 1 & 1 & 3 & 38 \\
0 & 0 & 1 & 5 & 0 & 1 & 1/2 & 8 \\
0 & 1 & 0 & 3 & 0 & 1/2 & 1/2 & 5
\end{bmatrix}
$$

There are no positive entries in the top row of the constraint columns. Therefore the final basic feasible solution is $x_1 = 5$, $x_2 = 8$, $x_4 = 38$, $x_3 = x_5 = x_6 = 0$, and the value $z = -60$ is minimal. ∎

We take time to note that a minimization program would seldom appear in the convenient form of the previous example. Indeed, even the maximization programs encountered in actual practice would usually not be exactly standard maximum in form. Thus on the surface an initial feasible simplex table would not normally be present. The thrust of this section is on how to surmount this difficulty, and we will return to it after formulating the simplex table in vector terms.

## THE SIMPLEX CONSTRAINTS AS A DEPENDENCY TABLE

We saw in Section 4.5 that the augmented matrix of a system of equations $A\mathbf{x} = \mathbf{b}$ can be viewed as a table whose column entries are the coefficients of the dependency relations giving the columns of $A$ and $\mathbf{b}$ in terms of some basis. Thus in this context the augmented matrix becomes a dependency table. We now look at the simplex algorithm from a dependency table point of view.

**EXAMPLE 2** Solve the linear program

$$
\begin{aligned}
\text{Minimize} \quad z = {} & 2x_1 - 6x_2 + 8x_3 \\
\text{subject to} \quad & -3x_1 + x_2 + 2x_3 \leqslant 5 \\
& 3x_1 + 3x_2 - 6x_3 \leqslant 3 \\
& 2x_1 - 3x_2 + 4x_3 \leqslant 9 \\
& x_1 \geqslant 0, \quad x_2 \geqslant 0, \quad x_3 \geqslant 0
\end{aligned}
$$

SOLUTION   We adjoin slack variables and write the system of equations

$$z - 2x_1 + 6x_2 - 8x_3 \qquad\qquad = 0$$
$$-3x_1 + x_2 + 2x_3 + x_4 \qquad\quad = 5$$
$$3x_1 + 3x_2 - 6x_3 \qquad + x_5 \quad = 3$$
$$2x_1 - 3x_2 + 4x_3 \qquad\qquad + x_6 = 9$$

The augmented matrix of this system is a simplex table, since three of the constraint variables appear only in a single row below the top row and with a "1" coefficient. That is, there are three basic variables present. In vector terms the constraint rows of a simplex table form a dependency table, and the columns that correspond to the basic variables form a basis. The vectors that are given by the columns of the slack variables in the constraint system are called **slack vectors**. Since the slack vectors are $a_4 = e_1, a_5 = e_2, a_6 = e_3$, a dependency table for the system in terms of a column basis of the system can immediately be written down. We emphasize that the top row is *not* part of the dependency table.

|        | $a_1$ | $a_2$ | $a_3$ | $a_4$ | $a_5$ | $a_6$ | $b$ |
|--------|-------|-------|-------|-------|-------|-------|-----|
|        | 1 | $-2$ | 6 | $-8$ | 0 | 0 | 0 | 0 |
| $a_4$ | 0 | $-3$ | 1 | 2 | 1 | 0 | 0 | 5 |
| $a_5$ | 0 | 3 | ③ | $-6$ | 0 | 1 | 0 | 3 |
| $a_6$ | 0 | 2 | $-3$ | 4 | 0 | 0 | 1 | 9 |

dependency table

The only possible pivot column is the $a_2$ column, and since $\frac{3}{5} < \frac{5}{1}$, the pivot is made on the 3 in this column. The new simplex table is

|        | $a_1$ | $a_2$ | $a_3$ | $a_4$ | $a_5$ | $a_6$ | $b$ |
|--------|-------|-------|-------|-------|-------|-------|-----|
|        | 1 | $-8$ | 0 | 4 | 0 | $-2$ | 0 | $-6$ |
| $a_4$ | 0 | $-4$ | 0 | ④ | 1 | $-1/3$ | 0 | 4 |
| $a_2$ | 0 | 1 | 1 | $-2$ | 0 | $1/3$ | 0 | 1 |
| $a_6$ | 0 | 5 | 0 | $-2$ | 0 | 1 | 1 | 12 |

The variable $x_2$ becomes basic, and the variable $x_5$ becomes nonbasic. In vector terms, $a_2$ enters the basis, and $a_5$ leaves the basis. Also, we obtain $b = 4a_4 + a_2 + 12a_6$ from the dependency table, and this corresponds to the new basic feasible solution $(0, 1, 0, 4, 0, 12)$ with $z = -6$. The next pivot must be made on the 4 in the $a_3$ column. The new simplex table is

|        | $a_1$ | $a_2$ | $a_3$ | $a_4$ | $a_5$ | $a_6$ | $b$ |
|--------|-------|-------|-------|-------|-------|-------|-----|
|        | 1 | $-4$ | 0 | 0 | $-1$ | $-5/3$ | 0 | $-10$ |
| $a_3$ | 0 | $-1$ | 0 | 1 | $1/4$ | $-1/12$ | 0 | 1 |
| $a_2$ | 0 | $-1$ | 1 | 0 | $1/2$ | $1/6$ | 0 | 3 |
| $a_6$ | 0 | 3 | 0 | 0 | $1/2$ | $5/6$ | 1 | 14 |

The variable $x_3$ becomes basic, and the variable $x_4$ becomes nonbasic. Thus

$\mathbf{a}_3$ enters the basis, and $\mathbf{a}_4$ leaves the basis. That is, $\mathbf{a}_3$ replaces $\mathbf{a}_4$ in the basis. We obtain $\mathbf{b} = \mathbf{a}_3 + 3\mathbf{a}_2 + 14\mathbf{a}_6$ from the dependency portion of the table, and the corresponding new basic feasible solution is $(0, 3, 1, 0, 0, 14)$ with $z = -10$. There are no pivot columns, and thus the new solution is minimal.

Since the constraint rows form a dependency table, we may check the accuracy of these rows at any stage by a direct computation. That is, for each column that is not in the basis, we can test the indicated linear combination of the basis vectors to see if it actually does produce the vector that is written at the top of the column. In this case we find that

$$-\mathbf{a}_3 - \mathbf{a}_2 + 3\mathbf{a}_6 = (-2, 6, -4) + (-1, -3, 3) + (0, 0, 3)$$
$$= (-3, 3, 2) = \mathbf{a}_1$$

$$(1/4)\mathbf{a}_3 + (1/2)\mathbf{a}_2 + (1/2)\mathbf{a}_6 = (1/2, -3/2, 1) + (1/2, 3/2, -3/2) + (0, 0, 1/2)$$
$$= (1, 0, 0) = \mathbf{a}_4$$

$$(-1/12)\mathbf{a}_3 + (1/6)\mathbf{a}_2 + (5/6)\mathbf{a}_6 = (-1/6, 1/2, -1/3) + (1/6, 1/2, -1/2) + (0, 0, 5/6)$$
$$= (0, 1, 0) = \mathbf{a}_5$$

$$\mathbf{a}_3 + 3\mathbf{a}_2 + 14\mathbf{a}_6 = (2, -6, 4) + (3, 9, -9) + (0, 0, 14)$$
$$= (5, 3, 9) = \mathbf{b}$$

Thus the constraint system rows are correct. Later in this section we will see how to check the top row as well. ▌▌

We observe that a constraint variable $x_j$ is basic if and only if the corresponding vector $\mathbf{a}_j$ is in the column basis. Thus the collection of basic variables corresponds to a column basis. In fact, the terminology "basic" as applied to variables comes from belonging to a basis or "basic" as applied to the corresponding vectors. In the linear programs that we have treated so far, the slack variables are the initial basic variables, and they correspond to the slack vectors $\mathbf{e}_1, \mathbf{e}_2, \ldots,$ which form an initial column basis. Then on each pivot a nonbasic variable becomes basic, and a basic variable becomes nonbasic; or from a vector point of view, a vector enters the basis, and a vector leaves the basis. That is, pivoting corresponds to vector replacement.

## THE ARTIFICIAL PROGRAM

We were able to start the simplex algorithm in the previous examples because the unit vectors $\mathbf{e}_1, \mathbf{e}_2, \mathbf{e}_3$ were present among the columns of the constraint system of equations and the equation constants were all nonnegative. Thus we were presented with an initial basic feasible solution and a dependency table. If we do not have an initial basic feasible solution and corresponding dependency table, then we will see how to use the simplex algorithm on an associated linear program, called the "artificial program," to obtain such a form for the constraint system or show that none exists. We will pursue this attack in this subsection.

Before we begin the discussion on finding nonnegative solutions to systems of equations, we will see how to convert an arbitrary system of constraints in nonnegative variables into a system of equations in nonnegative variables. We have already seen how a linear inequality such as

$$2x_1 + 3x_2 \leqslant 4$$

can be converted through the addition of a nonnegative slack variable, $x_3$, to the equation

$$2x_1 + 3x_2 + x_3 = 4$$

with the nonnegative equation constant 4. We now suppose that the inequality is reversed as in

$$3x_1 + 5x_2 \geqslant 5$$

We wish to convert this inequality into an equation with a nonnegative equation constant. Here we have the possibility of "too much" rather than "too little" as in the previous inequality, and we adjust for this situation by subtracting a nonnegative **surplus** variable $x_4$ from the left-hand side to obtain the equation

$$3x_1 + 5x_2 - x_4 = 5$$

We say that a system of equations is in **standard form** for linear programming if all the equation constants are nonnegative. We have, by means of addition of slack variables, subtraction of surplus variables, and negation of constraints, the means to convert any system of constraints into a system of equations in standard form. We give a brief example of the method.

**EXAMPLE 3**   Convert the constraint system

$$
\begin{aligned}
3x_1 + x_2 - 4x_3 &= -6 \\
-2x_1 + 4x_2 + 2x_3 &\leqslant 5 \\
5x_1 - 2x_2 + 3x_3 &\geqslant 4 \\
x_1 \geqslant 0, \quad x_2 \geqslant 0, \quad x_3 &\geqslant 0
\end{aligned}
$$

into a system of equations in standard form with nonnegative variables.

SOLUTION   We negate the equation, add the slack variable $x_4$ to the second constraint, and subtract the surplus variable $x_5$ from the third constraint to obtain

$$
\begin{aligned}
-3x_1 - x_2 + 4x_3 &= 6 \\
-2x_1 + 4x_2 + 2x_3 + x_4 &= 5 \\
5x_1 - 2x_2 + 3x_3 - x_5 &= 4 \\
x_1 \geqslant 0, \quad x_2 \geqslant 0, \quad x_3 \geqslant 0, \quad x_4 \geqslant 0, \quad x_5 \geqslant 0 \quad \blacksquare
\end{aligned}
$$

We now treat an example that leads into the procedure for finding a nonnegative solution to a system of equations in standard form.

**EXAMPLE 4**   Use the simplex algorithm to find a nonnegative solution and corresponding dependency table for the system of equations

$$x_1 + 2x_2 - 2x_3 + 2x_4 = 2$$
$$3x_1 - 4x_2 - x_3 + 2x_4 = -6$$

SOLUTION   First we negate the second equation so as to obtain a nonnegative equation constant and then adjoin the variable $y_1$ to the first equation and $y_2$ to the second equation. We will call $y_1$, $y_2$ "artificial variables" and the corresponding columns of the new constraint system "artificial vectors." We get the system

$$x_1 + 2x_2 - 2x_3 + 2x_4 + y_1 \qquad = 2$$
$$-3x_1 + 4x_2 + x_3 - 2x_4 \qquad + y_2 = 6$$

This system has the nonnegative solution $x_1 = 0$, $x_2 = 0$, $x_3 = 0$, $x_4 = 0$, $y_1 = 2$, $y_2 = 6$. However, since $y_1$ and $y_2$ are not 0, the $x_1, x_2, x_3, x_4$ values do not satisfy the original system of equations. Thus we attempt to find a nonnegative solution where $y_1$ and $y_2$ are both 0. To this end, we form the linear program

Minimize    $z = y_1 + y_2$

subject to    $x_1 + 2x_2 - 2x_3 + 2x_4 + y_1 \qquad = 2$
$-3x_1 + 4x_2 + x_3 - 2x_4 \qquad + y_2 = 6$
$x_1 \geqslant 0, \quad x_2 \geqslant 0, \quad x_3 \geqslant 0, \quad x_4 \geqslant 0, \quad y_1 \geqslant 0, \quad y_2 \geqslant 0$

This system has the augmented matrix

$$\begin{array}{ccccccc} \mathbf{a}_1 & \mathbf{a}_2 & \mathbf{a}_3 & \mathbf{a}_4 & \mathbf{a}_5 & \mathbf{a}_6 & \mathbf{b} \end{array}$$
$$\begin{array}{c} \\ \mathbf{a}_5 \\ \mathbf{a}_6 \end{array} \left[ \begin{array}{ccccc|cc|c} 1 & 0 & 0 & 0 & 0 & -1 & -1 & 0 \\ 0 & 1 & 2 & -2 & 2 & ① & 0 & 2 \\ 0 & -3 & 4 & 1 & -2 & 0 & ① & 6 \end{array} \right]$$

which would be a initial simplex table except for the $-1$s in the top row of the artificial variable columns. Moreover, if each of the rows below the top row is added to the top row (this is equivalent to a pivot on the 1s coefficients corresponding to each of $y_1$, $y_2$), we obtain

$$\begin{array}{ccccccc} \mathbf{a}_1 & \mathbf{a}_2 & \mathbf{a}_3 & \mathbf{a}_4 & \mathbf{a}_5 & \mathbf{a}_6 & \mathbf{b} \end{array}$$
$$\begin{array}{c} \\ \mathbf{a}_5 \\ \mathbf{a}_6 \end{array} \left[ \begin{array}{ccccc|cc|c} 1 & -2 & 6 & -1 & 0 & 0 & 0 & 8 \\ 0 & 1 & ② & -2 & 2 & 1 & 0 & 2 \\ 0 & -3 & 4 & 1 & -2 & 0 & 1 & 6 \end{array} \right]$$

This is now a simplex table for the linear program. Here we have $\mathbf{b} = 2\mathbf{a}_5 + 6\mathbf{a}_6$, and the corresponding basic feasible solution is $(0, 0, 0, 0, 2, 6)$ with value $z = 8$. The equation constants are entirely absorbed in the $y_1$, $y_2$ variables; or in vector terms, $\mathbf{b}$ is written entirely as a linear combination of artificial vectors. We see that $\mathbf{a}_2$ is a candidate to enter the basis, since the top row entry in this column is 6. Also, the quotient comparison $\frac{2}{2} < \frac{6}{4}$ dictates that the 2 will be the pivot and that $\mathbf{a}_5$ will leave the basis. The new table is

$$
\begin{array}{c}
 \\
 \\
\mathbf{a}_2 \\
\mathbf{a}_6
\end{array}
\begin{array}{|cccccc|c|}
 & \mathbf{a}_1 & \mathbf{a}_2 & \mathbf{a}_3 & \mathbf{a}_4 & \mathbf{a}_5 & \mathbf{a}_6 & \mathbf{b} \\
\hline
1 & -5 & 0 & 5 & -6 & -3 & 0 & 2 \\
0 & 1/2 & 1 & -1 & 1 & 1/2 & 0 & 1 \\
0 & -5 & 0 & ⑤ & -6 & -2 & 1 & 2
\end{array}
$$

The new basis is $\mathbf{a}_2, \mathbf{a}_6$ with corresponding basic variables $x_2, y_2$. We have that $\mathbf{b} = \mathbf{a}_2 + 2\mathbf{a}_6$ and the basic feasible solution is $(0, 1, 0, 0, 0, 2)$ with value $z = 2$. Thus $y_1, y_2$ now absorb only two units of the original equation constants.

There is a 5 in the $x_3$ column, and the only positive entry below it is the 5 in the third row. Thus this 5 is the pivot, and $\mathbf{a}_3$ will replace $\mathbf{a}_6$ in the basis. The new table is

$$
\begin{array}{c}
 \\
 \\
\mathbf{a}_2 \\
\mathbf{a}_3
\end{array}
\begin{array}{|cccccc|c|}
 & \mathbf{a}_1 & \mathbf{a}_2 & \mathbf{a}_3 & \mathbf{a}_4 & \mathbf{a}_5 & \mathbf{a}_6 & \mathbf{b} \\
\hline
1 & 0 & 0 & 0 & 0 & -1 & -1 & 0 \\
0 & -1/2 & 1 & 0 & -1/5 & 1/10 & 1/5 & 7/5 \\
0 & -1 & 0 & 1 & -6/5 & -2/5 & 1/5 & 2/5
\end{array}
$$

The new basis is $\mathbf{a}_2, \mathbf{a}_3$, and we have that $\mathbf{b} = \frac{7}{5}\mathbf{a}_2 + \frac{2}{5}\mathbf{a}_3$. The basic feasible solution is $(0, \frac{7}{5}, \frac{2}{5}, 0, 0, 0)$ with value $z = 0$. Thus $y_1$ and $y_2$ are both 0, and the remaining values $x_1 = 0, x_2 = \frac{7}{5}, x_3 = \frac{2}{5}, x_4 = 0$ solve the original system of equations. In vector terms we have that $\mathbf{b}$ has been written entirely in terms of columns of the system. ∎

We now generalize the scheme that was used in the example.

### Procedure to find a nonnegative solution to the equations

$$
\begin{aligned}
a_{11}x_1 + \cdots + a_{1n}x_n &= b_1 \\
&\vdots \\
a_{i1}x_1 + \cdots + a_{in}x_n &= b_i \\
&\vdots \\
a_{m1}x_1 + \cdots + a_{mn}x_n &= b_m
\end{aligned}
$$

**Step 1.**  Negate equations where necessary to obtain $b_i \geqslant 0$, $i = 1, \ldots, m$.

**Step 2.**  Form the linear program

$$
\begin{aligned}
\text{Minimize} \quad & z = y_1 + \cdots + y_i + \cdots + y_m \\
\text{subject to} \quad & a_{11}x_1 + \cdots + a_{1n}x_n + y_1 = b_1 \\
& \qquad\qquad\vdots \\
& a_{i1}x_1 + \cdots + a_{in}x_n \;\;\;\; + y_i = b_i \\
& \qquad\qquad\vdots \\
& a_{m1}x_1 + \cdots + a_{mn}x_n \;\;\;\;\;\;\;\; + y_m = b_m \\
& x_1 \geqslant 0, \;\; \ldots, \;\; x_n \geqslant 0, \;\; y_1 \geqslant 0, \;\; \ldots, \;\; y_m \geqslant 0
\end{aligned}
$$

The variables $y_1, \ldots, y_m$ are called the **artificial variables**, and the linear program is called the **artificial program**. In this context the constraint variables $x_1, \ldots, x_n$ are then called the **true variables**. The columns of the constraint system that correspond to the artificial variables are called the **artificial vectors**. Since the artificial vectors are $\mathbf{e}_1, \ldots, \mathbf{e}_m$, an initial dependency table is present for the artificial program.

**Step 3.**   Write the augmented matrix of the system of constraints and the objective function equation as

$$
\begin{array}{c}
\\
\\
\mathbf{e}_1 = \mathbf{a}_{n+1} \\
\\
\mathbf{e}_i = \mathbf{a}_{n+i} \\
\\
\mathbf{e}_m = \mathbf{a}_{n+m}
\end{array}
\begin{bmatrix}
\begin{array}{ccc|cccccc|c}
 & \mathbf{a}_1 & \cdots & \mathbf{a}_n & \mathbf{a}_{n+1} & & \mathbf{a}_{n+i} & & \mathbf{a}_{n+m} & \mathbf{b} \\
1 & 0 & \cdots & 0 & -1 & \cdots & -1 & \cdots & -1 & 0 \\
\hline
0 & a_{11} & \cdots & a_{1n} & 1 & & & & & b_1 \\
 & \vdots & & \vdots & & \ddots & & & & \vdots \\
0 & a_{i1} & \cdots & a_{in} & & & 1 & & & b_i \\
 & \vdots & & \vdots & & & & \ddots & & \vdots \\
0 & a_{m1} & \cdots & a_{mn} & & & & & 1 & b_m
\end{array}
\end{bmatrix}
$$

This would be a simplex table except for the $-1$s in the top row of the artificial variable columns. We put a vertical line between the true and artificial variable columns for ease in reading the table.

**Step 4.**   Add all rows below the top row to the top row to obtain an initial simplex table for the artificial program. (This is equivalent to pivoting on the 1s that correspond to the artificial variables.)

**Step 5.**   Solve the artificial program.

**Step 6.**   If all of the artificial variables are 0 in the minimum solution of the artificial program, then the values of the true variables in this solution will satisfy the original system. If one or more of the artificial variables is greater than 0 in the minimum solution, then the original system cannot be solved with nonnegative values.

We now apply this technique to another example.

**EXAMPLE 5**   Use the artificial program method to find a nonnegative solution and dependency table corresponding to this solution for the system of equations.

$$
\begin{aligned}
-3x_1 - 7x_2 - 2x_3 - 5x_4 + 3x_5 &= 12 \\
-2x_1 - 2x_2 + x_3 - 3x_4 - x_5 &= -2
\end{aligned}
$$

**SOLUTION**   First we negate the second equation, adjoin artificial variables, and form the linear program

Minimize   $z = y_1 + y_2$

subject to   
$$
\begin{aligned}
-3x_1 - 7x_2 - 2x_3 - 5x_4 + 3x_5 + y_1 \quad\;\; &= 12 \\
2x_1 + 2x_2 - x_3 + 3x_4 + x_5 \quad\; + y_2 &= 2
\end{aligned}
$$
$$
x_1 \geqslant 0, \quad x_2 \geqslant 0, \quad x_3 \geqslant 0, \quad x_4 \geqslant 0, \quad x_5 \geqslant 0, \quad y_1 \geqslant 0, \quad y_2 \geqslant 0
$$

The augmented matrix of this system is

$$
\begin{array}{c}
\\
\\
\mathbf{a}_6 \\
\mathbf{a}_7
\end{array}
\begin{array}{c}
\mathbf{a}_1 \quad \mathbf{a}_2 \quad \mathbf{a}_3 \quad \mathbf{a}_4 \quad \mathbf{a}_5 \qquad \mathbf{a}_6 \quad \mathbf{a}_7 \qquad \mathbf{b} \\
\left[
\begin{array}{cccccc|cc|c}
1 & 0 & 0 & 0 & 0 & 0 & -1 & -1 & 0 \\
\hline
0 & -3 & -7 & -2 & -5 & 3 & ① & 0 & 12 \\
0 & 2 & 2 & -1 & 3 & 1 & 0 & ① & 2
\end{array}
\right]
\end{array}
$$

Then we add both rows below the top row to the top row (pivot on the 1s corresponding to the artificial variables) to obtain the initial simplex table

$$
\begin{array}{c}
\\
\\
\mathbf{a}_6 \\
\mathbf{a}_7
\end{array}
\begin{array}{c}
\mathbf{a}_1 \quad \mathbf{a}_2 \quad \mathbf{a}_3 \quad \mathbf{a}_4 \quad \mathbf{a}_5 \quad \mathbf{a}_6 \; \mathbf{a}_7 \qquad \mathbf{b} \\
\left[
\begin{array}{cccccc|cc|c}
1 & -1 & -5 & -3 & -2 & 4 & 0 & 0 & 14 \\
\hline
0 & -3 & -7 & -2 & -5 & 3 & 1 & 0 & 12 \\
0 & 2 & 2 & -1 & 3 & ① & 0 & 1 & 2
\end{array}
\right]
\end{array}
$$

We observe that each of the entries in the top row in the columns of the true variables and in the column of constants is the sum of the entries below it. Therefore we could have formed this table in one step by forming the augmented matrix of the constraint system and then constructing the top row as follows. Place a 1 in the $z$ position and 0s in the positions corresponding to the artificial variables. In the remaining columns, sum the entries in the constraint system rows and place this sum in the top row.

We now solve the artificial program. The only choice of pivot column is the $\mathbf{a}_5$ column, and the quotient comparison $12/3 > 2/1$ determines that the 1 in the bottom row is the pivot. Thus $\mathbf{a}_5$ enters the basis, and the artificial vector $\mathbf{a}_7$ leaves. The new table is

$$
\begin{array}{c}
\\
\\
\mathbf{a}_6 \\
\mathbf{a}_5
\end{array}
\begin{array}{c}
\mathbf{a}_1 \quad \mathbf{a}_2 \quad \mathbf{a}_3 \quad \mathbf{a}_4 \quad \mathbf{a}_5 \quad \mathbf{a}_6 \quad \mathbf{a}_7 \qquad \mathbf{b} \\
\left[
\begin{array}{cccccc|cc|c}
1 & -9 & -13 & 1 & -14 & 0 & 0 & -4 & 6 \\
\hline
0 & -9 & -13 & ① & -14 & 0 & 1 & -3 & 6 \\
0 & 2 & 2 & -1 & 3 & 1 & 0 & 1 & 2
\end{array}
\right]
\end{array}
$$

The new basic feasible solution is $y_1 = 6, x_5 = 2, x_1 = x_2 = x_3 = x_4 = y_2 = 0$ with value $z = 6$, down from 14. The $\mathbf{a}_3$ column is the only possible pivot column, and the 1 in the second row is the only possible choice of pivot. In the basis, $\mathbf{a}_3$ replaces $\mathbf{a}_6$. The new table is

$$
\begin{array}{c}
\\
\\
\mathbf{a}_3 \\
\mathbf{a}_5
\end{array}
\begin{array}{c}
\mathbf{a}_1 \quad \mathbf{a}_2 \; \mathbf{a}_3 \quad \mathbf{a}_4 \; \mathbf{a}_5 \qquad \mathbf{a}_6 \quad \mathbf{a}_7 \qquad \mathbf{b} \\
\left[
\begin{array}{cccccc|cc|c}
1 & 0 & 0 & 0 & 0 & 0 & -1 & -1 & 0 \\
\hline
0 & -9 & -13 & 1 & -14 & 0 & 1 & -3 & 6 \\
0 & -7 & -11 & 0 & -11 & 1 & 1 & -2 & 8
\end{array}
\right]
\end{array}
$$

The new basic feasible solution is $x_3 = 6, x_5 = 8, x_1 = x_2 = x_4 = y_1 = y_2 = 0$ with value $z = 0$. The artificial variables are completely out of the solution.

Therefore the values $x_3 = 6$, $x_5 = 8$, $x_1 = x_2 = x_4 = 0$ furnish a nonnegative solution to the original system of equations. Further, the constraint rows furnish a dependency table for the original system of equations in terms of the basis $\mathbf{a}_3$, $\mathbf{a}_5$. We check the accuracy of the final dependency table below.

$$
\begin{aligned}
-9\mathbf{a}_3 - 7\mathbf{a}_5 &= (18,9) & +(-21,-7) &= (-3,2) = \mathbf{a}_1 \\
-13\mathbf{a}_3 - 11\mathbf{a}_5 &= (26,13) & +(-33,-11) &= (-7,2) = \mathbf{a}_2 \\
-14\mathbf{a}_3 - 11\mathbf{a}_5 &= (28,14) & +(-33,-11) &= (-5,3) = \mathbf{a}_4 \\
\mathbf{a}_3 + \mathbf{a}_5 &= (-2,-1) & +(3,1) &= (1,0) = \mathbf{a}_6 \\
-3\mathbf{a}_3 - 2\mathbf{a}_5 &= (6,3) & +(-6,-2) &= (0,1) = \mathbf{a}_7 \\
6\mathbf{a}_3 + 8\mathbf{a}_5 &= (-12,-6) & +(24,8) &= (12,2) = \mathbf{b} \quad \blacksquare
\end{aligned}
$$

We saw in the example that steps 3 and 4 could be combined to get the initial simplex table in a single operation. We now give a formal description of this technique.

**Combined steps 3 and 4.** Write the augmented matrix of the system of constraints. Form an objective function row at the top of this matrix as follows. Place a 1 in the entry corresponding to the $z$ position. Place 0s in the entries corresponding to the artificial variables. For each true variable, form the column sum and place it in the top row position corresponding to this variable. Sum the equation constants and place this sum in the entry corresponding to the objective function value.

We now treat an artificial program example in which we use the combined steps 3 and 4.

**EXAMPLE 6** Use the artificial program method to show that the following system of equations has no nonnegative solution.

$$
\begin{aligned}
-4x_1 + 2x_2 - 12x_3 &= 10 \\
2x_1 - x_2 + 4x_3 &= -3 \\
5x_1 - 2x_2 + 11x_3 &= 1
\end{aligned}
$$

**SOLUTION** We negate the second equation, adjoin artificial variables, and form the linear program

$$
\begin{aligned}
\text{Minimize} \quad & z = y_1 + y_2 + y_3 \\
\text{subject to} \quad & -4x_1 + 2x_2 - 12x_3 + y_1 = 10 \\
& -2x_1 + x_2 - 4x_3 + y_2 = 3 \\
& 5x_1 - 2x_2 + 11x_3 + y_3 = 1 \\
& x_1 \geq 0, \quad x_2 \geq 0, \quad x_3 \geq 0, \quad y_1 \geq 0, \quad y_2 \geq 0, \quad y_3 \geq 0
\end{aligned}
$$

The initial simplex table is

|        | $\mathbf{a}_1$ | $\mathbf{a}_2$ | $\mathbf{a}_3$ | $\mathbf{a}_4$ | $\mathbf{a}_5$ | $\mathbf{a}_6$ | $\mathbf{b}$ |
|--------|------|------|------|------|------|------|------|
|        | 1 | $-1$ | 1 | $-5$ | 0 | 0 | 0 | 14 |
| $\mathbf{a}_4$ | 0 | $-4$ | 2 | $-12$ | 1 | 0 | 0 | 10 |
| $\mathbf{a}_5$ | 0 | $-2$ | ① | $-4$ | 0 | 1 | 0 | 3 |
| $\mathbf{a}_6$ | 0 | 5 | $-2$ | 11 | 0 | 0 | 1 | 1 |

where we have used

$$
\begin{array}{ll}
(\mathbf{a}_1)\colon & -1 = -4 - 2 + 5 \\
(\mathbf{a}_2)\colon & 1 = 2 + 1 - 2 \\
(\mathbf{a}_3)\colon & -5 = -12 - 4 + 11 \\
(\mathbf{b})\colon & 14 = 10 + 3 + 1
\end{array}
$$

to complete the top row. The only possible pivot column is the $\mathbf{a}_2$ column, and the quotient comparison $10/2 > 3/1$ dictates that the pivot is to be made on the 1. Thus $\mathbf{a}_2$ replaces $\mathbf{a}_5$ in the basis. The new table is

|  | $\mathbf{a}_1$ | $\mathbf{a}_2$ | $\mathbf{a}_3$ | $\mathbf{a}_4$ | $\mathbf{a}_5$ | $\mathbf{a}_6$ | $\mathbf{b}$ |
|---|---|---|---|---|---|---|---|
|  | 1 | 1 | 0 | $-1$ | 0 | $-1$ | 0 | 11 |
| $\mathbf{a}_4$ | 0 | 0 | 0 | $-4$ | 1 | $-2$ | 0 | 4 |
| $\mathbf{a}_2$ | 0 | $-2$ | 1 | $-4$ | 0 | 1 | 0 | 3 |
| $\mathbf{a}_6$ | 0 | ① | 0 | 3 | 0 | 2 | 1 | 7 |

The new basic feasible solution is $y_1 = 4$, $x_2 = 3$, $y_3 = 7$, $x_1 = x_3 = y_2 = 0$ with objective function value $z = 11$ (the sum of $y_1$ and $y_3$). A pivot is to be made in the $\mathbf{a}_1$ column, and the 1 is the only choice of pivot. The vector $\mathbf{a}_1$ replaces the artificial vector $\mathbf{a}_6$ in the basis. The new table is

|  | $\mathbf{a}_1$ | $\mathbf{a}_2$ | $\mathbf{a}_3$ | $\mathbf{a}_4$ | $\mathbf{a}_5$ | $\mathbf{a}_6$ | $\mathbf{b}$ |
|---|---|---|---|---|---|---|---|
|  | 1 | 0 | 0 | $-4$ | 0 | $-3$ | $-1$ | 4 |
| $\mathbf{a}_4$ | 0 | 0 | 0 | $-4$ | 1 | $-2$ | 0 | 4 |
| $\mathbf{a}_2$ | 0 | 0 | 1 | 2 | 0 | 5 | 2 | 17 |
| $\mathbf{a}_1$ | 0 | 1 | 0 | 3 | 0 | 2 | 1 | 7 |

The new basic feasible solution is $y_1 = 4$, $x_2 = 17$, $x_1 = 7$, $x_3 = y_2 = y_3 = 0$ with objective function value $z = 4$ (contributed entirely by $y_1 = 4$). There is no possible pivot column, and thus the current basic feasible solution is a minimum. Since the objective function value is not 0, we see that there cannot be a nonnegative solution to the original system of equations. ∎

## APPLICATION

Many problems require nonnegative solutions to enable implementation. In the past we treated this requirement in an ad hoc manner. Here we use the artificial program method to ensure that any obtained solution will already have the nonnegativity conditions met.

**EXAMPLE 7**   The Zeta Research Corporation has determined that a certain blend of three frequencies produces the best background noise for efficient office work, and they have built five instruments that produce these frequencies in differing proportions.

The units of each frequency per unit of instrument are given in the following table

| | Instrument | | | | |
|---|---|---|---|---|---|
| Frequency | | 1 | 2 | 3 | 4 | 5 |
| 1 | 6 | 4 | 2 | 10 | 6 |
| 2 | 4 | 1 | 1 | 4 | 2 |
| 3 | 2 | 7 | 3 | 6 | 8 |

If the desired combination is 8 units of frequency 1, to 3 units of frequency 2, to 12 units of frequency 3, find a nonnegative combination of the instruments that will produce this combination.

SOLUTION    Let $x_1, x_2, x_3, x_4, x_5$ be the relative amounts of the five instruments. Then the system of equations to be solved is

$$6x_1 + 4x_2 + 2x_3 + 10x_4 + 6x_5 = 8$$
$$4x_1 + x_2 + x_3 + 4x_4 + 2x_5 = 3$$
$$2x_1 + 7x_2 + 3x_3 + 6x_4 + 8x_5 = 12$$

We adjoin artificial variables and form the linear program

Minimize    $z = y_1 + y_2 + y_3$
subject to    $6x_1 + 4x_2 + 2x_3 + 10x_4 + 6x_5 + y_1 \qquad\qquad = 8$
$\qquad\qquad 4x_1 + x_2 + x_3 + 4x_4 + 2x_5 \qquad + y_2 \qquad = 3$
$\qquad\qquad 2x_1 + 7x_2 + 3x_3 + 6x_4 + 8x_5 \qquad\qquad + y_3 = 12$
$x_1 \geqslant 0, \quad x_2 \geqslant 0, \quad x_3 \geqslant 0, \quad x_4 \geqslant 0, \quad x_5 \geqslant 0, \quad y_1 \geqslant 0, \quad y_2 \geqslant 0, \quad y_3 \geqslant 0$

Now we obtain the initial simplex table

| | $a_1$ | $a_2$ | $a_3$ | $a_4$ | $a_5$ | $a_6$ | $a_7$ | $a_8$ | $b$ |
|---|---|---|---|---|---|---|---|---|---|
| | 1 | 12 | 12 | 6 | 20 | 16 | 0 | 0 | 0 | 23 |
| $a_6$ | 0 | 6 | 4 | 2 | 10 | 6 | 1 | 0 | 0 | 8 |
| $a_7$ | 0 | 4 | 1 | ① | 4 | 2 | 0 | 1 | 0 | 3 |
| $a_8$ | 0 | 2 | 7 | 3 | 6 | 8 | 0 | 0 | 1 | 12 |

The initial basic feasible solution for the artificial program is $y_1 = 8$, $y_2 = 3$, $y_3 = 12$, $x_1 = x_2 = x_3 = x_4 = x_5 = 0$ with value $z = 23$. The standard basis vectors in this problem may be thought of as pure frequency generators. Thus all of the noise in the initial solution is created by the pure frequency generators.

Any of the true variable columns may be chosen as the pivot column. We take the $a_3$ column for numerical convenience. In this column the quotient

3/1 is the smallest, and the pivot is made on the 1. We obtain the table

|     | $a_1$ | $a_2$ | $a_3$ | $a_4$ | $a_5$ | $a_6$ | $a_7$ | $a_8$ | $b$ |
|-----|-----|-----|-----|-----|-----|-----|-----|-----|-----|
|     | 1 | $-12$ | 6 | 0 | $-4$ | 4 | 0 | $-6$ | 0 | 5 |
| $a_6$ | 0 | $-2$ | 2 | 0 | 2 | ② | 1 | $-2$ | 0 | 2 |
| $a_3$ | 0 | 4 | 1 | 1 | 4 | 2 | 0 | 1 | 0 | 3 |
| $a_8$ | 0 | $-10$ | 4 | 0 | $-6$ | 2 | 0 | $-3$ | 1 | 3 |

We have that $b = 2a_6 + 3a_3 + 3a_8$. That is, the noise can be created with 2 units of pure frequency 1, 3 units of the third instrument, and 3 units of pure frequency 3. The objective function value has fallen to 5, which indicates that 5 units of pure frequency are still being used to fill the gap between what the instruments generate and what is desired.

We pick the $a_5$ column for the pivot column (the $a_2$ column would also be a possibility), and the quotient comparison then dictates that the upper 2 is the pivot. The new table is

|     | $a_1$ | $a_2$ | $a_3$ | $a_4$ | $a_5$ | $a_6$ | $a_7$ | $a_8$ | $b$ |
|-----|-----|-----|-----|-----|-----|-----|-----|-----|-----|
|     | 1 | $-8$ | 2 | 0 | $-8$ | 0 | $-2$ | $-2$ | 0 | 1 |
| $a_5$ | 0 | $-1$ | 1 | 0 | 1 | 1 | 1/2 | $-1$ | 0 | 1 |
| $a_3$ | 0 | 6 | $-1$ | 1 | 2 | 0 | $-1$ | 3 | 0 | 1 |
| $a_8$ | 0 | $-8$ | ② | 0 | $-8$ | 0 | $-1$ | $-1$ | 1 | 1 |

We now have that $b = a_5 + a_3 + a_8$. That is, the noise can be created by 1 unit of instrument 5, 1 unit of instrument 3, and 1 unit of pure frequency 3. The objective function value of 1 reflects the fact that 1 unit of pure frequency is still being used in the noise generation.

The $a_2$ column is the only possible pivot column, and the quotients dictate a pivot on the 2 in this column. We have that $a_2$ replaces $a_8$ in the basis, or that instrument 2 replaces pure frequency 3 in the noise generation. The new table is

|     | $a_1$ | $a_2$ | $a_3$ | $a_4$ | $a_5$ | $a_6$ | $a_7$ | $a_8$ | $b$ |
|-----|-----|-----|-----|-----|-----|-----|-----|-----|-----|
|     | 1 | 0 | 0 | 0 | 0 | 0 | $-1$ | $-1$ | $-1$ | 0 |
| $a_5$ | 0 | 3 | 0 | 0 | 5 | 1 | 1 | $-1/2$ | $-1/2$ | 1/2 |
| $a_3$ | 0 | 2 | 0 | 1 | $-2$ | 0 | $-3/2$ | 5/2 | 1/2 | 3/2 |
| $a_2$ | 0 | $-4$ | 1 | 0 | $-4$ | 0 | $-1/2$ | $-1/2$ | 1/2 | 1/2 |

We have that $b = \frac{1}{2}a_5 + \frac{3}{2}a_3 + \frac{1}{2}a_2$, or that the desired noise can be created by $\frac{1}{2}$ unit from instrument 5, $\frac{3}{2}$ units from instrument 3, and $\frac{1}{2}$ unit from instrument 2. The objective function value of 0 reflects the fact that the noise is now being generated entirely by the instruments. The solution can be put in terms of whole units through multiplication by 2. Thus 1 instrument of type 5, to 3 instruments of type 3, to 1 instrument of type 2 will produce the desired noise. ∎

## THE TWO-PHASE METHOD

We now turn to the problem of solving a linear program that does not have a readily apparent initial simplex table. We will see that two linear programs have to be solved. First the artificial program is used to obtain an initial simplex table, and then the true objective function is adjoined, and the simplex algorithm is run again to obtain the best basic feasible solution. Thus the procedure has two phases.

**EXAMPLE 8**   Solve the linear program

$$\text{Minimize} \qquad z = -x_1 + x_2 + 2x_3 - 4x_4$$
$$\text{subject to} \qquad 3x_1 - x_2 + 2x_3 + 2x_4 = 10$$
$$x_1 + x_2 - 2x_3 + 2x_4 = 2$$
$$x_1 \geqslant 0, \quad x_2 \geqslant 0, \quad x_3 \geqslant 0, \quad x_4 \geqslant 0$$

**SOLUTION**

*Phase I.*   We first set aside the true objective function and form the artificial program

$$\text{Minimize} \qquad z = y_1 + y_2$$
$$\text{subject to} \qquad 3x_1 - x_2 + 2x_3 + 2x_4 + y_1 \qquad = 10$$
$$x_1 + x_2 - 2x_3 + 2x_4 \qquad + y_2 = 2$$
$$x_1 \geqslant 0, \quad x_2 \geqslant 0, \quad x_3 \geqslant 0, \quad x_4 \geqslant 0, \quad y_1 \geqslant 0, \quad y_2 \geqslant 0$$

This program has the initial simplex table

|  | $\mathbf{a}_1$ | $\mathbf{a}_2$ | $\mathbf{a}_3$ | $\mathbf{a}_4$ | $\mathbf{a}_5$ | $\mathbf{a}_6$ | $\mathbf{b}$ |
|---|---|---|---|---|---|---|---|
|  | 1 | 4 | 0 | 0 | 4 | 0 | 0 | 12 |
| $\mathbf{a}_5$ | 0 | 3 | −1 | 2 | 2 | 1 | 0 | 10 |
| $\mathbf{a}_6$ | 0 | ① | 1 | −2 | 2 | 0 | 1 | 2 |

We have initially that $\mathbf{b} = 10\mathbf{a}_5 + 2\mathbf{a}_6$. That is, the requirements of the $\mathbf{b}$ vector are met entirely by the artificial vectors.

There is a 4 in the top row of both the $\mathbf{a}_1$ and the $\mathbf{a}_4$ columns. Thus either will do for a pivot column. We arbitrarily take the $\mathbf{a}_1$ column. The quotients of interest are $\frac{10}{3} > \frac{2}{1}$. Thus the 1 is taken as the pivot, and $\mathbf{a}_1$ will replace $\mathbf{a}_6$ in the basis. We obtain the simplex table

|  | $\mathbf{a}_1$ | $\mathbf{a}_2$ | $\mathbf{a}_3$ | $\mathbf{a}_4$ | $\mathbf{a}_5$ | $\mathbf{a}_6$ | $\mathbf{b}$ |
|---|---|---|---|---|---|---|---|
|  | 1 | 0 | −4 | 8 | −4 | 0 | −4 | 4 |
| $\mathbf{a}_5$ | 0 | 0 | −4 | ⑧ | −4 | 1 | −3 | 4 |
| $\mathbf{a}_1$ | 0 | 1 | 1 | −2 | 2 | 0 | 1 | 2 |

We now have $\mathbf{b} = 4\mathbf{a}_5 + 2\mathbf{a}_1$, so that the requirements of $\mathbf{b}$ are only partially met by the artificial vectors.

The only choice for pivot column is the $\mathbf{a}_3$ column, and the 8 in this column is the only possible pivot. Thus $\mathbf{a}_3$ replaces $\mathbf{a}_5$ in the basis. We obtain the table

$$
\begin{array}{c}
\\
\\
\mathbf{a}_3 \\
\mathbf{a}_1
\end{array}
\begin{array}{cccccc|c}
\mathbf{a}_1 & \mathbf{a}_2 & \mathbf{a}_3 & \mathbf{a}_4 & \mathbf{a}_5 & \mathbf{a}_6 & \mathbf{b} \\
\hline
1 & 0 & 0 & 0 & 0 & -1 & -1 & 0 \\
0 & 0 & -1/2 & 1 & -1/2 & 1/8 & -3/8 & 1/2 \\
0 & 1 & 0 & 0 & 1 & 1/4 & 1/4 & 3
\end{array}
$$

We now have that $\mathbf{b} = \frac{1}{2}\mathbf{a}_3 + 3\mathbf{a}_1$, and we see that the artificial vectors are now completely out of the basis. Thus the constraint system is in a form in which the true objective function may again be considered and the initial simplex table formed.

**Phase II.** We delete the artificial variables and use the form of the constraints given by the last table of Phase I to write the linear program as

$$
\begin{aligned}
\text{Minimize} \quad & z = -x_1 + x_2 + 2x_3 - 4x_4 \\
\text{subject to} \quad & 0x_1 - (1/2)x_2 + x_3 - (1/2)x_4 = 1/2 \\
& x_1 + 0x_2 + 0x_3 + x_4 = 3 \\
& x_1 \geqslant 0, \quad x_2 \geqslant 0, \quad x_3 \geqslant 0, \quad x_4 \geqslant 0
\end{aligned}
$$

The augmented matrix of this system is

$$
\begin{array}{c}
\\
\\
\mathbf{a}_3 \\
\mathbf{a}_1
\end{array}
\begin{array}{cccc|c}
\mathbf{a}_1 & \mathbf{a}_2 & \mathbf{a}_3 & \mathbf{a}_4 & \mathbf{b} \\
\hline
1 & 1 & -1 & -2 & 4 & 0 \\
0 & 0 & -1/2 & 1 & -1/2 & 1/2 \\
0 & ① & 0 & 0 & 1 & 3
\end{array}
$$

This would be a simplex table except for the top row, where there is a 1 in the $\mathbf{a}_1$ column and a $-2$ in the $\mathbf{a}_3$ column. Therefore we will pivot on the 1s that correspond to the basic variables and obtain a simplex table. First we pivot on the 1 in the $\mathbf{a}_1$ column to obtain

$$
\begin{array}{c}
\\
\\
\mathbf{a}_3 \\
\mathbf{a}_1
\end{array}
\begin{array}{cccc|c}
\mathbf{a}_1 & \mathbf{a}_2 & \mathbf{a}_3 & \mathbf{a}_4 & \mathbf{b} \\
\hline
1 & 0 & -1 & -2 & 3 & -3 \\
0 & 0 & -1/2 & ① & -1/2 & 1/2 \\
0 & 1 & 0 & 0 & 1 & 3
\end{array}
$$

Next we pivot on the 1 in the $\mathbf{a}_3$ column and get the simplex table

$$
\begin{array}{c}
\\
\\
\mathbf{a}_3 \\
\mathbf{a}_1
\end{array}
\begin{array}{cccc|c}
\mathbf{a}_1 & \mathbf{a}_2 & \mathbf{a}_3 & \mathbf{a}_4 & \mathbf{b} \\
\hline
1 & 0 & -2 & 0 & 2 & -2 \\
0 & 0 & -1/2 & 1 & -1/2 & 1/2 \\
0 & 1 & 0 & 0 & ① & 3
\end{array}
$$

We observe that these pivots were not simplex pivots but were merely operations designed to produce 0s in the top row of the $\mathbf{a}_1$ and $\mathbf{a}_3$ columns so that the augmented matrix would be a simplex table. The basic feasible solution is $x_3 = 1/2$, $x_1 = 3$, $x_2 = x_4 = 0$ with value $z = -2$. The $\mathbf{a}_4$ column is a candidate to enter the basis, and since the 1 in the bottom row must be the pivot, $\mathbf{a}_1$ must leave the basis. The new table is

$$
\begin{array}{c} \\ \\ \mathbf{a}_3 \\ \mathbf{a}_4 \end{array}
\begin{array}{ccccc|c}
\mathbf{a}_1 & \mathbf{a}_2 & \mathbf{a}_3 & \mathbf{a}_4 & & \mathbf{b} \\
\hline
1 & -2 & -2 & 0 & 0 & -8 \\
0 & 1/2 & -1/2 & 1 & 0 & 2 \\
0 & 1 & 0 & 0 & 1 & 3
\end{array}
$$

We have that $\mathbf{b} = 2\mathbf{a}_3 + 3\mathbf{a}_4$ or that the new basic feasible solution is $x_3 = 2$, $x_4 = 3$, $x_1 = x_2 = 0$ with value $z = -8$. Since there are no candidates to enter the basis, this solution is minimal. ∎

We are now ready to detail a two-phase method for solving arbitrary linear programs. In Phase I the artificial program is used to find a basic feasible solution and dependency table for the constraint system. Then in Phase II the true objective function is adjoined to the dependency table, and the simplex algorithm (maximization or minimization form) is run to find the optimal (maximal or minimal) basic feasible solution.

### Procedure for the two-phase method

#### Phase I

**Step 1.** Use the artificial program method to find a feasible solution and dependency table for the constraint system.

**Step 2.** Discard the columns corresponding to the artificial variables.

#### Phase II

**Step 3.** Adjoin the true objective function equation to the constraint system in the form obtained from the artificial program. Form the augmented matrix for this system. Obtain a simplex table by pivoting on the 1s that correspond to the basic variables.

**Step 4.** Solve the program using the appropriate form of the simplex algorithm (maximization or minimization).

There is an alternate way to perform step 3 that is computationally easier and admits an interesting economic interpretation of the rule for the choice of pivot column. The method gives a construction and interpretation of the objective function row for any dependency table of the constraint system.

**Step 3\*.** (a) Start with a dependency table obtained by any means, insert a column of 0s on the left, and adjoin a top row that has only a 1 in the $z$ position.

(b) Let $z = c_1 x_1 + c_2 x_2 + \cdots + c_n x_n$ be the objective function. For each basic vector $\mathbf{a}_i$, write $c_i$ to the left of the table; and for each column $\mathbf{a}_j$ of the table, write $c_j$ above the column.

(c) For each column $\mathbf{a}_j$, take the product of the entry in each row with the $c_i$ on the left. Add these entries and call the sum $z_j$.

(d) Take the difference $z_j - c_j$ and put this number in the top row of the table in the $\mathbf{a}_j$ column. (Note that $z_j = c_j$ for any basic $\mathbf{a}_j$, and therefore this table will be a simplex table.)

(e) In the **b** column, take the product of the entry in each row with the $c_j$ on the left. Add these entries and call the sum $z_0$. Put $z_0$ in the **b** position of the top row, since it will be the value of the objective function for this basic feasible solution.

We will give a brief example of the use of step 3*. Let the objective function be

$$\text{minimize} \quad 2x_1 + 3x_2 - x_3 + x_4 - 2x_5$$

and suppose that we have obtained the dependency table

$$
\begin{array}{c}
\\
\mathbf{a}_3 \\
\mathbf{a}_2
\end{array}
\begin{array}{cccccc}
\mathbf{a}_1 & \mathbf{a}_2 & \mathbf{a}_3 & \mathbf{a}_4 & \mathbf{a}_5 & \mathbf{b} \\
\left[\begin{array}{ccccc|c}
-2 & 0 & 1 & 2 & 4 & 2 \\
3 & 1 & 0 & -1 & 1 & 4
\end{array}\right]
\end{array}
$$

for some linear program. Then insert two 0s on the left and put a 1 above them. Put the coefficient $c_3 = -1$ to the left of the basis vector $\mathbf{a}_3$ and the coefficient $c_2 = 3$ to the left of the basis vector $\mathbf{a}_2$. Write $c_1 = 2$ above $\mathbf{a}_1$, $c_2 = 3$ above $\mathbf{a}_2$, etc. The numbers

$$
\begin{aligned}
z_1 &= -1(-2) + 3(3) = 11, \\
z_2 &= -1(0) + 3(1) = 3, \\
z_3 &= -1(1) + 3(0) = -1, \\
z_4 &= -1(2) + 3(-1) = -5, \\
z_5 &= -1(4) + 3(1) = -1
\end{aligned}
$$

are placed below the table. Then the entries

$$
\begin{aligned}
z_1 - c_1 &= 11 - 2 = 9, \\
z_2 - c_2 &= 3 - 3 = 0, \\
z_3 - c_3 &= -1 - (-1) = 0, \\
z_4 - c_4 &= -5 - 1 = -6, \\
z_5 - c_5 &= -1 - (-2) = 1
\end{aligned}
$$

are placed in the top row. Finally, we compute

$$z_0 = -1(2) + 3(4) = 10$$

and put this value in the rightmost position of the top row. We then have the simplex table

$$
\begin{array}{c}
\\
\\
c_3 = -1 \quad \mathbf{a}_3 \\
c_2 = 3 \quad \mathbf{a}_2 \\
z_j
\end{array}
\begin{array}{cccccc}
2 & 3 & -1 & 1 & -2 & \\
\mathbf{a}_1 & \mathbf{a}_2 & \mathbf{a}_3 & \mathbf{a}_4 & \mathbf{a}_5 & \mathbf{b} \\
\left[\begin{array}{ccccc|c}
1 & 9 & 0 & 0 & -6 & 1 & 10 \\
0 & -2 & 0 & 1 & 2 & 4 & 2 \\
0 & 3 & 1 & 0 & -1 & 1 & 4
\end{array}\right] \\
& 11 & 3 & -1 & -5 & -1 & 10
\end{array}
$$

We now treat an example by the two-phase algorithm where step 3* is used to obtain the simplex table from the dependency table at the end of Phase I.

**EXAMPLE 9** Solve the linear program

$$\text{Minimize} \quad z = 3x_1 - 2x_2 - 3x_3 + 2x_4 + x_5$$
$$\text{subject to} \quad -8x_1 + 2x_2 + 4x_3 - 8x_4 - 4x_5 = 10$$
$$-2x_1 + 2x_2 + 2x_3 + 6x_4 + 4x_5 = 8$$
$$x_1 \geqslant 0, \quad x_2 \geqslant 0, \quad x_3 \geqslant 0, \quad x_4 \geqslant 0, \quad x_5 \geqslant 0$$

**SOLUTION**

**Phase I.** First we form the artificial program

$$\text{Minimize} \quad z = y_1 + y_2$$
$$\text{subject to} \quad -8x_1 + 2x_2 + 4x_3 - 8x_4 - 4x_5 + y_1 \qquad = 10$$
$$-2x_1 + 2x_2 + 2x_3 + 6x_4 + 4x_5 \qquad + y_2 = 8$$
$$x_1 \geqslant 0, \quad x_2 \geqslant 0, \quad x_3 \geqslant 0, \quad x_4 \geqslant 0, \quad x_5 \geqslant 0, \quad y_1 \geqslant 0, \quad y_2 \geqslant 0$$

and form the simplex table

$$
\begin{array}{c}
\phantom{a} \\
\phantom{a} \\
\mathbf{a}_6 \\
\mathbf{a}_7
\end{array}
\begin{bmatrix}
 & \mathbf{a}_1 & \mathbf{a}_2 & \mathbf{a}_3 & \mathbf{a}_4 & \mathbf{a}_5 & \mathbf{a}_6 & \mathbf{a}_7 & \mathbf{b} \\
1 & -10 & 4 & 6 & -2 & 0 & 0 & 0 & 18 \\
\hline
0 & -8 & 2 & 4 & -8 & -4 & 1 & 0 & 10 \\
0 & -2 & ② & 2 & 6 & 4 & 0 & 1 & 8
\end{bmatrix}
$$

The initial basis is made up entirely of the artificial vectors $\mathbf{a}_6$, $\mathbf{a}_7$. In the top row there is a 4 in the $\mathbf{a}_2$ column and a 6 in the $\mathbf{a}_3$ column. Thus either can be the pivot column. We arbitrarily choose the $\mathbf{a}_2$ column. Since $\frac{10}{2} > \frac{8}{2}$, we take the bottom 2 as the pivot. Then $\mathbf{a}_2$ replaces $\mathbf{a}_7$ in the basis. The new table is

$$
\begin{array}{c}
\phantom{a} \\
\phantom{a} \\
\mathbf{a}_6 \\
\mathbf{a}_2
\end{array}
\begin{bmatrix}
 & \mathbf{a}_1 & \mathbf{a}_2 & \mathbf{a}_3 & \mathbf{a}_4 & \mathbf{a}_5 & \mathbf{a}_6 & \mathbf{a}_7 & \mathbf{b} \\
1 & -6 & 0 & 2 & -14 & -8 & 0 & -2 & 2 \\
\hline
0 & -6 & 0 & ② & -14 & -8 & 1 & -1 & 2 \\
0 & -1 & 1 & 1 & 3 & 2 & 0 & 1/2 & 4
\end{bmatrix}
$$

The new basis is $\mathbf{a}_6$, $\mathbf{a}_2$. The $\mathbf{a}_3$ column is the only possible pivot column, and step 2 dictates that the 2 in the $\mathbf{a}_6$ row is the pivot. Thus $\mathbf{a}_3$ replaces $\mathbf{a}_6$ in the basis. We have

$$
\begin{array}{c}
\phantom{a} \\
\phantom{a} \\
\mathbf{a}_3 \\
\mathbf{a}_2
\end{array}
\begin{bmatrix}
 & \mathbf{a}_1 & \mathbf{a}_2 & \mathbf{a}_3 & \mathbf{a}_4 & \mathbf{a}_5 & \mathbf{a}_6 & \mathbf{a}_7 & \mathbf{b} \\
1 & 0 & 0 & 0 & 0 & 0 & -1 & -1 & 0 \\
\hline
0 & -3 & 0 & 1 & -7 & -4 & 1/2 & -1/2 & 1 \\
0 & 2 & 1 & 0 & 10 & 6 & -1/2 & 1 & 3
\end{bmatrix}
$$

The artificial vectors are now completely out of the basis. We have a dependency table for the constraint system that corresponds to a basic feasible solution. Thus Phase I ends.

***Phase II.*** We now adjoin the true objective function to the system of equations as presented in the last table of Phase I. We obtain

$$\text{Minimize} \quad z = 3x_1 - 2x_2 - 3x_3 + 2x_4 + x_5$$
$$\text{subject to} \quad -3x_1 + 0x_2 + 1x_3 - 7x_4 - 4x_5 = 1$$
$$2x_1 + 1x_2 + 0x_3 + 10x_4 + 6x_5 = 3$$
$$x_1 \geqslant 0, \quad x_2 \geqslant 0, \quad x_3 \geqslant 0 \quad x_4 \geqslant 0, \quad x_5 \geqslant 0$$

We now form the simplex table directly through use of step 3*. Form the augmented matrix with the top row left blank except for the 1 in the leftmost position. As an aid in the computation, we write the objective function coefficients above the table; and for each vector in the basis, we write the corresponding coefficient to the left of the vector. In addition we put a $z_j$ row below the table. Then we compute

$$z_1 = -3(-3) + (-2)2 = 5,$$
$$z_2 = -3(0) + (-2)1 = -2,$$
$$z_3 = -3(1) + (-2)0 = -3,$$
$$z_4 = -3(-7) + (-2)10 = 1,$$
$$z_5 = -3(-4) + (-2)6 = 0,$$
$$z_0 = -3(1) + (-2)3 = -9.$$

These numbers are placed in the $z_j$ row below the augmented matrix. The top row is now filled with the numbers

$$z_1 - c_1 = 5 - 3 = 2,$$
$$z_2 - c_2 = -2 - (-2) = 0,$$
$$z_3 - c_3 = -3 - (-3) = 0,$$
$$z_4 - c_4 = 1 - 2 = -1,$$
$$z_5 - c_5 = 0 - 1 = -1,$$
$$z_0 = -9,$$

in the $\mathbf{a}_1$ through $\mathbf{a}_5$ and $\mathbf{b}$ columns, respectively. The result is the simplex table

|  |  | 3 | −2 | −3 | 2 | 1 |  |
|---|---|---|---|---|---|---|---|
|  |  | $\mathbf{a}_1$ | $\mathbf{a}_2$ | $\mathbf{a}_3$ | $\mathbf{a}_4$ | $\mathbf{a}_5$ | $\mathbf{b}$ |
|  |  | 1 | 2 | 0 | 0 | −1 | −1 | −9 |
| $c_3 = -3$ | $\mathbf{a}_3$ | 0 | −3 | 0 | 1 | −7 | −4 | 1 |
| $c_2 = -2$ | $\mathbf{a}_2$ | 0 | ②  | 1 | 0 | 10 | 6 | 3 |
|  | $z_j$ |  | 5 | −2 | −3 | 1 | 0 | −9 |

We see that the $\mathbf{a}_1$ column is the only possible pivot column and that the 2 is the pivot. Thus $\mathbf{a}_1$ replaces $\mathbf{a}_2$ in the basis, and we obtain the new table

|  |  | $\mathbf{a}_1$ | $\mathbf{a}_2$ | $\mathbf{a}_3$ | $\mathbf{a}_4$ | $\mathbf{a}_5$ | $\mathbf{b}$ |
|---|---|---|---|---|---|---|---|
|  |  | 1 | 0 | −1 | 0 | −11 | −7 | −12 |
| $\mathbf{a}_3$ |  | 0 | 0 | 3/2 | 1 | 8 | 5 | 11/2 |
| $\mathbf{a}_1$ |  | 0 | 1 | 1/2 | 0 | 5 | 3 | 3/2 |

Now there are no possible pivot columns, and thus the minimum solution has been reached. That is, Phase II has ended. The minimal basis is $\mathbf{a}_3$, $\mathbf{a}_1$, and $\mathbf{b} = \frac{11}{2}\mathbf{a}_3 + \frac{3}{2}\mathbf{a}_1$. The basic feasible solution is $x_3 = \frac{11}{2}$, $x_1 = \frac{3}{2}$, $x_2 = x_4 = x_5 = 0$ with value $z = -12$. ∎

## PRODUCTION AT MINIMUM COST

In Section 1.5 of Chapter 1 we used a geometric analysis to examine the problem of meeting production demands at minimum cost. In Section 2.6 of Chapter 2 we did not return to treat this problem with the simplex algorithm because an initial simplex table is not immediate as in the case of the problem of maximizing revenue subject to available resources. Now that we have the two-phase technique, we are able to use the simplex algorithm to solve these problems. We illustrate this in the next example.

**EXAMPLE 10**   The Purity Drug Company manufactures aspirin and saccharin from the tars of five regional types of coal. The coal from region 1 can produce 6 units of aspirin and 15 units of saccharin per unit of tar; the coal from region 2 can produce 6 units of aspirin and 3 units of saccharin per unit of tar; the coal from region 3 can produce 3 units of aspirin and 6 units of saccharin per unit of tar; the coal from region 4 can produce 3 units of aspirin and 9 units of saccharin per unit of tar; and the coal from region 5 can produce 6 units of aspirin and 9 units of saccharin per unit of tar. One unit of tar from region 1 coal costs \$60,000; one unit from region 2 costs \$20,000; one unit from region 3 costs \$30,000; one unit from region 4 costs \$40,000 and one unit from region 5 costs \$60,000. Find the cheapest blend of the regional coals that will produce at least 9 units of aspirin and 24 units of saccharin.

**SOLUTION**   Let $x_1$, $x_2$, $x_3$, $x_4$, $x_5$ be the units of tar from the coals of region 1 through region 5, respectively, and let the costs be in units of \$10,000. Then the desired linear program is to

$$
\begin{aligned}
\text{Minimize} \quad & z = 6x_1 + 2x_2 + 3x_3 + 4x_4 + 6x_5 \\
\text{subject to} \quad & 6x_1 + 6x_2 + 3x_3 + 3x_4 + 6x_5 \geqslant 9 \\
& 15x_1 + 3x_2 + 6x_3 + 9x_4 + 9x_5 \geqslant 24 \\
& x_1 \geqslant 0, \quad x_2 \geqslant 0, \quad x_3 \geqslant 0, \quad x_4 \geqslant 0, \quad x_5 \geqslant 0
\end{aligned}
$$

We need to convert this system of linear inequalities into linear equations before we can start the simplex process. However, we cannot simply add slack variables as we did in Section 2.6 because the inequalities go the wrong way. In this case there is a potential for overproduction or surplus. Therefore we may obtain equations by subtracting a nonnegative surplus variable in each inequality. Thus we obtain the linear program

$$
\begin{aligned}
\text{Minimize} \quad & z = 6x_1 + 2x_2 + 3x_3 + 4x_4 + 6x_5 \\
\text{subject to} \quad & 6x_1 + 6x_2 + 3x_3 + 3x_4 + 6x_5 - x_6 \qquad = 9 \\
& 15x_1 + 3x_2 + 6x_3 + 9x_4 + 9x_5 \qquad - x_7 = 24 \\
& x_1 \geqslant 0, \quad x_2 \geqslant 0, \quad x_3 \geqslant 0, \quad x_4 \geqslant 0, \quad x_5 \geqslant 0, \quad x_6 \geqslant 0, \quad x_7 \geqslant 0
\end{aligned}
$$

There is no immediate initial simplex table for a basic feasible solution, but since the equation constants are nonnegative, we can adjoin the artificial variables $y_1, y_2 \geqslant 0$ and minimize the artificial objective function $z = y_1 + y_2$. This is Phase I. The artificial vectors are $\mathbf{a}_8$ and $\mathbf{a}_9$, which are artificial aspirin and artificial saccharin. The initial simplex table is

|  | | $\mathbf{a}_1$ | $\mathbf{a}_2$ | $\mathbf{a}_3$ | $\mathbf{a}_4$ | $\mathbf{a}_5$ | $\mathbf{a}_6$ | $\mathbf{a}_7$ | $\mathbf{a}_8$ | $\mathbf{a}_9$ | $\mathbf{b}$ |
|---|---|---|---|---|---|---|---|---|---|---|---|
| | 1 | 21 | 9 | 9 | 12 | 15 | $-1$ | $-1$ | 0 | 0 | 33 |
| $\mathbf{a}_8$ | 0 | 6 | 6 | ③ | 3 | 6 | $-1$ | 0 | 1 | 0 | 9 |
| $\mathbf{a}_9$ | 0 | 15 | 3 | 6 | 9 | 9 | 0 | $-1$ | 0 | 1 | 24 |

Here, we separate the surplus variables $x_6, x_7$ from the rest of the constraint variables with a vertical line for ease in reading the table.

Any of the $\mathbf{a}_1$ through $\mathbf{a}_5$ columns is a potential pivot column. We arbitrarily choose the $\mathbf{a}_3$ column. Since $\frac{9}{3} < \frac{24}{6}$, the 3 is the pivot. We replace $\mathbf{a}_8$ with $\mathbf{a}_3$ in the basis. The new table is

|  | | $\mathbf{a}_1$ | $\mathbf{a}_2$ | $\mathbf{a}_3$ | $\mathbf{a}_4$ | $\mathbf{a}_5$ | $\mathbf{a}_6$ | $\mathbf{a}_7$ | $\mathbf{a}_8$ | $\mathbf{a}_9$ | $\mathbf{b}$ |
|---|---|---|---|---|---|---|---|---|---|---|---|
| | 1 | 3 | $-9$ | 0 | 3 | $-3$ | 2 | $-1$ | $-3$ | 0 | 6 |
| $\mathbf{a}_3$ | 0 | 2 | 2 | 1 | 1 | 2 | $-1/3$ | 0 | $1/3$ | 0 | 3 |
| $\mathbf{a}_9$ | 0 | 3 | $-9$ | 0 | ③ | $-3$ | 2 | $-1$ | $-2$ | 1 | 6 |

The objective function value has decreased to $z = 6$, and the only artificial vector left in the basis is $\mathbf{a}_9$, artificial saccharin. That is, 6 units of the artificial vector $\mathbf{a}_9$ are contributing to the makeup of $\mathbf{b}$.

Now the pivot column can be either of $\mathbf{a}_1$, $\mathbf{a}_4$ or the surplus vector $\mathbf{a}_6$. We arbitrarily choose the $\mathbf{a}_4$ vector to enter the basis. Then the quotient comparison $\frac{3}{1} > \frac{6}{3}$ dictates that the 3 must be the pivot. Thus $\mathbf{a}_9$ will leave the basis. The new table is

|  | | $\mathbf{a}_1$ | $\mathbf{a}_2$ | $\mathbf{a}_3$ | $\mathbf{a}_4$ | $\mathbf{a}_5$ | $\mathbf{a}_6$ | $\mathbf{a}_7$ | $\mathbf{a}_8$ | $\mathbf{a}_9$ | $\mathbf{b}$ |
|---|---|---|---|---|---|---|---|---|---|---|---|
| | 1 | 0 | 0 | 0 | 0 | 0 | 0 | 0 | $-1$ | $-1$ | 0 |
| $\mathbf{a}_3$ | 0 | 1 | 5 | 1 | 0 | 3 | $-1$ | $1/3$ | 1 | $-1/3$ | 1 |
| $\mathbf{a}_4$ | 0 | 1 | $-3$ | 0 | 1 | $-1$ | $2/3$ | $-1/3$ | $-2/3$ | $1/3$ | 2 |

The new basis is $\mathbf{a}_3$, $\mathbf{a}_4$, and we see that Phase I has ended. The linear combination $\mathbf{b} = \mathbf{a}_3 + 2\mathbf{a}_4$ means that it is feasible to meet the production requirements with 1 unit of tar from region 3 and 2 units of tar from region 4.

*NOTE*:   If the $\mathbf{a}_1$ column had been chosen as the pivot column in the previous table, then the quotient comparison $\frac{3}{2} < \frac{6}{3}$ would have dictated that the 2 be the pivot. That is, we would have replaced $\mathbf{a}_3$ with $\mathbf{a}_1$, the artificial vector $\mathbf{a}_9$ would have remained in the basis, and another Phase I pivot (at least) would have been necessary. Thus we see that it may take more than $m$ simplex pivots to remove $m$ artificial vectors from the basis.

We now return the true objective function and begin Phase II. The constraint equations are taken in the final form of Phase I (without the artificial variables), and they are used to start the construction of the simplex table for Phase II. We use step 3* to complete the construction below.

| | | | 6 | 2 | 3 | 4 | 6 | 0 | 0 | |
|---|---|---|---|---|---|---|---|---|---|---|
| | | | $a_1$ | $a_2$ | $a_3$ | $a_4$ | $a_5$ | $a_6$ | $a_7$ | b |
| | | 1 | 1 | 1 | 0 | 0 | $-1$ | $-1/3$ | $-1/3$ | 11 |
| $c_3 = 3$ | $a_3$ | 0 | ① | 5 | 1 | 0 | 3 | $-1$ | $1/3$ | 1 |
| $c_4 = 4$ | $a_4$ | 0 | 1 | $-3$ | 0 | 1 | $-1$ | $2/3$ | $-1/3$ | 2 |
| | $z_j$ | | 7 | 3 | 3 | 4 | 5 | $-1/3$ | $-1/3$ | 11 |

Either the $a_1$ or the $a_2$ column can be the pivot column. We take the $a_1$ column for computational convenience. Then $1/1 < 2/1$, and the 1 in the $a_3$ row is the pivot.

*NOTE:* There is an economic interpretation of the simplex rules that may be seen in the present table. We have that $a_1 = a_3 + a_4$. This means that we can obtain synthetic region 1 coal tar from a mixture of one unit of region 3 coal tar and one unit of region 4 coal tar. The natural question to ask is "which is cheaper?". The cost of synthetic region 1 coal tar is $z_1 = 3(1) + 4(1) = 7$, and the cost of region 1 coal tar is $c_1 = 6$. Since $7 > 6$, the cost of region 1 coal tar, it makes sense to put some region 1 coal tar into the mixture. That is, put $a_1$ into the basis. We observe that $7 > 6$ is equivalent to $7 - 6 = 1 > 0$, and step 1 indicates that $a_1$ is a possible pivot column. In general, if $z_j > c_j$, then $z_j - c_j > 0$, and $a_j$ is a candidate to enter the basis. In other words, if synthetic item $j$ is more expensive than the real item $j$, then put some real item $j$ into the mixture. Now, step 2 comes into play. If equality is to be maintained when some coal tar from region 1 is put into the mixture, then something else has to be taken out. For each unit of $a_1$ that is put into the makeup of $b$, one unit of $a_3$ and one unit of $a_4$ must be removed. We see that the contribution from $a_3$ will be depleted first, and $a_3$ is removed from the basis. This is the essence of step 2. We are not allowed to remove more of a substance from the contribution to the $b$ vector than is present in the mixture.

The next simplex table is

| | | $a_1$ | $a_2$ | $a_3$ | $a_4$ | $a_5$ | $a_6$ | $a_7$ | b |
|---|---|---|---|---|---|---|---|---|---|
| | 1 | 0 | $-4$ | $-1$ | 0 | $-4$ | $2/3$ | $-2/3$ | 10 |
| $a_1$ | 0 | 1 | 5 | 1 | 0 | 3 | $-1$ | $1/3$ | 1 |
| $a_4$ | 0 | 0 | $-8$ | $-1$ | 1 | $-4$ | ⑤/③ | $-2/3$ | 1 |

We have that $b = a_1 + a_4$ with $z = 10$. That is, we have that the demands can be met with 1 unit of each of the region 1 and region 4 coal tars at a cost of \$100,000. The $a_6$ column is the only possible pivot column and the pivot must be the 5/3. Thus $a_6$ replaces $a_4$ in the basis. This means that coal tar from region 4 is replaced by more coal tar from region 1 and some overproduction of aspirin. The next simplex table is

|  | $a_1$ | $a_2$ | $a_3$ | $a_4$ | $a_5$ | $a_6$ | $a_7$ | $b$ |
|---|---|---|---|---|---|---|---|---|
|  | 1 | 0 | $-4/5$ | $-3/5$ | $-2/5$ | $-12/5$ | 0 | $-6/15$ | $48/5$ |
| $a_1$ | 0 | 1 | $1/5$ | $2/5$ | $3/5$ | $3/5$ | 0 | $-1/15$ | $8/5$ |
| $a_6$ | 0 | 0 | $-24/5$ | $-3/5$ | $3/5$ | $-12/5$ | 1 | $-2/5$ | $3/5$ |

We see that the minimal solution is given by $\mathbf{b} = \frac{8}{5}\mathbf{a}_1 + \frac{3}{5}\mathbf{a}_6$ with value $z = \frac{48}{5}$. That is, the minimum cost production schedule is obtained by using $\frac{8}{5}$ units of coal tar from region 1 at a cost of \$96,000. Since $x_6 = \frac{3}{5}$ in this schedule, we see that there is an overproduction of aspirin in this minimal cost schedule. ∎

## EXERCISES 4.7

In Exercises 1–6, use the minimization form of the simplex algorithm to solve the given linear program.

**1.** Minimize $\quad z = -8x_1 + 4x_2$
subject to
$$2x_1 - 2x_2 \leqslant 4$$
$$4x_1 - 2x_2 \leqslant 9$$
$$x_1 \geqslant 0, \quad x_2 \geqslant 0$$

**2.** Minimize $\quad z = \phantom{-}16x_1 - 9x_2$
subject to
$$-10x_1 + 6x_2 \leqslant 12$$
$$-6x_1 + 3x_2 \leqslant 3$$
$$x_1 \geqslant 0, \quad x_2 \geqslant 0$$

**3.** Minimize $\quad z = \phantom{-}x_1 - 4x_2 + 5x_3 + 4x_4$
subject to
$$3x_1 + \phantom{2}x_2 - \phantom{2}x_3 - 2x_4 \leqslant 3$$
$$2x_1 + 2x_2 + \phantom{2}x_3 - 2x_4 \leqslant 10$$
$$x_1 \geqslant 0, \quad x_2 \geqslant 0, \quad x_3 \geqslant 0, \quad x_4 \geqslant 0$$

**4.** Minimize $\quad z = -5x_1 + 13x_2 + x_3 + 18x_4$
subject to
$$3x_1 - \phantom{2}4x_2 + x_3 - 11x_4 \leqslant 10$$
$$x_1 - \phantom{2}2x_2 - x_3 - \phantom{1}3x_4 \leqslant 2$$
$$x_1 \geqslant 0, \quad x_2 \geqslant 0, \quad x_3 \geqslant 0, \quad x_4 \geqslant 0$$

**5.** Minimize $\quad z = \phantom{-}2x_1 + 10x_2 - 12x_3$
subject to
$$-3x_1 - \phantom{2}x_2 + 2x_3 \leqslant 16$$
$$2x_1 - \phantom{2}x_2 + \phantom{2}x_3 \leqslant 2$$
$$5x_1 - 3x_2 + 4x_3 \leqslant 12$$
$$x_1 \geqslant 0, \quad x_2 \geqslant 0, \quad x_3 \geqslant 0$$

**6.** Minimize $\quad z = -8x_1 + \phantom{2}x_2 + 2x_3$
subject to
$$x_1 + 3x_2 - \phantom{2}x_3 \leqslant 3$$
$$3x_1 + 3x_2 \phantom{- 2x_3} \leqslant 10$$
$$5x_1 + 10x_2 - 2x_3 \leqslant 20$$
$$x_1 \geqslant 0, \quad x_2 \geqslant 0, \quad x_3 \geqslant 0$$

In each of Exercises 7–12 a simplex table is given. Determine the column basis for the constraint system and the set of basic variables. Use the dependency portion of the table to write $\mathbf{b}$ and $\mathbf{a}_3$ in terms of the column basis.

7.

| | | $\mathbf{a}_1$ | $\mathbf{a}_2$ | $\mathbf{a}_3$ | $\mathbf{a}_4$ | $\mathbf{b}$ |
|---|---|---|---|---|---|---|
| | 1 | 6 | 0 | $-1$ | 0 | $-8$ |
| $\mathbf{a}_2$ | 0 | $-1$ | 1 | $1/4$ | 0 | 2 |
| $\mathbf{a}_4$ | 0 | 8 | 0 | $-1/2$ | 1 | 3 |

8.

| | | $\mathbf{a}_1$ | $\mathbf{a}_2$ | $\mathbf{a}_3$ | $\mathbf{a}_4$ | $\mathbf{b}$ |
|---|---|---|---|---|---|---|
| | 1 | $-10$ | 0 | $-2$ | 0 | $-6$ |
| $\mathbf{a}_2$ | 0 | 2 | 1 | $1/3$ | 0 | 1 |
| $\mathbf{a}_4$ | 0 | $-14$ | 0 | $-2$ | 1 | 12 |

9.

| | | $\mathbf{a}_1$ | $\mathbf{a}_2$ | $\mathbf{a}_3$ | $\mathbf{a}_4$ | $\mathbf{a}_5$ | $\mathbf{b}$ |
|---|---|---|---|---|---|---|---|
| | 1 | 0 | 0 | $-16$ | $-3$ | $-1/2$ | $-16$ |
| $\mathbf{a}_1$ | 0 | 1 | 0 | 3 | $1/2$ | $-1/4$ | 2 |
| $\mathbf{a}_2$ | 0 | 0 | 1 | 5 | 1 | $-1/4$ | $9/2$ |

10.

| | | $\mathbf{a}_1$ | $\mathbf{a}_2$ | $\mathbf{a}_3$ | $\mathbf{a}_4$ | $\mathbf{a}_5$ | $\mathbf{b}$ |
|---|---|---|---|---|---|---|---|
| | 1 | 0 | 0 | $-19$ | 1 | $-4$ | $-41$ |
| $\mathbf{a}_1$ | 0 | 1 | 0 | 3 | $-2/3$ | 1 | 9 |
| $\mathbf{a}_2$ | 0 | 0 | 1 | 2 | $-1/2$ | $1/2$ | 4 |

11.

| | | $\mathbf{a}_1$ | $\mathbf{a}_2$ | $\mathbf{a}_3$ | $\mathbf{a}_4$ | $\mathbf{a}_5$ | $\mathbf{a}_6$ | $\mathbf{b}$ |
|---|---|---|---|---|---|---|---|---|
| | 1 | 0 | 0 | $-12$ | 0 | $-2$ | 0 | $-18$ |
| $\mathbf{a}_4$ | 0 | 0 | 0 | $-4$ | 1 | $-1$ | 4 | 13 |
| $\mathbf{a}_2$ | 0 | 0 | 1 | 3 | 0 | $1/2$ | $-1$ | $1/2$ |
| $\mathbf{a}_1$ | 0 | 1 | 0 | $-14$ | 0 | $-2$ | 5 | 2 |

12.

| | | $\mathbf{a}_1$ | $\mathbf{a}_2$ | $\mathbf{a}_3$ | $\mathbf{a}_4$ | $\mathbf{a}_5$ | $\mathbf{a}_6$ | $\mathbf{b}$ |
|---|---|---|---|---|---|---|---|---|
| | 1 | 0 | 0 | 3 | $-2$ | 0 | 0 | $-18$ |
| $\mathbf{a}_1$ | 0 | 1 | 0 | 2 | 1 | $-2$ | 0 | 1 |
| $\mathbf{a}_2$ | 0 | 0 | 1 | $-7$ | $-2$ | 5 | 0 | 2 |
| $\mathbf{a}_6$ | 0 | 0 | 0 | $-8$ | $-2$ | 7 | 1 | 11 |

In Exercises 13–18, refer to the last simplex table of the indicated exercise. By direct computation, check the linear combinations giving the nonbasic columns and $\mathbf{b}$ in terms of the basis, and thereby verify that the numbers in the constraint rows are correct.

**13.** Exercise 1        **14.** Exercise 2        **15.** Exercise 3

**16.** Exercise 4        **17.** Exercise 5        **18.** Exercise 6

In Exercises 19–22, convert the given system of constraints into a system of equations in standard form with nonnegative variables.

**19.** $4x_1 - 2x_2 \leqslant 7$     $4x_1 - 2x_2 + x_3 = 7$
$3x_1 + 5x_2 \geqslant 4$
$6x_1 + 2x_2 = -4$     $3x_1 + 5x_2 - x_4 = 4$
$x_1 \geqslant 0, \quad x_2 \geqslant 0$

**20.** $-5x_1 + 4x_2 = -3$
$6x_1 + 2x_2 \leqslant 5$
$-2x_1 + 3x_2 \geqslant 4$
$x_1 \geqslant 0, \quad x_2 \geqslant 0$

**21.**  $4x_1 + x_2 + 3x_3 \geqslant -2$
$6x_1 - 5x_2 - 2x_3 \geqslant 4$
$-5x_1 + 3x_2 + x_3 \leqslant 2$
$-3x_1 + 4x_2 + 7x_3 \leqslant -5$
$5x_1 + 8x_2 - 2x_3 = 4$
$x_1 \geqslant 0, \quad x_2 \geqslant 0, \quad x_3 \geqslant 0$

**22.**  $9x_1 - 6x_2 + 3x_3 \leqslant -7$
$5x_1 + 3x_2 - x_3 \leqslant 3$
$4x_1 - x_2 - 4x_3 = 6$
$-8x_1 - 2x_2 + 6x_3 \geqslant 5$
$6x_1 + 3x_2 - 5x_3 \geqslant -2$
$x_1 \geqslant 0, \quad x_2 \geqslant 0, \quad x_3 \geqslant 0$

In Exercises 23–26 a system of constraints is given. (a) Set up the artificial program for these constraints, and (b) find the initial simplex table for this program.

**23.**  $2x_1 + 3x_2 - x_3 = 4$
$-3x_1 - 2x_2 + x_3 = 6$
$x_1 \geqslant 0, \quad x_2 \geqslant 0, \quad x_3 \geqslant 0$

**24.**  $4x_1 - 2x_2 - 3x_3 = 7$
$-6x_1 + x_2 + 2x_3 = 5$
$x_1 \geqslant 0, \quad x_2 \geqslant 0, \quad x_3 \geqslant 0$

**25.** $6x_1 + 2x_2 - 4x_3 = 3$
$x_1 + 3x_2 + 5x_3 = -4$
$5x_1 - 4x_2 - x_3 = 2$
$x_1 \geqslant 0, \quad x_2 \geqslant 0, \quad x_3 \geqslant 0$

**26.**  $4x_1 - 5x_2 - x_3 = 7$
$-8x_1 + 3x_2 + 4x_3 = 6$
$x_1 + 4x_2 - 2x_3 = -1$
$x_1 \geqslant 0, \quad x_2 \geqslant 0, \quad x_3 \geqslant 0$

In Exercises 27–34, use the artificial program method to find a nonnegative solution to the given system of constraints or to show that none exists.

**27.** $2x_1 + 4x_2 - 4x_3 = 4$
$4x_1 - 6x_2 - 6x_3 = 10$
$x_1 \geqslant 0, \quad x_2 \geqslant 0, \quad x_3 \geqslant 0$

**28.** $-8x_1 - 4x_2 + 6x_3 = 18$
$2x_1 - 2x_2 + 2x_3 = 2$
$x_1 \geqslant 0, \quad x_2 \geqslant 0, \quad x_3 \geqslant 0$

**29.** $-4x_1 - 2x_2 + 2x_3 - 6x_4 = 10$
$3x_1 - 2x_2 + x_3 + 2x_4 = 3$
$x_1 \geqslant 0, \quad x_2 \geqslant 0, \quad x_3 \geqslant 0, \quad x_4 \geqslant 0$

**30.** $-2x_1 + x_2 + 4x_3 - x_4 = 3$
$-7x_1 + 3x_2 - 6x_3 - 2x_4 = 12$
$x_1 \geqslant 0, \quad x_2 \geqslant 0, \quad x_3 \geqslant 0, \quad x_4 \geqslant 0$

**31.** $-2x_1 + 8x_2 + 2x_3 - 6x_4 = 8$
$-x_1 + 2x_2 + x_3 - 4x_4 = 3$
$5x_1 - 12x_2 - 2x_3 + 7x_4 = 2$
$x_1 \geqslant 0, \quad x_2 \geqslant 0, \quad x_3 \geqslant 0, \quad x_4 \geqslant 0,$

**32.** $-10x_1 + 4x_2 - 2x_3 - 3x_4 = 15$
$10x_1 - 10x_2 + 2x_3 - 2x_4 = 4$
$-4x_1 + 2x_2 - x_3 + x_4 = 2$
$x_1 \geqslant 0, \quad x_2 \geqslant 0, \quad x_3 \geqslant 0, \quad x_4 \geqslant 0$

**33.**  $6x_1 - 6x_2 + 2x_3 - 2x_4 = 8$
$-4x_1 + x_2 - x_3 - 4x_4 = 3$
$x_1 \geqslant 0, \quad x_2 \geqslant 0, \quad x_3 \geqslant 0, \quad x_4 \geqslant 0$

**34.** $-3x_1 - 2x_2 - 5x_3 + 6x_4 = 5$
$-3x_1 + 3x_2 + 6x_3 - 12x_4 = 9$
$x_1 \geqslant 0, \quad x_2 \geqslant 0, \quad x_3 \geqslant 0, \quad x_4 \geqslant 0$

**35.** Vacuglass Corporation manufactures thermopane picture windows in three sizes: (A) 36 × 36 inch, (B) 36 × 48 inch, and (C) 48 × 48 inch on five production lines. The windows are transported to central markets in their own customized railroad cars. The set of cars holds 1100 (A) windows, 500 (B) windows, and

1600 (C) windows; the table below gives the daily output of the production lines in 100s of windows.

|  | **Lines** | | | | |
|---|---|---|---|---|---|
|  | 1 | 2 | 3 | 4 | 5 |
| (A) | 5 | 2 | 5 | 4 | 3 |
| (B) | 2 | 1 | 2 | 2 | 3 |
| (C) | 3 | 3 | 6 | 7 | 8 |

Use the artificial program method to find a production schedule that will produce a train load of windows.

36. Stalwart Office Furniture Inc. manufactures desks, bookcases, and file cabinets at five locations. They have contracted to supply 2200 desks, 2200 bookcases, and 500 filing cabinets to the Marine Corps. The daily production capabilities of the plants (in 100s of units) are given in the table below.

|  | **Plant** | | | | |
|---|---|---|---|---|---|
|  | 1 | 2 | 3 | 4 | 5 |
| Desks | 6 | 9 | 10 | 9 | 3 |
| Bookcases | 11 | 10 | 6 | 9 | 4 |
| File cabinets | 3 | 2 | 1 | 2 | 1 |

Use the artificial program method to find a production schedule that will enable the firm to exactly meet the conditions of the contract.

In Exercises 37–40, use the two-phase method to solve the given linear program.

37. Minimize $z = 3x_1 + 2x_2 + 3x_3 + x_4$
    subject to
    $$8x_1 + 2x_2 + 2x_3 - 4x_4 = 4$$
    $$3x_1 - 3x_2 + x_3 - x_4 = 18$$
    $$x_1 \geqslant 0, \quad x_2 \geqslant 0, \quad x_3 \geqslant 0, \quad x_4 \geqslant 0$$

38. Minimize $z = 4x_1 + 2x_2 + x_3 - 5x_4$
    subject to
    $$x_1 - x_2 + 2x_3 - 5x_4 = 13$$
    $$3x_1 + 9x_2 - 6x_3 - 3x_4 = 3$$
    $$x_1 \geqslant 0, \quad x_2 \geqslant 0, \quad x_3 \geqslant 0, \quad x_4 \geqslant 0$$

39. Minimize $z = -x_1 - 3x_2 - 4x_3 - 4x_4$
    subject to
    $$x_1 - 2x_2 + 2x_3 - 2x_4 = 4$$
    $$4x_1 - 6x_2 + 9x_3 - 3x_4 = 17$$
    $$x_1 \geqslant 0, \quad x_2 \geqslant 0, \quad x_3 \geqslant 0, \quad x_4 \geqslant 0$$

40. Minimize $z = 2x_1 + 3x_2 + x_3 - 4x_4$
    subject to
    $$7x_1 - 5x_2 + 3x_3 - 2x_4 = 10$$
    $$2x_1 - 3x_2 + x_3 + x_4 = 3$$
    $$x_1 \geqslant 0, \quad x_2 \geqslant 0, \quad x_3 \geqslant 0, \quad x_4 \geqslant 0$$

In Exercises 41–42 a linear program and a dependency table for some basis of the constraint system are given. (a) Use step 3* to compute the top row entries of the corresponding simplex table. (b) Let the coefficients in each of the four columns of the constraint system represent parameters in some process, and compare the cost of the nonbasic processes with equivalent combinations of basic processes.

**41.** Minimize    $z = 3x_1 + 6x_2 + 2x_3 + 4x_4$
subject to    $x_1 + 4x_2 + 3x_3 + 5x_4 = 6$
$2x_1 + 9x_2 + 7x_3 + 11x_4 = 13$
$x_1 \geqslant 0, \quad x_2 \geqslant 0, \quad x_3 \geqslant 0, \quad x_4 \geqslant 0$

$$\begin{array}{c} \quad\ \mathbf{a}_1\ \mathbf{a}_2\ \mathbf{a}_3\ \mathbf{a}_4 \qquad \mathbf{b} \\ \begin{matrix} \mathbf{a}_1 \\ \mathbf{a}_3 \end{matrix} \left[ \begin{array}{cccc|c} 1 & 1 & 0 & 2 & 3 \\ 0 & 1 & 1 & 1 & 1 \end{array} \right] \end{array}$$

**42.** Minimize    $z = 6x_1 + 4x_2 + 2x_3 + x_4$
subject to    $12x_1 + 11x_2 + 5x_3 + 2x_4 = 12$
$5x_1 + 5x_2 + 2x_3 + x_4 = 5$
$x_1 \geqslant 0, \quad x_2 \geqslant 0, \quad x_3 \geqslant 0, \quad x_4 \geqslant 0$

$$\begin{array}{c} \quad\ \mathbf{a}_1\ \mathbf{a}_2\ \mathbf{a}_3\ \mathbf{a}_4 \qquad \mathbf{b} \\ \begin{matrix} \mathbf{a}_3 \\ \mathbf{a}_4 \end{matrix} \left[ \begin{array}{cccc|c} 2 & 1 & 1 & 0 & 2 \\ 1 & 3 & 0 & 1 & 1 \end{array} \right] \end{array}$$

**43.** The Greater Champaign Bottling Company has four lines that bottle cola and lemon-lime soft drinks. The capacities of the lines are given in the table below in 100s of cases per day.

|  | Line | | | |
|---|---|---|---|---|
|  | 1 | 2 | 3 | 4 |
| Cola | 15 | 7 | 9 | 2 |
| Lemon-lime | 7 | 3 | 4 | 1 |

The company has determined a need to bottle 6300 cases of cola and 2900 cases of lemon-lime. If the cost per day is $500 for line 1, $200 for line 2, $300 for line 3, and $100 for line 4, find a production schedule that will meet or exceed the cola and lemon-lime requirements at minimum cost.

**44.** Plasticap Corporation manufactures small and medium batting helmets at four plants. The daily capabilities of the plants are given in the table below in 1000s of helmets.

|  | Plant | | | |
|---|---|---|---|---|
|  | 1 | 2 | 3 | 4 |
| Small | 9 | 22 | 4 | 17 |
| Medium | 2 | 5 | 1 | 4 |

The company has a contract for 51,000 small and 12,000 medium helmets. If the daily costs are $3000 for plant 1, $9000 for plant 2, $2000 for plant 3, and $8000 for plant 4, find a production schedule that will meet or exceed the contract requirements at minimum cost.

# 5

# Orthogonality

In this chapter we develop one of the key concepts in the geometry of the vector space $R^n$, namely, the concept of orthogonality of vectors. Put briefly, orthogonality is the classical Euclidean concept of perpendicularity transferred to the context of vector spaces. It is necessary to have an algebraic condition for orthogonality so that it can be applied in the setting of vector spaces, and we will discuss this criterion in Section 5.1. To illustrate its use, we will show how equations of planes in $R^3$ can be derived by using orthogonality conditions.

In Section 5.2 we will discuss mutually perpendicular basis vectors, a concept that leads to the notion of orthonormal basis. An important technique of generating orthogonal vectors, called orthogonal projection, is analogous to dropping perpendiculars, and it is also described in Section 5.2. The idea of projection is then applied in Section 5.3 to derive the formulas for approximating a given set of data points in the plane by a straight line. This method of approximation is called least squares approximation. In Section 5.4 the approximation methods are extended, and certain types of nonlinear problems are treated. We will show in that section how approximate solutions of inconsistent systems can be obtained and how the concept of a generalized inverse matrix can be used to solve approximation problems.

## 5.1 SCALAR PRODUCTS AND ORTHOGONALITY

*The Scalar Product of Two Vectors, Orthogonality, Equations of Planes*

In this section we continue and extend the discussion of the geometry of vectors that was begun in Section 4.1. We will introduce the scalar product of two vectors and use it to obtain an algebraic condition for two vectors to be orthogonal (perpendicular). We will then apply the orthogonality condition to derive equations of planes in $R^3$.

**305**

## THE SCALAR PRODUCT OF TWO VECTORS

Let $\mathbf{u} = (u_1, u_2, \ldots, u_n)$ and $\mathbf{v} = (v_1, v_2, \ldots, v_n)$ be vectors in $R^n$. Then the **scalar product** of $\mathbf{u}$ and $\mathbf{v}$ is defined to be

$$\mathbf{u} \cdot \mathbf{v} = u_1 v_1 + u_2 v_2 + \cdots + u_n v_n$$

The terminology "scalar" product is appropriate, since the result of the product is a scalar, not a vector. The number $\mathbf{u} \cdot \mathbf{v}$ is also called the **dot product** (because of the dot notation) and the **inner product** of $\mathbf{u}$ and $\mathbf{v}$ in various textbooks. The scalar product is computed by adding the products of the respective components of the two vectors.

**EXAMPLE 1** Find the scalar product of the following pairs of vectors:

(a) $\mathbf{u} = (5, 1, -2)$ and $\mathbf{v} = (4, -3, 2)$

(b) $\mathbf{a} = (6, 1, 3, -4, -5)$ and $\mathbf{b} = (-1, 2, -4, 5, -7)$

SOLUTION We have from the definition that

(a) $\mathbf{u} \cdot \mathbf{v} = 5 \cdot 4 + 1 \cdot (-3) + (-2) \cdot 2 = 20 - 3 - 4 = 13$

and (b) $\mathbf{a} \cdot \mathbf{b} = -6 + 2 - 12 - 20 + 35 = -1$ ▮▮

The scalar product of two vectors in $R^n$ corresponds to the operation of matrix multiplication when the first vector is written as a row and the second vector is written as a column. For example, we can find the scalar product in part (a) of the preceding example by writing

$$[5 \quad 1 \quad -2] \begin{bmatrix} 4 \\ -3 \\ 2 \end{bmatrix} = [20 - 3 - 4] = [13]$$

Thus we can think of performing matrix multiplication as the calculation of the scalar products of the rows of the first matrix and the columns of the second matrix.

There are several properties of the scalar product that can be verified algebraically. We list them for convenience, but we suggest that the reader simply use experience with arithmetic properties of numbers to manipulate the scalar product correctly.

**THEOREM 1**

Let $\mathbf{u}$, $\mathbf{v}$, $\mathbf{w}$ be vectors in $R^n$ and let $a$ be a scalar. Then:

(i) $\mathbf{u} \cdot \mathbf{v} = \mathbf{v} \cdot \mathbf{u}$

(ii) $\mathbf{u} \cdot (\mathbf{v} + \mathbf{w}) = \mathbf{u} \cdot \mathbf{v} + \mathbf{u} \cdot \mathbf{w}$

(iii) $a(\mathbf{u} \cdot \mathbf{v}) = (a\mathbf{u}) \cdot \mathbf{v} = \mathbf{u} \cdot (a\mathbf{v})$

(iv) $\mathbf{0} \cdot \mathbf{u} = 0$

(v) $\mathbf{u} \cdot \mathbf{u} = |\mathbf{u}|^2$

The last item, property (v), relates scalar products and magnitude. For instance, if $\mathbf{u} = (2, -7, 5)$ in $R^3$, then

$$\mathbf{u} \cdot \mathbf{u} = 2^2 + (-7)^2 + 5^2 = 78 = |\mathbf{u}|^2$$

Thus magnitude can be calculated by using the scalar product.

The following example illustrates how the properties of Theorem 1 can be used in calculations.

**EXAMPLE 2** Let $\mathbf{u} = (1, 3)$, $\mathbf{v} = (-2, 2)$, $\mathbf{w} = (5, 1)$. Calculate $\mathbf{u} \cdot (4\mathbf{v} - 2\mathbf{w})$.

SOLUTION There are different ways to proceed. One is to calculate $4\mathbf{v} - 2\mathbf{w} = (-18, 6)$ and then find $\mathbf{u} \cdot (4\mathbf{v} - 2\mathbf{w}) = -18 + 18 = 0$. Another is to apply properties (ii) and (iii) of Theorem 1 to get $\mathbf{u} \cdot (4\mathbf{v} - 2\mathbf{w}) = 4\mathbf{u} \cdot \mathbf{v} - 2\mathbf{u} \cdot \mathbf{w} = 4 \cdot 4 - 2 \cdot 8 = 0$. ∎

There are two inequalities of some importance involving magnitudes and scalar products. We will not make great use of them in this book, but we state them here for completeness.

---

**THEOREM 2**

If $\mathbf{u}$, $\mathbf{v}$ are vectors in $R^n$, then

(i) $|\mathbf{u} \cdot \mathbf{v}| \leqslant |\mathbf{u}| |\mathbf{v}|$    (Schwarz's inequality)

(ii) $|\mathbf{u} + \mathbf{v}| \leqslant |\mathbf{u}| + |\mathbf{v}|$    (triangle inequality)

---

## ORTHOGONALITY

The geometric notion of perpendicularity of line segments is familiar from Euclidean geometry, and it has its counterpart in the theory of vector spaces. However, in the context of vectors the term "orthogonal" is used in place of "perpendicular." The two terms are essentially equivalent, but "orthogonality" connotes a more general situation than "perpendicularity."

***Orthogonality condition.*** The vectors $\mathbf{u} = (u_1, \ldots, u_n)$ and $\mathbf{v} = (v_1, \ldots, v_n)$ in $R^n$ are **orthogonal**, written $\mathbf{u} \perp \mathbf{v}$, if their scalar product is zero, that is, if

$$\mathbf{u} \cdot \mathbf{v} = u_1 v_1 + \cdots + u_n v_n = 0$$

We apply this condition for orthogonality in the following examples.

**EXAMPLE 3** Determine if the following pairs of vectors are orthogonal or not.

(a) $\mathbf{u} = (2, 1)$    and    $\mathbf{v} = (-1, 2)$    in $R^2$

(b) $\mathbf{u} = (3, -1, 1)$    and    $\mathbf{v} = (0, 4, 4)$    in $R^3$

(c) $\mathbf{u} = (1, 2, -3, 1)$    and    $\mathbf{v} = (4, 1, 2, -1)$    in $R^4$

SOLUTION  (a) Since $\mathbf{u} \cdot \mathbf{v} = -2 + 2 = 0$, the vectors are orthogonal. (See Figure 5.1(a).)

(b) Since $\mathbf{u} \cdot \mathbf{v} = 0 - 4 + 4 = 0$, the vectors are orthogonal. (See Figure 5.1(b).)

(c) Since $\mathbf{u} \cdot \mathbf{v} = 4 + 2 - 6 - 1 = -1$, the vectors are not orthogonal.  ∎

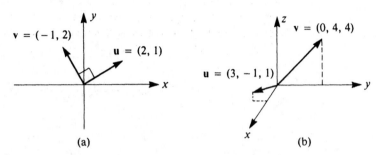

(a)                                              (b)

**FIGURE 5.1**                    *Orthogonal vectors*

**EXAMPLE 4**  Find the value of the number $k$ such that the vectors $\mathbf{u} = (5, 2, -3, k)$ and $\mathbf{v} = (3, k, 1, 2)$ are orthogonal.

SOLUTION  To be orthogonal, the vectors must satisfy

$$\mathbf{u} \cdot \mathbf{v} = 15 + 2k - 3 + 2k = 0$$

Hence we have $12 + 4k = 0$, so that $k = -3$.  ∎

**EXAMPLE 5**  Find a vector that is orthogonal to both of the vectors $\mathbf{u} = (1, 1, 1)$ and $\mathbf{v} = (1, 2, 3)$ in $R^3$.

SOLUTION  Let $\mathbf{w} = (x, y, z)$ be the vector we are looking for. Then we must have both

$$\mathbf{w} \cdot \mathbf{u} = x + y + z = 0$$
$$\mathbf{w} \cdot \mathbf{v} = x + 2y + 3z = 0$$

The system of equations has the solutions

$$x = t, \quad y = -2t, \quad z = t$$

where $t$ is arbitrary, as the reader can verify. Thus we have an entire line of solutions $\mathbf{w} = t(1, -2, 1)$. This is geometrically reasonable, since the span of the vectors $\mathbf{u}$ and $\mathbf{v}$ is a plane and the line will be perpendicular to this plane. To select a specific vector $\mathbf{w}$, we choose a particular value of $t$. For example, if we take $t = 1$, then we get the vector $\mathbf{w} = (1, -2, 1)$.  ∎

**EXAMPLE 6**  Show that if a vector $\mathbf{w}$ is orthogonal to both of the vectors $\mathbf{u}$ and $\mathbf{v}$, then $\mathbf{w}$ is orthogonal to all linear combinations of $\mathbf{u}$ and $\mathbf{v}$.

SOLUTION   We have $\mathbf{w} \cdot \mathbf{u} = 0$ and $\mathbf{w} \cdot \mathbf{v} = 0$. If $a$, $b$ are any scalars, then we have by Theorem 1 that

$$\mathbf{w} \cdot (a\mathbf{u} + b\mathbf{v}) = a\mathbf{w} \cdot \mathbf{u} + b\mathbf{w} \cdot \mathbf{v} = a \cdot 0 + b \cdot 0 = 0.$$

Hence $\mathbf{w}$ is orthogonal to any linear combination $a\mathbf{u} + b\mathbf{v}$.   ∎

To see how the orthogonality condition arises from geometric considerations, we now derive the condition for vectors in $R^2$. Let $\mathbf{u} = (a, b)$ and $\mathbf{v} = (c, d)$ be vectors in $R^2$ and let them be displayed as the position vectors $\overrightarrow{OP_1}$ and $\overrightarrow{OP_2}$, respectively, as in Figure 5.2. Then we have the vector $\overrightarrow{P_1 P_2} = (c - a, d - b)$, and the magnitudes of the vectors are

$$|\mathbf{u}| = \sqrt{a^2 + b^2}, \quad |\mathbf{v}| = \sqrt{c^2 + d^2}$$
$$|\overrightarrow{P_1 P_2}| = \sqrt{(c - a)^2 + (d - b)^2}$$

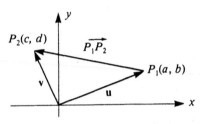

**FIGURE 5.2**          *The vectors* $\mathbf{u} = \overrightarrow{OP_1}$, $\mathbf{v} = \overrightarrow{OP_2}$, *and* $\overrightarrow{P_1 P_2}$

According to the Pythagorean Theorem, a triangle is a right triangle if and only if the sum of the squares of the lengths of the two legs is equal to the square of the length of the hypotenuse. Therefore the vectors $\mathbf{u} = \overrightarrow{OP_1}$ and $\mathbf{v} = \overrightarrow{OP_2}$ form a right angle if and only if

$$|\overrightarrow{P_1 P_2}|^2 = |\overrightarrow{OP_1}|^2 + |\overrightarrow{OP_2}|^2$$

In terms of components, this condition is

$$(c^2 - 2ac + a^2) + (d^2 - 2bd + b^2) = (a^2 + b^2) + (c^2 + d^2)$$

which becomes

$$-2(ac + bd) = 0$$

Thus the vectors $\mathbf{u}$ and $\mathbf{v}$ form a right angle if and only if

$$\mathbf{u} \cdot \mathbf{v} = ac + bd = 0$$

*REMARK* (for students who know trigonometry): If $\theta$ denotes the angle between $\mathbf{u}$ and $\mathbf{v}$, where $0 \leqslant \theta \leqslant 180°$, then the Law of Cosines can be used to show that the scalar product is related to $\cos(\theta)$ by the equation

$$\cos(\theta) = \frac{\mathbf{u} \cdot \mathbf{v}}{|\mathbf{u}||\mathbf{v}|}$$

The scalar product of two vectors thus determines the cosine of the angle between them, and therefore it determines the angle itself.

## EQUATIONS OF PLANES

In Chapter 2 we discussed the fact that planes in 3-space were given by linear equations in three variables, and we developed techniques for graphing planes and their lines of intersection. We now apply vector methods to derive equations of planes in $R^3$.

Any nonzero vector that is perpendicular to a plane is called a **normal vector** to the plane. A normal vector determines the inclination of a plane in space. If we have both a normal vector and a point on the plane, then the position of the plane is completely fixed, and we should be able to derive the equation of the plane. This is done as follows.

Suppose a plane has a normal vector $\mathbf{n} = (a, b, c)$ and contains the point $P_0(x_0, y_0, z_0)$. If $P(x, y, z)$ is a general point in the plane, then the vector $\overrightarrow{P_0P} = (x - x_0, y - y_0, z - z_0)$ must be orthogonal to the vector $\mathbf{n}$. See Figure 5.3. Thus we have

$$\mathbf{n} \cdot \overrightarrow{P_0P} = 0$$

which becomes

$$a(x - x_0) + b(y - y_0) + c(z - z_0) = 0$$

This is called the **point-normal** equation of the plane.

If we remove parentheses by multiplication and move the constant term to the other side of the equation, then we obtain the **general form** of the equation of the plane

$$ax + by + cz = d$$

where $d = ax_0 + by_0 + cz_0$.

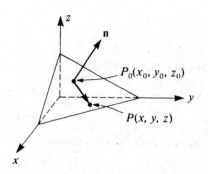

**FIGURE 5.3**          The plane $\mathbf{n} \cdot \overrightarrow{P_0P} = 0$

**EXAMPLE 7**  A plane has normal vector $\mathbf{n} = (2, 4, 3)$ and contains the point $P_0(1, 1, 2)$. Find the point-normal equation and the general equation of the plane.

SOLUTION   If $P(x, y, z)$ is an arbitrary point on the plane, then $\mathbf{n} \cdot \overrightarrow{P_0 P} = 0$ so that we obtain the point-normal equation

$$2(x - 1) + 4(y - 1) + 3(z - 2) = 0$$

If we take this equation one step further, we get

$$2x + 4y + 3z = 2 + 4 + 6 = 12$$

which is the general form of the equation of the plane. The graph of the plane is shown in Figure 5.4.  ▮▮

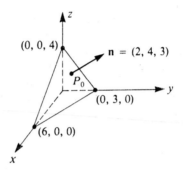

**FIGURE 5.4**                         *The plane* $2(x-1) + 4(y-1) + 3(z-2) = 0$

If a plane has the equation $ax + by + cz = d$, then $n = (a, b, c)$ is a normal vector. That is, *the coefficients of the variables are the components of a normal vector.* This statement is easy to verify by putting the equation into point-normal form. If we combine the constant $d$ with any term on the left, say, the first term, we obtain

$$(ax - d) + by + cz = 0$$

which may be written as

$$a(x - (d/a)) + b(y - 0) + c(z - 0) = 0$$

This is the equation of the plane with the normal vector $(a, b, c)$ and through the point $(d/a, 0, 0)$. If the $d$ had been combined with another term, we would still get the same normal vector but generally (except when $d = 0$) a different point. For example, to demonstrate that the plane $2x - 3y + 7z = 18$ has the normal vector $\mathbf{n} = (2, -3, 7)$, we can simply write the equation as

$$(2x - 18) - 3y + 7z = 0$$

which gives us the point-normal form

$$2(x - 9) - 3(y - 0) + 7(z - 0) = 0$$

If two planes have the same normal vector or proportional normal vectors, then the planes are parallel or identical. Thus by interpreting the coefficients as the components of a normal vector, we obtain a geometric insight into the parallelism condition given in Theorem 1 of Section 2.4.

**EXAMPLE 8**   Find an equation of the plane that is parallel to the plane $2x + 4y - 8z = 14$ and that contains the point $P_0(3, -4, -1)$.

SOLUTION   Since the desired plane is parallel to the given plane, it must have the same normal vector $\mathbf{n} = (2, 4, -8)$. Thus the equation is

$$2(x - 3) + 4(y + 4) - 8(z + 1) = 0$$

or

$$2x + 4y - 8z = -2 \quad \blacksquare$$

A plane is determined by three noncollinear points $P_1$, $P_2$, $P_3$. Since any normal vector $\mathbf{n}$ to the plane must be orthogonal to the vectors $\overrightarrow{P_1 P_2}$ and $\overrightarrow{P_1 P_3}$, we can find a normal vector $\mathbf{n}$ by solving the equations

$$\mathbf{n} \cdot \overrightarrow{P_1 P_2} = 0, \quad \mathbf{n} \cdot \overrightarrow{P_1 P_3} = 0$$

Consequently, an equation for the plane can be obtained from the three given points. The method is illustrated in the next example.

**EXAMPLE 9**   Find an equation of the plane that contains the three points $P_1(1, 1, 2)$, $P_2(2, 0, 3)$, $P_3(-1, 2, 4)$.

SOLUTION   We first find the vectors $\overrightarrow{P_1 P_2} = (1, -1, 1)$ and $\overrightarrow{P_1 P_3} = (-2, 1, 2)$. To find a normal vector $\mathbf{n} = (a, b, c)$, we solve the system

$$\mathbf{n} \cdot \overrightarrow{P_1 P_2} = \quad a - b + c = 0$$
$$\mathbf{n} \cdot \overrightarrow{P_1 P_3} = -2a + b + 2c = 0$$

The homogeneous system has the solutions $a = 3t$, $b = 4t$, $c = t$, where $t$ is a parameter. Any nonzero choice of $t$ will give us a normal to the plane. Let us take $t = 1$ and so obtain $\mathbf{n} = (3, 4, 1)$. If we use $\mathbf{n}$ along with the point $P_1(1, 1, 2)$, then we get the equation

$$3(x - 1) + 4(y - 1) + (z - 2) = 0$$

or

$$3x + 4y + z = 9$$

If we had chosen either of the points $P_2$ or $P_3$ instead of $P_1$, the same general form of the equation would be obtained, as the reader can verify.   $\blacksquare$

## EXERCISES 5.1

In Exercises 1–6, find the scalar product of the given vectors.

**1.** $(5, -3)$, $(8, 6)$

**2.** $(-4, 9)$, $(7, 2)$

**3.** $(7, -2, 4), (3, 9, 2)$

**4.** $(-6, 5, 1), (4, 7, -2)$

**5.** $(8, 2, -9, 3), (-7, 4, -5, -3)$

**6.** $(3, 6, 2, -5), (7, -2, 4, 3)$

In Exercises 7–10, write the scalar product of the given vectors as a matrix product.

**7.** $(2, -9) \cdot (6, 3)$

**8.** $(7, -4) \cdot (8, 10)$

**9.** $(6, -7, 3) \cdot (4, 2, -1)$

**10.** $(2, 9, 4) \cdot (-1, 3, -7)$

In Exercises 11–14, find $|\mathbf{u}|^2$.

**11.** $\mathbf{u} = (6, -5)$

**12.** $\mathbf{u} = (4, 2)$

**13.** $\mathbf{u} = (7, -1, 4)$

**14.** $\mathbf{u} = (3, 5, -6)$

In Exercises 15–18, find $\mathbf{u} \cdot \mathbf{v} + \mathbf{u} \cdot \mathbf{w}$ and $\mathbf{u} \cdot (\mathbf{v} + \mathbf{w})$.

**15.** $\mathbf{u} = (6, 1, -2), \quad \mathbf{v} = (3, -3, 5), \quad \mathbf{w} = (-6, 4, -1)$

**16.** $\mathbf{u} = (2, -4, 3), \quad \mathbf{v} = (5, 2, 4), \quad \mathbf{w} = (-7, 3, 6)$

**17.** $\mathbf{u} = (2, 7, 1), \quad \mathbf{v} = (5, -1, 7), \quad \mathbf{w} = (3, 2, -3)$

**18.** $\mathbf{u} = (4, 5, -3), \quad \mathbf{v} = (2, 1, 4), \quad \mathbf{w} = (-2, 3, -5)$

In Exercises 19–28, determine whether or not the given vectors are orthogonal.

**19.** $(6, 4), (-2, 3)$

**20.** $(8, 4), (-6, 12)$

**21.** $(4, 12), (6, 2)$

**22.** $(-3, 6), (5, 1)$

**23.** $(1, 7, -3), (4, 2, 6)$

**24.** $(-1, -5, 4), (1, 7, 9)$

**25.** $(7, 3, 4), (2, -2, 3)$

**26.** $(-5, -7, 2), (4, 3, 6)$

**27.** $(6, 8, 2, -4), (9, -6, 3, 3)$

**28.** $(4, -5, 8, -3), (7, 6, -2, -6)$

In Exercises 29–30, find a number $k$ such that the given vectors are orthogonal.

**29.** $(2, k, -2, 4), (3, -3, 7, k)$

**30.** $(k, -4, 6, 5), (3, 5, -k, -2)$

In Exercises 31–34, find a vector $(x, y, z)$ that is orthogonal to both of the given vectors.

**31.** $(2, 3, -3), (-4, -7, 10)$

**32.** $(3, -3, 6), (-9, 10, -15)$

**33.** $(4, 4, 8), (3, 5, 4)$

**34.** $(5, -5, 20), (2, -1, 12)$

In Exercises 35–38, find a point-normal form of the equation of the plane that contains the point $P_0$ and is normal to the vector $\mathbf{n}$. Then write the equation in general form.

**35.** $P_0(2, -4, 7), \quad \mathbf{n} = (5, -6, -3)$

**36.** $P_0(5, 9, -6), \quad \mathbf{n} = (-4, -8, -1)$

**37.** $P_0(4, -4, 3), \quad \mathbf{n} = (2, 8, 9)$

**38.** $P_0(-6, -5, 1), \quad \mathbf{n} = (-9, -4, -3)$

In Exercises 39–42, write the equation of the plane in point-normal form.

**39.** $4x - 3y + 5z = 8$

**40.** $6x + 2y + 3z = 12$

**41.** $5x + 2y - 7z = 6$

**42.** $-3x + 5y + 9z = 10$

In Exercises 43–44, find a vector that is perpendicular to the given plane.

**43.** $6x - 5y + 2z = 13$                   **44.** $3x + 7y - 5z = 11$

In Exercises 45–48, find an equation of the plane that is parallel to the given plane and contains the given point.

**45.**    $5x + 6y + \;\;6z = \;\;\;9, \quad P_0(5, -1, 3)$
**46.** $-8x + 2y - \;\;3z = \;\;\;5, \quad P_0(-4, 2, -2)$
**47.**    $2x - 7y - 11z = \;\;\;3, \quad P_0(-6, -9, -2)$
**48.**  $-x + 8y + \;\;3z = -5, \quad P_0(8, -3, -5)$

In Exercises 49–52, find an equation of the plane that contains the given points.

**49.** $P_1(-1, 1, -2), \quad P_2(-2, 2, 4), \quad P_3(0, 2, -2)$
**50.** $P_1(3, -2, -1), \quad P_2(5, 2, 7), \quad P_3(1, -4, 9)$
**51.** $P_1(2, 4, 2), \quad P_2(3, 8, -2), \quad P_3(4, 8, 10)$
**52.** $P_1(-2, 3, 2), \quad P_2(-1, 6, 5), \quad P_3(-3, -3, -4)$

In Exercises 53–58, determine if the given line intersects the given plane in 0, 1, or infinitely many points (i.e., if the line is parallel to the plane, has a unique intersection with the plane, or is contained in the plane). In the case of a single point of intersection, substitute the $x$, $y$, $z$ for the line into the equation of the plane and solve for $t$ to find the point of intersection.

**53.** Line: $(x, y, z) = (5 + 2t, 6 - t, 1 + t)$,       plane: $5x + 6y + z = 4$
**54.** Line: $(x, y, z) = (-3 + 3t, 2 + t, 4 + t)$,     plane: $-3x + 2y + 4z = 5$
**55.** Line: $(x, y, z) = (1 + 4t, 4 + t, 3 - 2t)$,      plane: $x - 2y + z = 6$
**56.** Line: $(x, y, z) = (-3 + 5t, 2 - 4t, -1 + 3t)$,   plane: $2x + y - 2z = 4$
**57.** Line: $(x, y, z) = (7 + t, -4 - 6t, 2 + 3t)$,    plane: $3x + y + z = 19$
**58.** Line: $(x, y, z) = (3 + 5t, -4 + 6t, 7 - t)$     plane: $5x - 4y + z = 38$

## 5.2 ORTHONORMAL VECTORS AND PROJECTIONS

*Unit Vectors, Orthonormal Vectors, Projections, Projections onto Subspaces, Orthonormalization of Vectors*

In Section 4.5 of Chapter 4 we discussed the concept of a basis for a subspace, namely, a set of linearly independent vectors that spanned the subspace. In this section we introduce a special type of basis, called an orthonormal basis, in which the vectors are mutually orthogonal and have magnitude 1. The standard basis vectors $\{e_1, \ldots, e_n\}$ for $R^n$ provide a model for the type of basis we will be discussing, since they are mutually orthogonal and each has magnitude equal to 1.

We will examine some properties of orthonormal bases, especially the ease with which a vector can be written as a linear combination of such basis vectors. Writing a vector as a linear combination of orthonormal vectors has a geometric interpretation related to the construction of perpendicular line segments in Euclidean geometry. The vector counterpart to the geometric construction of perpendiculars is called "orthogonal projection," an operation that has many useful applications. In this section we use it to convert a given set of vectors into orthonormal vectors, and in subsequent sections we will apply it to problems of approximation and the analysis of data.

## UNIT VECTORS

A vector is called a **unit vector** if $|\mathbf{u}| = 1$. For example, the vectors $\mathbf{e}_1, \mathbf{e}_2, \ldots, \mathbf{e}_n$ in $R^n$ are unit vectors because $|\mathbf{e}_1| = 1$, $|\mathbf{e}_2| = 1$, and so on. A nonzero vector $\mathbf{v}$ whose magnitude is not equal to 1 can be converted into a unit vector by dividing each of its components by the number $|\mathbf{v}|$, the length of the vector. That is, if we set $\mathbf{u} = \mathbf{v}/|\mathbf{v}|$, then $|\mathbf{u}| = 1$, so that $\mathbf{u}$ is a unit vector that has the same direction as $\mathbf{v}$. When a vector is converted to a unit vector in this manner, we say that it has been **normalized**.

**EXAMPLE 1**   Normalize the vector $\mathbf{v} = (6, -6, 7)$.

**SOLUTION**   First we calculate $|\mathbf{v}| = \sqrt{36 + 36 + 49} = \sqrt{121} = 11$, and then we define the vector $\mathbf{u}$ to be $\mathbf{u} = \frac{1}{11}\mathbf{v} = (\frac{6}{11}, -\frac{6}{11}, \frac{7}{11})$. To verify that $\mathbf{u}$ is a unit vector, we note that

$$|\mathbf{u}| = \frac{1}{11}|\mathbf{v}| = \frac{1}{11}11 = 1$$

Since $\mathbf{u}$ is obtained by multiplying $\mathbf{v}$ by a positive scalar, the two vectors have the same direction.   ∎

Frequently, it is necessary to normalize a vector in which the components have a common factor that complicates the arithmetic. In this case the absolute value of the common factor can be discarded, since it would merely be cancelled in the normalization process if carried along. For example, consider the vector $(-\frac{2}{11}, \frac{4}{11})$. To normalize, we write the vector as $\frac{2}{11}(-1, 2)$ and then discard the factor $\frac{2}{11}$. We simply normalize the vector $(-1, 2)$ to obtain $\frac{1}{\sqrt{5}}(-1, 2)$ as the normalization of the given vector.

## ORTHONORMAL VECTORS

A set of vectors that are mutually orthogonal and normalized so that each vector is a unit vector is called **orthonormal**. That is, the vectors $\mathbf{v}_1, \ldots, \mathbf{v}_k$ in $R^n$ are orthonormal if $\mathbf{v}_i \cdot \mathbf{v}_j = 0$ for $i \neq j$ and $|\mathbf{v}_i| = 1$ for each $i$. The normalization condition $|\mathbf{v}_i| = 1$ can also be written $\mathbf{v}_i \cdot \mathbf{v}_i = 1$ for all $i$.

For example, the standard basis vectors $\mathbf{e}_1, \mathbf{e}_2, \ldots, \mathbf{e}_n$ in $R^n$ constitute an orthonormal set of vectors. In the following examples we look at some other sets of orthonormal vectors.

**EXAMPLE 2**  Show that the vectors $\mathbf{v}_1 = \frac{1}{\sqrt{2}}(1, 1)$, $\mathbf{v}_2 = \frac{1}{\sqrt{2}}(1, -1)$ are orthonormal in $R^2$.

**SOLUTION**  Since $\mathbf{v}_1 \cdot \mathbf{v}_2 = \frac{1}{2}(1 - 1) = 0$, we see that $\mathbf{v}_1$ and $\mathbf{v}_2$ are orthogonal. Also, we have $\mathbf{v}_1 \cdot \mathbf{v}_1 = (\frac{1}{\sqrt{2}})^2(1 + 1) = 1$, and similarly $\mathbf{v}_2 \cdot \mathbf{v}_2 = 1$. Therefore the vectors $\mathbf{v}_1$, $\mathbf{v}_2$ are orthonormal. (See Figure 5.5.)  ∎

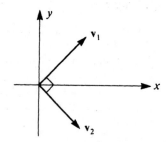

**FIGURE 5.5**  *The vectors $\mathbf{v}_1 = \frac{1}{\sqrt{2}}(1, 1)$, $\mathbf{v}_2 = \frac{1}{\sqrt{2}}(1, -1)$*

**EXAMPLE 3**  Show that the vectors

$$\mathbf{v}_1 = \frac{1}{\sqrt{3}}(1, 1, 1), \quad \mathbf{v}_2 = \frac{1}{\sqrt{2}}(1, -1, 0), \quad \mathbf{v}_3 = \frac{1}{\sqrt{6}}(1, 1, -2)$$

are orthonormal in $R^3$.

**SOLUTION**  First it must be shown that $\mathbf{v}_1 \cdot \mathbf{v}_2 = 0$, $\mathbf{v}_1 \cdot \mathbf{v}_3 = 0$, $\mathbf{v}_2 \cdot \mathbf{v}_3 = 0$, which can be done by direct calculation. For instance, we have

$$\mathbf{v}_1 \cdot \mathbf{v}_2 = \frac{1}{\sqrt{6}}(1 - 1 + 0) = 0$$

Furthermore, another calculation shows that $|\mathbf{v}_1| = 1$, $|\mathbf{v}_2| = 1$, $|\mathbf{v}_3| = 1$. For instance, we have $\mathbf{v}_1 \cdot \mathbf{v}_1 = \frac{1}{3}(1 + 1 + 1) = 1$, so that $|\mathbf{v}_1| = 1$. Thus the vectors $\mathbf{v}_1$, $\mathbf{v}_2$, $\mathbf{v}_3$ are orthonormal.  ∎

Orthonormal vectors have several significant advantages. One is the ease with which a given vector can be written as a linear combination of orthonormal vectors. Usually, to write $\mathbf{u}$ as a linear combination of the vectors $\mathbf{v}_1, \mathbf{v}_2, \ldots, \mathbf{v}_k$ it is necessary to solve a system of equations for the scalars $c_1, c_2, \ldots, c_k$ such that $\mathbf{u} = c_1\mathbf{v}_1 + \cdots + c_k\mathbf{v}_k$. However, if the vectors $\mathbf{v}_1, \ldots, \mathbf{v}_k$ are orthonormal, then we shall see that the task is quite simple.

Consider the case of two orthonormal vectors $\mathbf{v}_1$, $\mathbf{v}_2$, and suppose we wish to write the vector $\mathbf{u}$ as a linear combination

$$\mathbf{u} = c_1\mathbf{v}_1 + c_2\mathbf{v}_2$$

To obtain $c_1$, we take the scalar product of $\mathbf{u}$ with $\mathbf{v}_1$. Since $\mathbf{v}_1 \cdot \mathbf{v}_1 = 1$ and $\mathbf{v}_2 \cdot \mathbf{v}_1 = 0$, we get

$$\mathbf{u} \cdot \mathbf{v}_1 = (c_1\mathbf{v}_1 + c_2\mathbf{v}_2) \cdot \mathbf{v}_1$$
$$= c_1(\mathbf{v}_1 \cdot \mathbf{v}_1) + c_2(\mathbf{v}_2 \cdot \mathbf{v}_1)$$
$$= c_1 \cdot 1 + c_2 \cdot 0 = c_1$$

Hence we have $c_1 = \mathbf{u} \cdot \mathbf{v}_1$. In a similar way it can be shown that $c_2 = \mathbf{u} \cdot \mathbf{v}_2$.

In general, we have the following theorem.

### THEOREM 1

If $\mathbf{v}_1, \ldots, \mathbf{v}_k$ are orthonormal vectors whose span is $S$ and if $\mathbf{u}$ is in $S$, then

$$\mathbf{u} = (\mathbf{u} \cdot \mathbf{v}_1)\mathbf{v}_1 + \cdots + (\mathbf{u} \cdot \mathbf{v}_k)\mathbf{v}_k$$

Thus to write $\mathbf{u}$ as a linear combination of orthonormal vectors $\mathbf{v}_1, \ldots, \mathbf{v}_k$, we find the coefficients by calculating the scalar products $\mathbf{u} \cdot \mathbf{v}_1, \ldots, \mathbf{u} \cdot \mathbf{v}_k$ of $\mathbf{u}$ with the orthonormal vectors. There is no need to solve a system of equations. The method is illustrated in the next example.

**EXAMPLE 4**  Write the vector $\mathbf{u} = (4, 2)$ as a linear combination of the vectors $\mathbf{v}_1 = \frac{1}{\sqrt{2}}(1, 1)$ and $\mathbf{v}_2 = \frac{1}{\sqrt{2}}(1, -1)$.

SOLUTION   We saw in Example 2 that $\mathbf{v}_1, \mathbf{v}_2$ are orthonormal. We calculate the scalar products

$$\mathbf{u} \cdot \mathbf{v}_1 = \frac{1}{\sqrt{2}}(4 + 2) = \frac{6}{\sqrt{2}}$$

$$\mathbf{u} \cdot \mathbf{v}_2 = \frac{1}{\sqrt{2}}(4 - 2) = \frac{2}{\sqrt{2}}$$

and thus we have by Theorem 1 that

$$\mathbf{u} = \left(\frac{6}{\sqrt{2}}\right)\mathbf{v}_1 + \left(\frac{2}{\sqrt{2}}\right)\mathbf{v}_2$$

See Figure 5.6.  ∎

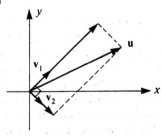

**FIGURE 5.6**                    *An orthonormal combination*

An important property of orthonormal vectors is that they are automatically linearly independent, a fact that may seem obvious from a geometric viewpoint. Note that if we apply Theorem 1 to the zero vector in the relation

$$\mathbf{0} = c_1\mathbf{v}_1 + \cdots + c_k\mathbf{v}_k$$

we obtain

$$c_1 = \mathbf{0} \cdot \mathbf{v}_1 = 0, \quad \ldots, \quad c_k = \mathbf{0} \cdot \mathbf{v}_k = 0$$

which implies by theorem 2 of Section 4.4 that $\mathbf{v}_1, \ldots, \mathbf{v}_k$ are linearly independent. Hence we have the following theorem.

### THEOREM 2

If the vectors $\mathbf{v}_1, \ldots, \mathbf{v}_k$ are orthonormal, then they are linearly independent.

If an orthonormal set of vectors spans a subspace $S$, then since the vectors are linearly independent, the orthonormal set is a basis for $S$. We call it an **orthonormal basis** for $S$. Thus a set of orthonormal vectors is an orthonormal basis for its span. The standard basis vectors $\mathbf{e}_1, \ldots, \mathbf{e}_n$ in $R^n$ comprise an orthonormal basis for $R^n$. Also, the vectors in Example 2 form an orthonormal basis for $R^2$, and the vectors in Example 3 form an orthonormal basis for $R^3$. Many different orthonormal bases are possible for the same space.

## PROJECTIONS

There is a geometric interpretation that gives us insight into the representation of a vector as a linear combination of orthonormal vectors. If a vector $\mathbf{u}$ is written as a linear combination of the orthonormal vectors $\mathbf{v}_1$, $\mathbf{v}_2$, then $\mathbf{u}$ is the sum of the orthogonal vectors $(\mathbf{u} \cdot \mathbf{v}_1)\mathbf{v}_1$ and $(\mathbf{u} \cdot \mathbf{v}_2)\mathbf{v}_2$. The geometric relationships are shown in Figure 5.7. We see that $(\mathbf{u} \cdot \mathbf{v}_1)\mathbf{v}_1$ is obtained by dropping a perpendicular from the tip of $\mathbf{u}$ to the line with direction $\mathbf{v}_1$, and $(\mathbf{u} \cdot \mathbf{v}_2)\mathbf{v}_2$ is obtained similarly. We can interpret the relationships by thinking of $\mathbf{u}$ as being "projected" onto the vectors $\mathbf{v}_1$ and $\mathbf{v}_2$.

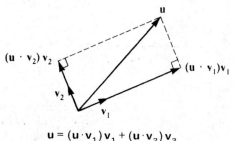

**FIGURE 5.7**

$$\mathbf{u} = (\mathbf{u} \cdot \mathbf{v}_1)\mathbf{v}_1 + (\mathbf{u} \cdot \mathbf{v}_2)\mathbf{v}_2$$

The preceding observations motivate the idea of projecting one vector onto another.

### DEFINITION

If **v** is a unit vector, then the (orthogonal) **projection** of a vector **u** onto **v** is defined to be the vector

$$\text{Proj}_v(\mathbf{u}) = (\mathbf{u} \cdot \mathbf{v})\mathbf{v}$$

We extend the definition as follows. In the case that **v** is *not* a unit vector, we first normalize **v** and then apply the definition of the projection of **u** onto the unit vector **v**/|**v**|. If we replace **v** by **v**/|**v**| in the formula and collect terms, then the projection of **u** onto **v** is given by the formula

$$\text{Proj}_v(\mathbf{u}) = \left(\frac{\mathbf{u} \cdot \mathbf{v}}{|\mathbf{v}|^2}\right)\mathbf{v}$$

**EXAMPLE 5**   Find the projection of $\mathbf{u} = (3, 4)$ onto each of the vectors (a) $\mathbf{v} = (1, 0)$ and (b) $\mathbf{v} = (2, 1)$.

**SOLUTION**   (a) The vector $\mathbf{v} = (1, 0)$ is the standard basis vector $\mathbf{e}_1$, which is a unit vector. Thus the projection of **u** onto **v** is the vector

$$\text{Proj}_v(\mathbf{u}) = (\mathbf{u} \cdot \mathbf{v})\mathbf{v} = 3\mathbf{e}_1 = (3, 0)$$

See Figure 5.8(a). In general, the projections of a vector **u** onto the standard basis vectors are determined by the coordinates of **u**.

(b) We calculate the magnitude of $\mathbf{v} = (2, 1)$ and find that $|\mathbf{v}| = \sqrt{5}$, so that **v** is not a unit vector. Therefore the projection of **u** onto **v** is the vector

$$\text{Proj}_v(\mathbf{u}) = \left(\frac{\mathbf{u} \cdot \mathbf{v}}{|\mathbf{v}|^2}\right)\mathbf{v} = \frac{10}{5}(2, 1) = (4, 2)$$

See Figure 5.8(b).   ∎

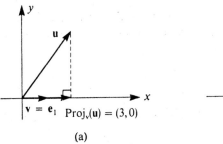

(a)

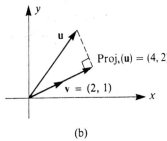

(b)

**FIGURE 5.8**

*The projections of* $\mathbf{u} = (3, 4)$ *onto*
*(a)* $\mathbf{v} = \mathbf{e}_1$ *and (b)* $\mathbf{v} = (2, 1)$

The notion of orthogonal projection corresponds to the construction of a perpendicular in Euclidean geometry. If the vector **u** is projected onto the vector

**v**, then as shown in Figure 5.9, the vector counterpart of the perpendicular is the vector

$$\mathbf{u}' = \mathbf{u} - \text{Proj}_v(\mathbf{u})$$

The fact that **u**′ is orthogonal to **v** is readily verified. Note that if **v** is a unit vector, then the orthogonality follows from the calculation

$$\mathbf{u}' \cdot \mathbf{v} = (\mathbf{u} - (\mathbf{u} \cdot \mathbf{v})\mathbf{v}) \cdot \mathbf{v} = \mathbf{u} \cdot \mathbf{v} - \mathbf{u} \cdot \mathbf{v} = 0$$

A similar calculation shows that $\mathbf{u}' \cdot \mathbf{v} = 0$ for a general nonzero vector **v**.

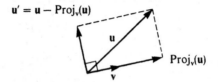

**FIGURE 5.9**            $\mathbf{u}' = \mathbf{u} - \text{Proj}_v(\mathbf{u})$ *is orthogonal to* **v**

We will call **u**′ the **orthogonal complement** of **u** relative to **v**. Since the distance between a point and a line is the perpendicular distance, the magnitude of **u**′ gives us the distance from the tip of **u** to the line through the origin that has the direction of **v**. Again see Figure 5.9.

**EXAMPLE 6**    Project $\mathbf{u} = (1, 1, 3)$ onto $\mathbf{v} = (\frac{1}{3}, \frac{2}{3}, \frac{2}{3})$ and find the orthogonal complement **u**′ of **u** relative to **v**. Then find the distance from the point $P(1, 1, 3)$ to the line determined by **v**.

**SOLUTION**    Since **v** is a unit vector, the projection of **u** onto **v** is given by

$$\text{Proj}_v(\mathbf{u}) = (\mathbf{u} \cdot \mathbf{v})\mathbf{v} = 3\mathbf{v} = (1, 2, 2)$$

The orthogonal complement of **u** relative to **v** is the vector

$$\mathbf{u}' = \mathbf{u} - (\mathbf{u} \cdot \mathbf{v})\mathbf{v} = (1, 1, 3) - (1, 2, 2)$$
$$= (0, -1, 1)$$

The distance from $P(1, 1, 3)$ to the line is therefore $|\mathbf{u}'| = \sqrt{2}$. The configuration is shown in Figure 5.10. ∎

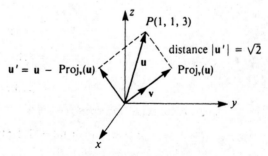

**FIGURE 5.10**            *The distance from* $P(1, 1, 3)$ *is*
$$|\mathbf{u} - \text{Proj}_v(\mathbf{u})| = \sqrt{2}$$

## PROJECTIONS ONTO SUBSPACES

The notion of projection can be extended to subspaces as follows. Let $v_1$, $v_2$ be orthonormal vectors in $R^3$ and let $S$ be the subspace spanned by $v_1$, $v_2$. If the vector $u$ does *not* lie in $S$, then we define the projection of $u$ onto $S$ to be

$$\text{Proj}_S(u) = (u \cdot v_1)v_1 + (u \cdot v_2)v_2$$

Thus we simply add the projections of $u$ onto the vectors $v_1$ and $v_2$. Geometrically, we are dropping a perpendicular from the tip of $u$ to the plane $S$. See Figure 5.11.

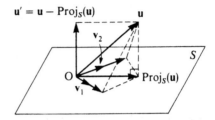

**FIGURE 5.11**                    *The projection of $u$ onto the subspace $S$*

The vector

$$u' = u - \text{Proj}_S(u) = u - (u \cdot v_1)v_1 - (u \cdot v_2)v_2$$

is then orthogonal to both $v_1$ and $v_2$, and therefore it is orthogonal to the plane $S$. See Figure 5.11 again. The magnitude of $u - \text{Proj}_S(u)$ then gives us the distance from the tip of $u$ to the plane $S$.

**EXAMPLE 7**   Find the projection of $u = (2, 1, 5)$ onto the plane $S$ spanned by the orthonormal vectors

$$v_1 = (1, 0, 0), \quad v_2 = \frac{1}{\sqrt{2}}(0, 1, 1)$$

Then find the distance from $P(2, 1, 5)$ to the plane $S$.

**SOLUTION**   From the definition we have

$$\text{Proj}_S(u) = (u \cdot v_1)v_1 + (u \cdot v_2)v_2$$
$$= 2(1, 0, 0) + \left(\frac{6}{\sqrt{2}}\right)\left(\frac{1}{\sqrt{2}}\right)(0, 1, 1)$$
$$= (2, 3, 3)$$

See Figure 5.12. The vector

$$u' = u - \text{Proj}_S(u) = (2, 1, 5) - (2, 3, 3) = (0, -2, 2)$$

is orthogonal to $S$, and its magnitude $|u'| = \sqrt{8} = 2\sqrt{2}$ is the distance from $P(2, 1, 5)$ to the plane.   ∎

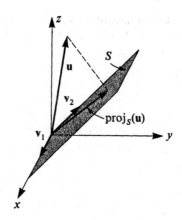

**FIGURE 5.12**                    *The projection of* **u** *onto S*

In general, if the orthonormal vectors $\mathbf{v}_1, \ldots, \mathbf{v}_k$ form a basis for the subspace $S$ and if $\mathbf{u}$ is a vector that does not lie in $S$, then the projection of $\mathbf{u}$ onto $S$ is the vector

$$\text{Proj}_S(\mathbf{u}) = (\mathbf{u} \cdot \mathbf{v}_1)\mathbf{v}_1 + \cdots + (\mathbf{u} \cdot \mathbf{v}_k)\mathbf{v}_k$$

Moreover, the vector

$$\mathbf{u}' = \mathbf{u} - \text{Proj}_S(\mathbf{u})$$

is orthogonal to each $\mathbf{v}_i$ and thus to every vector in the space $S$. Thus this notion of projection generalizes the geometric construction of perpendicular line segments to higher dimensions. We state this fact as a theorem.

**THEOREM 3**

If $S$ is a subspace of $R^n$ and if the vector $\mathbf{u}$ is not in $S$, then the vector

$$\mathbf{u}' = \mathbf{u} - \text{Proj}_S(\mathbf{u})$$

is orthogonal to every vector in $S$. Furthermore, the magnitude of $\mathbf{u}'$ is the distance from the terminal point of the position vector $\mathbf{u}$ to $S$.

Of course, if the vector $\mathbf{u}$ belongs to $S$, then $\mathbf{u}$ is the same as its projection. In this case we have $\mathbf{u}' = \mathbf{0}$, which is trivially orthogonal to every vector in the space.

## ORTHONORMALIZATION OF VECTORS

We now apply the notion of projection to the construction of orthonormal vectors from a given set of vectors. The method is based on the fact that subtraction of projections creates orthogonality.

The procedure of orthonormalization is called the **Gram - Schmidt** process. Given linearly independent vectors $\mathbf{u}_1, \mathbf{u}_2, \mathbf{u}_3, \ldots$ whose span is $S$, we wish to construct orthonormal vectors $\mathbf{v}_1, \mathbf{v}_2, \mathbf{v}_3, \ldots$ with the same span. The steps are as follows.

***Step 1.*** Normalize $\mathbf{u}_1$ to get $\mathbf{v}_1$.

***Step 2.*** Calculate $\mathbf{u}_2' = \mathbf{u}_2 - (\mathbf{u}_2 \cdot \mathbf{v}_1)\mathbf{v}_1$. Then normalize $\mathbf{u}_2'$ to get $\mathbf{v}_2 = \mathbf{u}_2'/|\mathbf{u}_2'|$. (Then $\mathbf{v}_1, \mathbf{v}_2$ are orthonormal, and they span the same subspace as $\mathbf{u}_1, \mathbf{u}_2$.)

***Step 3.*** Calculate $\mathbf{u}_3' = \mathbf{u}_3 - (\mathbf{u}_3 \cdot \mathbf{v}_1)\mathbf{v}_1 - (\mathbf{u}_3 \cdot \mathbf{v}_2)\mathbf{v}_2$. Then normalize $\mathbf{u}_3'$ to get $\mathbf{v}_3 = \mathbf{u}_3'/|\mathbf{u}_3'|$. (Then $\mathbf{v}_1, \mathbf{v}_2, \mathbf{v}_3$ are orthonormal, and they span the same subspace as $\mathbf{u}_1, \mathbf{u}_2, \mathbf{u}_3$.)

If additional vectors are given, the process continues in the same manner.
The following examples illustrate the Gram–Schmidt process.

**EXAMPLE 8**   The plane $S$ with equation $x - y + 2z = 0$ is a subspace of $R^3$. Find an orthonormal basis for $S$.

SOLUTION   Since each $(x, y, z)$ in $S$ is given by

$$\begin{bmatrix} x \\ y \\ z \end{bmatrix} = \begin{bmatrix} y - 2z \\ y \\ z \end{bmatrix} = y\begin{bmatrix} 1 \\ 1 \\ 0 \end{bmatrix} + z\begin{bmatrix} -2 \\ 0 \\ 1 \end{bmatrix}$$

we see that the vectors $\mathbf{u}_1 = (1, 1, 0)$ and $\mathbf{u}_2 = (-2, 0, 1)$ form a basis for $S$. To find an orthonormal basis, we apply the Gram-Schmidt process. First, we normalize $\mathbf{u}_1$ to get

$$\mathbf{v}_1 = \frac{1}{\sqrt{2}}(1, 1, 0)$$

Second, we subtract the projection of $\mathbf{u}_2$ onto $\mathbf{v}_1$ from $\mathbf{u}_2$ to get

$$\mathbf{u}_2' = \mathbf{u}_2 - (\mathbf{u}_2 \cdot \mathbf{v}_1)\mathbf{v}_1$$
$$= (-2, 0, 1) - \left(-\frac{2}{\sqrt{2}}\right)\left(\frac{1}{\sqrt{2}}\right)(1, 1, 0)$$
$$= (-2, 0, 1) + (1, 1, 0)$$
$$= (-1, 1, 1)$$

The vector $\mathbf{u}_2'$ lies in $S$ and is orthogonal to $\mathbf{v}_1$. Third, we normalize $\mathbf{u}_2'$ to get

$$\mathbf{v}_2 = \left(\frac{1}{|\mathbf{u}_2'|}\right)\mathbf{u}_2' = \frac{1}{\sqrt{3}}(-1, 1, 1)$$

The vectors $\mathbf{v}_1, \mathbf{v}_2$ form an orthonormal basis for $S$.  ∎

**EXAMPLE 9**   Apply the Gram–Schmidt process to orthonormalize the vectors $\mathbf{u}_1 = (1, 0, 1)$, $\mathbf{u}_2 = (1, 1, 0)$, $\mathbf{u}_3 = (1, 1, 1)$.

SOLUTION First, we normalize $\mathbf{u}_1$ to get

$$\mathbf{v}_1 = \frac{1}{\sqrt{2}}(1,0,1)$$

Second, we subtract the projection of $\mathbf{u}_2$ onto $\mathbf{v}_1$ from $\mathbf{u}_2$ to get

$$\mathbf{u}_2' = \mathbf{u}_2 - (\mathbf{u}_2 \cdot \mathbf{v}_1)\mathbf{v}_1$$
$$= (1,1,0) - \left(\frac{1}{\sqrt{2}}\right)\left(\frac{1}{\sqrt{2}}\right)(1,0,1)$$
$$= \frac{1}{2}(1,2,-1)$$

Then $|\mathbf{u}_2'| = \sqrt{6}/2$, so that normalizing $\mathbf{u}_2'$ gives us

$$\mathbf{v}_2 = \frac{1}{\sqrt{6}}(1,2,-1)$$

Third, we subtract the projections of $\mathbf{u}_3$ onto $\mathbf{v}_1$ and $\mathbf{v}_2$ from $\mathbf{u}_3$ to get

$$\mathbf{u}_3' = \mathbf{u}_3 - (\mathbf{u}_3 \cdot \mathbf{v}_1)\mathbf{v}_1 - (\mathbf{u}_3 \cdot \mathbf{v}_2)\mathbf{v}_2$$
$$= (1,1,1) - \left(\frac{2}{\sqrt{2}}\right)\left(\frac{1}{\sqrt{2}}\right)(1,0,1) - \left(\frac{2}{\sqrt{6}}\right)\left(\frac{1}{\sqrt{6}}\right)(1,2,-1)$$
$$= (1,1,1) - (1,0,1) - \frac{1}{3}(1,2,-1)$$
$$= \frac{1}{3}(-1,1,1)$$

Since $|\mathbf{u}_3'| = \sqrt{3}/3 = 1/\sqrt{3}$, we get the normalized vector

$$\mathbf{v}_3 = \frac{1}{\sqrt{3}}(-1,1,1)$$

Then $\mathbf{v}_1, \mathbf{v}_2, \mathbf{v}_3$ are the orthonormalized vectors obtained from $\mathbf{u}_1, \mathbf{u}_2, \mathbf{u}_3$. ∎

## EXERCISES 5.2

In Exercises 1–6, normalize the given vector.

1. $(3,4)$      2. $(-4,3)$      3. $(1,-2,4)$

4. $(3,-1,5)$      5. $(-1,-2,4,1)$      6. $(5,-3,1,-2)$

In Exercises 7–12, show that the given vectors are orthonormal.

7. $\dfrac{1}{\sqrt{40}}(6,2), \dfrac{1}{\sqrt{10}}(-1,3)$      8. $\dfrac{1}{\sqrt{80}}(8,4), \dfrac{1}{\sqrt{45}}(3,-6)$

**9.** $\dfrac{1}{\sqrt{59}}(7, 1, 3),\ \dfrac{1}{\sqrt{18}}(-1, 4, 1)$

**10.** $\dfrac{1}{\sqrt{29}}(3, 4, -2),\ \dfrac{1}{\sqrt{30}}(2, 1, 5)$

**11.** $\dfrac{1}{3}(1, 2, 2),\ \dfrac{1}{3}(-2, -1, 2),\ \dfrac{1}{3}(-2, 2, -1)$

**12.** $\dfrac{1}{\sqrt{6}}(2, 1, 1),\ \dfrac{1}{\sqrt{11}}(-1, -1, 3),\ \dfrac{1}{\sqrt{66}}(-4, 7, 1)$

In Exercises 13–16, write the given vector as a linear combination of the ortho-normal vectors $v_1 = (1/\sqrt{5})(1, -2)$, $v_2 = (1/\sqrt{5})(2, 1)$.

**13.** $(7, 3)$       **14.** $(5, 2)$       **15.** $(-3, 1)$       **16.** $(2, -3)$

In Exercises 17–20, write the given vector as a linear combination of the ortho-normal vectors $v_1 = (1/\sqrt{6})(-1, 2, 1)$, $v_2 = (1/\sqrt{11})(3, 1, 1)$, $v_3 = (1/\sqrt{66})(1, 4, -7)$.

**17.** $(2, 2, -3)$    **18.** $(3, -2, -1)$    **19.** $(-2, 4, 3)$    **20.** $(4, -4, 1)$

In Exercises 21–24, find $\text{Proj}_v(u)$, $u' = u - \text{Proj}_v(u)$, and then sketch the four vectors.

**21.** $u = (2, 4),$    $v = (2, 2)$      **22.** $u = (2, 3),$    $v = (5, 1)$

**23.** $u = (-4, 3),$    $v = (-3, 1)$      **24.** $u = (1, -4),$    $v = (5, -3)$

In Exercises 25–30, find $\text{Proj}_v(u)$, $u' = u - \text{Proj}_v(u)$, and then verify by direct compu-tation that $u'$ is orthogonal to $\text{Proj}_v(u)$.

**25.** $u = (-7, 3),$    $v = \dfrac{1}{\sqrt{41}}(4, 5)$      **26.** $u = (2, 9),$    $v = \dfrac{1}{\sqrt{45}}(6, -3)$

**27.** $u = (1, 5, -2),$    $v = (-2, 2, 6)$      **28.** $u = (-3, -2, 4)$    $v = (7, 1, 4)$

**29.** $u = (2, 2, 5),$    $v = \dfrac{1}{\sqrt{69}}(7, 2, -4)$

**30.** $u = (-1, -4, -2),$    $v = \dfrac{1}{\sqrt{65}}(5, 2, -6)$

In Exercises 31–34, find $\text{Proj}_S(u)$ where $S$ is the space spanned by $v_1 = (1/3)(2, 1, 2)$ and $v_2 = (1/3)(-2, 2, 1)$. Find the orthogonal complement, $u'$, of $u$ relative to $S$.

**31.** $u = (3, 2, -3)$            **32.** $u = (4, 1, -2)$

**33.** $u = (1, 3, -3)$            **34.** $u = (1, 2, -4)$

In Exercises 35–36, find the distance, $|u - \text{Proj}_S(u)|$, from the tip of $u$ to the space $S$ spanned $v_1 = (1/\sqrt{3})(1, -1, 1)$, $v_2 = (1/\sqrt{6})(2, 1, -1)$.

**35.** $\mathbf{u} = (2, 3, -1)$         **36.** $\mathbf{u} = (2, 2, 3)$

In Exercises 37–40, use the Gram–Schmidt process to find an orthonormal basis for the space spanned by the given vectors.

**37.** $(4, 3), (-1, 3)$          **38.** $(3, 2), (7, 1)$

**39.** $(1, 1, 2), (2, 1, 1), (1, 2, 1)$     **40.** $(1, 1, -1), (-9, 3, -3), (1, -2, 4)$

In Exercises 41–44, use the Gram–Schmidt process to find an orthonormal basis for the subspace of $R^3$ that satisfies the given equation.

**41.** $5x + 5y + 2z = 0$        **42.** $x + 2y - 2z = 0$

**43.** $2x - 6y + 8z = 0$        **44.** $x - 4y + 2z = 0$

## 5.3 LEAST SQUARES APPROXIMATION

*Linear Approximation, The Least Squares Line, Applications*

In the analysis of many business and industrial problems, it is very important to know relationships between variables so that the values of certain quantities can be calculated in terms of other quantities. For example, sales revenue of a product may depend on the price of the product or it may depend on the amount of advertising that is used. Similarly, the cost of manufacturing a product depends upon the number of units of the product that are made or upon the changing costs of raw materials or labor. It is common practice to try to predict other values, such as future sales or the future value of an asset, on the basis of past performances.

In general, these relationships are not available in the form of ready-made formulas but must be derived from the collection of raw numerical data. The problem is thus one of finding an equation that best fits the given data. If the information is plotted as points in the plane, then the problem can be described graphically as one of finding a curve that best fits the data points. The resulting equation or curve will not be exact in general, but it will approximate the data, and there are a number of methods that can be used to obtain an approximation and a measure of its accuracy. In this section we discuss one method, known as least squares approximation, that is based on the notion of vector projection. We will restrict our attention in this section to the case of linear approximation and indicate a method for dealing with the problem of fitting other curves in the next section.

### LINEAR APPROXIMATION

Suppose that the data points $(x_1, y_1), (x_2, y_2), \ldots, (x_n, y_n)$ have been obtained from past records, market surveys, experimentation, or some other means and we would like to deduce a general relationship between the variables $x$ and $y$. A first step may be to plot the points in the plane to see if a qualitative relationship can be sensed. For example, the points shown in Figure 5.13 suggest that $x$ and $y$ may have an approximately linear relation, since the points almost lie on a line.

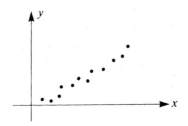

**FIGURE 5.13**                    *The data points suggest a linear relation*

In the situation pictured in Figure 5.13, we would like to find the equation $y = mx + b$ of a line that comes close to fitting the given points. If the line actually contained the data points, then we would have a system of equations that we could solve for the slope $m$ and the $y$-intercept $b$, namely,

$$mx_1 + b = y_1$$
$$mx_2 + b = y_2$$
$$\vdots \qquad \vdots \qquad \vdots$$
$$mx_n + b = y_n$$

However, since in practice the data points usually do not lie nicely on a line, the system of equations is usually inconsistent. Consider the following example involving three points.

**EXAMPLE 1**    Write the problem of finding a line $y = mx + b$ that passes through the three points $(1, 1), (2, 3), (6, 5)$ as a system of equations. Determine if the system is consistent or not.

SOLUTION    The system of equations for the slope $m$ and the intercept $b$ of the line is

$$m + b = 1$$
$$2m + b = 3$$
$$6m + b = 5$$

which has the matrix form

$$\begin{bmatrix} 1 & 1 \\ 2 & 1 \\ 6 & 1 \end{bmatrix} \begin{bmatrix} m \\ b \end{bmatrix} = \begin{bmatrix} 1 \\ 3 \\ 5 \end{bmatrix}$$

After several row operations the augmented matrix

$$\left[\begin{array}{cc|c} 1 & 1 & 1 \\ 2 & 1 & 3 \\ 6 & 1 & 5 \end{array}\right] \text{ becomes } \left[\begin{array}{cc|c} 1 & 1 & 1 \\ 0 & 1 & -1 \\ 0 & 0 & -6 \end{array}\right]$$

and we conclude from the third row that the system is inconsistent. The points do not lie on a line. ∎

Since an exact fit is not generally possible, we seek a line that will closely approximate the data points. By interpreting the problem in terms of vectors, we can apply the notion of orthogonal projection to find a good line of approximation.

## THE LEAST SQUARES LINE

Given the data points $(x_1, y_1)$, $(x_2, y_2)$, ..., $(x_n, y_n)$, we introduce the vectors

$$\mathbf{x} = \begin{bmatrix} x_1 \\ x_2 \\ \vdots \\ x_n \end{bmatrix}, \quad \mathbf{y} = \begin{bmatrix} y_1 \\ y_2 \\ \vdots \\ y_n \end{bmatrix}, \quad \mathbf{1} = \begin{bmatrix} 1 \\ 1 \\ \vdots \\ 1 \end{bmatrix}$$

Then the system of equations for $m$ and $b$ can be written as the vector equation

$$m\mathbf{x} + b\mathbf{1} = \mathbf{y}$$

If the points do not lie on a line, then a solution does not exist, which means, from a vector viewpoint, that the vector $\mathbf{y}$ does not belong to the span of $\{\mathbf{x}, \mathbf{1}\}$. (See Theorem 1 of Section 4.2.) At this stage we project the vector $\mathbf{y}$ onto the subspace spanned by $\{\mathbf{x}, \mathbf{1}\}$; and by replacing $\mathbf{y}$ with its orthogonal projection, we obtain a new problem that does have a solution. This is done as follows.

We let $S$ denote the subspace spanned by $\{\mathbf{x}, \mathbf{1}\}$, and we let $\text{Proj}_S(\mathbf{y})$ denote the projection of $\mathbf{y}$ onto $S$. Then we consider the vector equation

$$m\mathbf{x} + b\mathbf{1} = \text{Proj}_S(\mathbf{y})$$

Since $\text{Proj}_S(\mathbf{y})$ is a linear combination of $\mathbf{x}$ and $\mathbf{1}$, this equation has a solution $(m, b)$. See Figure 5.14 for a geometric view of the situation.

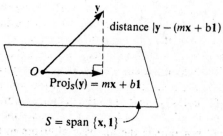

**FIGURE 5.14**    *The projection of $\mathbf{y}$ onto the span $S$ of $\{\mathbf{x}, \mathbf{1}\}$*

By taking the orthogonal projection of **y** onto $S$, we have chosen that vector in $S$ that is closest to **y**. The minimum distance from **y** to $S$ is the orthogonal distance, and thus the solution $(m, b)$ minimizes the distance from **y** to $S$. That is, if $m'\mathbf{x} + b'\mathbf{1}$ is an arbitrary vector in $S$, then

$$|\mathbf{y} - (m\mathbf{x} + b\mathbf{1})| \leqslant |\mathbf{y} - (m'\mathbf{x} + b'\mathbf{1})|$$

See Figure 5.15. Therefore we have the inequality

$$\sqrt{(y_1 - (mx_1 + b))^2 + \cdots + (y_n - (mx_n + b))^2}$$
$$\leqslant \sqrt{(y_1 - (m'x_1 + b'))^2 + \cdots + (y_n - (m'x_n + b'))^2}$$

and by taking squares we obtain

$$(y_1 - (mx_1 + b))^2 + \cdots + (y_n - (mx_n + b))^2$$
$$\leqslant (y_1 - (m'x_1 + b'))^2 + \cdots + (y_n - (m'x_n + b'))^2$$

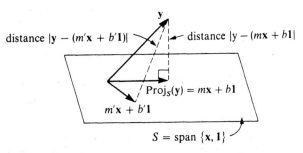

distance $|\mathbf{y} - (m'\mathbf{x} + b'\mathbf{1})|$     distance $|\mathbf{y} - (m\mathbf{x} + b\mathbf{1}|$

$\text{Proj}_S(\mathbf{y}) = m\mathbf{x} + b\mathbf{1}$

$m'\mathbf{x} + b'\mathbf{1}$

$S = \text{span } \{\mathbf{x}, \mathbf{1}\}$

**FIGURE 5.15**

*The minimum distance from* **y** *to S is*
$|\mathbf{y} - (m\mathbf{x} + b\mathbf{1})|$

Thus the solution $(m, b)$ that gives us $\text{Proj}_S(\mathbf{y}) = m\mathbf{x} + b\mathbf{1}$ produces the least value of the expression

$$e = (y_1 - (mx_1 + b))^2 + \cdots + (y_n - (mx_n + b))^2$$

This is the reason that the resulting line of approximation is called the **least squares line of approximation**. The number $e$ can be used to measure the accuracy of the approximation.

There is a nice geometric interpretation of the sum of squares, which we have denoted by $e$. In Figure 5.16 we have displayed the least squares line of approximation to the data points that are shown. The vertical lines from the data points to the line represent the vertical distances from the points to the line. The distance from a point $(x_i, y_i)$ to the line $y = mx + b$ is given by $|y_i - (mx_i + b)|$, and thus the number $e$ is the sum of the squares of the distances. Clearly, if this sum of squares is small, then the distance from any particular point to the line is small, and the line would be regarded as a good approximation to the data points. We will not pursue the analysis of errors in this brief introduction to least squares approximation.

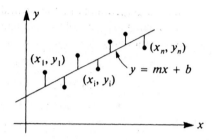

**FIGURE 5.16**

*The least squares line approximates the data points*

*REMARK:* In the field of statistics the fitting of a line to given data is called *linear regression*, and the line is called the *regression line* for the data. The term "regression" was first used in the nineteenth century by the Englishman Francis Dalton in connection with his study of the relationship between the heights of fathers and sons. He observed that tall men are likely to have shorter sons and short men are likely to have taller sons, so that the heights over generations tend to "regress" toward an average.

We will now derive formulas for the slope $m$ and the intercept $b$ of the line that best fits the given data in the sense of least squares. The formulas, which are given in Theorem 1 below, are derived by using the fact that the vector

$$\mathbf{y} - (m\mathbf{x} + b\mathbf{1}) = \mathbf{y} - \text{Proj}_S(\mathbf{y})$$

is orthogonal to $\mathbf{x}$ and $\mathbf{1}$. The scalar products of $\mathbf{x}$ and $\mathbf{1}$ with this vector are zero, so that we have the system

$$\mathbf{x} \cdot [\mathbf{y} - (m\mathbf{x} + b\mathbf{1})] = 0$$
$$\mathbf{1} \cdot [\mathbf{y} - (m\mathbf{x} + b\mathbf{1})] = 0$$

which can be written as

$$\mathbf{x} \cdot (m\mathbf{x} + b\mathbf{1}) = \mathbf{x} \cdot \mathbf{y}$$
$$\mathbf{1} \cdot (m\mathbf{x} + b\mathbf{1}) = \mathbf{1} \cdot \mathbf{y}$$

An additional simplification gives us the system

$$(\mathbf{x} \cdot \mathbf{x})m + (\mathbf{x} \cdot \mathbf{1})b = \mathbf{x} \cdot \mathbf{y}$$
$$(\mathbf{1} \cdot \mathbf{x})m + (\mathbf{1} \cdot \mathbf{1})b = \mathbf{1} \cdot \mathbf{y}$$

which can easily be solved (by Cramer's Rule, for example) for $m$ and $b$. The solution is given in the following theorem. In the formulas we have used the fact that $\mathbf{1} \cdot \mathbf{1} = n$.

**THEOREM 1**

The slope $m$ and intercept $b$ of the least squares line of approximation for the data points $(x_1, y_1), \ldots, (x_n, y_n)$ are given by

$$m = \frac{n\mathbf{x} \cdot \mathbf{y} - (\mathbf{1} \cdot \mathbf{x})(\mathbf{1} \cdot \mathbf{y})}{n\mathbf{x} \cdot \mathbf{x} - (\mathbf{1} \cdot \mathbf{x})^2}$$

$$b = \frac{(\mathbf{x} \cdot \mathbf{x})(\mathbf{1} \cdot \mathbf{y}) - (\mathbf{x} \cdot \mathbf{y})(\mathbf{1} \cdot \mathbf{x})}{n\mathbf{x} \cdot \mathbf{x} - (\mathbf{1} \cdot \mathbf{x})^2}$$

The scalar products in the formulas of Theorem 1 involve sums that are usually expressed in terms of the summation symbol $\Sigma$, which is the capital Greek letter sigma (for sum). It is a convenient shorthand to write

$$\Sigma x = x_1 + x_2 + \cdots + x_n = \mathbf{1} \cdot \mathbf{x}$$
$$\Sigma y = y_1 + y_2 + \cdots + y_n = \mathbf{1} \cdot \mathbf{y}$$
$$\Sigma xy = x_1 y_1 + x_2 y_2 + \cdots + x_n y_n = \mathbf{x} \cdot \mathbf{y}$$
$$\Sigma x^2 = x_1{}^2 + x_2{}^2 + \cdots + x_n{}^2 = \mathbf{x} \cdot \mathbf{x}$$

Thus the formulas can be written

$$m = \frac{n\Sigma xy - (\Sigma x)(\Sigma y)}{n\Sigma x^2 - (\Sigma x)^2}$$

$$b = \frac{(\Sigma x^2)(\Sigma y) - (\Sigma xy)(\Sigma x)}{n\Sigma x^2 - (\Sigma x)^2}$$

For a large number of data points, these formulas are best applied with the help of a calculator or computer. Some calculators are available with buttons that will perform these computations after the data is entered.

The following example illustrates the computations for three data points.

**EXAMPLE 2**    Find the least squares line of approximation for the data points $(1, 1)$, $(2, 3)$, $(6, 5)$. Then find the value of $y$ when $x = 4$.

**SOLUTION**    We have $\mathbf{x} = (1, 2, 6)$, $\mathbf{y} = (1, 3, 5)$, $\mathbf{1} = (1, 1, 1)$, and $n = 3$. We first calculate the sums by means of a table, where the terms in the $x$ and $y$ columns are listed first, then the terms in the $x^2$ and $xy$ columns are calculated, and then the sums are found.

| $x$ | $y$ | $x^2$ | $xy$ |
|---|---|---|---|
| 1 | 1 | 1 | 1 |
| 2 | 3 | 4 | 6 |
| 6 | 5 | 36 | 30 |
| Totals 9 | 9 | 41 | 37 |

Thus we have $\mathbf{1} \cdot \mathbf{x} = \Sigma x = 9$, $\mathbf{1} \cdot \mathbf{y} = \Sigma y = 9$, $\mathbf{x} \cdot \mathbf{x} = \Sigma x^2 = 41$, and $\mathbf{x} \cdot \mathbf{y} = \Sigma xy = 37$. Upon substituting these values into the formulas, we obtain

$$m = \frac{3 \cdot 37 - 9 \cdot 9}{3 \cdot 41 - 81} = \frac{30}{42} = \frac{5}{7}$$

$$b = \frac{41 \cdot 9 - 37 \cdot 9}{3 \cdot 41 - 81} = \frac{36}{42} = \frac{6}{7}$$

Thus the least squares line has the equation

$$y = \frac{5}{7} x + \frac{6}{7}$$

See Figure 5.17. For the value $x = 4$, we find the value of $y$ to be

$$y = \frac{5}{7} \cdot 4 + \frac{6}{7} = \frac{26}{7} \quad \blacksquare$$

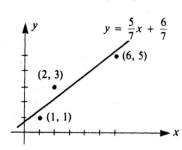

**FIGURE 5.17**

The least squares line is $y = \frac{5}{7}x + \frac{6}{7}$

## APPLICATIONS

The following examples illustrate how the notion of least squares approximation can be applied. In applications some restraint must be exercised so that estimates made far away from the given data are not taken seriously. The approximation becomes less reliable as we move farther away from the data points. The future should not be predicted too far in advance.

**EXAMPLE 3** In a pilot marketing analysis for a new handyman drill, the King Hardware Company distributed the drill for a month in four different cities at different prices. The demand for the drill is given in the table

| Price ($x$) | 20 | 25 | 30 | 35 |
|---|---|---|---|---|
| Demand ($y$) | 84 | 74 | 62 | 50 |

Find the least squares line that relates demand to price. Estimate the demand $y$ and the revenue $xy$ when the price is $x = \$28.50$.

**SOLUTION** With a calculator we obtain the following table (note that $xy$ represents revenue)

| | $x$ | $y$ | $x^2$ | $xy$ |
|---|---|---|---|---|
| | 20 | 84 | 400 | 1680 |
| | 25 | 74 | 625 | 1850 |
| | 30 | 62 | 900 | 1860 |
| | 35 | 50 | 1225 | 1750 |
| Totals | 110 | 270 | 3150 | 7140 |

Putting these values into the formulas, we get

$$m = \frac{4 \cdot 7140 - 110 \cdot 270}{4 \cdot 3150 - 110 \cdot 110} = -\frac{1140}{500} = -2.28$$

$$b = \frac{3150 \cdot 270 - 7140 \cdot 110}{4 \cdot 3150 - 110 \cdot 110} = \frac{65,100}{500} = 130.2$$

Hence the equation of the least squares line is

$$y = -2.28x + 130.2$$

Note that the negative slope indicates that demand goes down as the price increases. At the price $x = \$28.50$ we project demand to be $y = 65.22$ and the corresponding revenue to be $xy = \$1858.77$. ∎

The formulas for slope and intercept become much simpler if we have $\Sigma x = 0$. In this case they are

$$m = \frac{\Sigma xy}{\Sigma x^2}, \quad b = \frac{1}{n}\Sigma y$$

Thus if the values $x_1, x_2, \ldots, x_n$ are equally spaced and coded so that they are symmetrically located about 0, then the computations are simplified. For example, if the $x_i$ represent years, we can choose an appropriate code for them as in the following example.

**EXAMPLE 4**   The Eastern Import Auto Corporation had sales of $800,000 in 1979, $1,400,000 in 1980, $2,100,000 in 1981, $3,000,000 in 1982, and $3,600,000 in 1983. Find the least squares line that relates dollar volume of car sales to year. Use the equation to project sales for 1984.

**SOLUTION**   We code the years by letting $x_1 = -2$ stand for 1979, $x_2 = -1$ stand for 1980, and so on. This symmetric coding about 0 gives us a sum of zero so that the simplified formulas can be used. We will let the sales units be $1,000,000. Then the data points are $(-2, .8), (-1, 1.4), (0, 2.1), (1, 3), (2, 3.6)$, and we use a calculator to obtain the table

| $x$ | $y$ | $x^2$ | $xy$ |
|---|---|---|---|
| $-2$ | .8 | 4 | $-1.6$ |
| $-1$ | 1.4 | 1 | $-1.4$ |
| 0 | 2.1 | 0 | 0 |
| 1 | 3 | 1 | 3 |
| 2 | 3.6 | 4 | 7.2 |
| Totals    0 | 10.9 | 10 | 7.2 |

The formulas then give us

$$m = \frac{\Sigma xy}{\Sigma x^2} = .72, \quad b = \frac{1}{5}\Sigma y = 2.18$$

The equation of the least square line is

$$y = .72x + 2.18$$

To estimate sales in 1984, we set $x = 3$ and find $y = 4.34$. Thus we project sales of $4,340,000 in 1984. ∎

## EXERCISES 5.3

In Exercises 1–4, show that the given points do not lie on a line, and find the least squares line of approximation. Sketch the given points and the approximating line.

**1.** $(1, 2), (-2, 3), (5, 1)$            **2.** $(2, 2), (0, 0), (-3, -2)$

**3.** $(-2, 4), (-1, 1), (2, -6)$           **4.** $(4, 3), (6, 6), (8, 7)$

In Exercises 5–8, find the least squares line of approximation to the given data points.

**5.** $(-1, -1), (-4, 1), (4, -3), (6, -4)$

**6.** $(-3, -2), (-1, 0), (0, 1), (2, 2)$

**7.** $(-4, 1), (-2, 0), (-1, -1), (0, -2), (1, -3)$

**8.** $(-1, -3), (5, 1), (8, 3), (10, 6), (13, 8)$

In Exercises 9–12, find the least squares line of approximation to the given points. Note that $\Sigma x = 0$, and use the simplified formulas.

**9.** $(-2, 1), (-1, 1.2), (0, 1.3), (1, 1.5), (2, 1.6)$

**10.** $(-2, 3), (-1, 2.7), (0, 2.6), (1, 2.4), (2, 2.3)$

**11.** $(-3, -2), (-2, -1.6), (-1, -1), (1, -.6), (2, -.4), (3, 0)$

**12.** $(-3, 3), (-2, 2.5), (-1, 2.1), (1, 1.8), (2, 1.3), (3, 1)$

In Exercises 13–18, code the data points $(x, y)$ so that $\Sigma x = 0$ and determine an appropriate measure on the $y$-axis. Assume that the conditions existing during the period of the data collection will hold into the prediction period of the future.

**13.** Building lots in the "Sunset Acres" development sold for $4500 in 1972, $4800 in 1973, and $5000 in 1974. Find the line of least squares fit that relates selling price to year, and use it to determine the selling price for lots in 1975.

**14.** The Flivver Auto Corporation had sales of 2,200,000 autos in 1978, 3,000,000 autos in 1979, and 4,000,000 autos in 1980. Find the line of least squares fit that relates auto sales to year, and use it to project sales for 1981.

**15.** Paula Gehring bought 100 shares of RANTEC Corporation for $1000 on March 15. On April 15 the financial page showed that 100 shares of RANTEC sold for $1030; and on May 15, 100 shares sold for $1080. Paula has decided to sell on the first fifteenth of the month that 100 shares sell for more than $1120. Find the line of least squares fit that relates selling price to month, and use it to determine when Paula will sell. For how much will she sell the shares?

16. Jack Jones bought a used VAROOME SPEEDSTER in 1976 for $19,000. In 1977 Jack saw an advertisement for his model car that asked for $17,000 (firm), and in 1978 there was one offered for $16,000. Jack wants to sell his car after the value falls below $13,000. Find the line of least squares fit that relates the value of the car to the year, and use it to determine when Jack will sell. For how much will the car sell? Assume that all advertisements and sales occur in the spring of the year.

17. The Galaxy Television Company has test marked their new 19-inch "Colorburst" television set at different prices in five comparable markets. A table relating price and sales is given below.

| Price ($x$) | $450 | $475 | $500 | $525 | $550 |
|---|---|---|---|---|---|
| Sales ($y$) | 920 | 910 | 890 | 880 | 860 |

Find the line of least squares fit that relates sales to price. Estimate the sales when the price is $510, and find the total revenue, $xy$, at this price.

18. The Purity Dairy Company has test marketed their new dietetic "SlimGlow" milk at five different prices in comparable sales areas. A table relating sales in gallons to price is given below.

| Price ($x$) | $1.95 | $2.00 | $2.05 | $2.10 | $2.15 |
|---|---|---|---|---|---|
| Sales ($y$) | 965 | 930 | 900 | 875 | 840 |

Find the line of least squares fit that relates sales to price. Estimate the sales when the price is $2.07 per gallon, and find the total revenue, $xy$, at this price.

## 5.4  LEAST SQUARES APPROXIMATION AND GENERALIZED INVERSES (OPTIONAL)

*Least Squares Solutions of Inconsistent Systems, Generalized Inverses, Application, Linear Approximations, Quadratic and Other Approximations, Application*

In this section we extend the ideas of the preceding section to more general approximation problems. Since the attempt to fit curves exactly to data points leads to an inconsistent system, we will first consider inconsistent linear systems; and by applying the technique of orthogonal projections, we will obtain vectors that can be regarded as "solutions" in the sense of least squares approximation. The method will give rise to the notion of a "generalized" inverse matrix so that the least squares solution of an inconsistent system can be expressed in terms of the generalized inverse of the coefficient matrix. The generalized inverse of a matrix coincides with the actual inverse in the case that the matrix is invertible, and it extends the concept of inverting a matrix to some matrices that are not invertible in the usual sense. It will also be used to obtain a matrix formula for the projection of a vector onto the column space of a matrix.

The method of "solving" inconsistent systems is then applied to the problem of approximating data points by a curve that best fits the points in the sense of least squares. For linear approximation this yields an alternative method of finding the least squares line of approximation that was discussed in the preceding section. We will also consider nonlinear approximation problems, including a method for fitting a quadratic curve to given data points in the plane and an application to estimation of sales.

## LEAST SQUARES SOLUTION OF INCONSISTENT SYSTEMS

A system of linear equations $A\mathbf{x} = \mathbf{b}$ is inconsistent if it has no solutions. This occurs if the vector $\mathbf{b}$ cannot be written as a linear combination of the column vectors of $A$ or, in other words, if $\mathbf{b}$ does not belong to the column space of the matrix $A$. (See Sections 4.2 and 4.3.) However, in the same spirit as the preceding section we can take the orthogonal projection of $\mathbf{b}$ into the subspace spanned by the column vectors of $A$ and thereby obtain a system of equations that is consistent.

In the ensuing discussion we will assume that the column vectors of the matrix $A$ are linearly independent and will refer to this property of $A$ by saying that $A$ has **full column rank**. The columns of such a matrix form a basis for the column space so that any vector in the column space of $A$ can be written as a linear combination of the column vectors in only one way. Note that a matrix with full column rank cannot have more columns than rows.

Now suppose that we have an inconsistent system $A\mathbf{x} = \mathbf{b}$. The vector $\mathbf{b}$ lies outside the column space of $A$; but if we let $\mathrm{Proj}_A(\mathbf{b})$ denote the orthogonal projection of $\mathbf{b}$ onto the column space, then we can create the consistent system

$$A\mathbf{x} = \mathrm{Proj}_A(\mathbf{b})$$

Since $A$ has full column rank, this system will have a unique solution. We will denote this unique solution by $\mathbf{u}$, and we will call $\mathbf{u}$ the **least squares solution** of the system $A\mathbf{x} = \mathbf{b}$. Thus the vector $\mathbf{u}$ satisfies

$$A\mathbf{u} = \mathrm{Proj}_A(\mathbf{b})$$

and it yields the least (orthogonal) distance from $\mathbf{b}$ to the column space of the matrix $A$. That is, we have the inequality

$$|A\mathbf{u} - \mathbf{b}| \leqslant |A\mathbf{x} - \mathbf{b}|$$

for any other vector $\mathbf{x}$. See Figure 5.18.

We now derive a method for finding the least squares solution, which we denote by $\mathbf{u}$, of the system $A\mathbf{x} = \mathbf{b}$. Since the vector $\mathbf{b} - A\mathbf{u}$ is orthogonal to the column space of $A$, we have for all vectors $\mathbf{x}$ that

$$(A\mathbf{x}) \cdot (\mathbf{b} - A\mathbf{u}) = 0$$

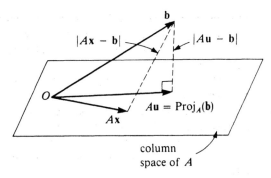

**FIGURE 5.18**                    *The least squares solution of A$\mathbf{x}$ = $\mathbf{b}$*

We can think of the scalar product of two vectors as matrix multiplication if we have a row vector times a column vector. Therefore if we transpose the column vector $A\mathbf{x}$ to the row vector $(A\mathbf{x})^t = \mathbf{x}^t A^t$, then we can write the scalar product as

$$(\mathbf{x}^t A^t)(\mathbf{b} - A\mathbf{u}) = 0$$

Rearranging terms, we can write this in the form

$$\mathbf{x}^t [A^t \mathbf{b} - (A^t A)\mathbf{u}] = 0$$

Because this equation holds for all vectors $\mathbf{x}$, the expression in brackets must be zero, so that we have

$$A^t \mathbf{b} - (A^t A)\mathbf{u} = \mathbf{0}$$

which is the same as

$$(A^t A)\mathbf{u} = A^t \mathbf{b}$$

We have the following theorem.

### THEOREM 1

The least squares solution $\mathbf{u}$ of the system $A\mathbf{x} = \mathbf{b}$ is the solution of the consistent system

$$(A^t A)\mathbf{x} = A^t \mathbf{b}$$

also the projection of $\mathbf{b}$ onto the column space of $A$ is the vector $A\mathbf{u}$.

To find the solution of the system given in Theorem 1, we first calculate the product $A^t A$ and the vector $A^t \mathbf{b}$. Then we find the solution $\mathbf{u}$ by row reducing the augmented matrix $[A^t A | A^t \mathbf{b}]$. The projection $\text{Proj}_A(\mathbf{b})$ is then found by calculating $A\mathbf{u}$. The following example provides an illustration.

**EXAMPLE 1**  Find the least squares solution of the inconsistent system $A\mathbf{x} = \mathbf{b}$ where

$$A = \begin{bmatrix} 1 & 1 \\ 1 & 2 \\ 0 & 1 \end{bmatrix} \quad \text{and} \quad \mathbf{b} = \begin{bmatrix} 2 \\ 1 \\ 3 \end{bmatrix}$$

Then find the projection of $\mathbf{b}$ onto the column space of $A$.

**SOLUTION**  We calculate the matrix

$$A^t A = \begin{bmatrix} 1 & 1 & 0 \\ 1 & 2 & 1 \end{bmatrix} \begin{bmatrix} 1 & 1 \\ 1 & 2 \\ 0 & 1 \end{bmatrix} = \begin{bmatrix} 2 & 3 \\ 3 & 6 \end{bmatrix}$$

and the vector

$$A^t \mathbf{b} = \begin{bmatrix} 1 & 1 & 0 \\ 1 & 2 & 1 \end{bmatrix} \begin{bmatrix} 2 \\ 1 \\ 3 \end{bmatrix} = \begin{bmatrix} 3 \\ 7 \end{bmatrix}$$

Then the system $(A^t A)\mathbf{x} = A^t \mathbf{b}$ has the augmented matrix

$$\begin{bmatrix} 2 & 3 & | & 3 \\ 3 & 6 & | & 7 \end{bmatrix}$$

which can be put into the reduced echelon form

$$\begin{bmatrix} 1 & 0 & | & -1 \\ 0 & 1 & | & 5/3 \end{bmatrix}$$

Hence the least squares solution of $A\mathbf{x} = \mathbf{b}$ is the vector $\mathbf{u} = (-1, \frac{5}{3})$. The projection of $\mathbf{b}$ onto the column space of $A$ is the vector

$$\text{Proj}_A \mathbf{b} = A\mathbf{u} = \begin{bmatrix} 1 & 1 \\ 1 & 2 \\ 0 & 1 \end{bmatrix} \begin{bmatrix} -1 \\ 5/3 \end{bmatrix} = \begin{bmatrix} 2/3 \\ 7/3 \\ 5/3 \end{bmatrix} \quad \blacksquare$$

## GENERALIZED INVERSES

We have seen that the least squares solution of an inconsistent system is obtained by solving the consistent system

$$(A^t A)\mathbf{x} = A^t \mathbf{b}$$

It can be proved that if the matrix $A$ has full column rank, then the square matrix

$A^tA$ is invertible. Accepting this result, we can multiply both sides of the equation by the inverse of $A^tA$ to get the least squares solution

$$\mathbf{u} = (A^tA)^{-1}A^t\mathbf{b}$$

This formula for $\mathbf{u}$ leads to the following definition.

### DEFINITION

If $A$ is a matrix with full column rank, then the matrix

$$A^\dagger = (A^tA)^{-1}A^t$$

is called the **generalized inverse** of $A$.

In the case that $A$ is a square matrix that possesses an inverse $A^{-1}$ in the usual sense, then the formula for $A^\dagger$ gives us

$$A^\dagger = (A^tA)^{-1}A^t = A^{-1}(A^t)^{-1}A^t = A^{-1}I = A^{-1}$$

Hence the generalized inverse is the same as the usual inverse when $A$ is invertible.

In general, if $A$ is an $m \times n$ matrix, then $A^t$ is an $n \times m$ matrix, so that $A^tA$ and $(A^tA)^{-1}$ are $n \times n$ matrices. Then the product $(A^tA)^{-1}A^t$ is an $n \times m$ matrix. Thus the generalized inverse $A^\dagger$ of an $m \times n$ matrix $A$ is an $n \times m$ matrix.

When we multiply $A$ on the left by $A^\dagger$, we obtain

$$A^\dagger A = (A^tA)^{-1}(A^tA) = I$$

so that the generalized inverse $A^\dagger$ acts as an inverse when it premultiplies $A$. This fact can be used to check the calculations when we are finding the generalized inverse of a matrix.

**EXAMPLE 2**   Find the generalized inverse $A^\dagger$ of the matrix

$$A = \begin{bmatrix} 1 & 3 \\ 2 & 1 \\ 2 & 1 \end{bmatrix}$$

SOLUTION   We first find the product

$$A^tA = \begin{bmatrix} 1 & 2 & 2 \\ 3 & 1 & 1 \end{bmatrix} \begin{bmatrix} 1 & 3 \\ 2 & 1 \\ 2 & 1 \end{bmatrix} = \begin{bmatrix} 9 & 7 \\ 7 & 11 \end{bmatrix}$$

and then compute its inverse

$$(A^tA)^{-1} = (1/50) \begin{bmatrix} 11 & -7 \\ -7 & 9 \end{bmatrix}$$

Then the generalized inverse of $A$ is

$$A^\dagger = (A^t A)^{-1} A^t$$

$$= (1/50) \begin{bmatrix} 11 & -7 \\ -7 & 9 \end{bmatrix} \begin{bmatrix} 1 & 2 & 2 \\ 3 & 1 & 1 \end{bmatrix}$$

$$= (1/50) \begin{bmatrix} -10 & 15 & 15 \\ 20 & -5 & -5 \end{bmatrix}$$

$$= (1/10) \begin{bmatrix} -2 & 3 & 3 \\ 4 & -1 & -1 \end{bmatrix}$$

As a check on the calculation, the reader should verify that

$$A^\dagger A = \begin{bmatrix} 1 & 0 \\ 0 & 1 \end{bmatrix} \quad \blacksquare$$

If the system $A\mathbf{x} = \mathbf{b}$ is inconsistent and if $A$ has full column rank, then the least squares solution is the vector

$$\mathbf{u} = (A^t A)^{-1} A^t \mathbf{b} = A^\dagger \mathbf{b}$$

Thus the generalized inverse can be used in much the same way that the usual inverse is used to solve a consistent system.

When $A$ is multiplied on the left by $A^\dagger$, we obtain $A^\dagger A = I$, as was noted earlier. The product $A A^\dagger$ in the opposite order is not the identity, but it does have a significant application. By the definition of least squares solution, the vector $A\mathbf{u}$ is the projection of $\mathbf{b}$ onto the column space of $A$. That is, we have

$$\text{Proj}_A(\mathbf{b}) = A\mathbf{u}$$

If we now substitute $\mathbf{u} = A^\dagger \mathbf{b}$, we get

$$\text{Proj}_A(\mathbf{b}) = A A^\dagger \mathbf{b}$$

Hence the projection of $\mathbf{b}$ onto the column space of $A$ is obtained by multiplying the vector $\mathbf{b}$ by the matrix $A A^\dagger$. For this reason the matrix $A A^\dagger$ is called the **projection matrix** onto the column space of $A$. Thus instead of finding an orthonormal basis and calculating projections as we did in Section 5.2, we can use the projection matrix $A A^\dagger$ instead.

We summarize these facts in the following theorem, which is a parallel to Theorem 1.

### THEOREM 2

If $A$ has full column rank and if $A^\dagger$ is its generalized inverse, then the least squares solution of $A\mathbf{x} = \mathbf{b}$ is

$$\mathbf{u} = A^\dagger \mathbf{b}$$

also the projection of $\mathbf{b}$ onto the column space of $A$ is

$$\text{Proj}_A(\mathbf{b}) = A A^\dagger \mathbf{b}$$

The following example illustrates the role of the generalized inverse.

**EXAMPLE 3**  Find the generalized inverse $A^\dagger$ of the matrix

$$A = \begin{bmatrix} 1 & 0 \\ 1 & 2 \\ 1 & 1 \\ 0 & 1 \end{bmatrix}$$

Use $A^\dagger$ to find the least squares solution of the system $A\mathbf{x} = \mathbf{b}$ where

$$\mathbf{b} = \begin{bmatrix} 5 \\ 6 \\ 7 \\ 2 \end{bmatrix}$$

and find the projection of $\mathbf{b}$ onto the column space of $A$.

**SOLUTION**   First we calculate

$$A^t A = \begin{bmatrix} 3 & 3 \\ 3 & 6 \end{bmatrix}$$

and then find the inverse

$$(A^t A)^{-1} = (1/3) \begin{bmatrix} 2 & -1 \\ -1 & 1 \end{bmatrix}$$

Then the generalized inverse of $A$ is

$$A^\dagger = (1/3) \begin{bmatrix} 2 & -1 \\ -1 & 1 \end{bmatrix} \begin{bmatrix} 1 & 1 & 1 & 0 \\ 0 & 2 & 1 & 1 \end{bmatrix}$$

$$= (1/3) \begin{bmatrix} 2 & 0 & 1 & -1 \\ -1 & 1 & 0 & 1 \end{bmatrix}$$

Thus the system $A\mathbf{x} = \mathbf{b}$ has the least squares solution

$$\mathbf{u} = A^\dagger \mathbf{b}$$

$$= (1/3) \begin{bmatrix} 2 & 0 & 1 & -1 \\ -1 & 1 & 0 & 1 \end{bmatrix} \begin{bmatrix} 5 \\ 6 \\ 7 \\ 2 \end{bmatrix}$$

$$= \begin{bmatrix} 5 \\ 1 \end{bmatrix}$$

The projection of $\mathbf{b}$ onto the column space of $A$ is

$$\text{Proj}_A(\mathbf{b}) = A A^\dagger \mathbf{b} = A\mathbf{u}$$

$$= \begin{bmatrix} 1 & 0 \\ 1 & 2 \\ 1 & 1 \\ 0 & 1 \end{bmatrix} \begin{bmatrix} 5 \\ 1 \end{bmatrix} = \begin{bmatrix} 5 \\ 7 \\ 6 \\ 1 \end{bmatrix} \quad \blacksquare$$

*REMARK:* We have discussed the notion of generalized inverse under the assumption that the matrix $A$ has full column rank, an assumption that is satisfied in many applications. If $A$ does not have full column rank, then it is still possible to define a generalized inverse, but the construction is much more complicated. If $A$ does not have full column rank, then the system $A\mathbf{x} = \text{Proj}_A(\mathbf{b})$ may have infinitely many solutions, and one of these solutions is selected by applying another least squares procedure. This uniquely chosen solution is called the least squares solution, and a matrix formula can be derived for it. The resulting formula is used to define the generalized inverse in this case. Because of the complicated nature of the construction, we will not go into any more detail.

## APPLICATION

We now consider the problem of a contract whose terms cannot be satisfied exactly, but for which an approximation will suffice if it is close enough to the specified requirements.

**EXAMPLE 4**   The Great American Boat Works is preparing a bid on a government contract to manufacture Missile Frigates from "mothballed" Liberty Ships and Battleships. The steel in the Missile Frigates is to be 20 tons iron to 2 tons chromium to 2 tons molybdenum. The available steel in the Liberty Ships is 25 tons iron to 2 tons chromium to 1 ton molybdenum; and the steel in the Battleships is 20 tons iron to 3 tons chromium to 2 tons molybdenum. The specifications on the Missile Frigates do not have to be met exactly, but there are penalties based on the degree of the discrepancy. How closely can the specifications be matched with the alloys from the mothballed ships, and what are the relative proportions of each that should be used to produce the closest match?

SOLUTION   Let $x_1$, $x_2$ be the relative tonnage of Liberty Ships and Battleships to be used. Then we seek the least squares solution to the system of equations

$$\begin{bmatrix} 25 & 20 \\ 2 & 3 \\ 1 & 2 \end{bmatrix} \begin{bmatrix} x_1 \\ x_2 \end{bmatrix} = \begin{bmatrix} 20 \\ 2 \\ 2 \end{bmatrix}$$

We let the above system be denoted by $A\mathbf{x} = \mathbf{b}$, and we wish to solve the system

$$A^t A \mathbf{u} = A^t \mathbf{b}$$

We find first that

$$A^t A = \begin{bmatrix} 630 & 508 \\ 508 & 413 \end{bmatrix}$$

and then we compute the inverse

$$(A^t A)^{-1} = (1/2126) \begin{bmatrix} 413 & -508 \\ -508 & 630 \end{bmatrix}$$

Next we obtain

$$A^t \mathbf{b} = \begin{bmatrix} 506 \\ 410 \end{bmatrix}$$

Then we get the least squares solution

$$\mathbf{u} = (A^t A)^{-1} A^t \mathbf{b}$$

$$= (1/2126) \begin{bmatrix} 413 & -508 \\ -508 & 630 \end{bmatrix} \begin{bmatrix} 506 \\ 410 \end{bmatrix} = \begin{bmatrix} .3283 \\ .5889 \end{bmatrix}$$

Therefore we blend .3283 tons of Liberty Ship to .5889 tons of Battleship. In order to find the closeness of fit, we compute

$$A A^\dagger \mathbf{b} = A\mathbf{u}$$

$$= \begin{bmatrix} 25 & 20 \\ 2 & 3 \\ 1 & 2 \end{bmatrix} \begin{bmatrix} .3283 \\ .5889 \end{bmatrix} = \begin{bmatrix} 19.986 \\ 2.423 \\ 1.506 \end{bmatrix}$$

That is, the approximate alloy will be 19.986 tons of iron to 2.423 tons of chromium to 1.506 tons of molybdenum. ❚❚

## LINEAR APPROXIMATIONS

The methods of this section provide an alternative approach for finding the least squares line of approximation for data points in the plane that was discussed in Section 5.3. The search for a line $y = mx + b$ to fit the data points $(x_1, y_1), (x_2, y_2),$ $\ldots, (x_n, y_n)$ leads to the system of equations

$$\begin{bmatrix} x_1 & 1 \\ x_2 & 1 \\ \vdots & \vdots \\ x_n & 1 \end{bmatrix} \begin{bmatrix} m \\ b \end{bmatrix} = \begin{bmatrix} y_1 \\ y_2 \\ \vdots \\ y_n \end{bmatrix}$$

If the points are noncollinear, then the system is inconsistent, and the least squares line of approximation is determined by the least squares solution. Thus we may obtain the line by using the generalized inverse of the coefficient matrix. The following theorem is the matrix counterpart to Theorem 1 of Section 5.3 in which formulas for $m$ and $b$ were given.

### THEOREM 3

The slope and intercept of the least squares line of approximation $y = mx + b$ for the noncollinear data points $(x_1, y_2), (x_2, y_2), \ldots, (x_n, y_n)$ are given by

$$\begin{bmatrix} m \\ b \end{bmatrix} = A^\dagger \mathbf{y} = (A^t A)^{-1} A^t \mathbf{y}$$

where

$$A = \begin{bmatrix} x_1 & 1 \\ x_2 & 1 \\ \vdots & \vdots \\ x_n & 1 \end{bmatrix} \quad \text{and} \quad \mathbf{y} = \begin{bmatrix} y_1 \\ y_2 \\ \vdots \\ y_n \end{bmatrix}$$

This matrix method for finding the least squares line of approximation is illustrated in the following example.

**EXAMPLE 5**    Find the least squares line of approximation to the data points $(1, 5)$, $(3, 4)$, $(4, 3)$, $(6, 1)$.

SOLUTION    We have

$$A = \begin{bmatrix} 1 & 1 \\ 3 & 1 \\ 4 & 1 \\ 6 & 1 \end{bmatrix} \quad \text{and} \quad y = \begin{bmatrix} 5 \\ 4 \\ 3 \\ 1 \end{bmatrix}$$

We find the generalized inverse of $A$ by first calculating

$$A^t A = \begin{bmatrix} 62 & 14 \\ 14 & 4 \end{bmatrix}$$

and its inverse

$$(A^t A)^{-1} = (1/52) \begin{bmatrix} 4 & -14 \\ -14 & 62 \end{bmatrix} = (1/26) \begin{bmatrix} 2 & -7 \\ -7 & 31 \end{bmatrix}$$

Then we obtain the generalized inverse

$$A^\dagger = (A^t A)^{-1} A^t = (1/26) \begin{bmatrix} -5 & -1 & 1 & 5 \\ 24 & 10 & 3 & -11 \end{bmatrix}$$

Thus we have

$$\begin{bmatrix} m \\ b \end{bmatrix} = A^\dagger y = (1/26) \begin{bmatrix} -21 \\ 158 \end{bmatrix} = \begin{bmatrix} -21/26 \\ 158/26 \end{bmatrix}$$

Hence the least squares line of approximation has the equation.

$$y = \frac{-21}{26} x + \frac{158}{26} = -0.808x + 6.077 \quad \blacksquare$$

We note that the formulas for $m$ and $b$ given in Section 5.3 can be derived from the matrix formula of Theorem 3. In fact, we have

$$A^t A = \begin{bmatrix} \Sigma x^2 & \Sigma x \\ \Sigma x & n \end{bmatrix}, \quad A^t y = \begin{bmatrix} \Sigma xy \\ \Sigma y \end{bmatrix}$$

so that

$$\begin{bmatrix} m \\ b \end{bmatrix} = A^\dagger y = (A^t A)^{-1} A^t y$$

$$= \frac{1}{n\Sigma x^2 - (\Sigma x)^2} \begin{bmatrix} n & -\Sigma x \\ -\Sigma x & \Sigma x^2 \end{bmatrix} \begin{bmatrix} \Sigma xy \\ \Sigma y \end{bmatrix}$$

Carrying out the multiplication will result in precisely the formulas that were used in Section 5.3.

## QUADRATIC AND OTHER APPROXIMATIONS

The matrix approach to least squares approximation has the advantage of being applicable to nonlinear as well as linear problems. It often happens that plotted data points do not have a linear appearance and some other type of curve is more appropriate. We first discuss the fitting of a quadratic curve to a given set of data points.

The graph of a quadratic equation of the form

$$y = ax^2 + bx + c, \qquad a \neq 0$$

is a parabola that opens upwards if $a > 0$ and downwards if $a < 0$. Recall from algebra that the axis of symmetry is the line $x = -b/2a$ and the vertex is the point at the intersection of this line and the curve. Thus the $y$-coordinate of the vertex is found by setting $x = -b/2a$ in the equation. The spread of the parabola can be determined by plotting some other point and its symmetrically located partner. See Figure 5.19 for two typical-looking graphs. In the second figure we have used the $y$-intercept and its symmetrically located point to indicate the spread.

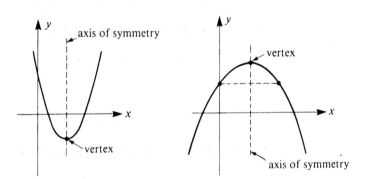

**FIGURE 5.19**                    *Typical graphs of $y = ax^2 + bx + c$*

**EXAMPLE 6**   Graph the quadratic equation $y = x^2 - 4x + 5$.

SOLUTION   We have $a = 1$, $b = -4$, $c = 5$. The axis of symmetry is the line $x = -b/2a = 2$. To find the vertex, we set $x = 2$ in the equation and get $y = 4 - 8 + 5 = 1$; thus the vertex is the point $(2, 1)$. If $x = 0$, then $y = 5$, so that the point $(0, 5)$ is the $y$-intercept of the graph. Then the symmetrically located point $(4, 5)$ is also on the graph. The parabola is shown in Figure 5.20 on the next page.   ■

Now suppose that the data points $(x_1, y_1), (x_2, y_2), \ldots, (x_n, y_n)$ have a general parabolic appearance. We wish to find the coefficients $a, b, c$ such that the quadratic equation

$$y = ax^2 + bx + c$$

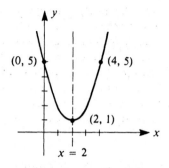

**FIGURE 5.20**                    *The graph of $y = x^2 - 4x + 5$*

provides a least squares approximation to the data points. If we substitute each data point into the equation, then we get the system

$$ax_1^2 + bx_1 + c = y_1$$
$$ax_2^2 + bx_2 + c = y_2$$
$$\vdots \qquad \vdots \qquad \vdots \qquad \vdots$$
$$ax_n^2 + bx_n + c = y_n$$

If we let

$$A = \begin{bmatrix} x_1^2 & x_1 & 1 \\ x_2^2 & x_2 & 1 \\ \vdots & \vdots & \vdots \\ x_n^2 & x_n & 1 \end{bmatrix}, \quad \mathbf{u} = \begin{bmatrix} a \\ b \\ c \end{bmatrix}, \quad \mathbf{y} = \begin{bmatrix} y_1 \\ y_2 \\ \vdots \\ y_n \end{bmatrix}$$

then the system can be written in the matrix form

$$A\mathbf{u} = \mathbf{y}$$

If the given points do not lie on a single quadratic curve, then the system will be inconsistent, and the methods of least squares approximation can be applied. Using the generalized inverse as in Theorem 2, we obtain the following theorem.

### THEOREM 4

If the data points $(x_1, y_1)$, $(x_2, y_2)$, ... , $(x_n, y_n)$ do not all lie on a quadratic curve, then the least squares quadratic approximation to the points is

$$y = ax^2 + bx + c$$

where the coefficients $a$, $b$, $c$ are given by

$$\begin{bmatrix} a \\ b \\ c \end{bmatrix} = A^\dagger \mathbf{y} = (A^t A)^{-1} A^t \mathbf{y}$$

where the matrix $A$ and vector $\mathbf{y}$ are as given above.

Note that $(A^tA)^{-1}A^t$ depends entirely on the $x$-coordinates of the data points. Therefore it needs to be computed only once if the $x$-coordinates remain fixed in successive periods of data collection.

It is possible to derive explicit formulas for the coefficients $a$, $b$, $c$ in the quadratic approximation, but since $A^tA$ is a $3 \times 3$ matrix having nine entries, the formulas are rather messy. The computations are just as easily done in matrix form, with a calculator providing numerical assistance. One type of simplification that is sometimes possible is noted later in the section in connection with Theorem 5.

**EXAMPLE 7**  Find the least squares quadratic approximation to the data points $(-1, 2)$, $(0, -1)$, $(1, 0)$, $(2, 4)$.

**SOLUTION**  For these points we have $x_1 = -1$, $x_2 = 0$, $x_3 = 1$, $x_4 = 2$ and $y_1 = 2$, $y_2 = -1$, $y_3 = 0$, $y_4 = 4$. Thus we have

$$A = \begin{bmatrix} 1 & -1 & 1 \\ 0 & 0 & 1 \\ 1 & 1 & 1 \\ 4 & 2 & 1 \end{bmatrix}, \quad y = \begin{bmatrix} 2 \\ -1 \\ 0 \\ 4 \end{bmatrix}$$

Now we calculate the product

$$A^tA = \begin{bmatrix} 18 & 8 & 6 \\ 8 & 6 & 2 \\ 6 & 2 & 4 \end{bmatrix}$$

The inverse, which can be found by using cofactors and the adjoint matrix (or row operations), is the matrix

$$(A^tA)^{-1} = (1/20)\begin{bmatrix} 5 & -5 & -5 \\ -5 & 9 & 3 \\ -5 & 3 & 11 \end{bmatrix}$$

Instead of finding the generalized inverse $A^\dagger$ at this stage, we can slightly reduce the amount of calculation by finding

$$A^ty = \begin{bmatrix} 18 \\ 6 \\ 5 \end{bmatrix}$$

Then we have

$$\begin{bmatrix} a \\ b \\ c \end{bmatrix} = A^\dagger y = (A^tA)^{-1}(A^ty) = (1/20)\begin{bmatrix} 35 \\ -21 \\ -17 \end{bmatrix} = \begin{bmatrix} 1.75 \\ -1.05 \\ -0.85 \end{bmatrix}$$

Thus the least squares quadratic approximation is

$$y = 1.75x^2 - 1.05x - .85$$

The graph and the data points are shown in Figure 5.21. We have plotted the points on the graph that correspond to the given data points. ▮▮

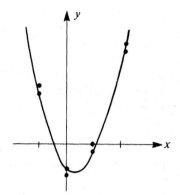

| $x$ | $y$ (data) | $y$ (curve) |
|---|---|---|
| −1 | 2 | 1.95 |
| 0 | −1 | −.85 |
| 1 | 0 | −.15 |
| 2 | 4 | 4.05 |

**FIGURE 5.21**

*The least squares quadratic approximation*
$$y = 1.75x^2 - 1.05x - 0.85$$

The same general method can be used to fit other types of curves to data points as long as the relationships among the unknown coefficients are linear. For example, polynomial curves, such as quadratic, cubic, and higher order polynomials, are determined by coefficients that are linearly related. The following example illustrates the idea for another type of curve.

**EXAMPLE 8** Find a curve of the form

$$y = \frac{a}{x} + b$$

that approximates the points $(1, 7)$, $(3, 3)$, $(6, 1)$.

**SOLUTION** The data points give us the following system of equations in $a$ and $b$:

$$\frac{a}{1} + b = 7$$

$$\frac{a}{3} + b = 3$$

$$\frac{a}{6} + b = 1$$

This system can be written

$$\begin{bmatrix} 1 & 1 \\ 1/3 & 1 \\ 1/6 & 1 \end{bmatrix} \begin{bmatrix} a \\ b \end{bmatrix} = \begin{bmatrix} 7 \\ 3 \\ 1 \end{bmatrix}$$

If we let $A$ denote the coefficient matrix, then we have

$$A^t A = \begin{bmatrix} 41/36 & 9/6 \\ 9/6 & 3 \end{bmatrix} = (1/36) \begin{bmatrix} 41 & 54 \\ 54 & 108 \end{bmatrix}$$

so that

$$(A^t A)^{-1} = (1/42) \begin{bmatrix} 108 & -54 \\ -54 & 41 \end{bmatrix}$$

and

$$A^\dagger = (A^t A)^{-1} A^t = (1/42) \begin{bmatrix} 54 & -18 & -36 \\ -13 & 23 & 32 \end{bmatrix}$$

Hence we obtain

$$\begin{bmatrix} a \\ b \end{bmatrix} = A^\dagger \mathbf{y} = (1/42) \begin{bmatrix} 288 \\ 10 \end{bmatrix} = \begin{bmatrix} 6.86 \\ .24 \end{bmatrix}$$

so that the approximating curve is $y = 6.86/x + .24$. The curve and the data points are shown in Figure 5.22. ∎

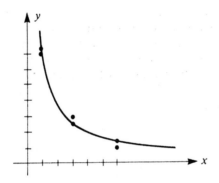

| $x$ | $y$ (data) | $y$ (curve) |
|---|---|---|
| 1 | 7 | 7.1 |
| 3 | 3 | 2.53 |
| 6 | 1 | 1.38 |

**FIGURE 5.22**                    *The approximating curve $y = 6.86/x + .24$*

*REMARK*:   In fitting curves to data points, it is not always clear which type of curve is most appropriate. In certain situations it may be advisable to fit several types of curves and then examine the least squares error for each type. The curve that resulted in the smallest error would be selected. There are other measures of accuracy that can be used, but the least squares fit has a natural interpretation in statistics, and it is the most widely used method of approximation. These and other issues can be examined in a study of regression analysis.

## APPLICATION

In this section we will treat an optimal pricing problem for a new product where the sales figures suggest that a parabola will provide the best fit.

First, however, it is advantageous to restate the quadratic approximation theorem (Theorem 4) in an equation format and derive formulas for the special case that $\Sigma x = \Sigma x^3 = 0$. Since it is frequently possible in applications to code the quantities $x_1, \ldots, x_n$ so that they are equally spaced and symmetrically located about the origin, this will be a useful formula.

As in the previous discussion, suppose that the data points $(x_1, y_1), \ldots, (x_m, y_n)$ have a general parabolic appearance and that we wish to find coefficients $a, b, c$ such that

$$y = ax^2 + bx + c$$

provides a least squares approximation to these points. Let $\mathbf{u} = (a, b, c)$ be the solution to the system

$$(A^t A)\mathbf{x} = A^t \mathbf{y}$$

where $A$ and $\mathbf{y}$ are as defined in Theorem 4. Then

$$A^t A = \begin{bmatrix} \Sigma x^4 & \Sigma x^3 & \Sigma x^2 \\ \Sigma x^3 & \Sigma x^2 & \Sigma x \\ \Sigma x^2 & \Sigma x & n \end{bmatrix}, \quad A^t \mathbf{y} = \begin{bmatrix} \Sigma x^2 y \\ \Sigma xy \\ \Sigma y \end{bmatrix}$$

and we obtain the following restatement of Theorem 4.

### THEOREM 5

If the data points $(x_1, y_1), (x_2, y_2), \ldots, (x_m, y_n)$ do not all lie on a quadratic curve, then the least squares approximation to the points is

$$y = ax^2 + bx + c$$

where the coefficients $a$, $b$, $c$ are solutions of the system of equations.

$$a\Sigma x^4 + b\Sigma x^3 + c\Sigma x^2 = \Sigma x^2 y$$
$$a\Sigma x^3 + b\Sigma x^2 + c\Sigma x = \Sigma xy$$
$$a\Sigma x^2 + b\Sigma x + cn = \Sigma y$$

If the quantities $x_1, \ldots, x_n$ are coded so that they are equally spaced and symmetrically located about the origin, then $\Sigma x = \Sigma x^3 = 0$, and we obtain the simplified system

$$a\Sigma x^4 \qquad + c\Sigma x^2 = \Sigma x^2 y$$
$$b\Sigma x^2 \qquad = \Sigma xy$$
$$a\Sigma x^2 \qquad + cn = \Sigma y$$

The first and third equations may be solved independently of the second equation. Thus we obtain

$$b = \frac{\Sigma xy}{\Sigma x^2}$$

and by Cramer's Rule

$$a = \frac{n\Sigma x^2 y - \Sigma x^2 \Sigma y}{n\Sigma x^4 - (\Sigma x^2)^2}, \quad c = \frac{\Sigma x^4 \Sigma y - \Sigma x^2 \Sigma x^2 y}{n\Sigma x^4 - (\Sigma x^2)^2}$$

We will use the simplified formulas in the following example.

**EXAMPLE 9** The Excelsior Margarine Company has test marketed their product at different prices in seven specially selected supermarkets located in different areas of Elmira. The prices went from 45¢ to 75¢ inclusive in 5¢ increments, and the corresponding sales figures were 6000, 6600, 7200, 7500, 7800, 7600, 7000 pounds of margarine, respectively. Find the parabolic curve of best fit, and determine the price that will result in the greatest sales.

SOLUTION   Let the prices be coded as $-3$ for 45¢, $-2$ for 50¢, etc., and let the sales be in thousands of pounds. Then the data points are $(-3, 6)$, $(-2, 6.6)$, $(-1, 7.2)$, $(0, 7.5)$, $(1, 7.8)$, $(2, 7.6)$, $(3, 7)$. We have that $\Sigma x = \Sigma x^3 = 0$, and we may use the simplified formulas. We form the table

| $x$ | $y$ | $xy$ | $x^2$ | $x^2 y$ | $x^4$ |
|---|---|---|---|---|---|
| $-3$ | 6 | $-18$ | 9 | 54 | 81 |
| $-2$ | 6.6 | $-13.2$ | 4 | 26.4 | 16 |
| $-1$ | 7.2 | $-7.2$ | 1 | 7.2 | 1 |
| 0 | 7.5 | 0 | 0 | 0 | 0 |
| 1 | 7.8 | 7.8 | 1 | 7.8 | 1 |
| 2 | 7.6 | 15.2 | 4 | 30.4 | 16 |
| 3 | 7 | 21 | 9 | 63 | 81 |
| Totals   0 | 49.7 | 5.6 | 28 | 188.8 | 196 |

Then we obtain

$$b = \frac{5.6}{28} = .2$$

$$a = \frac{7(188.8) - 28(49.7)}{7(196) - 28^2} = \frac{-70}{588} = -.119$$

$$c = \frac{196(49.7) - 28(188.8)}{588} = \frac{4454.8}{588} = 7.576$$

The equation is

$$y = -.119x^2 + .2x + 7.576$$

The axis of symmetry of the parabola is given by $x = -b/2a = .84$, which is roughly 64¢ per pound. The sales figure at this price would be

$$y = -.119(.84)^2 + .2(.84) + 7.576 = 7.66$$

or 7660 pounds. This maximum sales is lower than the measured sales for 65¢ per pound and reflects the fact that given the sales at the other prices, this one measurement is probably a little high. See Figure 5.23. ∎

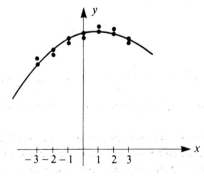

| $x$ | $y$ (data) | $y$ (curve) |
|---|---|---|
| $-3$ | 6.0 | 5.9 |
| $-2$ | 6.6 | 6.7 |
| $-1$ | 7.2 | 7.3 |
| 0 | 7.5 | 7.6 |
| 1 | 7.8 | 7.7 |
| 2 | 7.6 | 7.5 |
| 3 | 7.0 | 7.1 |

**FIGURE 5.23**                    *Excelsior sales versus price*

## EXERCISE 5.4

In Exercises 1–4, form the augmented matrix $[A^tA|A^tb]$ and find the least squares solution $\mathbf{u}$ of the inconsistent system of equations $A\mathbf{x} = \mathbf{b}$. Find the projection of $\mathbf{b}$ onto the column space of $A$.

**1.**
$$A = \begin{bmatrix} -1 & 2 \\ 2 & 2 \\ 1 & 4 \end{bmatrix}, \quad \mathbf{b} = \begin{bmatrix} 1 \\ -6 \\ 1 \end{bmatrix}$$

**2.**
$$A = \begin{bmatrix} 2 & 2 \\ 1 & 2 \\ -1 & 0 \end{bmatrix}, \quad \mathbf{b} = \begin{bmatrix} 3 \\ -8 \\ 4 \end{bmatrix}$$

**3.**
$$A = \begin{bmatrix} -1 & 3 \\ 1 & 3 \\ -1 & 3 \end{bmatrix}, \quad \mathbf{b} = \begin{bmatrix} 2 \\ 4 \\ -1 \end{bmatrix}$$

**4.**
$$A = \begin{bmatrix} 2 & 3 \\ 2 & 1 \\ -2 & 1 \end{bmatrix}, \quad \mathbf{b} = \begin{bmatrix} -6 \\ 1 \\ 1 \end{bmatrix}$$

In Exercises 5–8, find the generalized inverse of the given matrix. Verify by direct computation that $A^\dagger A = I$.

**5.**
$$\begin{bmatrix} 1 & -1 \\ 0 & 1 \\ -1 & 2 \end{bmatrix}$$

**6.**
$$\begin{bmatrix} 3 & 2 \\ -2 & -2 \\ 1 & 2 \end{bmatrix}$$

**7.**
$$\begin{bmatrix} -1 & 2 \\ 2 & 0 \\ 1 & 1 \\ 0 & 1 \end{bmatrix}$$

**8.**
$$\begin{bmatrix} 2 & 1 \\ 0 & -1 \\ 2 & 1 \\ -2 & -1 \end{bmatrix}$$

In Exercises 9–12, use the generalized inverse to find the least squares solution of the system $A\mathbf{x} = \mathbf{b}$ where $\mathbf{b}$ is given and $A$ is the matrix of the indicated exercise.

**9.** Exercise 5, $\mathbf{b} = (4, 3, 2)$

**10.** Exercise 6, $\mathbf{b} = (-1, -2, 3)$

**11.** Exercise 7, $\mathbf{b} = (6, 0, 4 - 2)$

**12.** Exercise 8, $\mathbf{b} = (3, 2, -2, 4)$

**13.** The Laclede Bottling Company bottles pancake syrup under the label "Mom's Old Fashioned Table Delight," a local favorite. Laclede attempts to obtain a mixture for "Mom's" that is as close as possible to 85% corn syrup, 13% fructose, and 2% maple sugar syrup. Laclede has determined the availability of cheap sources of syrup in the mixture 88% corn syrup, 11% fructose, and 1% maple syrup and in the mixture 80% corn syrup, 15% fructose, and 5% maple syrup. Find the blend of these syrups that will produce the closest approximation to "Mom's," and determine the relative amounts of each type of sugar syrup that will be present in the mixture.

**14.** The SAVE SOME Company packages a cat chow that they want to be 28 parts protein to 9 parts fat to 5 parts fiber. They have located two sources of chow, which they hope to blend to an approximation of their specifications. The first is 32 parts protein to 6 parts fat to 7 parts fiber; the second is 25 parts protein to 10 parts fat to 6 parts fiber. Find a blend of these chows that will produce the closest approximation to the SAVE SOME specifications, and determine the relative amount of each ingredient that will be present in the blend.

In Exercises 15–16, use the generalized inverse to find the line of approximation to the given data points. Note that $A^\dagger$ is completely determined by the $x$-coordinates of the data points and thus is the same for both problems.

**15.** $(-2, 2), (-1, 1.2), (0, 0), (1, -0.8), (2, -2)$

**16.** $(-2, 1), (-1, 1.4), (0, 1.9), (1, 2.4), (2, 3)$

In Exercises 17–20, use the generalized inverse to find a least squares approximation of the given data points with a curve of the form $y = ax^2 + bx + c$, $a \neq 0$. Find the vertex of the parabola. Note that $A^\dagger$ depends only on the $x$-coordinates of the data points and therefore needs to be computed only once.

**17.** $(-2, 1.4), (-1, .8), (0, .6), (1, 1)$

**18.** $(-2, .3), (-1, -0.8), (0, -0.6), (1, .4)$

**19.** $(-2, -0.6), (-1, 1.2), (0, 1), (1, -0.2)$

**20.** $(-2, .8), (-1, 2.2), (0, 3), (1, 1.4)$

In Exercises 21–22, use the generalized inverse to find a curve of the form $y = a/x + b$, $a \neq 0$, that approximates the given data points.

**21.** $(2, 5), (3, 3), (6, 2)$   **22.** $(2, 6), (3, 3), (6, -3)$

In Exercises 23–24, find the parabolic curve of best fit, and determine the price that will result in the greatest sales. Code the data points so that $\Sigma x = \Sigma x^3 = 0$ and use the simplified formulas from Theorem 5. Pick your units of sales so as to help keep the numbers manageable.

**23.** Tri-Star Electronics has test marketed their new telephone in five comparable discount department stores in Ohio. The phones were priced at $16.50, $17, $17.50, $18, and $18.50 with the resulting sales 200, 210, 230, 220, 210, respectively.

**24.** The Parker Sisters Soap Company has test marketed their new "Scottish Highlands" face soap at five drug centers in the "Basin" area. The soap was sold at 30, 35, 40, 45, and 50 cents per bar, and the respective sales were 1000, 1200, 1300, 1100, and 900 bars.

# 6

# Eigenvalues and Eigenvectors

For a square matrix $A$ there is often no obvious relationship between a vector $\mathbf{x}$ and the vector $A\mathbf{x}$ obtained by multiplying $\mathbf{x}$ by $A$. However, it can happen for certain vectors that $A\mathbf{x}$ is a multiple of $\mathbf{x}$, and in this case we have a relationship $A\mathbf{x} = \lambda\mathbf{x}$ for a scalar $\lambda$. This special type of vector is called an "eigenvector", and the scalar is called an "eigenvalue" of the matrix $A$. In this chapter we will be concerned with the study of these notions and some of their applications.

In Section 6.1 we will be interested mainly in how the eigenvalues and eigenvectors of a matrix are calculated, and we will discuss methods for doing this. In Section 6.2 we will show how eigenvectors can be used to convert certain types of matrices into diagonal matrices, where the eigenvalues are displayed as the diagonal entries and all other entries are zero. Since a diagonal matrix is the simplest type of matrix to work with, the fact that matrices can be transformed in this way is an indication of the power of the theory of eigenvalues.

A note on terminology. The words "eigenvalue" and "eigenvector" are hybrids of German and English. The German prefix "eigen-" means proper or characteristic, so that the terms "proper value" and "characteristic value" are often used in place of the term "eigenvalue." The term "eigenvector" has similar counterparts. However, since the words eigenvalue and eigenvector are the most commonly used, we give them preference.

## 6.1 EIGENVALUES AND EIGENVECTORS

*Introduction, Finding Eigenvalues, Finding Eigenvectors, Multiplicity*

In this section we define the notions of eigenvalue and eigenvector for a square matrix, and then we describe methods for calculating them. Eigenvalues are found by solving equations that arise from determinants, and eigenvectors are found by solving certain systems of homogeneous equations. We wish to emphasize that we will be concerned only with square matrices.

## INTRODUCTION

The basic definitions are as follows. A number $\lambda$ is called an **eigenvalue** of the square matrix $A$ if there exists a nonzero vector $\mathbf{x}$ such that $A\mathbf{x} = \lambda\mathbf{x}$. If $\lambda$ is an eigenvalue of $A$, then any vector $\mathbf{x} \neq \mathbf{0}$ that satisfies $A\mathbf{x} = \lambda\mathbf{x}$ is called an **eigenvector** of $A$ associated with $\lambda$.

**EXAMPLE 1**   Show that $\vec{\mathbf{x}} = (2, 3)$ is an eigenvector of the matrix

$$A = \begin{bmatrix} 1 & 2 \\ 3 & 2 \end{bmatrix}$$

What is the eigenvalue corresponding to the eigenvector $\mathbf{x}$?

**SOLUTION**   To show that $\vec{\mathbf{x}}$ is an eigenvector of $A$, we must show that $A\mathbf{x}$ is a multiple of $\vec{\mathbf{x}}$. We calculate

$$A\mathbf{x} = \begin{bmatrix} 1 & 2 \\ 3 & 2 \end{bmatrix} \begin{bmatrix} 2 \\ 3 \end{bmatrix} = \begin{bmatrix} 8 \\ 12 \end{bmatrix} = 4 \begin{bmatrix} 2 \\ 3 \end{bmatrix} = 4\mathbf{x}$$

Hence we conclude that the vector $\mathbf{x}$ is an eigenvector for $A$, and since $A\mathbf{x} = 4\mathbf{x}$, the corresponding eigenvalue is $\lambda = 4$.   ∎

An eigenvector $\mathbf{x}$ of a matrix $A$ can be viewed as determining a direction of stability for $A$. If $A\mathbf{x}$ is the scalar multiple $\lambda\mathbf{x}$ of $\mathbf{x}$, the direction of $A\mathbf{x}$ is the same as the direction of $\mathbf{x}$ if $\lambda$ is positive and the direction is reversed if $\lambda$ is negative. Since $A\mathbf{x} = \lambda\mathbf{x}$, the effect of $A$ on $\mathbf{x}$ is to leave $\mathbf{x}$ fixed if $\lambda = 1$, or to stretch or shrink the vector $\mathbf{x}$ depending on whether $\lambda > 1$ or $0 < \lambda < 1$; and if $\lambda$ is negative, there are similar actions but with the direction reversed. See Figure 6.1 for the geometric interpretation in the plane.

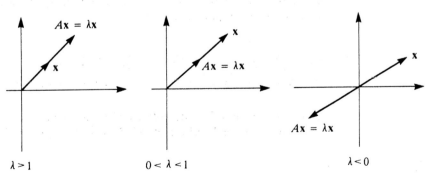

**FIGURE 6.1**                    *A geometric view of eigenvectors*

There is a type of matrix for which the problem of finding the eigenvalues is very easy. Recall from Chapter 3 that a diagonal matrix is one in which all of the entries that lie off the main diagonal are zero. In this case the eigenvalues are simply the entries along the main diagonal. For example, if $A$ is the diagonal matrix

$$A = \begin{bmatrix} 2 & 0 & 0 \\ 0 & 3 & 0 \\ 0 & 0 & -5 \end{bmatrix}$$

then we have $A\mathbf{e}_1 = 2\mathbf{e}_1$, $A\mathbf{e}_2 = 3\mathbf{e}_2$, and $A\mathbf{e}_3 = -5\mathbf{e}_3$, where $\mathbf{e}_1$, $\mathbf{e}_2$, $\mathbf{e}_3$ are the standard basis vectors for $R^3$. Hence the eigenvalues of $A$ are $\lambda_1 = 2$, $\lambda_2 = 3$, and $\lambda_3 = -5$, and the vectors $\mathbf{e}_1$, $\mathbf{e}_2$, and $\mathbf{e}_3$ are eigenvectors.

In general, the problem of finding the eigenvalues of a matrix is not nearly as transparent as it is for diagonal matrices. We will now describe a method for finding the eigenvalues of a matrix that is based on determinants; later in this section we will turn to the problem of finding the associated eigenvectors.

## FINDING EIGENVALUES

The condition for $\lambda$ to be an eigenvalue of the matrix $A$ is that there exists a vector $\mathbf{x} \neq \mathbf{0}$ such that $A\mathbf{x} = \lambda\mathbf{x}$. We wish to reformulate the condition in such a way that we can solve for $\lambda$ without involving the accompanying vectors. This is done as follows.

First we write $\lambda\mathbf{x} = \lambda I\mathbf{x}$ so that the equation becomes $A\mathbf{x} = \lambda I\mathbf{x}$ where $I$ is the identity matrix of the same order as $A$. Then by moving the term $\lambda I\mathbf{x}$ to the left-hand side and factoring, we get

$$(A - \lambda I)\mathbf{x} = \mathbf{0}$$

Thus we have a homogeneous system of equations with coefficient matrix $A - \lambda I$ obtained by subtracting $\lambda$ from the main diagonal entries of $A$. For example, if $A = [a_{ij}]$ is a $3 \times 3$ matrix, then the system has the appearance

$$(A - \lambda I)\mathbf{x} = \begin{bmatrix} a_{11} - \lambda & a_{12} & a_{13} \\ a_{21} & a_{22} - \lambda & a_{23} \\ a_{31} & a_{32} & a_{33} - \lambda \end{bmatrix} \begin{bmatrix} x_1 \\ x_2 \\ x_3 \end{bmatrix} = \begin{bmatrix} 0 \\ 0 \\ 0 \end{bmatrix}$$

For $\lambda$ to be an eigenvalue of $A$, this homogeneous system must have nonzero solutions. This occurs if and only if the coefficient matrix $A - \lambda I$ fails to be invertible or, equivalently, if and only if its determinant is zero. (See Section 3.5.) Hence we have derived the following condition for $\lambda$ to be an eigenvalue for $A$.

---

### THEOREM 1

A number $\lambda$ is an eigenvalue of the square matrix $A$ if and only if it is a root of the equation

$$\det(A - \lambda I) = 0$$

---

The theorem gives us a method for finding eigenvalues of a matrix. We regard $\lambda$ as a variable and form the matrix $A - \lambda I$ by subtracting $\lambda$ from the diagonal entries of $A$. We then set the determinant of $A - \lambda I$ equal to zero, thus getting a polynomial equation in $\lambda$. This polynomial equation in $\lambda$ is called the **characteristic equation** of the matrix $A$. The roots of the characteristic equation are the eigenvalues of $A$.

**EXAMPLE 2**    Find the eigenvalues of the matrix

$$A = \begin{bmatrix} 1 & 4 \\ 3 & 2 \end{bmatrix}$$

SOLUTION    First we form the matrix

$$A - \lambda I = \begin{bmatrix} 1 & 4 \\ 3 & 2 \end{bmatrix} - \begin{bmatrix} \lambda & 0 \\ 0 & \lambda \end{bmatrix} = \begin{bmatrix} 1 - \lambda & 4 \\ 3 & 2 - \lambda \end{bmatrix}$$

Then we set the determinant equal to zero to get the characteristic equation

$$\det(A - \lambda I) = (1 - \lambda)(2 - \lambda) - 12 = \lambda^2 - 3\lambda - 10 = 0$$

This quadratic equation in $\lambda$ can be solved by writing it in factored form:

$$(\lambda - 5)(\lambda + 2) = 0$$

Hence the eigenvalues of $A$ are $\lambda_1 = 5$ and $\lambda_2 = -2$.  ∎

Thus we see that the problem of finding the eigenvalues of $A$ becomes one of finding the roots of a polynomial equation. If $A$ is an $n \times n$ matrix, then its characteristic equation is a polynomial equation of degree $n$. If $n = 2$, then we have a quadratic equation, and the quadratic formula can be used; recall that the roots of $a\lambda^2 + b\lambda + c = 0$ are given by the formula

$$\lambda = \frac{-b \pm \sqrt{b^2 - 4ac}}{2a}$$

We will consider only real numbers as eigenvalues, so that if imaginary numbers arise, we will ignore them as eigenvalues. The theory can be extended to include such eigenvalues, but we will not do so in this book.

**EXAMPLE 3**    Find the eigenvalues of

$$A = \begin{bmatrix} 1 & 2 \\ -2 & 3 \end{bmatrix}$$

SOLUTION    The characteristic equation is

$$\det(A - \lambda I) = \det \begin{bmatrix} 1 - \lambda & 2 \\ -2 & 3 - \lambda \end{bmatrix} = \lambda^2 - 4\lambda + 7 = 0$$

The quadratic equation gives us the roots

$$\lambda = \frac{4 \pm \sqrt{16 - 28}}{2} = 2 \pm \sqrt{-3}$$

The negative number under the square root means that imaginary numbers are involved. We conclude that $A$ has no real eigenvalues. ∎∎

The calculation of characteristic polynomials for large-order matrices can be rather messy, since determinants are involved. We will deal only with $2 \times 2$ and $3 \times 3$ matrices in the examples and exercises.

If $A = [a_{ij}]$ is a $3 \times 3$ matrix, then the calculation of $\det(A - \lambda I)$ can be done directly, or the following formulas for the coefficients can be used. By collecting terms we can put the determinant of $A - \lambda I$ into the form

$$\det(A - \lambda I) = -\lambda^3 + \text{tr}(A)\lambda^2 - \text{pm}(A)\lambda + \det(A)$$

where the coefficients of $\lambda^2$ and $\lambda$ are as follows:

$$\text{tr}(A) = a_{11} + a_{22} + a_{33}$$

is the sum of the diagonal entries, called the **trace** of $A$, and

$$\text{pm}(A) = M_{11} + M_{22} + M_{33}$$
$$= \det\begin{bmatrix} a_{22} & a_{23} \\ a_{32} & a_{33} \end{bmatrix} + \det\begin{bmatrix} a_{11} & a_{13} \\ a_{31} & a_{33} \end{bmatrix} + \det\begin{bmatrix} a_{11} & a_{12} \\ a_{21} & a_{22} \end{bmatrix}$$

is the sum of the minors of the main diagonal entries, called the principal minors of $A$.

For example, if

$$A = \begin{bmatrix} 2 & 1 & 0 \\ -3 & 4 & -1 \\ 1 & 2 & 3 \end{bmatrix}$$

then we have

$$\text{tr}(A) = 2 + 4 + 3 = 9$$

and

$$M_{11} = 12 + 2 = 14, \quad M_{22} = 6 - 0 = 6, \quad M_{33} = 8 + 3 = 11$$

so that

$$\text{pm}(A) = 14 + 6 + 11 = 31$$

and finally

$$\det(A) = 36$$

Thus the characteristic equation is

$$-\lambda^3 + 9\lambda^2 - 31\lambda + 36 = 0$$

If $A$ is a $3 \times 3$ matrix, then its characteristic equation is a cubic equation; and though there is a general procedure for solving cubic equations, it is complicated, and we will not employ it. Since our main purpose is to illustrate eigenvalue theory and not to delve into the subtleties of polynomial equations, we will use examples and problems that can be handled by the following technique.

If we have a cubic equation

$$\lambda^3 + a\lambda^2 + b\lambda + c = 0$$

with leading coefficient 1 and integer coefficients $a$, $b$, $c$ and if $\lambda = r$ is an integer root, then a theorem of algebra states that $r$ must be a divisor of the constant term $c$. A cubic equation of this type need not have an integer root in general, but if it does, then that root must divide the constant term. For example, if the cubic equation

$$\lambda^3 + 7\lambda^2 + 8\lambda - 4 = 0$$

has an integer root, then it must be one of the six divisors of $-4$, namely, the numbers $\pm 1$, $\pm 2$, $\pm 4$. If we test these possible roots one at a time, we find that $\lambda = -2$ is indeed a root. We now divide the polynomial by $\lambda - (-2) = \lambda + 2$ to obtain the factored form

$$(\lambda + 2)(\lambda^2 + 5\lambda - 2) = 0$$

and then we can apply the quadratic formula to the quadratic factor to determine the remaining roots $\frac{1}{2}(-5 \pm \sqrt{33})$.

The same procedure works for higher order polynomials as long as the leading coefficient is 1 and the other coefficients are integers. If there are integer roots, this technique can be used to find them in succession, since each factorization will reduce the degree by one. We apply the method to find the eigenvalues of a $3 \times 3$ matrix.

**EXAMPLE 4**   Find the eigenvalues of the matrix

$$A = \begin{bmatrix} 3 & -1 & 2 \\ -1 & 1 & 0 \\ 2 & 0 & 1 \end{bmatrix}$$

SOLUTION   The characteristic equation of $A$ is

$$\det(A - \lambda I) = \det \begin{bmatrix} 3 - \lambda & -1 & 2 \\ -1 & 1 - \lambda & 0 \\ 2 & 0 & 1 - \lambda \end{bmatrix}$$

$$= -\lambda^3 + 5\lambda^2 - 2\lambda - 2 = 0$$

Multiplying by $-1$, we get the cubic equation

$$\lambda^3 - 5\lambda^2 + 2\lambda + 2 = 0$$

Testing the possible integer roots $\pm 1$, $\pm 2$, we find that $\lambda = 1$ is a root. Dividing by $\lambda - 1$, we obtain the factored form

$$(\lambda - 1)(\lambda^2 - 4\lambda - 2) = 0$$

Using the quadratic formula on the second factor, we get $\lambda = 2 \pm \sqrt{6}$. Thus the eigenvalues of $A$ are $\lambda_1 = 1$, $\lambda_2 = 2 + \sqrt{6}$, $\lambda_3 = 2 - \sqrt{6}$.  ∎

In actual practice, polynomial equations do not usually factor conveniently, and approximation methods are used to find the roots. If $n$ is very large, then solving the characteristic equation may not be a practical method of finding eigenvalues, and computer oriented approximation procedures are applied instead.

## FINDING EIGENVECTORS

We now turn to the problem of finding the eigenvectors associated with the eigenvalues of a matrix. If $\lambda$ is an eigenvalue of a matrix $A$, then its associated eigenvectors are the nonzero solutions of the homogeneous system of equations

$$(A - \lambda I)\mathbf{x} = \mathbf{0}$$

The solution space of the system, which is the same as the null space of the matrix $A - \lambda I$, is a subspace consisting of the eigenvectors associated with $\lambda$ together with the zero vector. This subspace is called the **eigenspace** for the eigenvalue $\lambda$.

To find the eigenspace for a given eigenvalue, we simply apply the methods of solving a homogeneous system and represent the solution vectors as linear combinations of basis vectors. The technique is illustrated in the examples that follow. Since a matrix will usually have more than one eigenvalue, the procedure must be applied to each of the eigenvalues in turn.

**EXAMPLE 5**  The eigenvalues of the matrix

$$A = \begin{bmatrix} 1 & 4 \\ 3 & 2 \end{bmatrix}$$

are $\lambda_1 = 5$ and $\lambda_2 = -2$. (See Example 2.) Find the associated eigenvectors for each eigenvalue.

**SOLUTION**  First we take $\lambda_1 = 5$, which gives us the homogeneous system

$$(A - 5I)\mathbf{x} = \begin{bmatrix} 1-5 & 4 \\ 3 & 2-5 \end{bmatrix} \begin{bmatrix} x_1 \\ x_2 \end{bmatrix} = \begin{bmatrix} -4 & 4 \\ 3 & -3 \end{bmatrix} \begin{bmatrix} x_1 \\ x_2 \end{bmatrix} = \begin{bmatrix} 0 \\ 0 \end{bmatrix}$$

The solution space consists of all vectors $\mathbf{x} = (x_1, x_2)$ such that $-x_1 + x_2 = 0$, that is, $x_1 = x_2$. Thus we may take $\mathbf{v}_1 = (1, 1)$ as a basis vector for the eigenspace, so that the vectors can be written as

$$\mathbf{x} = t\mathbf{v}_1 = t \begin{bmatrix} 1 \\ 1 \end{bmatrix}$$

The eigenvectors for $\lambda_1 = 5$ are the nonzero multiples of $\mathbf{v}_1$, that is, the vectors $\mathbf{x} = t\mathbf{v}_1$ where $t \neq 0$.

We next consider the eigenvalue $\lambda_2 = -2$, which gives us the homogeneous system

$$(A - 2I)\mathbf{x} = \begin{bmatrix} 1+2 & 4 \\ 3 & 2+2 \end{bmatrix} \begin{bmatrix} x_1 \\ x_2 \end{bmatrix} = \begin{bmatrix} 3 & 4 \\ 3 & 4 \end{bmatrix} \begin{bmatrix} x_1 \\ x_2 \end{bmatrix} = \begin{bmatrix} 0 \\ 0 \end{bmatrix}$$

The eigenspace consists of all vectors $\mathbf{x} = (x_1, x_2)$ such that $3x_1 + 4x_2 = 0$. It is convenient to select the vector $\mathbf{v}_2 = (4, -3)$ with integer components as the basis vector. Then the eigenspace for $\lambda_2 = -2$ consists of all vectors of the form

$$\mathbf{x} = t\mathbf{v}_2 = t\begin{bmatrix} 4 \\ -3 \end{bmatrix}$$

and the eigenvectors are the multiples of $\mathbf{v}_2$ where $t \neq 0$. The eigenspaces for $\lambda_1 = 5$ and $\lambda_2 = -2$ can be displayed as lines in the plane as shown in Figure 6.2. ∎

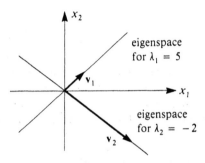

**FIGURE 6.2**            *The eigenspaces for $\lambda_1 = 5$ and $\lambda_2 = -2$*

## MULTIPLICITY

When the characteristic equation is put into factored form, it sometimes happens that a factor is repeated and we have a multiple root of the equation. The number of times that the root is repeated is called the **multiplicity** of the root. For example, the equation

$$(\lambda - 4)^3 (\lambda + 3)^2 (\lambda - 5) = 0$$

has the root $\lambda_1 = 4$ of multiplicity three, the root $\lambda_2 = -3$ of multiplicity two, and the simple root $\lambda_3 = 5$.

When an eigenvalue appears as a multiple root of the characteristic equation, the dimension of the corresponding eigenspace may or may not be equal to the multiplicity of the root. However, the dimension of the eigenspace never exceeds the multiplicity of the eigenvalue as a root of the characteristic equation. For example, an eigenvalue of multiplicity three can have an eigenspace of dimension 1, 2, or 3, depending on the nature of the particular matrix. For example, the $3 \times 3$ identity matrix $I_3$ has the characteristic equation $(1 - \lambda)^3 = 0$, and the corresponding eigenspace is all of $R^3$. The following examples illustrate some of the other possibilities.

**EXAMPLE 6** Find the eigenvectors and the corresponding eigenspaces of the matrix

$$A = \begin{bmatrix} 2 & 3 & 5 \\ 0 & 2 & -1 \\ 0 & 0 & 3 \end{bmatrix}$$

SOLUTION The matrix is an upper triangular matrix, and the eigenvalues of this type of matrix are just the entries on the main diagonal. This can be seen by calculating the determinant

$$\det(A - \lambda I) = \det \begin{bmatrix} 2-\lambda & 3 & 5 \\ 0 & 2-\lambda & -1 \\ 0 & 0 & 3-\lambda \end{bmatrix} = (2-\lambda)^2(3-\lambda)$$

Thus the characteristic equation, which can be written as

$$(\lambda - 2)^2(\lambda - 3) = 0$$

has the root $\lambda_1 = 2$ of multiplicity two and the root $\lambda_2 = 3$.

To find the eigenvectors for $\lambda_1 = 2$, we must solve the system

$$(A - 2I)\mathbf{x} = \begin{bmatrix} 0 & 3 & 5 \\ 0 & 0 & -1 \\ 0 & 0 & 1 \end{bmatrix} \begin{bmatrix} x_1 \\ x_2 \\ x_3 \end{bmatrix} = \begin{bmatrix} 0 \\ 0 \\ 0 \end{bmatrix}$$

The reduced echelon form of the coefficient matrix is

$$\begin{bmatrix} 0 & 1 & 0 \\ 0 & 0 & 1 \\ 0 & 0 & 0 \end{bmatrix}$$

so that $x_3 = 0, x_2 = 0$, and $x_1 = t$ is arbitrary. Thus the eigenspace for $\lambda_1 = 2$ consists of all vectors

$$\mathbf{x} = t \begin{bmatrix} 1 \\ 0 \\ 0 \end{bmatrix}$$

Consequently, the eigenspace has dimension 1 even though $\lambda_1 = 2$ has multiplicity two as a root of the characteristic equation.

The eigenvalue $\lambda_2 = 3$ will necessarily have a 1-dimensional eigenspace. The homogeneous system

$$(A - 3I)\mathbf{x} = \begin{bmatrix} -1 & 3 & 5 \\ 0 & -1 & -1 \\ 0 & 0 & 0 \end{bmatrix} \begin{bmatrix} x_1 \\ x_2 \\ x_3 \end{bmatrix} = \begin{bmatrix} 0 \\ 0 \\ 0 \end{bmatrix}$$

has a coefficient matrix whose reduced echelon form is

$$\begin{bmatrix} 1 & 0 & -2 \\ 0 & 1 & 1 \\ 0 & 0 & 0 \end{bmatrix}$$

Thus if we let $x_3 = t$, we get $x_2 = -t$ and $x_1 = 2t$, so that the solutions are given by

$$\mathbf{x} = t \begin{bmatrix} 2 \\ -1 \\ 1 \end{bmatrix}$$

Thus the eigenspace for $\lambda_2 = 3$ is 1-dimensional.  ■

**EXAMPLE 7**   Find the eigenvalues and the corresponding eigenspaces of the matrix

$$A = \begin{bmatrix} 3 & -2 & -2 \\ -2 & 3 & 2 \\ 3 & -3 & -2 \end{bmatrix}$$

SOLUTION   We calculate the determinant

$$\det(A - \lambda I) = \det \begin{bmatrix} 3-\lambda & -2 & -2 \\ -2 & 3-\lambda & 2 \\ 3 & -3 & -2-\lambda \end{bmatrix}$$

$$= -\lambda^3 + 4\lambda^2 - 5\lambda + 2$$

Then multiplying by $-1$, we get the cubic equation

$$\lambda^3 - 4\lambda^2 + 5\lambda - 2 = 0$$

Testing the numbers $\pm 1$, $\pm 2$ for roots, we find that $\lambda_1 = 1$ and $\lambda_2 = 2$ are roots, and we obtain the factored form

$$(\lambda - 1)^2(\lambda - 2) = 0$$

Thus we have the eigenvalues $\lambda_1 = 1$ and $\lambda_2 = 2$, where $\lambda_1 = 1$ has multiplicity two.

For $\lambda_1 = 1$ we get the system

$$(A - I)\mathbf{x} = \begin{bmatrix} 2 & -2 & -2 \\ -2 & 2 & 2 \\ 3 & -3 & -3 \end{bmatrix} \begin{bmatrix} x_1 \\ x_2 \\ x_3 \end{bmatrix} = \begin{bmatrix} 0 \\ 0 \\ 0 \end{bmatrix}$$

The coefficient matrix has the echelon form

$$\begin{bmatrix} 1 & -1 & -1 \\ 0 & 0 & 0 \\ 0 & 0 & 0 \end{bmatrix}$$

Therefore we may set $x_3 = t$, $x_2 = s$ and get $x_1 = s + t$. Thus the eigenspace for $\lambda_1 = 1$ consists of all vectors of the form

$$\mathbf{x} = s \begin{bmatrix} 1 \\ 1 \\ 0 \end{bmatrix} + t \begin{bmatrix} 1 \\ 0 \\ 1 \end{bmatrix}$$

The eigenspace is therefore 2-dimensional.

For the eigenvalue $\lambda_2 = 2$ we have the system

$$(A - 2I)\mathbf{x} = \begin{bmatrix} 1 & -2 & -2 \\ -2 & 1 & 2 \\ 3 & -3 & -4 \end{bmatrix} \begin{bmatrix} x_1 \\ x_2 \\ x_3 \end{bmatrix} = \begin{bmatrix} 0 \\ 0 \\ 0 \end{bmatrix}$$

We leave it to the reader to verify that the solutions are all vectors of the form

$$\mathbf{x} = t \begin{bmatrix} 2 \\ -2 \\ 3 \end{bmatrix} \quad \blacksquare$$

## EXERCISES 6.1

In Exercises 1–6, show that the given vector $\mathbf{x}$ is an eigenvector of the given matrix $A$. Find the corresponding eigenvalue.

**1.** $\begin{bmatrix} 6 & -3 \\ 2 & 1 \end{bmatrix}$, $(3, 2)$

**2.** $\begin{bmatrix} 3 & 5 \\ 3 & 1 \end{bmatrix}$, $(-1, 1)$

**3.** $\begin{bmatrix} 2 & 1 \\ 8 & -5 \end{bmatrix}$, $(1, 1)$

**4.** $\begin{bmatrix} 2 & 3 \\ 4 & 3 \end{bmatrix}$, $(3, 4)$

**5.** $\begin{bmatrix} 2 & -3 & -10 \\ -1 & 4 & -8 \\ -2 & 2 & 2 \end{bmatrix}$, $(4, 2, 1)$

**6.** $\begin{bmatrix} -3 & 2 & -6 \\ 3 & -4 & -15 \\ 6 & -2 & 9 \end{bmatrix}$, $(2, 3, -1)$

In Exercises 7–22, compute the characteristic equation and find the eigenvalues of the given matrix.

**7.** $\begin{bmatrix} -7 & -10 \\ 5 & 8 \end{bmatrix}$

**8.** $\begin{bmatrix} 6 & 10 \\ -5 & -9 \end{bmatrix}$

**9.** $\begin{bmatrix} 10 & -8 \\ 12 & -10 \end{bmatrix}$

**10.** $\begin{bmatrix} 9 & 6 \\ -12 & -9 \end{bmatrix}$

**11.** $\begin{bmatrix} 5 & 3 \\ -2 & -3 \end{bmatrix}$

**12.** $\begin{bmatrix} 2 & 5 \\ 1 & -4 \end{bmatrix}$

**13.** $\begin{bmatrix} 6 & 2 \\ -4 & 3 \end{bmatrix}$

**14.** $\begin{bmatrix} 5 & -7 \\ 4 & 3 \end{bmatrix}$

**15.** $\begin{bmatrix} 3 & 5 & 2 \\ -2 & -8 & -4 \\ 4 & 14 & 7 \end{bmatrix}$

**16.** $\begin{bmatrix} -6 & 8 & -8 \\ -2 & 5 & -4 \\ 2 & -1 & 2 \end{bmatrix}$

**17.** $\begin{bmatrix} 2 & -1 & -1 \\ -2 & 3 & 2 \\ 4 & -4 & -3 \end{bmatrix}$

**18.** $\begin{bmatrix} 4 & -4 & 4 \\ 4 & -6 & 8 \\ 2 & -4 & 6 \end{bmatrix}$

**19.** $\begin{bmatrix} 5 & -5 & 6 \\ -2 & 2 & -4 \\ 3 & -4 & 8 \end{bmatrix}$

**20.** $\begin{bmatrix} -1 & 2 & 2 \\ 3 & -1 & -1 \\ -3 & 3 & 6 \end{bmatrix}$

**21.** $\begin{bmatrix} 1 & 2 & -2 \\ 1 & 2 & 1 \\ -1 & -3 & -1 \end{bmatrix}$

**22.** $\begin{bmatrix} -4 & 2 & -2 \\ 3 & 1 & 1 \\ 8 & -5 & 4 \end{bmatrix}$

In Exercises 23–36, determine the characteristic equation, the eigenvalues, and the eigenspace for each eigenvalue of the given matrix.

**23.** $\begin{bmatrix} 1 & 2 \\ -4 & 7 \end{bmatrix}$
**24.** $\begin{bmatrix} -3 & 5 \\ -10 & 12 \end{bmatrix}$
**25.** $\begin{bmatrix} -12 & -4 \\ 12 & 2 \end{bmatrix}$

**26.** $\begin{bmatrix} 1 & 1 \\ -12 & -6 \end{bmatrix}$
**27.** $\begin{bmatrix} -1 & -2 \\ 8 & 7 \end{bmatrix}$
**28.** $\begin{bmatrix} -11 & 3 \\ -27 & 7 \end{bmatrix}$

**29.** $\begin{bmatrix} 4 & 2 & -3 \\ 2 & 1 & -1 \\ 4 & 4 & -4 \end{bmatrix}$
**30.** $\begin{bmatrix} 6 & 3 & -2 \\ 2 & -1 & -1 \\ 2 & 6 & 1 \end{bmatrix}$

**31.** $\begin{bmatrix} 5 & -3 & -3 \\ -6 & 8 & 6 \\ 12 & -12 & -10 \end{bmatrix}$
**32.** $\begin{bmatrix} -4 & 6 & -6 \\ -6 & 11 & -12 \\ -3 & 6 & -7 \end{bmatrix}$

**33.** $\begin{bmatrix} 5 & -2 & -4 \\ -2 & 1 & 2 \\ 2 & -2 & -1 \end{bmatrix}$
**34.** $\begin{bmatrix} -4 & 4 & -1 \\ 6 & -2 & 3 \\ 10 & -8 & 3 \end{bmatrix}$

**35.** $\begin{bmatrix} -2 & 5 & 1 \\ -2 & 4 & 1 \\ 6 & -9 & 2 \end{bmatrix}$
**36.** $\begin{bmatrix} -1 & 3 & 1 \\ -1 & 2 & 1 \\ 2 & -9 & -4 \end{bmatrix}$

**37.** Let $b$ be a nonzero number and show that the repeated root $\lambda = a, a$ has the corresponding eigenspace $t(1,0)$ for the matrix

$$\begin{bmatrix} a & b \\ 0 & a \end{bmatrix}$$

**38.** Show that there are eigenvalues $a + b$, $a - b$ and corresponding eigenvectors $(1, 1)$, $(1, -1)$ for the matrix

$$\begin{bmatrix} a & b \\ b & a \end{bmatrix}$$

Let the square matrix $A$ have the characteristic equation

$$c_n \lambda^n + c_{n-1} \lambda^{n-1} + \cdots + c_1 \lambda + c_0 = 0$$

Then the **Cayley-Hamilton Theorem** states that

$$c_n A^n + c_{n-1} A^{n-1} + \cdots + c_1 A + c_0 I = O$$

That is, every square matrix satisfies its characteristic equation. Verify the truth of this theorem for the matrices in Exercise 39–42.

**39.** $\begin{bmatrix} 2 & -3 \\ 4 & 1 \end{bmatrix}$
**40.** $\begin{bmatrix} -1 & 4 \\ 5 & -2 \end{bmatrix}$

**41.** $\begin{bmatrix} 1 & 3 & -2 \\ 0 & 2 & 4 \\ -2 & -5 & 0 \end{bmatrix}$     **42.** $\begin{bmatrix} 3 & 4 & 0 \\ -1 & 2 & 5 \\ 0 & 3 & -2 \end{bmatrix}$

**43.** Show that if $A\mathbf{v} = \lambda\mathbf{v}$, then $A^2\mathbf{v} = \lambda^2\mathbf{v}$.

**44.** Show that if $A\mathbf{v} = \lambda\mathbf{v}$, $\mathbf{v} \neq \mathbf{0}$, and if $A$ is invertible, then $\lambda \neq 0$ and $A^{-1}\mathbf{v} = \dfrac{1}{\lambda}\mathbf{v}$.

## 6.2 DIAGONALIZATION OF MATRICES

*Diagonalizing a Matrix, The Diagonalization Procedure, Symmetric Matrices*

In this section we apply the notions of eigenvector and eigenvalue to convert a square matrix into a diagonal matrix. This conversion cannot be accomplished for all matrices, but it can be done for a large class of them. The basic idea is to form a certain type of matrix $P$ so that $P$ and its inverse $P^{-1}$ will give us $P^{-1}AP = D$, where $D$ is a diagonal matrix that displays the eigenvalues of $A$ along the main diagonal. Since diagonal matrices are quite elementary in nature, the process of diagonalizing a matrix can be very useful, as we will see in the next section. The last topic of this section concerns the special class of matrices known as symmetric matrices, for which the diagonalization procedure employs eigenvectors that are orthonormal.

### DIAGONALIZING A MATRIX

The essential technique of diagonalizing a matrix is illustrated in the following example. We use eigenvectors of the matrix $A$ to create a matrix $P$ such that the product matrix $P^{-1}AP$ is a diagonal matrix where the diagonal entries are the eigenvalues of $A$.

**EXAMPLE 1**   Diagonalize the matrix

$$A = \begin{bmatrix} 1 & 4 \\ 3 & 2 \end{bmatrix}$$

SOLUTION   In the preceding section we calculated the eigenvalues and eigenvectors of $A$. In Example 2 we found the eigenvalues $\lambda_1 = 5$ and $\lambda_2 = -2$, and in Example 5 we found the associated eigenvectors to be the nonzero multiples of the vectors

$$\mathbf{v}_1 = \begin{bmatrix} 1 \\ 1 \end{bmatrix} \quad \text{and} \quad \mathbf{v}_2 = \begin{bmatrix} 4 \\ -3 \end{bmatrix}$$

We use $\mathbf{v}_1$ and $\mathbf{v}_2$ to form the matrix

$$P = [\mathbf{v}_1, \mathbf{v}_2] = \begin{bmatrix} 1 & 4 \\ 1 & -3 \end{bmatrix}$$

Note that the columns of $P$ are linearly independent, so that $P$ is an invertible matrix. We now verify that $P^{-1}AP$ is a diagonal matrix. The inverse of $P$ is

$$P^{-1} = (-1/7)\begin{bmatrix} -3 & -4 \\ -1 & 1 \end{bmatrix}$$

If we calculate the product $P^{-1}AP$, we obtain

$$P^{-1}AP = (-1/7)\begin{bmatrix} -3 & -4 \\ -1 & 1 \end{bmatrix}\begin{bmatrix} 1 & 4 \\ 3 & 2 \end{bmatrix}\begin{bmatrix} 1 & 4 \\ 1 & -3 \end{bmatrix}$$

$$= (-1/7)\begin{bmatrix} -15 & -20 \\ 2 & -2 \end{bmatrix}\begin{bmatrix} 1 & 4 \\ 1 & -3 \end{bmatrix}$$

$$= \begin{bmatrix} 5 & 0 \\ 0 & -2 \end{bmatrix}$$

Hence we have obtained a diagonal matrix with the eigenvalues of $A$ displayed on the diagonal. ∎

A square matrix $A$ is said to be **diagonalizable** if there exists an invertible matrix $P$ such that

$$D = P^{-1}AP$$

is a diagonal matrix. Not every matrix can be diagonalized. The criterion for diagonalization, which was indicated in the previous example, is that there are enough linearly independent eigenvectors so that an invertible matrix $P$ can be created to perform the task. For emphasis we state this criterion as a theorem.

**THEOREM 1**

An $n \times n$ matrix $A$ is diagonalizable if and only if $A$ has $n$ linearly independent eigenvectors.

The eigenvectors of a matrix are found by the methods of the preceding section. First we find the eigenvalues of the matrix, and then we select basis vectors for each of the eigenspaces. It can be proved that eigenvectors associated with distinct eigenvalues are automatically linearly independent. For example, if the nonzero vectors $v_1$, $v_2$ satisfy $Av_1 = \lambda_1 v_1$ and $Av_2 = \lambda_2 v_2$ and if $\lambda_1 \neq \lambda_2$, then $v_1$, $v_2$ are linearly independent. A similar conclusion is valid for three or more eigenvectors associated with distinct eigenvalues. We omit the proof.

Therefore if an $n \times n$ matrix has $b$ distinct eigenvalues, the collection of basic eigenvectors, one from each of the 1-dimensional eigenspaces, will automatically be linearly independent, and therefore the matrix can be diagonalized. However, if an eigenvalue is a repeated root of the characteristic equation, then the dimension of the eigenspace may or may not be the same as the multiplicity of the eigenvalue. If an eigenspace fails to have as many basis vectors as the multiplicity of the corresponding eigenvalue, then it is not possible to diagonalize the matrix. The following example deals with a matrix of this type.

**EXAMPLE 2**  Show that the matrix

$$A = \begin{bmatrix} 1 & 4 & -2 \\ 0 & 3 & 1 \\ 0 & 0 & 3 \end{bmatrix}$$

cannot be diagonalized.

SOLUTION   The characteristic equation for $A$ can be shown to be

$$\det(A - \lambda I) = (1 - \lambda)(3 - \lambda)^2 = 0$$

so that the eigenvalues are $\lambda_1 = 1$ and $\lambda_2 = 3$. The eigenvalue $\lambda_2 = 3$ has multiplicity two, and we must examine its associated eigenspace. The solutions of the system

$$(A - 3I)\mathbf{x} = \begin{bmatrix} -2 & 4 & -2 \\ 0 & 0 & 1 \\ 0 & 0 & 0 \end{bmatrix} \begin{bmatrix} x_1 \\ x_2 \\ x_3 \end{bmatrix} = \begin{bmatrix} 0 \\ 0 \\ 0 \end{bmatrix}$$

are given by

$$\mathbf{x} = t \begin{bmatrix} 2 \\ 1 \\ 0 \end{bmatrix}$$

so that the eigenspace for $\lambda_2 = 3$ is only 1-dimensional. Therefore the matrix $A$ has only two linearly independent eigenvectors, one associated with $\lambda_1 = 1$ and one other associated with $\lambda_2 = 3$. Consequently, by Theorem 1 the matrix cannot be diagonalized.  ▌▌

## THE DIAGONALIZATION PROCEDURE

If an $n \times n$ matrix $A$ has $n$ linearly independent eigenvectors, then they can be used as the columns of a matrix $P$. The independence of the columns assure us that $P$ is an invertible matrix. The following procedure then gives us a diagonal matrix that displays the eigenvalues.

### *Procedure for diagonalizing an $n \times n$ matrix A*

***Step 1.***   Solve the characteristic equation to find the eigenvalues

$$\lambda_1, \lambda_2, \ldots, \lambda_n$$

where each eigenvalue is repeated according to its multiplicity.

***Step 2.***   Find a basis for the eigenspaces corresponding to the eigenvalues to obtain $n$ linearly independent eigenvectors

$$\mathbf{v}_1, \mathbf{v}_2, \ldots, \mathbf{v}_n$$

where $A\mathbf{v}_i = \lambda_i \mathbf{v}_i$ for $i = 1, \ldots, n$. (If there are fewer than $n$ independent eigenvectors, the matrix is not diagonalizable, and we stop.)

***Step 3.***   Form the matrix

$$P = [\mathbf{v}_1, \mathbf{v}_2, \ldots, \mathbf{v}_n]$$

whose columns are the independent eigenvectors found in step 2, and invert it. Then the product $P^{-1}AP$ is the diagonal matrix

$$P^{-1}AP = \begin{bmatrix} \lambda_1 & 0 & \cdots & 0 \\ 0 & \lambda_2 & \cdots & 0 \\ \vdots & \vdots & \ddots & \vdots \\ 0 & 0 & \cdots & \lambda_n \end{bmatrix}$$

It is interesting to note that it does not matter which particular basis vectors are chosen in step 2. Even though there is some freedom of choice in the selection of basis vectors for the eigenspaces, we can use any set of independent eigenvectors to form the matrix $P$, and the same diagonal matrix will be obtained. However, if the vectors are rearranged and put in a different order, then the eigenvalues will appear down the diagonal in the corresponding order. That is, the position of the eigenvalue on the diagonal will match up with the column of $P$ in which the corresponding eigenvector is located.

**EXAMPLE 3**   Find a matrix that diagonalizes the matrix

$$A = \begin{bmatrix} 3 & -2 & -2 \\ -2 & 3 & 2 \\ 3 & -3 & -2 \end{bmatrix}$$

**SOLUTION**   It was shown in Example 7 of the preceding section that the eigenvalues of $A$ are

$$\lambda_1 = 1, \quad \lambda_2 = 1, \quad \lambda_3 = 2$$

and the associated eigenvectors are

$$\mathbf{v}_1 = \begin{bmatrix} 1 \\ 1 \\ 0 \end{bmatrix}, \quad \mathbf{v}_2 = \begin{bmatrix} 1 \\ 0 \\ 1 \end{bmatrix}, \quad \mathbf{v}_3 = \begin{bmatrix} 2 \\ -2 \\ 3 \end{bmatrix}$$

That is, we found that $\lambda_1 = 1$ is an eigenvalue of multiplicity two and that its eigenspace is 2-dimensional with the basis vectors $\mathbf{v}_1$ and $\mathbf{v}_2$. We also found that $\mathbf{v}_3$ spans the eigenspace for $\lambda_3 = 2$. We now use the vectors $\mathbf{v}_1$, $\mathbf{v}_2$, $\mathbf{v}_3$ to form the matrix

$$P = \begin{bmatrix} 1 & 1 & 2 \\ 1 & 0 & -2 \\ 0 & 1 & 3 \end{bmatrix}$$

Unless mistakes in arithmetic have been made, we know without further work that $P$ will give us the diagonal matrix

$$P^{-1}AP = \begin{bmatrix} 1 & 0 & 0 \\ 0 & 1 & 0 \\ 0 & 0 & 2 \end{bmatrix}$$

where $\lambda_1 = 1$, $\lambda_2 = 1$, $\lambda_3 = 2$ are the eigenvalues that correspond to the eigenvectors $v_1$, $v_2$, $v_3$, respectively.

However, we can check the result by finding the inverse

$$P^{-1} = \begin{bmatrix} 2 & -1 & -2 \\ -3 & 3 & 4 \\ 1 & -1 & -1 \end{bmatrix}$$

and verifying that the product $P^{-1}AP$ actually is the desired diagonal matrix. We leave these calculations to the reader.  ▌▌

By reversing the diagonalization procedure we can construct matrices that have specific eigenvalues and eigenvectors. The following example shows how this is done.

**EXAMPLE 4**    Find a 2 × 2 matrix $A$ whose eigenvalues are $\lambda_1 = 3$, $\lambda_2 = 4$ with associated eigenvectors

$$v_1 = \begin{bmatrix} 2 \\ 5 \end{bmatrix} \quad \text{and} \quad v_2 = \begin{bmatrix} 1 \\ 3 \end{bmatrix}$$

**SOLUTION**    The matrix $A$ must be diagonalized by the matrix

$$P = \begin{bmatrix} 2 & 1 \\ 5 & 3 \end{bmatrix}$$

whose columns are the given eigenvectors. Since we have

$$P^{-1}AP = D = \begin{bmatrix} 3 & 0 \\ 0 & 4 \end{bmatrix}$$

we can find $A$ by premultiplying $D$ by $P$ and postmultiplying $D$ by $P^{-1}$. That is, we have

$$A = PDP^{-1}$$

Since the inverse of $P$ is

$$P^{-1} = \begin{bmatrix} 3 & -1 \\ -5 & 2 \end{bmatrix}$$

we have

$$A = PDP^{-1} = \begin{bmatrix} 2 & 1 \\ 5 & 3 \end{bmatrix} \begin{bmatrix} 3 & 0 \\ 0 & 4 \end{bmatrix} \begin{bmatrix} 3 & -1 \\ -5 & 2 \end{bmatrix}$$

$$= \begin{bmatrix} 2 & 1 \\ 5 & 3 \end{bmatrix} \begin{bmatrix} 9 & -3 \\ -20 & 8 \end{bmatrix}$$

$$= \begin{bmatrix} -2 & 2 \\ -15 & 9 \end{bmatrix} \quad \blacksquare$$

To see why the diagonalization procedure works, consider a $3 \times 3$ matrix $A$ with linearly independent eigenvectors $\mathbf{v}_1, \mathbf{v}_2, \mathbf{v}_3$ corresponding to the eigenvalues $\lambda_1, \lambda_2, \lambda_3$, respectively. Then we have

$$A\mathbf{v}_1 = \lambda_1 \mathbf{v}_1, \quad A\mathbf{v}_2 = \lambda_2 \mathbf{v}_2, \quad A\mathbf{v}_3 = \lambda_3 \mathbf{v}_3$$

If we let

$$P = [\mathbf{v}_1, \mathbf{v}_2, \mathbf{v}_3]$$

then by definition of matrix multiplication, the product $AP$ has columns $A\mathbf{v}_1, A\mathbf{v}_2, A\mathbf{v}_3$. That is, we have

$$AP = [A\mathbf{v}_1, A\mathbf{v}_2, A\mathbf{v}_3]$$

$$= [\lambda_1 \mathbf{v}_1, \lambda_2 \mathbf{v}_2, \lambda_3 \mathbf{v}_3]$$

$$= [\mathbf{v}_1, \mathbf{v}_2, \mathbf{v}_3] \begin{bmatrix} \lambda_1 & 0 & 0 \\ 0 & \lambda_2 & 0 \\ 0 & 0 & \lambda_3 \end{bmatrix}$$

$$= PD$$

where $D$ is the diagonal matrix with the eigenvalues $\lambda_1, \lambda_2, \lambda_3$ on the diagonal. Hence we have

$$AP = PD$$

and multiplying on the left by $P^{-1}$ gives us

$$P^{-1}AP = D$$

Therefore we obtain the diagonal matrix containing the eigenvalues of $A$ as stated.


## SYMMETRIC MATRICES

A square matrix $A$ is called **symmetric** if it is the same as its transpose, that is,
$$A^t = A$$

In terms of entries this means that $A = [a_{ij}]$ is symmetric if $a_{ij} = a_{ji}$ for all $i \neq j$. (We always have that $a_{ij}$ equals $a_{ji}$ for $i = j$, since each represents the same diagonal entry.) More simply stated, $A$ is symmetric if the entries located symmetrically with respect to the main diagonal are equal. For example, the matrix

$$A = \begin{bmatrix} 1 & 2 & -4 \\ 2 & 3 & 0 \\ -4 & 0 & 5 \end{bmatrix}$$

is symmetric, since $a_{12} = a_{21} = 2$, $a_{13} = a_{31} = -4$, and $a_{23} = a_{32} = 0$.

It was noted in the previous section that some matrices may have eigenvalues that include imaginary numbers. This cannot occur with symmetric matrices, since it can be proved that all of the eigenvalues of a symmetric matrix are real numbers. Furthermore, symmetric matrices have special properties concerning the diagonalization procedure. The key features are summarized in the following theorem, which we state without proof. One important aspect of symmetric matrices is that they can always be diagonalized.

### THEOREM 2

Each $n \times n$ symmetric matrix $A$ has $n$ eigenvectors $v_1, \ldots, v_n$ that are orthonormal. The matrix $Q = [v_1, \ldots, v_n]$ has the property that $Q^{-1} = Q^t$, and the product $Q^t A Q$ is a diagonal matrix whose diagonal entries are the eigenvalues of $A$.

The item of special interest in the theorem is that the transpose $Q^t$ is used in the diagonalization $Q^t A Q$ of $A$. The reasons behind this fact will be discussed after we illustrate the theorem with an example.

**EXAMPLE 5**   Diagonalize the symmetric matrix

$$A = \begin{bmatrix} 1 & 3 \\ 3 & 1 \end{bmatrix}$$

**SOLUTION**   The characteristic equation for $A$ is

$$\det \begin{bmatrix} 1-\lambda & 3 \\ 3 & 1-\lambda \end{bmatrix} = \lambda^2 - 2\lambda - 8 = (\lambda - 4)(\lambda + 2) = 0$$

Thus the eigenvalues for $A$ are $\lambda_1 = 4$ and $\lambda_2 = -2$. The eigenvectors associated with $\lambda_1 = 4$ are the nonzero solutions of the system

$$(A - 4I)x = \begin{bmatrix} -3 & 3 \\ 3 & -3 \end{bmatrix} \begin{bmatrix} x_1 \\ x_2 \end{bmatrix} = \begin{bmatrix} 0 \\ 0 \end{bmatrix}$$

so that we have $-x_1 + x_2 = 0$. Thus the eigenspace consists of all multiples of the vector $(1, 1)$. Since we need unit vectors, we normalize to get

$$v_1 = (1/\sqrt{2}) \begin{bmatrix} 1 \\ 1 \end{bmatrix}$$

The eigenvectors associated with $\lambda_2 = -2$ are the nonzero solutions of the system

$$(A + 2I)\mathbf{x} = \begin{bmatrix} 3 & 3 \\ 3 & 3 \end{bmatrix} \begin{bmatrix} x_1 \\ x_2 \end{bmatrix} = \begin{bmatrix} 0 \\ 0 \end{bmatrix}$$

so that we have $x_1 + x_2 = 0$. Thus the eigenspace consists of all multiples of the vector $(-1, 1)$. Again we normalize to get

$$\mathbf{v}_2 = (1/\sqrt{2}) \begin{bmatrix} -1 \\ 1 \end{bmatrix}$$

Also note that $\mathbf{v}_1 \cdot \mathbf{v}_2 = 0$, so that $\mathbf{v}_1, \mathbf{v}_2$ are orthonormal.

We now define the matrix

$$Q = [\mathbf{v}_1, \mathbf{v}_2] = (1/\sqrt{2}) \begin{bmatrix} 1 & -1 \\ 1 & 1 \end{bmatrix} = \begin{bmatrix} 1/\sqrt{2} & -1/\sqrt{2} \\ 1/\sqrt{2} & 1/\sqrt{2} \end{bmatrix}$$

whose columns are orthonormal eigenvectors of $A$. Then $Q^{-1} = Q^t$, and we obtain

$$Q^t A Q = \begin{bmatrix} \lambda_1 & 0 \\ 0 & \lambda_2 \end{bmatrix} = \begin{bmatrix} 4 & 0 \\ 0 & -2 \end{bmatrix}$$

The reader should verify this result by direct computation. ∎

The matrix $Q$ in Theorem 2 has the special property that $Q^{-1} = Q^t$, so that the usually tedious calculation of the inverse matrix is avoided. The reason for this phenomenon is the fact that the columns of $Q$ are orthonormal vectors $\mathbf{v}_1$, $\dots$, $\mathbf{v}_n$. Since the transpose $Q^t$ of $Q$ has these vectors as rows, the entries of the product matrix $Q^t Q$ are the scalar products

$$\mathbf{v}_i \cdot \mathbf{v}_j = \begin{cases} 0 & \text{if } i \neq j \text{ (orthogonal vectors)} \\ 1 & \text{if } i = j \text{ (unit vectors)} \end{cases}$$

Therefore we have $Q^t Q = I$ so that the inverse of $Q$ is $Q^{-1} = Q^t$.

A matrix $Q$ of this type is called an **orthogonal** matrix, and we say that a symmetric matrix is **orthogonally diagonalized** by $Q$ when $Q^t A Q$ equals the diagonal matrix of eigenvalues. The selection of orthonormal eigenvectors needed to create $Q$ can entail a little extra computation in the case of repeated eigenvalues, but the effort is worthwhile because the inverse of $Q$ is so easily found.

It can be proved that if $A$ is a symmetric matrix, the eigenvectors that are associated with *distinct* eigenvalues are mutually orthogonal. Therefore if an $n \times n$ symmetric matrix has $n$ distinct eigenvalues, the associated eigenvectors are automatically orthogonal. In this case we need only normalize each vector to get an orthonormal set of eigenvectors, and thus the matrix is easily obtained. This occurred in Example 5. However, if we encounter a multiple eigenvalue, then the eigenspace has dimension greater than one, and the basis vectors found by solving the corresponding homogeneous system in the usual manner of elimination are not normally orthogonal. In this case we orthonormalize the basis vectors by applying the Gram–Schmidt process as in Section 5.2. The following example illustrates how this case is treated.

**EXAMPLE 6**  Find an orthogonal matrix $Q$ that diagonalizes the symmetric matrix

$$A = \begin{bmatrix} 5 & 1 & -1 \\ 1 & 5 & 1 \\ -1 & 1 & 5 \end{bmatrix}$$

**SOLUTION**  The characteristic equation for $A$ is

$$\det(A - \lambda I) = -\lambda^3 + 15\lambda^2 - 72\lambda + 108 = (3 - \lambda)(6 - \lambda)^2 = 0$$

Therefore the eigenvalues of $A$ are $\lambda_1 = 3$, $\lambda_2 = 6$, $\lambda_3 = 6$.
For $\lambda_1 = 3$ we get the system

$$(A - 3I)\mathbf{x} = \begin{bmatrix} 2 & 1 & -1 \\ 1 & 2 & 1 \\ -1 & 1 & 2 \end{bmatrix} \begin{bmatrix} x_1 \\ x_2 \\ x_3 \end{bmatrix} = \begin{bmatrix} 0 \\ 0 \\ 0 \end{bmatrix}$$

The coefficient matrix has the reduced echelon form

$$\begin{bmatrix} 1 & 0 & -1 \\ 0 & 1 & 1 \\ 0 & 0 & 0 \end{bmatrix}$$

so that if $x_3 = t$, then $x_2 = -t$ and $x_1 = t$. Thus the eigenspace for $\lambda_1 = 3$ is the set of vectors

$$\mathbf{x} = t \begin{bmatrix} 1 \\ -1 \\ 1 \end{bmatrix}$$

where $t$ is arbitrary. To get a unit vector, we take $t = 1/\sqrt{3}$. Thus we have

$$\mathbf{v}_1 = (1/\sqrt{3}) \begin{bmatrix} 1 \\ -1 \\ 1 \end{bmatrix}$$

For $\lambda_2 = \lambda_3 = 6$ we have the system

$$(A - 6I)\mathbf{x} = \begin{bmatrix} -1 & 1 & -1 \\ 1 & -1 & 1 \\ -1 & 1 & -1 \end{bmatrix} \begin{bmatrix} x_1 \\ x_2 \\ x_3 \end{bmatrix} = \begin{bmatrix} 0 \\ 0 \\ 0 \end{bmatrix}$$

The coefficient matrix has the reduced echelon form

$$\begin{bmatrix} 1 & -1 & 1 \\ 0 & 0 & 0 \\ 0 & 0 & 0 \end{bmatrix}$$

If we set $x_3 = t$, $x_2 = s$, then $x_1 = s - t$, so that the eigenspace consists of all vectors of the form

$$s \begin{bmatrix} 1 \\ 1 \\ 0 \end{bmatrix} + t \begin{bmatrix} -1 \\ 0 \\ 1 \end{bmatrix}$$

where $s$ and $t$ are parameters. Thus the eigenspace is 2-dimensional, and we have the basis vectors

$$\mathbf{u}_2 = \begin{bmatrix} 1 \\ 1 \\ 0 \end{bmatrix}, \quad \mathbf{u}_3 = \begin{bmatrix} -1 \\ 0 \\ 1 \end{bmatrix}$$

Note that $\mathbf{u}_2, \mathbf{u}_3$ are both orthogonal to the eigenvector $\mathbf{v}_1$ found earlier, but they are not orthogonal to each other. To obtain orthonormal vectors, we apply the Gram–Schmidt process to $\mathbf{u}_2$ and $\mathbf{u}_3$. (See Section 5.2.) First we normalize $\mathbf{u}_2$ to get

$$\mathbf{v}_2 = (1/\sqrt{2}) \begin{bmatrix} 1 \\ 1 \\ 0 \end{bmatrix}$$

Then we subtract the projection of $\mathbf{u}_3$ onto $\mathbf{v}_2$ from $\mathbf{u}_2$ to get

$$\mathbf{u}_3' = \mathbf{u}_3 - (\mathbf{u}_3 \cdot \mathbf{v}_2)\mathbf{v}_2 = \begin{bmatrix} -1 \\ 0 \\ 1 \end{bmatrix} + (1/2) \begin{bmatrix} 1 \\ 1 \\ 0 \end{bmatrix} = (1/2) \begin{bmatrix} -1 \\ 1 \\ 2 \end{bmatrix}$$

Normalizing $\mathbf{u}_3'$ gives us

$$\mathbf{v}_3 = (1/\sqrt{6}) \begin{bmatrix} -1 \\ 1 \\ 2 \end{bmatrix}$$

Thus we obtain the orthonormal vectors $\mathbf{v}_1, \mathbf{v}_2, \mathbf{v}_3$ where $\mathbf{v}_1$ is an eigenvector for $\lambda_1 = 3$ and $\mathbf{v}_2, \mathbf{v}_3$ are eigenvectors for $\lambda_2 = \lambda_3 = 6$.

We now define the matrix $Q$ to be

$$Q = [\mathbf{v}_1, \mathbf{v}_2, \mathbf{v}_3] = \begin{bmatrix} 1/\sqrt{3} & 1/\sqrt{2} & -1/\sqrt{6} \\ -1/\sqrt{3} & 1/\sqrt{2} & 1/\sqrt{6} \\ 1/\sqrt{3} & 0 & 2/\sqrt{6} \end{bmatrix}$$

Then $Q$ is an orthogonal matrix, and

$$Q'AQ = \begin{bmatrix} 3 & 0 & 0 \\ 0 & 6 & 0 \\ 0 & 0 & 6 \end{bmatrix} \quad \blacksquare$$

## EXERCISES 6.2

In Exercises 1–4 a matrix $A$ and a set of its independent eigenvectors are given. Use the eigenvectors to form a matrix $P$ such that $P^{-1}AP = D$, where $D$ is a diagonal matrix. Check your work by direct computation. What are the eigenvalues corresponding to each eigenvector?

1. $\begin{bmatrix} 2 & -15 \\ 2 & -9 \end{bmatrix}$, $\begin{bmatrix} 3 \\ 1 \end{bmatrix}$, $\begin{bmatrix} 5 \\ 2 \end{bmatrix}$

2. $\begin{bmatrix} -21 & 30 \\ -12 & 17 \end{bmatrix}$, $\begin{bmatrix} 3 \\ 2 \end{bmatrix}$, $\begin{bmatrix} 5 \\ 3 \end{bmatrix}$

3. $\begin{bmatrix} 7 & -20 & 8 \\ 2 & -7 & 4 \\ -2 & 2 & 3 \end{bmatrix}$, $\begin{bmatrix} -4 \\ -2 \\ -1 \end{bmatrix}$, $\begin{bmatrix} 1 \\ 1 \\ 2 \end{bmatrix}$, $\begin{bmatrix} -2 \\ -1 \\ -1 \end{bmatrix}$

4. $\begin{bmatrix} -3 & -5 & -10 \\ 2 & 2 & 2 \\ 0 & -1 & -5 \end{bmatrix}$, $\begin{bmatrix} -5 \\ 4 \\ -1 \end{bmatrix}$, $\begin{bmatrix} -5 \\ 3 \\ -1 \end{bmatrix}$, $\begin{bmatrix} 4 \\ -2 \\ 1 \end{bmatrix}$

In Exercises 5–8, show that the given matrix cannot be diagonalized.

5. $\begin{bmatrix} 5 & -3 \\ 3 & -1 \end{bmatrix}$

6. $\begin{bmatrix} -7 & 2 \\ -8 & 1 \end{bmatrix}$

7. $\begin{bmatrix} 1 & -1 & -3 \\ -2 & -2 & 2 \\ -4 & -1 & 2 \end{bmatrix}$

8. $\begin{bmatrix} 5 & 1 & 2 \\ -4 & 3 & -4 \\ -6 & -1 & -3 \end{bmatrix}$

In Exercises 9–12 a matrix and its eigenvalues are given. Find the corresponding eigenvectors and use them to construct a matrix $P$ such that $P^{-1}AP = D$ where $D$ is a diagonal matrix. Check your work by direct computation.

9. $\begin{bmatrix} 24 & -28 \\ 15 & -17 \end{bmatrix}$, $\lambda = 3, 4$

10. $\begin{bmatrix} -22 & 30 \\ -20 & 27 \end{bmatrix}$, $\lambda = 3, 2$

11. $\begin{bmatrix} 1 & 22 & -38 \\ -2 & -5 & 2 \\ -1 & -5 & 6 \end{bmatrix}$, $\lambda = -1, 5, -2$

12. $\begin{bmatrix} 9 & 6 & -1 \\ -16 & -13 & 4 \\ -18 & -18 & 8 \end{bmatrix}$, $\lambda = 3, -1, 2$

In Exercises 13–16, diagonalize the given matrix.

13. $\begin{bmatrix} -14 & 24 \\ -10 & 17 \end{bmatrix}$

14. $\begin{bmatrix} 12 & -21 \\ 10 & -17 \end{bmatrix}$

15. $\begin{bmatrix} 3 & -1 & -3 \\ -4 & 3 & 6 \\ 4 & -1 & -4 \end{bmatrix}$

16. $\begin{bmatrix} -1 & 6 & -4 \\ -4 & -3 & 8 \\ -4 & 0 & 5 \end{bmatrix}$

In Exercises 17–20, find a matrix with the given eigenvalues and eigenvectors

17. $\lambda = 2, (11, 7)$;  $\lambda = 1, (3, 2)$

18. $\lambda = 3, (12, 7)$;  $\lambda = 2, (5, 3)$

19. $\lambda = 1, (1, -1, 1)$;  $\lambda = -2, (-1, 2, 1)$;  $\lambda = -1, (-3, 4, 0)$

20. $\lambda = -1, (1, 3, -1)$;  $\lambda = 3, (-3, -9, 4)$;  $\lambda = 2, (-2, -7, 3)$

In Exercises 21–28, find a matrix $Q$ such that $Q^t AQ = D$ where $D$ is a diagonal matrix and $QQ^t = I$. Check your answer by direct computation.

21. $\begin{bmatrix} 2 & 5 \\ 5 & 2 \end{bmatrix}$

22. $\begin{bmatrix} -3 & 1 \\ 1 & -3 \end{bmatrix}$

**23.** $\begin{bmatrix} 2 & \sqrt{2} \\ \sqrt{2} & 3 \end{bmatrix}$

**24.** $\begin{bmatrix} 1 & \sqrt{3} \\ \sqrt{3} & 3 \end{bmatrix}$

**25.** $\begin{bmatrix} -1 & -3 & 1 \\ -3 & -1 & 1 \\ 1 & 1 & -5 \end{bmatrix}$, $\lambda = -3, 2, -6$

**26.** $\begin{bmatrix} 2 & 6 & 1 \\ 6 & 2 & 1 \\ 1 & 1 & 7 \end{bmatrix}$, $\lambda = 9, 6, -4$

**27.** $\begin{bmatrix} 1 & -4 & 2 \\ -4 & 1 & -2 \\ 2 & -2 & -2 \end{bmatrix}$, $\lambda = -3, -3, 6$

**28.** $\begin{bmatrix} 2 & 1 & -2 \\ 1 & 2 & 2 \\ -2 & 2 & -1 \end{bmatrix}$, $\lambda = -3, 3, 3$

In Exercises 29–30, refer to Exercises 37–38 of Section 6.1.

**29.** Show that the matrix

$$\begin{bmatrix} a & b \\ 0 & a \end{bmatrix}$$

where $b \neq 0$, is not diagonalizable.

**30.** Let

$$A = \begin{bmatrix} a & b \\ b & a \end{bmatrix}$$

Find a matrix $P$ such that $P^{-1}AP = D$, a diagonal matrix.

## 6.3 APPLICATIONS TO MARKOV ANALYSIS

*Calculating Powers, Markov Analysis, Application*

In this section we examine the role of eigenvalues and eigenvectors in the study of Markov analysis, which was introduced in Section 3.6 of Chapter 3. We will first show how the diagonalization of a matrix provides a convenient method of calculating the powers $A^n$ of a square matrix $A$, a technique that can be applied in any situation in which the powers of a matrix arise. We will apply the diagonalization method to examine the powers of a transition matrix for a Markov chain and show how the eigenvectors lead us naturally to the stable vector and the limiting form of the transition matrix. To keep the calculations at a reasonable level, we will deal mainly with the case of $2 \times 2$ matrices.

### CALCULATING POWERS

As one example of the utility of diagonalizing a matrix, we apply it to the task of raising a matrix to powers. In general, to find the powers $A^n$ of a square matrix $A$, such as $A^5$, $A^{10}$, $A^{30}$, and so on, requires a great deal of calculation, since the definition of matrix multiplication is not amenable to repeated application.

The powers of a diagonal matrix $D$ are quite easy to find, since we need only raise the diagonal entries to the given power. For example, if

$$D = \begin{bmatrix} -1 & 0 & 0 \\ 0 & 2 & 0 \\ 0 & 0 & 3 \end{bmatrix}$$

then it is quite easy to find

$$D^5 = \begin{bmatrix} (-1)^5 & 0 & 0 \\ 0 & 2^5 & 0 \\ 0 & 0 & 3^5 \end{bmatrix} = \begin{bmatrix} -1 & 0 & 0 \\ 0 & 32 & 0 \\ 0 & 0 & 243 \end{bmatrix}$$

If $A$ is a diagonalizable matrix, then its powers can be calculated in a fairly painless way as follows. Suppose we have found a matrix $P$ that diagonalizes $A$, so that

$$P^{-1}AP = D$$

where $D$ denotes a diagonal matrix. If we square both sides of the equation, then we obtain

$$(P^{-1}AP)(P^{-1}AP) = D^2$$

which is the same as

$$P^{-1}A(PP^{-1})AP = D^2$$

Since $PP^{-1} = I$, the identity matrix, the middle term in the product drops out, and we have

$$P^{-1}A^2P = D^2$$

If we now multiply on the left by $P$ and on the right by $P^{-1}$, we obtain

$$A^2 = PD^2P^{-1}$$

Any power $A^n$ of $A$ can be found in a similar manner. In the product

$$(P^{-1}AP)(P^{-1}AP)\cdots(P^{-1}AP) = D^n$$

the adjacent matrices $P$ and $P^{-1}$ combine to give us the identity matrix $I$; and since $I$ leaves products unchanged, it can be dropped. Thus the product becomes $P^{-1}A^nP = D^n$; and if we multiply by $P$ and $P^{-1}$ as before, we see that the power $A^n$ is given by

$$A^n = PD^nP^{-1}$$

The matrix $D^n$ is easily calculated, so that the computation of $A^n$ is reduced to finding the product of three matrices, one of which is a diagonal matrix. The technique is illustrated in the following example.

**EXAMPLE 1**   Find the power $A^5$ of the matrix

$$A = \begin{bmatrix} 3 & -2 & -2 \\ -2 & 3 & 2 \\ 3 & -3 & -2 \end{bmatrix}$$

SOLUTION   In Example 3 of Section 6.2 we diagonalized $A$ by using the matrix

$$P = \begin{bmatrix} 1 & 1 & 2 \\ 1 & 0 & -2 \\ 0 & 1 & 3 \end{bmatrix}$$

and its inverse

$$P^{-1} = \begin{bmatrix} 2 & -1 & -2 \\ -3 & 3 & 4 \\ 1 & -1 & -1 \end{bmatrix}$$

It was shown that

$$P^{-1}AP = D = \begin{bmatrix} 1 & 0 & 0 \\ 0 & 1 & 0 \\ 0 & 0 & 2 \end{bmatrix}$$

The matrix $D^5$ has diagonal entries $1, 1, 32$. Therefore the power $A^5$ is given by

$$A^5 = PD^5P^{-1} = \begin{bmatrix} 1 & 1 & 2 \\ 1 & 0 & -2 \\ 0 & 1 & 3 \end{bmatrix} \begin{bmatrix} 1 & 0 & 0 \\ 0 & 1 & 0 \\ 0 & 0 & 32 \end{bmatrix} \begin{bmatrix} 2 & -1 & -2 \\ -3 & 3 & 4 \\ 1 & -1 & -1 \end{bmatrix}$$

Note that multiplying $P^{-1}$ on the left by a diagonal matrix has the effect of multiplying each row of $P^{-1}$ by the corresponding diagonal entry. Thus the product is quickly reduced to the product of two matrices, and we obtain

$$A^5 = \begin{bmatrix} 1 & 1 & 2 \\ 1 & 0 & -2 \\ 0 & 1 & 3 \end{bmatrix} \begin{bmatrix} 2 & -1 & -2 \\ -3 & 3 & 4 \\ 32 & -32 & -32 \end{bmatrix}$$

$$= \begin{bmatrix} 63 & -62 & -62 \\ -62 & 63 & 62 \\ 93 & -93 & -92 \end{bmatrix} \quad \blacksquare$$

## MARKOV ANALYSIS

We now relate the notions of eigenvalue and eigenvector to the subject of Markov analysis, which was discussed in Section 3.6 of Chapter 3. In that section we described the general ideas of Markov analysis and some of the basic properties concerning limiting behavior and steady state distributions. (See Theorem 2 of Section 3.6.) These properties can be explained and clarified by applying the theory of eigenvalues.

Let us review the main aspects of a Markov chain. Recall that a Markov chain is determined by a transition matrix $T$ whose entries are nonnegative and whose columns add up to 1. A distribution vector **s** is a vector that has nonnegative components whose sum is 1. For example, the percentage shares (in decimals) of a market among competing companies defines a distribution vector. The change in distributions over fixed time intervals is then found by applying the matrix $T$. That is, if we have a distribution vector **s** at some stage, then the distribution at the next stage is given by the vector $T\mathbf{s}$. If $\mathbf{s}_0$ denotes an initial distribution, then the successive distribution vectors are determined by the powers of $T$ so that we have the chain

$$\mathbf{s}_0, \quad \mathbf{s}_1 = T\mathbf{s}_0, \quad \mathbf{s}_2 = T^2\mathbf{s}_0, \quad \dots, \quad \mathbf{s}_n = T^n\mathbf{s}_0, \quad \dots$$

Thus if the powers $T^n$ of $T$ are known, then the chain of distribution vectors is known for any initial distribution. By diagonalizing the transition matrix $T$, we can readily obtain the powers $T^n$ as in the following example.

**EXAMPLE 2**   Suppose a Markov chain has the transition matrix

$$T = \begin{bmatrix} .7 & .4 \\ .3 & .6 \end{bmatrix}$$

Diagonalize $T$ and then find an expression for $T^n$. Calculate the power $T^6$ explicitly.

**SOLUTION**   First we find the eigenvalues of $T$ by solving the characteristic equation

$$\det(T - \lambda I) = \det \begin{bmatrix} .7 - \lambda & .4 \\ .3 & .6 - \lambda \end{bmatrix} = \lambda^2 - 1.3\lambda + .3 = 0$$

If we use the quadratic formula, we obtain

$$\lambda = \frac{1.3 \pm \sqrt{.49}}{2} = \frac{1.3 \pm .7}{2} = 1, .3$$

Hence we see that $T$ has the eigenvalues $\lambda_1 = 1$ and $\lambda_2 = .3$. By solving the corresponding homogeneous systems of equations, we obtain the associated eigenvectors

$$\mathbf{v}_1 = \begin{bmatrix} 4 \\ 3 \end{bmatrix}, \quad \mathbf{v}_2 = \begin{bmatrix} 1 \\ -1 \end{bmatrix}$$

Thus the diagonalization of $T$ is accomplished by the matrix

$$P = \begin{bmatrix} 4 & 1 \\ 3 & -1 \end{bmatrix}$$

and its inverse

$$P^{-1} = (1/7) \begin{bmatrix} 1 & 1 \\ 3 & -4 \end{bmatrix}$$

Then we have

$$P^{-1}TP = \begin{bmatrix} 1 & 0 \\ 0 & .3 \end{bmatrix}$$

so that the powers of $T$ are given by

$$T^n = P\begin{bmatrix} 1 & 0 \\ 0 & .3^n \end{bmatrix}P^{-1}$$

$$= (1/7)\begin{bmatrix} 4 & 1 \\ 3 & -1 \end{bmatrix}\begin{bmatrix} 1 & 0 \\ 0 & .3^n \end{bmatrix}\begin{bmatrix} 1 & 1 \\ 3 & -4 \end{bmatrix}$$

$$= (1/7)\begin{bmatrix} 4 + 3(.3)^n & 4 - 4(.3)^n \\ 3 - 3(.3)^n & 3 + 4(.3)^n \end{bmatrix}$$

For the value $n = 6$ we have $(.3)^n = .000729$, so that

$$T^6 = (1/7)\begin{bmatrix} 4.002187 & 3.997084 \\ 2.997813 & 3.002916 \end{bmatrix} = \begin{bmatrix} .571741 & .571012 \\ .428259 & .428988 \end{bmatrix} \quad \blacksquare\blacksquare$$

In the preceding example the matrix $T$ had the eigenvalue $\lambda_1 = 1$ and a second eigenvalue $\lambda_2$ smaller than one. Since the powers $\lambda_2{}^n$ approach zero as $n$ gets large, the long-term behavior is determined by the eigenvalue $\lambda_1 = 1$ and its eigenvector. The stable vector for $T$ is the distribution vector $\mathbf{s}$ such that

$$T\mathbf{s} = \mathbf{s}$$

and thus $\mathbf{s}$ is an eigenvector for $\lambda_1 = 1$. The components of $\mathbf{s}$ are positive and their sum is 1, so that a particular eigenvector is determined by these conditions. Furthermore, as $n$ tends to infinity, the powers $T^n$ tend to the limiting matrix, which we will denote by $T^\infty$, whose columns are all equal to the stable vector $\mathbf{s}$. Let us continue the preceding example to see how this occurs.

**EXAMPLE 3**   For the transition matrix $T$ of Example 2, find the stable vector $\mathbf{s}$ and the limiting matrix $T^\infty$ of $T^n$ as $n \to \infty$.

SOLUTION   In Example 2 we obtained an eigenvector $\mathbf{v}_1 = (4, 3)$ for the eigenvalue $\lambda_1 = 1$. To get the stable vector, we must convert $\mathbf{v}_1$ into a distribution vector by introducing a factor so that its components add up to 1. The components of $\mathbf{v}_1$ have the sum $4 + 3 = 7$, so we multiply by $\frac{1}{7}$ and thereby obtain

$$\mathbf{s} = (1/7)\mathbf{v}_1 = \begin{bmatrix} 4/7 \\ 3/7 \end{bmatrix}$$

The vector $\mathbf{s}$ is a distribution vector and $T\mathbf{s} = \mathbf{s}$, so that it is the stable vector.
        Turning to the powers $T^n$, we note that the numbers $(.3)^n$ tend to zero as $n$ gets large. Therefore as $n$ tends to infinity, the matrix

$$T^n = (1/7)\begin{bmatrix} 4 + 3(.3)^n & 4 - 4(.3)^n \\ 3 - 3(.3)^n & 3 + 4(.3)^n \end{bmatrix}$$

approaches the limiting matrix

$$T^\infty = (1/7)\begin{bmatrix} 4 & 4 \\ 3 & 3 \end{bmatrix} = \begin{bmatrix} 4/7 & 4/7 \\ 3/7 & 3/7 \end{bmatrix} = [\mathbf{s}, \mathbf{s}]$$

whose columns equal the stable vector **s**.

In order to determine at what stage stability occurs to some fixed degree of accuracy, we look at the largest term that is dependent on $n$. In this case it is $\frac{4}{7}(.3)^n$. When this number is less than $.5 \times 10^{-4}$, for example, we will have four-place accuracy. (The .5 compensates for rounding.) We use the relation $\frac{4}{7}(.3)^{n+1} = [\frac{4}{7}(.3)^n](.3)$ to form the table

| $n$ | $\frac{4}{7}(.3)^n$ |
|-----|---------------------|
| 1 | .17143 |
| 2 | .05143 |
| 3 | .01543 |
| 4 | .00463 |
| 5 | .00139 |
| 6 | .00042 |
| 7 | .00012 |
| 8 | .00004 |

Since $\frac{4}{7}(.3)^8 < .5 \times 10^{-4}$, we see that $T^8$ will be stable to within four decimal places. ∎

The case of a $2 \times 2$ transition matrix can be treated in general. Since the column sums must equal one, each $2 \times 2$ transition matrix can be written in the form

$$T = \begin{bmatrix} 1-a & b \\ a & 1-b \end{bmatrix}$$

where we assume that $a$, $b$ are strictly between 0 and 1. Then we have the characteristic equation

$$\det(T - \lambda I) = \lambda^2 - (2 - a - b)\lambda + (1 - a - b) = 0$$

which has the roots

$$\lambda_1 = 1, \quad \lambda_2 = 1 - a - b$$

The eigenvectors for $\lambda_1 = 1$ are solutions of the system

$$(T - I)\mathbf{x} = \begin{bmatrix} -a & b \\ a & -b \end{bmatrix} \begin{bmatrix} x_1 \\ x_2 \end{bmatrix} = \begin{bmatrix} 0 \\ 0 \end{bmatrix}$$

and we choose the eigenvector

$$\mathbf{v}_1 = \begin{bmatrix} b \\ a \end{bmatrix}$$

The stable vector for $T$ is therefore

$$\mathbf{s} = 1/(a+b) \begin{bmatrix} b \\ a \end{bmatrix} = \begin{bmatrix} b/(a+b) \\ a/(a+b) \end{bmatrix}$$

The eigenvectors for $\lambda_2 = 1 - a - b$ are solutions of the system

$$(T - (1 - a - b)I)\mathbf{x} = \begin{bmatrix} b & b \\ a & a \end{bmatrix} \begin{bmatrix} x_1 \\ x_2 \end{bmatrix} = \begin{bmatrix} 0 \\ 0 \end{bmatrix}$$

and we choose

$$\mathbf{v}_2 = \begin{bmatrix} 1 \\ -1 \end{bmatrix}$$

Thus $T$ is diagonalized by

$$P = \begin{bmatrix} b & 1 \\ a & -1 \end{bmatrix} \quad \text{and} \quad P^{-1} = 1/(a+b) \begin{bmatrix} 1 & 1 \\ a & -b \end{bmatrix}$$

so that we have

$$P^{-1}TP = \begin{bmatrix} 1 & 0 \\ 0 & 1-a-b \end{bmatrix}$$

Then we have the powers $T^n$ given by

$$T^n = P \begin{bmatrix} 1 & 0 \\ 0 & (1-a-b)^n \end{bmatrix} P^{-1}$$

$$= \frac{1}{(a+b)} \begin{bmatrix} b + a(1-a-b)^n & b - b(1-a-b)^n \\ a - a(1-a-b)^n & a + b(1-a-b)^n \end{bmatrix}$$

If $0 < a < 1$ and $0 < b < 1$, then $|1 - a - b| < 1$, so that $(1 - a - b)^n$ tends to 0 as $n$ tends to infinity. Thus the powers $T^n$ tend to the limiting matrix

$$T^\infty = 1/(a+b) \begin{bmatrix} b & b \\ a & a \end{bmatrix} = [\mathbf{s}, \mathbf{s}]$$

The quantities

$$\left| \frac{a(1-a-b)^n}{a+b} \right| \quad \text{and} \quad \left| \frac{b(1-a-b)^n}{a+b} \right|$$

represent the discrepancies between the entries in $T^n$ and the stable positions of $T^\infty$. Thus stability can be determined to any degree of precision by examining these quantities. For example, when the larger of the two is less than $.5 \times 10^{-4}$, we will have stability to four decimal places.

There is, however, a more relevant way of looking at the error. That is, it is more significant to look at the error in comparison to the total quantity than it is to look at the error alone. For example, an absolute error of .01 in a total measurement of 1000 is reasonably small, but the same absolute error of .01 in a total measurement of 0.1 may be unreasonable. Therefore it is desirable to have a measure of error that takes both the absolute error and the total quantity into account. We define the **relative error** to be the ratio of the absolute error to the total quantity. In this case, one may show that the largest relative error in $T^n$ is given by the absolute value of $k(1 - a - b)^n$ where $k$ is the larger of the ratios $a/b$ and $b/a$. We will treat this issue numerically in the next example.

**EXAMPLE 4**  Find the stable vector, the power $T^5$, and the limiting matrix $T^\infty$ for the transition matrix

$$T = \begin{bmatrix} .2 & .4 \\ .8 & .6 \end{bmatrix}$$

Then find the largest absolute and relative errors in $T^5$.

**SOLUTION**  If we write $T$ in the form

$$T = \begin{bmatrix} 1-a & b \\ a & 1-b \end{bmatrix}$$

then we have $a = .8$ and $b = .4$. Thus the eigenvectors are $\lambda_1 = 1$ and $\lambda_2 = 1 - a - b = -0.2$. The stable vector is

$$1/(a+b)\begin{bmatrix} b \\ a \end{bmatrix} = (1/1.2)\begin{bmatrix} .4 \\ .8 \end{bmatrix} = \begin{bmatrix} 1/3 \\ 2/3 \end{bmatrix}$$

Using a calculator, we find for $n = 5$ that $(1 - a - b)^5 = (-0.2)^5 = -0.00032$, and

$$T^5 = (1/1.2)\begin{bmatrix} .4 - .8(.00032) & .4 + .4(.00032) \\ .8 + .8(.00032) & .8 - .4(.00032) \end{bmatrix}$$

$$= \begin{bmatrix} .33312 & .33344 \\ .66688 & .66656 \end{bmatrix}$$

The limiting matrix is

$$T^\infty = 1/(a+b)\begin{bmatrix} b & b \\ a & a \end{bmatrix} = \begin{bmatrix} 1/3 & 1/3 \\ 2/3 & 2/3 \end{bmatrix}$$

We see that the largest absolute error is $.8(.00032)/1.2 = .0002133$, and the largest relative error is

$$\frac{\dfrac{.8(.00032)}{1.2}}{\dfrac{.4}{1.2}} = \frac{.8}{.4}(.00032) = .00064$$

Thus the relative error is larger than the absolute error, since the quantity being approximated, $.4/1.2$, is itself small.  ∎

*REMARK:*  For transition matrices that are larger than $2 \times 2$ matrices, there are no longer any convenient formulas, but the general approach and conclusions are the same. If $T$ is a regular transition matrix (that is, some power of $T$ has all entries nonzero), then $T$ has an eigenvalue $\lambda_1 = 1$, and the other eigenvalues have absolute value less than 1. The stable vector for $T$ is an eigenvector for $\lambda = 1$ and the powers of $T$ can often be found by diagonalizing $T$. However, as the size of $T$ gets larger, the calculations become increasingly messy. The stable vector can be readily found, but the other eigenvalues and eigenvectors needed for diagonalization can cause calculational difficulties. Moreover, not every transition matrix can be diagonalized. The theory of eigenvalues can be used to provide theoretical insights into Markov analysis, but its value as a computational method is limited for large matrices.

## APPLICATION

Markov analysis is applied in a great variety of areas, some of which were noted in Section 3.6. The following example is concerned with the transmission of information, in this case the spread of a rumor. The general issue of how accurately information is transmitted, whether from person to person, broker to client, bank to bank, person to computer, or whatever, can be vitally important. The example illustrates how information can become unreliable when it is passed along through a succession of people.

**EXAMPLE 5**   A corporation executive informs his aide that a long-awaited decision will be announced the next day as to whether or not a large contract will be awarded to General Construction Company. The executive tells the aide what the decision will be. The aide relates the information to his assistant, who tells the secretary, who tells a friend, and so on. In this manner the information reaches the President of General Construction after it has been relayed 12 times. Suppose that in each transmission of the information there is a 10% chance that the message was misunderstood. What is the likelihood that the President of General Construction knows the correct decision?

SOLUTION   To be specific, let us assume that the contract decision is yes. Then, starting with the executive telling the aide, each transmission of the information can be represented by the transition matrix

$$T = \begin{matrix} & \text{yes} & \text{no} \\ \begin{matrix} \text{yes} \\ \text{no} \end{matrix} & \left[\begin{matrix} .9 & .1 \\ .1 & .9 \end{matrix}\right] & \begin{matrix} \text{yes} \\ \text{no} \end{matrix} \end{matrix}$$

In other words, if a person thought the decision was yes, then he or she would correctly relay the information "yes" with probability .9 and the information "no" with probability .1. On the other hand, if the person thought that the decision was no, then the relayed information would be "no" with probability .9 and "yes" with probability .1.

If we use the formula that was derived earlier for $T^n$ with $a = .1$ and $b = .1$, then we have

$$T^n = \begin{bmatrix} .5 + .5(.8)^n & .5 - .5(.8)^n \\ .5 - .5(.8)^n & .5 + .5(.8)^n \end{bmatrix}$$

Since $(.8)^n$ tends to 0 as $n$ tends to infinity, the limiting matrix is

$$T^\infty = \begin{bmatrix} .5 & .5 \\ .5 & .5 \end{bmatrix}$$

Thus as the information is relayed by more and more people, the likelihood that one correctly understands the information nears 50%. For the particular value $n = 12$ we have

$$T^{12} = \begin{bmatrix} .5034 & .4656 \\ .4656 & .5034 \end{bmatrix}$$

We conclude that it is almost an even chance that the President of General Construction, the twelfth person to hear the rumor, knows the correct information concerning the contract. ∎

It is interesting to note that if the probable accuracy of transmission in the preceding example were increased from .9 to .95, the limiting matrix $T^{\infty}$ would still be

$$T^{\infty} = \begin{bmatrix} .5 & .5 \\ .5 & .5 \end{bmatrix}$$

However, it would take more steps to approach $T^{\infty}$ with a high degree of accuracy. For example, if $a = b = .05$, then

$$T^n = \begin{bmatrix} .5 + .5(.9)^n & .5 - .5(.9)^n \\ .5 - .5(.9)^n & .5 + .5(.9)^n \end{bmatrix}$$

and for $n = 12$ we have

$$T^{12} = \begin{bmatrix} .6412 & .3588 \\ .3588 & .6412 \end{bmatrix}$$

In fact, for any $p$ such that $0 < p < 1$, the transition matrix

$$T = \begin{bmatrix} 1 - p & p \\ p & 1 - p \end{bmatrix}$$

will have the property that its limit matrix is

$$T^{\infty} = \begin{bmatrix} .5 & .5 \\ .5 & .5 \end{bmatrix}$$

This can be interpreted to mean that even extremely reliable transmission systems will eventually garble information.

## EXERCISES 6.3

In Exercises 1–4 a diagonal matrix $D$ is given. Find $D^7$.

1. $\begin{bmatrix} -1.1 & 0 \\ 0 & 2 \end{bmatrix}$
   
2. $\begin{bmatrix} -2 & 0 \\ 0 & 1.2 \end{bmatrix}$

3. $\begin{bmatrix} 1 & 0 & 0 \\ 0 & .9 & 0 \\ 0 & 0 & .85 \end{bmatrix}$
   
4. $\begin{bmatrix} 1 & 0 & 0 \\ 0 & -0.7 & 0 \\ 0 & 0 & .95 \end{bmatrix}$

In Exercises 5–8 a matrix, $A$, is given together with its eigenvalues and eigenvectors. Use this information to find $A^6$.

5. $\begin{bmatrix} -28 & 45 \\ -18 & 29 \end{bmatrix}$  $\lambda = -1, (5, 3)$  $\lambda = 2, (3, 2)$

6. $\begin{bmatrix} 44 & -105 \\ 18 & -43 \end{bmatrix}$  $\lambda = 2, (5, 2)$  $\lambda = -1, (7, 3)$

7. $\begin{bmatrix} 14 & -3 & 3 \\ 45 & -10 & 9 \\ -19 & 5 & -2 \end{bmatrix}$ $\lambda = 2, (1, 3, -1)$
$\lambda = 1, (-3, -9, 4)$
$\lambda = -1, (-2, -7, 3)$

8. $\begin{bmatrix} 9 & -6 & -34 \\ -14 & 7 & 46 \\ 5 & -3 & -18 \end{bmatrix}$ $\lambda = -1, (-1, 4, -1)$
$\lambda = 1, (-2, 3, -1)$
$\lambda = -2, (2, -2, 1)$

In Exercises 9–12, find $T^5$ and $T^\infty$ for the given transition matrix, $T$. Find the smallest number $k$ such that $T^k$ approximates $T^\infty$ to four decimal places. What is the relative error in $T^k$?

9. $\begin{bmatrix} .8 & .5 \\ .2 & .5 \end{bmatrix}$    10. $\begin{bmatrix} .6 & .2 \\ .4 & .8 \end{bmatrix}$    11. $\begin{bmatrix} .1 & .7 \\ .9 & .3 \end{bmatrix}$    12. $\begin{bmatrix} .4 & .8 \\ .6 & .2 \end{bmatrix}$

13. Suppose that information about accounts delinquent or nondelinquent is (1) keyed at a terminal, (2) encoded by a modem, (3) transmitted over a phone line, (4) decoded by a modem, (5) processed by a district computer, (6) encoded by a modem, (7) transmitted over a phone line, (8) decoded by a modem, and (9) processed and stored by a national computer. Let the possibility that an error is made in the status of an account be 1% at each stage. Find the transition matrix of this Markov chain and determine the probability that the correct information is stored by the national computer.

14. The Armageddon Retaliatory Missile System (ARMS) receives "fire," "no fire" information from the President through the chain consisting of (1) the Secretary of State, (2) the Chief of Staff, (3) the Base Commander, (4) the Company Commander, (5) the Platoon Sergeant, and finally to (6) Corporal Jones. If the probability is .95 that any person in the chain will receive the sense of the order as transmitted, find the transition matrix of the Markov chain and determine the probability that "Jonesy" will push the right button.

# 7

# Linear Transformations

In this chapter we look at matrices from a geometric viewpoint, as transformations that carry vectors from one space to another space. Because we are dealing with matrices, these transformations are a very special type, called linear transformations.

The notion of linear transformation is introduced in Section 7.1, with emphasis placed on geometric properties. In Section 7.2, we show how this type of transformation can be represented by matrices. The ideas are applied in Section 7.3 to the issue of expressing a vector as a linear combination of basis vectors. This idea of coordinates relative to a basis was discussed in Section 4.5. We now see that when a basis is changed the change in coordinates can be done by a change of basis matrix. In Section 7.4, we use these new methods to take another look at the simplex method in linear programming.

## 7.1  LINEAR TRANSFORMATIONS

By a *transformation* or a *mapping* from $R^n$ to $R^n$ we mean a rule which gives a unique vector of $R^n$ for each vector of $R^n$.

Thus in $R^3$ let

$$T(x, y, z) = (2x + 3y - z, 3z, 2y)$$

Then

$$T(1, -2, 5) = (2(1) + 3(-2) - 5, 3(5), 2(-2))$$
$$= (-9, 15, -4)$$

Or in $R^4$ let

$$T(x, y, z, w) = (xy, zw, x + z, y - w).$$

Then

$$T(-2, 3, 5, 4) = (-6, 20, 3, -1)$$

A transformation $T$ from $R^n$ to $R^n$ is called a **linear transformation** if for all $\mathbf{u}, \mathbf{v} \in R^n$ and $c$ a constant it is true that

(1)                           $$T(\mathbf{u} + \mathbf{v}) = T(\mathbf{u}) + T(\mathbf{v})$$

(2)                           $$T(c\mathbf{u}) = cT(\mathbf{u})$$

A linear transformation is also called a *linear mapping* or, in more advanced texts, a *linear operator*.

**EXAMPLE 1**    Let $T(x, y) = (2x + y, x - y)$. Then

(1)
$$T((x_1, y_1) + (x_2, y_2)) = T(x_1 + x_2, y_1 + y_2)$$
$$= (2(x_1 + x_2) + y_1 + y_2, x_1 + x_2 - (y_1 + y_2))$$
$$= (2x_1 + y_1, x_1 - y_1) + (2x_2 + y_2, x_2 - y_2)$$
$$= T(x_1, y_1) + T(x_2, y_2)$$

(2)                  $$T(c(x_1, y_1)) = T(cx_1, cy_1)$$
$$= (2cx_1 + cy_1, cx_1 - cy_1)$$
$$= c(2x_1 + y_1, x_1 - y_1)$$
$$= cT(x_1, y_1).$$

Therefore $T$ is linear.                                                ▮▮

The conditions for linearity can be condensed into a single test.

**THEOREM 1**

A transformation $T$ from $R^n$ to $R^n$ is linear if and only if

(*)                 for all $\mathbf{u}, \mathbf{v} \in R^n$ and constants $c_1, c_2$ it is true that

$$T(c_1\mathbf{u} + c_2\mathbf{v}) = c_1 T(\mathbf{u}) + c_2 T(\mathbf{v}).$$

*Proof.* Let $T$ be linear, then

$$T(c_1\mathbf{u} + c_2\mathbf{v}) = T(c_1\mathbf{u}) + T(c_2\mathbf{v})$$
$$= c_1 T(\mathbf{u}) + c_2 T(\mathbf{v})$$

Conversely, let (*) hold. Then letting $c_1 = c_2 = 1$ gives

$$T(\mathbf{u} + \mathbf{v}) = T(\mathbf{u}) + T(\mathbf{v})$$

and letting $c_2 = 0$ gives

$$T(c_1\mathbf{u}) = c_1 T(\mathbf{u})$$

Thus $T$ is linear.

As one might expect, a linear transformation takes lines into lines. For example, let a line $L$ be given by

$$x = x_0 + ta, \quad y = y_0 + tb, \quad z = z_0 + tc$$

in $R^3$. Then

$$T(x, y, z) = T((x_0, y_0, z_0) + t(a, b, c))$$
$$= T(x_0, y_0, z_0) + tT(a, b, c)$$

which is again the equation of a line.

**EXAMPLE 2**  Let $T(x, y, z) = (x + y, y + z, z + x)$. Then

$$T(c_1(x_1, y_1, z_1) + c_2(x_2, y_2, z_2))$$
$$= T(c_1 x_1 + c_2 x_2, c_1 y_1 + c_2 y_2, c_1 z_1 + c_2 z_2)$$
$$= (c_1 x_1 + c_2 x_2 + c_1 y_1 + c_2 y_2, c_1 y_1 + c_2 y_2 + c_1 z_1 + c_2 z_2, c_1 z_1 + c_2 z_2 + c_1 x_1 + c_2 x_2)$$
$$= (c_1 x_1 + c_1 y_1, c_1 y_1 + c_1 z_1, c_1 z_1 + c_1 x_1)$$
$$\quad + (c_2 x_2 + c_2 y_2, c_2 y_2 + c_2 z_2, c_2 z_2 + c_2 x_2)$$
$$= c_1(x_1 + y_1, y_1 + z_1, z_1 + x_1)$$
$$\quad + c_2(x_2 + y_2, y_2 + z_2, z_2 + x_2)$$
$$= c_1 T(x_1, y_1, z_1) + c_2 T(x_2, y_2, z_2)$$

and therefore $T$ is linear.

Also, $T$ takes the line

$$x = 3 + t(2), \quad y = -1 + t(4), \quad z = 5 + t(1)$$

into the line

$$T((3, -1, 5) + t(2, 4, 1)) = T(3, -1, 5) + tT(2, 4, 1)$$
$$= (2, 4, 8) + t(6, 5, 3) \qquad \blacksquare$$

A class of linear transformations is given by multiplication of all vectors by some constant. In general, if we let

$$T(\mathbf{u}) = k\mathbf{u}, \quad k \text{ a constant,}$$

then

$$T(c_1\mathbf{u} + c_2\mathbf{v}) = k(c_1\mathbf{u} + c_2\mathbf{v})$$
$$= c_1(k\mathbf{u}) + c_2(k\mathbf{v})$$
$$= c_1 T(\mathbf{u}) + c_2 T(\mathbf{v})$$

and $T$ is a linear transformation.

$T$ is called a *stretching* if $k > 1$ and a *shrinking* if $0 < k < 1$. If $k = 0$ then all vectors are mapped into the origin, and if $k = 1$ every vector is mapped into itself. The latter transformation is called the *identity* transformation. Finally, if $k < 0$, then all vectors are reflected about the origin.

**EXAMPLE 3**   Let $T(\mathbf{u}) = 2\mathbf{u}$ for all $\mathbf{u}$ in $R^2$. Then each vector is doubled. For example, $(3, 2)$ is mapped into $(6, 4)$. See Figure 7.1. $\qquad \blacksquare$

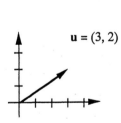
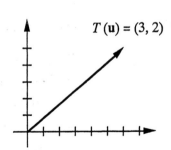

**FIGURE 7.1**

Many common geometric notions in the plane are given by linear transformations.

**EXAMPLE 4**  Let $T(x, y) = (-x, y)$. This is a reflection in the $y$-axis. It is easily seen to be linear since

$$\begin{aligned}
T(c_1(x_1, y_1) + c_2(x_2, y_2)) &= T(c_1 x_1 + c_2 x_2, c_1 y_1 + c_2 y_2) \\
&= (-c_1 x_1 - c_2 x_2, c_1 y_1 + c_2 y_2) \\
&= (-c_1 x_1, c_1 y_1) + (-c_2 x_2, c_2 y_2) \\
&= c_1(-x_1, y_1) + c_2(-x_2, y_2) \\
&= c_1 T(x_1, y_1) + c_2 T(x_2, y_2)
\end{aligned}$$ ∎

**EXAMPLE 5**  A rotation of $90°$ in the plane is given by $T(x, y) = (-y, x)$. See Figure 7.2. This is linear since

$$\begin{aligned}
T(c_1(x_1, y_1) + c_2(x_2, y_2)) &= T(c_1 x_1 + c_2 x_2, c_1 y_1 + c_2 y_2) \\
&= (-c_1 y_1 - c_2 y_2, c_1 x_1 + c_2 x_2) \\
&= c_1(-y_1, x_1) + c_2(-y_2, x_2)
\end{aligned}$$ ∎

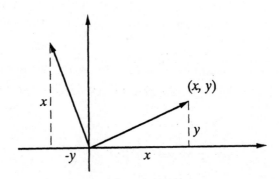

**FIGURE 7.2**

It is easily seen that not all transformations are linear.

**EXAMPLE 6**  Let $T(x, y) = (xy, y)$. Then

$$T((1, 0) + (0, 1)) = T(1, 1) = (1, 1)$$

and

$$T(1, 0) + T(0, 1) = (0, 0) + (0, 1) = (0, 1)$$

Therefore $T((1, 0) + (0, 1)) \neq T(1, 0) + T(0, 1)$ and $T$ is not linear.  ∎

**EXAMPLE 7**  Let $T(x, y) = (x - h, y - k)$ where $h$, $k$ are constants not both 0. Then

$$T(0(0,0)) = T(0,0)$$
$$= (-h, -k) \neq \mathbf{0} = 0 \cdot T(0,0)$$  ∎

Multiplication of $\mathbf{x}$ in $R^n$ by an $n \times n$ matrix $A$ is a linear transformation of $R^n$ to $R^n$ since

$$A(c_1\mathbf{x} + c_2\mathbf{y}) = A(c_1\mathbf{x}) + A(c_2\mathbf{y})$$
$$= c_1 A\mathbf{x} + c_2 A\mathbf{y}$$

**EXAMPLE 8**  Let $T(\mathbf{x}) = A\mathbf{x}$ where $A = \begin{bmatrix} 1 & 5 \\ -2 & 3 \end{bmatrix}$. Then

$$T(4,2) = \begin{bmatrix} 1 & 5 \\ -2 & 3 \end{bmatrix} \begin{bmatrix} 4 \\ 2 \end{bmatrix} = \begin{bmatrix} 14 \\ -2 \end{bmatrix}$$

and

$$T(\mathbf{e}_1) = \begin{bmatrix} 1 & 5 \\ -2 & 3 \end{bmatrix} \begin{bmatrix} 1 \\ 0 \end{bmatrix} = \begin{bmatrix} 1 \\ -2 \end{bmatrix}$$

∎

## EXERCISES 7.1.

1. Let $T(x, y, z) = (x + 2z, z - y, 3x)$. Find

    (a) $T(4, -2, 1)$  (b) $T(-3, 3, 2)$

2. Let $T(x, y, z) = (3y + z, x + 2y, 2y)$. Find

    (a) $T(-2, 2, 5)$  (b) $T(5, 4, -3, )$

3. Let $T(x, y) = (2x + y, 2x - y)$. Show that $T$ is linear.

4. Let $T(x, y) = (-x + 3y, x - 3y)$. Show that $T$ is linear.

5. Let $T(x, y) = (2x + 1, y - 1)$. Show that $T$ is not linear.

6. Let $T(x, y) = (x - 2, y + 2)$. Show that $T$ is not linear.

7. Let $T(x, y) = (x^2, y)$. Show that $T$ is not linear.

8. Let $T(x, y) = (x, xy)$. Show that $T$ is not linear.

9. Show that $T(x, y) = (x, 0)$ is linear.

10. Show that $T(x, y) = (0, y)$ is linear.

11. Let $T(x, y) = (x, -y)$. Show that $T$ is linear.

12. Let $T(x, y) = (y, x)$. Show that $T$ is linear.

13. Let $T(\mathbf{x}) = A\mathbf{x}$ where $A = \begin{bmatrix} 1 & -1 & 0 \\ 0 & -1 & 1 \\ 1 & 0 & 1 \end{bmatrix}$. Find

    (a) $T(1, -3, 2)$                 (b) $T(2, -2, 4)$

14. Let $T(\mathbf{x}) = A\mathbf{x}$ where $A = \begin{bmatrix} 1 & 0 & 1 \\ -1 & -1 & 0 \\ 0 & 1 & 1 \end{bmatrix}$. Find

    (a) $T(4, -2, 3)$                 (b) $T(-1, 3, 1)$

15. Let a line in $R^2$ be given by $\mathbf{x} = (2, 1) + t(3, -2)$. Find the image of the line under the linear transformation $T(x, y) = (x + y, x + 2y)$.

16. Let a line in $R^2$ be given by $\mathbf{x} = (-3, 2) + t(-1, 4)$. Find the image of the line under the linear transformation $T(x, y) = (x - 2y, 2x - y)$.

## 7.2 A MATRIX REPRESENTATION OF A LINEAR TRANSFORMATION

In the previous section we saw that multiplication of a vector in $R^n$ by an $n \times n$ matrix was a linear transformation from $R^n$ to $R^n$. It is further true that every linear transformation from $R^n$ to $R^n$ can be given by suitable matrix multiplication.

### DEFINITION

If $T(\mathbf{x}) = A\mathbf{x}$, then $A$ is called a **matrix representation** of the linear transformation $T$.

We now turn to the problem of constructing a matrix representation $A$ for a given linear transformation $T$.

First we note that the definition of linearity extends to arbitrary linear combinations by induction since

$$c_1\mathbf{x}_1 + (c_2\mathbf{x}_2 + \cdots c_n\mathbf{x}_n) = T(c_1\mathbf{x}_1) + T(c_2\mathbf{x}_2 + \cdots + c_n\mathbf{x}_n)$$
$$= c_1 T(\mathbf{x}_1) + c_2 T(\mathbf{x}_2) + \cdots + c_n T(\mathbf{x}_n)$$

For example, if $T$ is linear then

$$T(5\mathbf{x}_1 - 3\mathbf{x}_2 + \mathbf{x}_3) = 5T(\mathbf{x}_1) - 3T(\mathbf{x}_2) + T(\mathbf{x}_3)$$

The above result may be restated as "The transform of a linear combination of vectors is the linear combination of the transforms."

### THEOREM 1

Let $\mathbf{e}_1, \mathbf{e}_2, \ldots, \mathbf{e}_n$ be the standard basis for $R^n$, and let

$$T(\mathbf{e}_j) = \mathbf{a}_j = (a_{1j}, a_{2j}, \ldots, a_{nj})$$

for $j = 1, \ldots, n$. Then
$$T(\mathbf{x}) = A\mathbf{x}$$

where $A$ is the matrix $A = (\mathbf{a}_1 \ \mathbf{a}_2 \cdots \mathbf{a}_j \cdots \mathbf{a}_n)$, with columns $\mathbf{a}_j$, $j = 1, 2, \ldots, n$.

*Proof.* Let $\mathbf{x} = (x_j)$. Then

$$
\begin{aligned}
A\mathbf{x} &= x_1\mathbf{a}_1 + x_2\mathbf{a}_2 + \cdots + x_j\mathbf{a}_j + \cdots x_n\mathbf{a}_n \\
&= x_1 T(\mathbf{e}_1) + x_2 T(\mathbf{e}_2) + \cdots + x_j T(\mathbf{e}_j) + \cdots + x_n T(\mathbf{e}_n) \\
&= T(x_1\mathbf{e}_1 + x_2\mathbf{e}_2 + \cdots + x_j\mathbf{e}_j + \cdots + x_n\mathbf{e}_n) \\
&= T(\mathbf{x}).
\end{aligned}
$$

NOTE: It is very important to recognize that the vectors $\mathbf{a}_j = T(\mathbf{e}_j)$ are the *columns* of $A$ even though we write them initially as row vectors. These vectors must be written as columns when constructing the matrix $A$ that represents $T$. This is illustrated in the following examples.

**EXAMPLE 1**  In $R^2$ let $T(x, y) = (x - y, x + y)$. We find

$$
\begin{aligned}
T(\mathbf{e}_1) &= T(1, 0) = (1, 1) \\
T(\mathbf{e}_2) &= T(0, 1) = (-1, 1)
\end{aligned}
$$

Then the images of $\mathbf{e}_1$ and $\mathbf{e}_2$ form the 1st and 2nd columns of $A$. Thus

$$A = \begin{bmatrix} 1 & -1 \\ 1 & 1 \end{bmatrix}$$

As a check we see that

$$\begin{bmatrix} 1 & -1 \\ 1 & 1 \end{bmatrix} \begin{bmatrix} x \\ y \end{bmatrix} = \begin{bmatrix} x - y \\ x + y \end{bmatrix}$$

This shows the linearity of $T$ as well.    ∎

**EXAMPLE 2** In $R^2$ let
$$T(x, y) = (-y, x)$$
Find a matrix representation of $T$.

**SOLUTION** We have
$$T(\mathbf{e}_1) = T(1, 0) = (0, 1)$$
$$T(\mathbf{e}_2) = T(0, 1) = (-1, 0)$$

Therefore, writing these as columns, we get the matrix
$$A = \begin{bmatrix} 0 & -1 \\ 1 & 0 \end{bmatrix}$$

Again we note that
$$A \begin{bmatrix} x \\ y \end{bmatrix} = \begin{bmatrix} 0 & -1 \\ 1 & 0 \end{bmatrix} \begin{bmatrix} x \\ y \end{bmatrix} = \begin{bmatrix} -y \\ x \end{bmatrix}$$

■

**EXAMPLE 3** In $R^3$ let
$$T(x, y, z) = (2x + z, x + 3z, x + 4y - z)$$
Find a matrix representation of $T$.

**SOLUTION** We have
$$T(\mathbf{e}_1) = (2, 1, 1)$$
$$T(\mathbf{e}_2) = (0, 0, 4)$$
$$T(\mathbf{e}_3) = (1, 3, -1)$$

Therefore
$$A = \begin{bmatrix} 2 & 0 & 1 \\ 1 & 0 & 3 \\ 1 & 4 & -1 \end{bmatrix}$$

As a check we see that
$$A \begin{bmatrix} x \\ y \\ z \end{bmatrix} = \begin{bmatrix} 2 & 0 & 1 \\ 1 & 0 & 3 \\ 1 & 4 & -1 \end{bmatrix} \begin{bmatrix} x \\ y \\ z \end{bmatrix} = \begin{bmatrix} 2x + z \\ x + 3z \\ x + 4y - z \end{bmatrix}$$

■

In the previous cases, the transformations were all linear. Thus, the procedure of Theorem 1 produced a matrix representation. If the transformation is not linear, then an incorrect matrix representation must come out of the procedure.

**EXAMPLE 4**    In $R^2$ let

$$T(x, y) = (x - 2, y + 1).$$

Show that $T$ is not linear, by showing that the procedure of Theorem 1 does not produce a matrix representation of the transformation.

**SOLUTION**

$$T(\mathbf{e_1}) = (-1, 1)$$
$$T(\mathbf{e_2}) = (-2, 2)$$
$$A = \begin{bmatrix} -1 & -2 \\ 1 & 2 \end{bmatrix}$$
$$A \begin{bmatrix} x \\ y \end{bmatrix} = \begin{bmatrix} -x - 2y \\ x + 2y \end{bmatrix} \neq T(x, y)$$

∎

Many of the notions about functions on the real numbers to the real numbers carry over to transformations of vectors. For example, we define the composition of $T_2$ with $T_1$ to be

$$T_2 \circ T_1(\mathbf{x}) = T_2(T_1(\mathbf{x}))$$

Thus we see that the composition of $T_2$ with $T_1$ is simply the performance of $T_1$ followed by the performance of $T_2$.

*THEOREM 2*

If $T_1$ and $T_2$ are linear transformations of $R^n$ to $R^n$, then $T_2 \circ T_1$ is a linear transformation of $R^n$ to $R^n$.

*Proof.*

$$T_2 \circ T_1(c_1\mathbf{x} + c_2\mathbf{y})$$
$$= T_2(T_1(c_1\mathbf{x} + c_2\mathbf{y})$$
$$= T_2(c_1T_1(\mathbf{x}) + c_2T_1(\mathbf{y}))$$
$$= c_1T_2 \circ T_1(\mathbf{x}) + c_2T_2 \circ T_1(\mathbf{y})$$

*THEOREM 3*

If $A_1$, $A_2$ are the respective matrix representations of the linear transformations $T_1$, $T_2$, then $A_2 A_1$ is the matrix representation of $T_2 \circ T_1$.

*Proof.*

$$T_2 \circ T_1(\mathbf{x}) = T_2(T_1(\mathbf{x}))$$
$$= T_2(A_1\mathbf{x})$$
$$= A_2(A_1\mathbf{x})$$
$$= (A_2 A_1)\mathbf{x}$$

**EXAMPLE 5** Let $T_1(x, y) = (2x - y, x + 2y)$ and $T_2(x, y) = (-x - 4y, 3x + y)$. Find the matrix representation of the composite linear transformation

**SOLUTION** Since

$$T_1(\mathbf{e_1}) = (2, 1), \quad T_1(\mathbf{e_2}) = (-1, 2)$$

We have

$$A_1 = \begin{bmatrix} 2 & -1 \\ 1 & 2 \end{bmatrix}$$

Also, since

$$T_2(\mathbf{e_1}) = (-1, 3), \quad T_2(\mathbf{e_2}) = (-4, 1)$$

we have

$$A_2 = \begin{bmatrix} -1 & -4 \\ 3 & 1 \end{bmatrix}$$

Then

$$T_2 \circ T_1(\mathbf{x}) = \begin{bmatrix} -1 & -4 \\ 3 & 1 \end{bmatrix} \begin{bmatrix} 2 & -1 \\ 1 & 2 \end{bmatrix} \begin{bmatrix} x \\ y \end{bmatrix}$$
$$= \begin{bmatrix} -6 & -7 \\ 7 & -1 \end{bmatrix} \begin{bmatrix} x \\ y \end{bmatrix}$$
$$= (-6x - 7y, 7x - y)$$

∎

NOTE: The composite transformation can be found directly by

$$T_2 \circ T_1(x) = T_2(2x - y, x + 2y)$$
$$= (-(2x - y) - 4(x + 2y), 3(2x - y) + (x + 2y))$$
$$= (-6x - 7y, 7x - y)$$

A transformation $T$ is said to be *one-to-one* $(1:1)$ if every vector of $R^n$ is mapped onto exactly one vector of $R^n$. For example, a rotation of the plane is a $1:1$ transformation whereas the mappings

$$T(x, y) = (x, 2x + 3)$$

which takes all of the plane into the line $y = 2x + 3$ is not $1:1$.

If $T$ is $1:1$, then each $y$ in $R^n$ is the image of exactly one $x$ in $R^n$. That is to say, if $T(x_1) = y$ and $T(x_2) = y$ then $x_1 = x_2$. Thus it is possible to define an *inverse* transformation, $T^{-1}$, by

$$T^{-1}(T(x)) = x$$

As with real functions it is also true that

$$T(T^{-1}(x)) = x$$

## THEOREM 4

The inverse of a linear transformation is a linear transformation.

*Proof.* Let $T(x_1) = y_1$, $T(x_2) = y_2$. Then

$$
\begin{aligned}
T^{-1}(c_1 y_1 + c_2 y_2)) &= T^{-1}(c_1 T(x_1) + c_2 T(x_2)) \\
&= T^{-1}(T(c_1 x_1 + c_2 x_2)) \\
&= c_1 x_1 + c_2 x_2 \\
&= c_1 T^{-1}(y_1) + c_2 T^{-1}(y_2)
\end{aligned}
$$

## THEOREM 5

The matrix representation of $T^{-1}$ is the inverse of the matrix representation of $T$.

*Proof.* Let $A_T$ and $A_{T^{-1}}$ be the matrix representation of $T$, $T^{-1}$ reprectively. Then for all $x$ in $R^n$, we have

$$(T^{-1} \circ T)(x) = x$$
$$A_{T^{-1}} A_T x = x$$

and therefore

$$A_{T^{-1}} = (A_T)^{-1}$$

**EXAMPLE 6**  Let $T(\mathbf{x}) = (x + y, y, 2y + z)$ in $R^3$. Find the matrix representation for the inverse $T^{-1}$.

**SOLUTION**  We have

$$T(\mathbf{e_1}) = (1, 0, 0)$$
$$T(\mathbf{e_2}) = (1, 1, 2)$$
$$T(\mathbf{e_3}) = (0, 0, 1)$$

Then

$$A = \begin{bmatrix} 1 & 1 & 0 \\ 0 & 1 & 0 \\ 0 & 2 & 1 \end{bmatrix}$$

and

$$A^{-1} = \begin{bmatrix} 1 & -1 & 0 \\ 0 & 1 & 0 \\ 0 & -2 & 1 \end{bmatrix}.$$

As a check we see that

$$T^{-1}(T(\mathbf{x})) = \begin{bmatrix} 1 & -1 & 0 \\ 0 & 1 & 0 \\ 0 & -2 & 1 \end{bmatrix} \begin{bmatrix} 1 & 1 & 0 \\ 0 & 1 & 0 \\ 0 & 2 & 1 \end{bmatrix} \mathbf{x}$$

$$= \begin{bmatrix} 1 & 0 & 0 \\ 0 & 1 & 0 \\ 0 & 0 & 1 \end{bmatrix} \mathbf{x}$$

$$= I\mathbf{x}$$

$$= \mathbf{x}$$

**EXERCISE 7.2.**

In exercises 1-6, find the matrix $A$ such that $A\mathbf{x} = T(\mathbf{x})$.

1. $T(x, y) = (4x - 3y, 5x + 2y)$       2. $T(x, y) = (-x + 2y, 7x - 5y)$

3. $T(x, y) = (-6x - 3y, 2x + y)$       4. $T(x, y) = (8x - y, 3x + 2y)$

5. $T(x, y, z) = (x + 2z, z, -2y)$       6. $T(x, y, z) = (-z, 2x + y, 3x)$

In Exercises 7-10 show that $T$ is not linear by attempting to find the matrix $A$ such that $A\mathbf{x} = T(\mathbf{x})$.

7. $T(x, y) = (x + 3, y - 6)$

8. $T(x, y) = (x + 2, y + 1)$

9. $T(x, y) = (xy, y)$

10. $T(x, y) = (x, y^2)$

11. Let $T_1(x, y) = (3x - 2y, 2x + y)$ and $T_2(x, y) = (x + 3y, x - 2y)$.

 Find

 (a) $T_2 \circ T_1(\mathbf{x})$            (b) $T_1 \circ T_2(\mathbf{x})$

12. Let $T_1(x, y) = (5x - y, -2x + 2y)$ and $T_2(x, y) = (-4x + 3y, 2x - 3y)$.

 Find

 (a) $T_2 \circ T_1(\mathbf{x})$            (b) $T_1 \circ T_2(\mathbf{x})$

13. Find the the matrices of the linear transformation for $T_1$, $T_2$, $T_2 \circ T_1$, $T_1 \circ T_2$ in Exercise 11.

14. Find the the matrices of the linear transformation for $T_1$, $T_2$, $T_2 \circ T_1$, $T_1 \circ T_2$ in Exercise 12.

15. Let $T(x, y) = (5x + 7y, 3x + 4y)$. Find $T^{-1}$.

16. Let $T(x, y) = (5x + 8y, 3x + 5y)$. Find $T^{-1}$.

17. Let $T(x, y, z) = (-x + 2y + z, y + 3z, -x + 4y + 8z)$. Find $T^{-1}$.

18. Let $T(x, y, z) = (x - 2y + 4z, 2x - 5y + 6z, -3x + 9y - 7z)$. Find $T^{-1}$.

## 7.3  CHANGE OF BASIS

We have seen that $\mathbf{e}_1, \mathbf{e}_2, \cdots, \mathbf{e}_n$ is but one of infinitely many possible basis for $R^n$. Often it is convenient or advantageous to express the vectors under consideration in terms of some different bases.

For example, the vector

$$\mathbf{x} = (5, 7) = 5\mathbf{e}_1 + 7\mathbf{e}_2$$

which is stated in terms of coordinates based on $\mathbf{e}_1, \mathbf{e}_2$, can also be given in terms of the basis $\mathbf{u}_1 = (-1, 4)$, $\mathbf{u}_2 = (2, 1)$ as

$$\mathbf{x} = \mathbf{u}_1 + 3\mathbf{u}_2.$$

We would like to give this representation of $\mathbf{x}$ in terms of coordinates as well.

*DEFINITION*

Let $u_1, u_2, \cdots, u_n$ be an ordered basis for $R^n$ and let $\mathbf{B} = (u_1, u_2, \ldots, u_n)$ stand for this basis in the same order. If

$$x = c_1 u_1 + c_2 u_2 + \cdots + c_n u_n$$

then

$$x_\mathbf{B} = (c_i)$$

is called the **coordinate vector** or **coordinate representation** for **x** in terms of **B**.

In the above example $x_\mathbf{B} = (1, 3)$ is the coordinate vector of x for the ordered basis $\mathbf{B} = (u_1, u_2) = ((-1, 4), (2, 1))$.

Many problems involve converting from the standard basis $e_1, e_2, \ldots, e_n$ to another basis $\mathbf{B} = (u_1, u_2, \ldots, u_n)$ or the converse. Let x be a coordinate vector with respect to the standard basis and $x_\mathbf{B}$ the coordinate representation of the same vector with respect to $\mathbf{B} = (u_1, u_2, \ldots, u_n)$. We let $B = [u_1 u_2 \cdots u_n]$ be the $n \times n$ matrix with the vector $u_j$ as the $j$th column. We call $B$ the **basis matrix** for the basis **B**. Let

$$x = c_1 u_1 + c_2 u_2 + \cdots + c_n u_n$$

Then

$$x_\mathbf{B} = (c_1, c_2, \ldots, c_n)$$

and

$$x = [u_1 u_2 \cdots u_n] x_\mathbf{B} = B x_\mathbf{B}$$

Thus, the coordinate vector with respect to the standard basis is given by the basis matrix for $u_1, u_2, \ldots, u_n$ times the coordinates vector for x with respect to the ordered basis $u_1, u_2, \ldots, u_n$.

**EXAMPLE 1**  Let

$$x_\mathbf{B} = (2, -3, 1)$$

where $\mathbf{B} = (u_1, u_2, u_3)$, $u_1 = (1, -1, 2)$, $u_2 = (2, -3, 3)$, $u_3 = (-2, 4, -1)$. Find the coordinate vector with respect to the standard basis.

SOLUTION    The basis matrix for **B** is

$$B = \begin{bmatrix} 1 & 2 & -2 \\ -1 & -3 & 4 \\ 2 & 3 & -1 \end{bmatrix}$$

and

$$\mathbf{x} = 2\mathbf{u}_1 - 3\mathbf{u}_2 + \mathbf{u}_3$$
$$= 2(1, -1, 2) - 3(2, -3, 3) + (-2, 4, -1)$$
$$= \begin{bmatrix} 1 & 2 & -2 \\ -1 & -3 & 4 \\ 2 & 3 & -1 \end{bmatrix} \begin{bmatrix} 2 \\ -3 \\ 1 \end{bmatrix} = \begin{bmatrix} -6 \\ 11 \\ -10 \end{bmatrix}$$

We have seen that $\mathbf{x} = B\mathbf{x_B}$ converts the coordinate vector with respect to $\mathbf{u}_1, \mathbf{u}_2, \ldots, \mathbf{u}_n$ into the coordinate vector with respect to the standard basis. Now we shall see how to achieve the converse.

Since $B$ is an invertible matrix we can multiply $\mathbf{x} = B\mathbf{x_B}$ by $B^{-1}$ to obtain

$$\mathbf{x_B} = B^{-1}\mathbf{x}$$

Thus the inverse of the basis matrix times the coordinate vector for $\mathbf{e}_1$, $\mathbf{e}_2, \ldots, \mathbf{e}_n$ gives the coordinate vector for $\mathbf{u}_1, \mathbf{u}_2, \ldots, \mathbf{u}_n$.

---

**DEFINITION**

The inverse of the basis matrix $B = [\mathbf{u}_1 \mathbf{u}_2 \cdots \mathbf{u}_n]$ is called the **change of basis matrix** for the conversion of coordinate vectors with respect to the standard basis to the coordinate vectors with respect to the basis $\mathbf{u}_1, \mathbf{u}_2, \ldots, \mathbf{u}_n$.

---

In words we can say that "the change of basis matrix is the inverse of the basis matrix."

**EXAMPLE 2**    In the previous example we had $\mathbf{u}_1 = (1, -1, 2)$, $\mathbf{u}_2 = (2, -3, 3)$, $\mathbf{u}_3 = (-2, 4, 1)$. Find the change of basis matrix to convert a standard coordinate vector $\mathbf{x}$ into a coordinate vector $\mathbf{x_B}$ with respect to the basis $\mathbf{B} = (\mathbf{u}_1, \mathbf{u}_2, \mathbf{u}_3)$. Convert $\mathbf{x} = (3, -1, 5)$.

SOLUTION    We have that

$$B = \begin{bmatrix} 1 & 2 & -2 \\ -1 & -3 & 4 \\ 2 & 3 & -1 \end{bmatrix}$$

Then, by the methods of section 3.2 we find

$$B^{-1} = \begin{bmatrix} 9 & 4 & -2 \\ -7 & -3 & 2 \\ -3 & -1 & 1 \end{bmatrix}$$

Then for $\mathbf{x} = (3, -1, 5)$ we have

$$\mathbf{x_B} = B^{-1}\mathbf{x} = \begin{bmatrix} 9 & 4 & -2 \\ -7 & -3 & 2 \\ -3 & -1 & 1 \end{bmatrix} \begin{bmatrix} 3 \\ -1 \\ 5 \end{bmatrix} = \begin{bmatrix} 13 \\ -8 \\ -3 \end{bmatrix}$$

∎

The matrix of a linear transformation is not unique, but depends on the basis being used for the coordinate vectors.

**EXAMPLE 3** Let the linear transformation $T$ be given by

$$T(x, y) = (-4x + y, x - 2y)$$

Then the matrix of the transformation with respect to the standard basis is

$$A = \begin{bmatrix} -4 & 1 \\ 1 & -2 \end{bmatrix}$$

Then we may transform any vector, say $\mathbf{x} = (-1, -1)$ by

$$A\mathbf{x} = A \begin{bmatrix} -1 \\ -1 \end{bmatrix} = \begin{bmatrix} -4 & 1 \\ 1 & -2 \end{bmatrix} \begin{bmatrix} -1 \\ -1 \end{bmatrix} = \begin{bmatrix} 3 \\ 1 \end{bmatrix}$$

Now consider the basis $\mathbf{B} = (\mathbf{u_1}, \mathbf{u_2})$ where $\mathbf{u_1} = (2, 3)$, $\mathbf{u_2} = (3, 4)$. Since $\mathbf{u_1} - \mathbf{u_2} = (2, 3) - (3, 4) = (-1, -1)$, the coordinate vector $(-1, -1)$ becomes $\mathbf{x_B} = (1, -1)$ with respect to $\mathbf{u_1}, \mathbf{u_2}$.

Suppose that we use the matrix

$$A' = \begin{bmatrix} 8 & 17 \\ -7 & -14 \end{bmatrix}$$

to transform $\mathbf{x_B}$. Then

$$A'\mathbf{x_B} = \begin{bmatrix} 8 & 17 \\ -7 & -14 \end{bmatrix} \begin{bmatrix} 1 \\ -1 \end{bmatrix}_{\mathbf{B}} = \begin{bmatrix} -9 \\ 7 \end{bmatrix}_{\mathbf{B}}$$

Also we have

$$\begin{bmatrix} -9 \\ 7 \end{bmatrix}_{\mathbf{B}} = -9\mathbf{u_1} + 7\mathbf{u_2} = -9(2, 3) + 7(3, 4) = (3, 1)$$

Thus $A\mathbf{x}$ and $A'\mathbf{x_B}$ are the same vector, but in different coordinates. We shall show that $A'$ is the matrix of the given linear transformation with respect to the basis $\mathbf{u_1}, \mathbf{u_2}$. ∎

We will develop a procedure to convert a matrix of a linear transformation with respect to a given basis into the matrix of the linear transformation with respect to another basis. First we will construct the matrix for the preceding $R^2$ example.

**EXAMPLE 4**    Show that the matrix of the linear transformation of the previous example with respect to the basis $\mathbf{u}_1 = (2, 3)$, $\mathbf{u}_2 = (3, 4)$ is $A' = \begin{bmatrix} 8 & 17 \\ -7 & -14 \end{bmatrix}$.

**SOLUTION**    Let $T(\mathbf{x}) = \mathbf{y}$ where $\mathbf{x}, \mathbf{y}$ are coordinate vectors with respect to $\mathbf{e}_1, \mathbf{e}_2$. Now $B = \begin{bmatrix} 2 & 3 \\ 3 & 4 \end{bmatrix}$, $B^{-1} = \begin{bmatrix} -4 & 3 \\ 3 & -2 \end{bmatrix}$ so that

$$\mathbf{x} = \begin{bmatrix} 2 & 3 \\ 3 & 4 \end{bmatrix} \mathbf{x_B} \quad \text{and} \quad \mathbf{y} = \begin{bmatrix} 2 & 3 \\ 3 & 4 \end{bmatrix} \mathbf{y_B}$$

Therefore, we can substitute into

$$\mathbf{y} = A\mathbf{x}$$

to obtain

$$\begin{bmatrix} 2 & 3 \\ 3 & 4 \end{bmatrix} \mathbf{y_B} = \begin{bmatrix} -4 & 1 \\ 1 & -2 \end{bmatrix} \begin{bmatrix} 2 & 3 \\ 3 & 4 \end{bmatrix} \mathbf{x_B}$$

or

$$\mathbf{y_B} = \begin{bmatrix} 2 & 3 \\ 3 & 4 \end{bmatrix}^{-1} \begin{bmatrix} -4 & 1 \\ 1 & -2 \end{bmatrix} \begin{bmatrix} 2 & 3 \\ 3 & 4 \end{bmatrix} \mathbf{x_B}$$

$$= \begin{bmatrix} -4 & 3 \\ 3 & -2 \end{bmatrix} \begin{bmatrix} -5 & -8 \\ -4 & -5 \end{bmatrix} \mathbf{x_B}$$

$$= \begin{bmatrix} 8 & 17 \\ -7 & -14 \end{bmatrix} \mathbf{x_B}$$

So that $\mathbf{x}$ in $\mathbf{B}$ coordinates is transformed by $\begin{bmatrix} 8 & 17 \\ -7 & -14 \end{bmatrix}$ into $\mathbf{y}$ in $\mathbf{B}$ coordinates.    ∎

Suppose that $A$ is the matrix of a linear transformation $T$ with respect to the standard basis $\mathbf{e}_1, \mathbf{e}_2, \ldots, \mathbf{e}_n$. Let $\mathbf{B}$ be the ordered basis $(\mathbf{u}_1, \mathbf{u}_2, \ldots, \mathbf{u}_n)$ and find the matrix of $T$ with respect to $\mathbf{B}$. Let $\mathbf{x}$ be any vector in $R^n$ and $T(\mathbf{x}) = \mathbf{y}$ be its image under $T$, where $\mathbf{x}, \mathbf{y}$ are given in standard coordinates. If $B = [\mathbf{u}_1 \mathbf{u}_2 \ldots \mathbf{u}_n]$, then we have

$$\mathbf{y} = A\mathbf{x}, \quad \mathbf{y} = B\mathbf{y_B} \quad \text{and} \quad \mathbf{x} = B\mathbf{x_B}$$

On substituting in the first equation for **x** and **y** we find that

$$B\mathbf{y_B} = AB\mathbf{x_B}$$

and

$$\mathbf{y_B} = (B^{-1}AB)\mathbf{x_B}$$

So that $B^{-1}AB$ is the matrix of $T$ with respect to the basis **B**.

**EXAMPLE 5**  Consider the linear transformation

$$T(x, y) = (3x + 2y, 2x - y)$$

Find the matrix of $T$ with respect to the basis $\mathbf{B} = (\mathbf{u_1}, \mathbf{u_2})$ where $\mathbf{u_1} = (1, -3)$, $\mathbf{u_2} = (-2, 7)$.

**SOLUTION**   The matrix of $T$ with respect to $e_2$, $e_2$ is

$$A = \begin{bmatrix} 3 & 2 \\ 2 & -1 \end{bmatrix}$$

Then

$$B = \begin{bmatrix} 1 & -2 \\ -3 & 7 \end{bmatrix} \quad \text{and} \quad B^{-1} = \begin{bmatrix} 7 & 2 \\ 3 & 1 \end{bmatrix}$$

Then

$$\begin{aligned}
B^{-1}AB &= \begin{bmatrix} 7 & 2 \\ 3 & 1 \end{bmatrix} \begin{bmatrix} 3 & 2 \\ 2 & -1 \end{bmatrix} \begin{bmatrix} 1 & -2 \\ -3 & 7 \end{bmatrix} \\
&= \begin{bmatrix} 25 & 12 \\ 11 & 5 \end{bmatrix} \begin{bmatrix} 1 & -2 \\ -3 & 7 \end{bmatrix} \\
&= \begin{bmatrix} -11 & 34 \\ -4 & 13 \end{bmatrix}
\end{aligned}$$

∎

**EXAMPLE 6**   Let

$$A = \begin{bmatrix} 3 & -2 & -2 \\ -2 & 3 & 2 \\ 3 & -3 & -2 \end{bmatrix}$$

be the matrix of a linear transformation $T$ with respect to the standard basis.  Find the matrix of $T$ with respect to the basis $\mathbf{u_1} = (1, 1, 0)$, $\mathbf{u_2} = (1, 0, 1)$, $\mathbf{u_3} = (2, -2, 3)$.

**SOLUTION**   We have

$$B = \begin{bmatrix} 1 & 1 & 2 \\ 1 & 0 & -2 \\ 0 & 1 & 3 \end{bmatrix}$$

and we can check that

$$B^{-1} = \begin{bmatrix} 2 & -1 & -2 \\ -3 & 3 & 4 \\ 1 & -1 & -1 \end{bmatrix}$$

Then the matrix of the transformation with respect to $u_1$, $u_2$, $u_3$ is

$$B^{-1}AB = \begin{bmatrix} 1 & 0 & 0 \\ 0 & 1 & 0 \\ 0 & 0 & 2 \end{bmatrix}$$

∎

The matrix found in the last example had the particularly simple form of a diagonal matrix. The basis which produced this form comes from the eigenvectors of $A$ which we studied in the previous chapter.

If two matrices $A_1$ and $A_2$ represent the same linear transformation $T$ with respect to different basis then they are said to be **similar**. Let $u_1$, $u_2, \ldots, u_n$ and $v_1, v_2, \ldots, v_n$ be the bases for $A_1$ and $A_2$ respectively. Let $A$ be the matrix of $T$ with respect to $e_1, \ldots, e_n$. If $B_1 = [u_1 u_2 \ldots u_2]$ and $B_2 = [v_1 v_2 \cdots v_n]$ then

$$A_1 = B_1^{-1}AB_1 \quad \text{and} \quad A_2 = B_2^{-1}AB_2$$

so that

$$A = B_1 A_1 B_1^{-1} \quad \text{and} \quad A = B_2 A_2 B_2^{-1}.$$

Then

$$B_1 A_1 B_1^{-1} = B_2 A_2 B_2^{-1}$$

and

$$A_1 = B_1^{-1} B_2 A_2 B_2^{-1} B_1.$$

If we let

$$P = B_2^{-1} B_1$$

then

$$P^{-1} = B_1^{-1} B_2$$

and

$$A_1 = P^{-1} A_2 P$$

where $P$ is some invertible matrix. A study of similarity is beyond the scope of this text.

## EXERCISES 7.3.

In Exercises 1-4 find the coordinate vector of $x_B$ with respect to the standard basis.

1. $x_B = (5, -1)$ where $B = ((4, 2), (-1, 3))$.

2. $x_B = (-3, 6)$ where $B = ((6, 3), (2, 4))$.

3. $x_B = (1, -3, -4)$ where $B = ((4, 3, -1), (12, 7, -2), (-5, -3, 1))$.

4. $x_B = (2, -1, 3)$ where $B = ((-1, 1, -1), (2, -3, 4), (1, -5, 8))$.

In Exercises 5-8 find the change of basis matrix which will convert a vector in standard coordinates into a coordinate vector for the given basis, $B$. Convert the vector $x$ into $x_B$.

5. $u_1 = (5, 6)$, $u_2 = (6, 7)$, $x = (3, 4)$.

6. $u_1 = (4, 7)$, $u_2 = (5, 9)$, $x = (5, 2)$.

7. $u_1 = (1, 2, 4)$, $u_2 = (3, 7, 10)$, $u_3 = (-2, -2, -13)$, $x = (1, 2, -3)$.

8. $u_1 = (-2, 1, 2)$, $u_2 = (7, -3, -8)$, $u_3 = (-6, 2, 9)$, $x = (4, 2, -2)$.

In Exercises 9-16 let $B$ be the basis given in the noted exercise. Let $A$ as shown be the matrix of a linear transformation $T$ with respect to the standard basis. Find the matrix of $T$ with respect to the basis $B$.

9. $B$ from Exercise 1. $A = \begin{bmatrix} 2 & -1 \\ 5 & 3 \end{bmatrix}$.

10. $B$ from Exercise 5. $A = \begin{bmatrix} 5 & 3 \\ 9 & 1 \end{bmatrix}$.

11. $B$ from Exercise 2. $A = \begin{bmatrix} 4 & -1 \\ -2 & 6 \end{bmatrix}$.

12. $B$ from Exercise 6. $A = \begin{bmatrix} -3 & 5 \\ 2 & -1 \end{bmatrix}$.

13. $B$ from Exercise 3. $A = \begin{bmatrix} 0 & 0 & 5 \\ 1 & 2 & 4 \\ 0 & 1 & 6 \end{bmatrix}$.

14. $B$ from Exercise 4. $A = \begin{bmatrix} 2 & 3 & 0 \\ -1 & 0 & -2 \\ 1 & 2 & 1 \end{bmatrix}$.

15. $B$ from Exercise 7. $A = \begin{bmatrix} 1 & -1 & 0 \\ 4 & -5 & 1 \\ 1 & -1 & -2 \end{bmatrix}$

16. $B$ from Exercise 8. $A = \begin{bmatrix} 1 & 2 & 3 \\ -1 & -1 & -2 \\ 1 & -1 & 0 \end{bmatrix}$

17. Let $A = \begin{bmatrix} 3 & -1 & -3 \\ -4 & 3 & 6 \\ 4 & -1 & -4 \end{bmatrix}$ be the matrix of the linear transformation $T$
with respect to the standard basis. Find the matrix of $T$ with respect to the basis $\mathbf{u}_1 = (1, -1, 1)$, $\mathbf{u}_2 = (1, -2, 1)$, $\mathbf{u}_3 = (1, -2, 2)$.

18. Let $A = \begin{bmatrix} -1 & 6 & -4 \\ -4 & -3 & 8 \\ -4 & 0 & 5 \end{bmatrix}$ be the matrix of the linear transformation $T$
with respect to the standard basis. Find the matrix of $T$ with respect to the basis $\mathbf{u}_1 = (1, 2, 2)$, $\mathbf{u}_2 = (2, 0, 1)$, $\mathbf{u}_3 = (1, 1, 1)$.

## 7.4   THE REVISED SIMPLEX METHOD

The dependency table used in the simplex method expresses each column vector of the constraint system in terms of a given basis and a pivot replaces a single vector in the basis with another column vector. There are times when the desired basis is known in advance and one wants to find the dependency table by a more direct or otherwise better method then the succession of simplex pivots. For example, it may happen that precision is lost after a number of simplex pivots, and the resulting dependency table is suspect. Then the table can be reconstructed from the basis in a way which will preserve the precision. We now develop the mechanics of the reconstruction.

Since a pivot is composed of a sequence of elementary row operations, we return to a study of them.

Suppose that we perform the multiplication $RT$ where

$$R = \begin{bmatrix} 0 & 0 & 1 \\ 0 & 1 & 0 \\ 1 & 0 & 0 \end{bmatrix}, \quad T = \begin{bmatrix} 5 & 2 & 8 & -1 \\ 4 & 1 & -6 & -2 \\ -9 & 7 & 3 & 6 \end{bmatrix}$$

We find that

$$RT = \begin{bmatrix} -9 & 7 & 3 & 6 \\ 4 & 1 & -6 & -2 \\ 5 & 2 & 8 & -1 \end{bmatrix}$$

which is the matrix $T$ with the first and third rows exchanged.

In general, if $R$ is the $n \times n$ identity with the $h$ and $k$th rows exchanged, and $T$ is $n \times m$, then $RT$ will be the same as $T$ except that the $h$ and $k$th rows will be exchanged. Thus the exchange of two rows in a matrix can be accomplished by premultiplication by a properly chosen square matrix.

Now let $T$ be the $3 \times 4$ matrix above and

$$S = \begin{bmatrix} 1 & 0 & 0 \\ 0 & 2 & 0 \\ 0 & 0 & 1 \end{bmatrix}$$

Then

$$ST = \begin{bmatrix} 5 & 2 & 8 & -1 \\ 8 & 2 & -12 & -4 \\ -9 & 7 & 3 & 6 \end{bmatrix}$$

is the same as $T$ except that the second row has been multiplied by 2.

In general, if $S$ is the $n \times n$ identity with the $h$th row multiplied by $c$, and $T$ is $n \times m$, then $ST$ is the same as $T$ except that the $h$th row is multiplied by $c$. Thus the multiplication of a row by a non zero constant can be accomplished by premultiplication by a properly chosen square matrix.

Finally let $T$ be the $3 \times 4$ matrix above and

$$Q = \begin{bmatrix} 1 & 0 & 3 \\ 0 & 1 & 0 \\ 0 & 0 & 1 \end{bmatrix}$$

Then

$$QT = \begin{bmatrix} -22 & 23 & 17 & 17 \\ 4 & 1 & -6 & -2 \\ -9 & 7 & 3 & 6 \end{bmatrix}$$

is the same as $T$ except 3 times the third row has been added to the first row.

In general if $Q$ is the identity except for a constant $c$ in the $h, k$ position then $QT$ is the same as $T$ except that the $h$th row has been replaced by the sum of the $h$th and $c$ times the $k$th row. Thus the addition of a multiple of a row to another row can be accomplished though premultiplication by a properly chosen square matrix.

## DEFINITION

Let the premultiplication of $T$ by a square matrix $E$ perform an elementary row operation. Then we call $E$ an **elementary (row) matrix**.

We note that $R$, $S$ and $Q$ above are the elementary row matrices which, respectively, correspond to exchanging two rows, adding a multiple of a row to another row and multiplying a row by a non-zero constant. The identity matrix is an elementary matrix which corresponds to multiplying any row by 1.

Suppose that the succession of elementary row operations represented by $E_1, E_2, \ldots, E_r$ accomplishes a complete pivot on a dependency table $T_1$. That is

$$T_2 = E_r \cdots E_2 E_1 T_1$$

is the matrix $T_1$ after a pivot has been performed. If

$$P = E_r \cdots E_2 E_1$$

then

$$T_2 = PT_1$$

and we call $P$ a **pivot matrix**.

**EXAMPLE 1**  Construct the pivot matrix for the pivot on the circled element in the following matrix

$$A = \begin{bmatrix} 2 & -1 & 5 \\ 6 & ② & -2 \\ -4 & 3 & 7 \end{bmatrix}$$

**SOLUTION**  First multiply by

$$E_1 = \begin{bmatrix} 1 & 0 & 0 \\ 0 & 1/2 & 0 \\ 0 & 0 & 1 \end{bmatrix}$$

to obtain $E_1 A =$

$$\begin{bmatrix} 1 & 0 & 0 \\ 0 & 1/2 & 0 \\ 0 & 0 & 1 \end{bmatrix} \begin{bmatrix} 2 & -1 & 5 \\ 6 & 2 & -2 \\ -4 & 3 & 7 \end{bmatrix} = \begin{bmatrix} 2 & -1 & 5 \\ 3 & 1 & -1 \\ -4 & 3 & 7 \end{bmatrix}$$

Then multiply by

$$E_2 = \begin{bmatrix} 1 & 1 & 0 \\ 0 & 1 & 0 \\ 0 & 0 & 1 \end{bmatrix} \quad \text{and} \quad E_3 = \begin{bmatrix} 1 & 0 & 0 \\ 0 & 1 & 0 \\ 0 & -3 & 1 \end{bmatrix}$$

to obtain $E_3 E_2 E_1 A$

$$= \begin{bmatrix} 1 & 0 & 0 \\ 0 & 1 & 0 \\ 0 & -3 & 1 \end{bmatrix} \begin{bmatrix} 1 & 1 & 0 \\ 0 & 1 & 0 \\ 0 & 0 & 1 \end{bmatrix} \begin{bmatrix} 2 & -1 & 5 \\ 3 & 1 & -1 \\ -4 & 3 & 7 \end{bmatrix}$$

$$= \begin{bmatrix} 5 & 0 & 4 \\ 3 & 1 & -1 \\ -13 & 0 & 10 \end{bmatrix}$$

The pivot matrix is

$$P = E_3 E_2 E_1$$

$$= \begin{bmatrix} 1 & 0 & 0 \\ 0 & 1 & 0 \\ 0 & -3 & 1 \end{bmatrix} \begin{bmatrix} 1 & 1 & 0 \\ 0 & 1 & 0 \\ 0 & 0 & 1 \end{bmatrix} \begin{bmatrix} 1 & 0 & 0 \\ 0 & 1/2 & 0 \\ 0 & 0 & 1 \end{bmatrix}$$

$$= \begin{bmatrix} 1 & 1/2 & 0 \\ 0 & 1/2 & 0 \\ 0 & -3/2 & 1 \end{bmatrix}$$

As a check we see that $PA$

$$= \begin{bmatrix} 1 & 1/2 & 0 \\ 0 & 1/2 & 0 \\ 0 & -3/2 & 1 \end{bmatrix} \begin{bmatrix} 2 & -1 & 5 \\ 6 & 2 & -2 \\ -4 & 3 & 7 \end{bmatrix}$$

$$= \begin{bmatrix} 5 & 0 & 4 \\ 3 & 1 & -1 \\ -13 & 0 & 10 \end{bmatrix}$$

■

Since

$$P = E_r \cdots E_2 E_1$$
$$= E_r \cdots E_2 E_1 I$$

the pivot matrix can always be obtained by performing the desired row operations on the identity matrix $I$.

**EXAMPLE 2**  Construct the pivot matrix for the pivot on the circled element in the matrix below

$$A = \begin{bmatrix} 1 & 5 & -2 & -3 \\ 2 & 3 & 1 & 7 \\ 6 & -6 & ③ & 9 \end{bmatrix}$$

First, the third row of $I$ is divided by 3 to obtain

$$\begin{bmatrix} 1 & 0 & 0 \\ 0 & 1 & 0 \\ 0 & 0 & 1/3 \end{bmatrix}$$

Then, the third row is subtracted from the second row and two times the third row is added to the first row to get

$$\begin{bmatrix} 1 & 0 & 2/3 \\ 0 & 1 & -1/3 \\ 0 & 0 & 1/3 \end{bmatrix}$$

As a check we see that

$$PA = \begin{bmatrix} 1 & 0 & 2/3 \\ 0 & 1 & -1/3 \\ 0 & 0 & 1/3 \end{bmatrix} \begin{bmatrix} 1 & 5 & -2 & -3 \\ 2 & 3 & 1 & 7 \\ 6 & -6 & ③ & 9 \end{bmatrix}$$

$$= \begin{bmatrix} 5 & 1 & 0 & 3 \\ 0 & 5 & 0 & 4 \\ 2 & -2 & 1 & 3 \end{bmatrix}$$

∎

NOTE: The pivot matrix $P$, differs from the identity matrix only in the $h$th column, where $h$ is the index of the pivot row. The entries there are easily checked since $Pc = e_h$ where $c$ is the pivot column.

Suppose that one begins with a dependency table $T_1$ in terms of the basis $e_1, e_2, \ldots, e_n$ and performs a pivot $P_1$ to obtain the new table

$$T_2 = P_1 T_1.$$

And then in sucession one performs pivots $P_2, \ldots, P_r$ to obtain

$$T_3 = P_2 T_2 = (P_2 P_1) T_2$$
$$T_4 = P_3 T_3 = (P_3 P_2 P_1) T_1$$

$$\vdots$$

$$T_{r+1} = P_r T_r = (P_r \cdots P_2 P_1) T_1$$

The columns of the dependency table are the coordinate vectors of the constraint system with respect to basis listed on the left. As we pivot from dependency table to dependency table, the basis changes by one vector each time. If the final basis is denoted by **B** and $B$ is the basis matrix for **B** then since

$$B^{-1}T_1 = T_{r+1}$$

it must be true that

$$P_r \cdots P_2 P_1 = B^{-1}$$

**EXAMPLE 3**  Suppose that we start with the matrix

$$T_1 = \begin{bmatrix} 1 & 1 & 5 \\ 1 & -1 & 3 \end{bmatrix}$$

Writing $T_1$ as a dependency table we obtain

$$
\begin{array}{c}
\quad\ \ \mathbf{a_1} \quad \mathbf{a_2} \quad \mathbf{a_3} \\
\begin{array}{c} \mathbf{e_1} \\ \mathbf{e_2} \end{array}
\begin{bmatrix} ① & 1 & 5 \\ 1 & -1 & 3 \end{bmatrix}
\end{array}
$$

If a pivot is to be made on the "1" in the 1, 1 position then the pivot matrix is

$$P_1 = \begin{bmatrix} 1 & 0 \\ -1 & 1 \end{bmatrix}$$

and

$$T_2 = P_1 T_1 = \begin{bmatrix} 1 & 0 \\ -1 & 1 \end{bmatrix} \begin{bmatrix} 1 & 1 & 5 \\ 1 & -1 & 3 \end{bmatrix}$$

$$
= \begin{array}{c}
\quad\ \ \mathbf{a_1} \quad \mathbf{a_2} \quad \mathbf{a_3} \\
\begin{array}{c} \mathbf{a_1} \\ \mathbf{e_2} \end{array}
\begin{bmatrix} 1 & 1 & 5 \\ 0 & ⊝2 & -2 \end{bmatrix}
\end{array}
$$

Then let a pivot be made on the "$-2$" in the 2, 2 position. The pivot matrix is

$$P_2 = \begin{bmatrix} 1 & +1/2 \\ 0 & -1/2 \end{bmatrix}$$

Then

$$T_2 = P_2 T_2 = \begin{bmatrix} 1 & 1/2 \\ 0 & -1/2 \end{bmatrix} \begin{bmatrix} 1 & 1 & 5 \\ 0 & -2 & -2 \end{bmatrix}$$

$$\begin{array}{c} & \begin{array}{ccc} \mathbf{a}_1 & \mathbf{a}_2 & \mathbf{a}_3 \end{array} \\ = \begin{array}{c} \mathbf{a}_1 \\ \mathbf{a}_2 \end{array} & \begin{bmatrix} 1 & 0 & 4 \\ 0 & 1 & 1 \end{bmatrix} \end{array}$$

Since

$$T_3 = (P_2 P_1)T_1$$

we must have that $B^{-1} = P_2 P_1$ where $B$ is the basis matrix

$$B = [\mathbf{a}_1 \mathbf{a}_2] = \begin{bmatrix} 1 & 1 \\ 1 & -1 \end{bmatrix}$$

As a check we see that

$$P_2 P_1 = \begin{bmatrix} 1 & 1/2 \\ 0 & -1/2 \end{bmatrix} \begin{bmatrix} 1 & 0 \\ -1 & 1 \end{bmatrix} = \begin{bmatrix} 1/2 & 1/2 \\ 1/2 & -1/2 \end{bmatrix}$$

and

$$B^{-1} = \begin{bmatrix} 1 & 1 \\ 1 & -1 \end{bmatrix}^{-1} = -\frac{1}{2} \begin{bmatrix} -1 & -1 \\ -1 & 1 \end{bmatrix} = \begin{bmatrix} 1/2 & 1/2 \\ 1/2 & -1/2 \end{bmatrix}$$

∎

We have seen in Section 4.7 that the Simplex Table of a linear program for a given basis can be formed from the dependency table of the constraint system which corresponds to that basis. Since we have just shown how to construct the dependency for a basis we can construct the entire Simplex Table for the basis.

**EXAMPLE 4**    Consider the linear program

$$\text{minimize } z = -x_1 + x_2 + 2x_3 - 4x_4$$
$$\text{subject to} \quad 3x_1 - x_2 + 2x_3 + 2x_4 = 10$$
$$x_1 + x_2 - 2x_3 + 2x_4 = 2$$

$$x_1 \geq 0, \quad x_2 \geq 0, \quad x_3 \geq 0, \quad x_4 \geq 0$$

Find the Simplex Table which corresponds to the basis $\mathbf{a}_3$, $\mathbf{a}_4$ and determined whether or not the solution is optimal.

**SOLUTION**   First let

$$B = (a_3, a_4) = \begin{bmatrix} 2 & 2 \\ -2 & 2 \end{bmatrix}$$

Then, the change of basis matrix is

$$B^{-1} = \frac{1}{8} \begin{bmatrix} 2 & -2 \\ 2 & 2 \end{bmatrix} = \begin{bmatrix} 1/4 & -1/4 \\ 1/4 & 1/4 \end{bmatrix}$$

Therefore, the dependency table of the constraint system is

$$\begin{bmatrix} 1/4 & -1/4 \\ 1/4 & 1/4 \end{bmatrix} \begin{bmatrix} 3 & -1 & 2 & 2 & 10 \\ 1 & 1 & -2 & 2 & 2 \end{bmatrix}$$

$$\begin{array}{ccccc} & a_1 & a_2 & a_3 & a_4 & b \\ = & a_3 \\ & a_4 \end{array} \begin{bmatrix} 1/2 & -1/2 & 1 & 0 & 2 \\ 1 & 0 & 0 & 1 & 3 \end{bmatrix}$$

By the methods of Section 7.4 Step 3* the Simplex Table is found to be

| | | $-1$ | $1$ | $2$ | $-4$ | |
|---|---|---|---|---|---|---|
| | | $a_1$ | $a_2$ | $a_3$ | $a_4$ | $b$ |
| | | $1$ | $-2$ | $-2$ | $0$ | $0$ | $-8$ |
| $c_3 = 2$ | $a_3$ | $0$ | $1/2$ | $-1/2$ | $1$ | $0$ | $2$ |
| $c_4 = -4$ | $a_4$ | $0$ | $1$ | $0$ | $0$ | $1$ | $3$ |
| | $z_j$ | | $-3$ | $-1$ | $2$ | $-4$ | $-8$ |

We see that the basic feasible solution $x_1 = 0$, $x_2 = 0$, $x_3 = 2$, $x_4 = 3$ is optimal with value $z = -8$.   ▌▌

We now turn to the **Revised Simplex Method.** Suppose that the current dependency table of the constraint system is given by $T$, the initial table by $T_1$ and the change of basis matrix by $B^{-1}$. Then

$$T = B^{-1}T_1$$

If a pivot, given by $P$, is performed on $T$, then the new table is

$$T' = PT = P(B^{-1}T_1) = (PB^{-1})T_1$$

so that the change of basis matrix for the table $T'$ is given by

$$(B^{-1})' = PB^{-1}$$

We see that the new dependency table can be obtained by performing the pivot on the change of basis matrix to get the new change of basis matrix, and then $(B^{-1})'$ is multiplied into $T_1$ to get $T'$. This is the essence of the revised simplex method. The original table is never modified and so retains all of the original precision. If a lack of precision is detected at some stage, then the basis matrix can be inverted by precision preserving methods, to obtain a better form of the change of basis matrix.

**EXAMPLE 5**  Consider the linear program

$$
\begin{aligned}
\text{minimize} \quad z = \quad & 3x_1 - 2x_2 - 3x_3 + 2x_4 + x_5 \\
\text{subject to} \quad & -8x_1 + 2x_2 + 4x_3 - 8x_4 - 4x_5 = 10 \\
& -2x_1 + 2x_2 + 2x_3 + 6x_4 + 4x_5 = 8
\end{aligned}
$$

$$
x_1 \geq 0, \quad x_2 \geq 0, \quad x_3 \geq 0, \quad x_4 \geq 0, \quad x_5 \geq 0
$$

Suppose that the basis $a_3$, $a_2$ has been reached. For this basis find the change of basis matrix, construct the Simplex Table, and perform a Revised Simplex pivot to obtain a new Simplex Table.

**SOLUTION**  The change of basis matrix is

$$
B^{-1} = \begin{bmatrix} 4 & 2 \\ 2 & 2 \end{bmatrix}^{-1} = 1/4 \begin{bmatrix} 2 & -2 \\ -2 & 4 \end{bmatrix} = \begin{bmatrix} 1/2 & -1/2 \\ -1/2 & 1 \end{bmatrix}
$$

Then, the dependency table for this basis is

$$
\begin{aligned}
& \begin{bmatrix} 1/2 & -1/2 \\ -1/2 & 1 \end{bmatrix} \begin{bmatrix} -8 & 2 & 4 & -8 & -4 & 10 \\ -2 & 2 & 2 & 6 & 4 & 8 \end{bmatrix} \\
& = \begin{matrix} a_3 \\ a_2 \end{matrix} \begin{bmatrix} -3 & 0 & 1 & -7 & -4 & 1 \\ 2 & 1 & 0 & 10 & 6 & 3 \end{bmatrix}
\end{aligned}
$$

The Simplex table is

|  |  | | 3 | −2 | −3 | 2 | 1 | |
|---|---|---|---|---|---|---|---|---|
|  |  |  | $a_1$ | $a_2$ | $a_3$ | $a_4$ | $a_5$ | b |
|  |  | 1 | 2 | 0 | 0 | −1 | −1 | −9 |
| $c_3 = -3$ | $a_3$ | 0 | −3 | 0 | 1 | −7 | −4 | 1 |
| $c_2 = -2$ | $a_2$ | 0 | ② | 1 | 0 | 10 | 6 | 3 |
| | $z_j$ | | 5 | −2 | −3 | 1 | 0 | −9 |

The Simplex rules call for a pivot on the 2 in the $\mathbf{a}_1$ column. The pivot matrix is

$$P = \begin{bmatrix} 1 & 3/2 \\ 0 & 1/2 \end{bmatrix}.$$

The new change of basis matrix is

$$(B^{-1})' = PB^{-1} = \begin{bmatrix} 1 & 3/2 \\ 0 & 1/2 \end{bmatrix} \begin{bmatrix} 1/2 & -1/2 \\ -1/2 & 1 \end{bmatrix}$$

$$= \begin{bmatrix} -1/4 & 1 \\ -1/4 & 1/2 \end{bmatrix}.$$

The new dependency table is

$$\begin{bmatrix} -1/4 & 1 \\ -1/4 & 1/2 \end{bmatrix} \begin{bmatrix} -8 & 2 & 4 & -8 & -4 & | & 10 \\ -2 & 2 & 2 & 6 & 4 & | & 8 \end{bmatrix}$$

$$= \begin{array}{c} \mathbf{a}_3 \\ \mathbf{a}_1 \end{array} \begin{bmatrix} 0 & 3/2 & 1 & 8 & 5 & | & 22/4 \\ 1 & 1/2 & 0 & 5 & 3 & | & 6/4 \end{bmatrix}$$

Finally, the new Simplex table is

|  |  | 3 | −2 | −3 | 2 | 1 |  |
|---|---|---|---|---|---|---|---|
|  |  | $\mathbf{a}_1$ | $\mathbf{a}_2$ | $\mathbf{a}_3$ | $\mathbf{a}_4$ | $\mathbf{a}_5$ | $\mathbf{b}$ |
|  |  | 1 | 0 | −1 | 0 | −11 | −7 | −12 |
| $c_3 = -3$ | $\mathbf{a}_3$ | 0 | 0 | 3/2 | 1 | 8 | 5 | 11/2 |
| $c_1 = 3$ | $\mathbf{a}_1$ | 0 | 1 | 1/2 | 0 | 5 | 3 | 3/2 |
|  | $z_j$ | 3 | −3 | −3 | −9 | −6 | −12 |

We see that the solution $x_1 = 3$, $x_2 = 0$, $x_3 = -3$, $x_4 = 0$, $x_5 = 0$ with value $z = -12$ is optimal. ∎

## EXERCISES 7.4

In Exercises 1-8 construct the indicated pivot matrix.

1. $\begin{bmatrix} 4 & ① & 7 \\ -3 & 2 & 6 \end{bmatrix}$

2. $\begin{bmatrix} 7 & -5 & 3 \\ 4 & -3 & ① \end{bmatrix}$

3. $\begin{bmatrix} 6 & 9 & 3 \\ ② & 5 & -1 \end{bmatrix}$

4. $\begin{bmatrix} 5 & 4 & ③ \\ 7 & 2 & -3 \end{bmatrix}$

5. $\begin{bmatrix} 3 & -7 & 2 & 5 \\ 1 & -3 & ① & 7 \\ 4 & -2 & -3 & 6 \end{bmatrix}$

6. $\begin{bmatrix} 7 & -5 & 8 & -9 \\ 2 & 4 & 5 & 6 \\ -2 & ① & 3 & 4 \end{bmatrix}$

7. $\begin{bmatrix} -6 & 1 & 7 & 8 \\ 4 & 5 & -2 & 1 \\ ② & 3 & 4 & 3 \end{bmatrix}$
   8. $\begin{bmatrix} 1 & 5 & 9 & 3 \\ 9 & 2 & ③ & 1 \\ 7 & 8 & -6 & 4 \end{bmatrix}$

In Exercises 9-12 find the change of basis matrix which will take the given initial dependency table into the one for the given basis. Use the change of basis matrix to find the new dependency table.

9. $\begin{array}{c} e_1 \\ e_2 \end{array} \left[ \begin{array}{cccc|c} 5 & 7 & 2 & -4 & 2 \\ 1 & -5 & 6 & 3 & 1 \end{array} \right]$    basis $a_4, a_2$

10. $\begin{array}{c} e_1 \\ e_2 \end{array} \left[ \begin{array}{cccc|c} 5 & 6 & 3 & 8 & 8 \\ 2 & 3 & 4 & 3 & 3 \end{array} \right]$    basis $a_4, a_1$

11. $\begin{array}{c} e_1 \\ e_2 \\ e_3 \end{array} \left[ \begin{array}{ccccc|c} 1 & 7 & 1 & 1 & 0 & 5 \\ 1 & 8 & 0 & 1 & 1 & 4 \\ 0 & 3 & 1 & 4 & 1 & 7 \end{array} \right]$    basis $a_1, a_3\ a_5$

12. $\begin{array}{c} e_1 \\ e_2 \\ e_3 \end{array} \left[ \begin{array}{ccccc|c} 1 & -2 & 1 & 2 & -1 & 2 \\ 1 & 6 & -1 & 4 & 1 & 6 \\ -1 & 2 & 1 & -4 & 1 & 4 \end{array} \right]$    basis $a_1, a_3\ a_5$

13. Suppose that the change of basis matrix

$$B^{-1} = \begin{bmatrix} 1 & -1 & 3 \\ 2 & 4 & -4 \\ -1 & 1 & -2 \end{bmatrix}$$

is used to take an initial dependency table into

$$\begin{array}{c} a_4 \\ a_1 \\ a_2 \end{array} \left[ \begin{array}{ccccc|c} 0 & 0 & 5 & 1 & -4 & 7 \\ 1 & 0 & -8 & 0 & 2 & 5 \\ 0 & 1 & 1 & 0 & 6 & 18 \end{array} \right]$$

Find the change of basis matrix which will take the initial table into the dependency table for the basis $a_4, a_5, a_2$.

14. Suppose that the change of basis matrix

$$B^{-1} = \begin{bmatrix} -3 & 6 & 12 \\ 3 & -7 & -10 \\ 6 & 2 & 15 \end{bmatrix}$$

is used to take an initial dependency table into

$$
\begin{array}{c}
\mathbf{a_2} \\
\mathbf{a_5} \\
\mathbf{a_1}
\end{array}
\left[
\begin{array}{ccccc|c}
0 & 1 & 3 & 5 & 0 & 3 \\
0 & 0 & -3 & 7 & 1 & 2 \\
1 & 0 & 6 & 9 & 0 & 8
\end{array}
\right]
$$

Find the change of basis matrix which will take the initial table into the dependency table for the basis $\mathbf{a_3}, \mathbf{a_5}, \mathbf{a_1}$.

In Exercises 15 and 16 consider the given linear program. Find the change of basis matrix for the given basis. Use this matrix to construct the Simplex Table of the linear program for the given basis.

15.

$$\text{minimize} \quad z = 3x_1 + 2x_2 + 3x_3 + x_4$$
$$\text{subject to} \quad 8x_1 + 2x_2 + 2x_3 - 4x_4 = 4$$
$$3x_1 - 3x_2 + x_3 - x_4 = 18$$
$$x_1 \geq 0, \quad x_2 \geq 0, \quad x_3 \geq 0, \quad x_4 \geq 0.$$
$$\text{basis} \quad \mathbf{a_1}, \mathbf{a_4}.$$

16.

$$\text{minimize} \quad z = -x_1 - 3x_2 - 4x_3 - 4x_4$$
$$\text{subject to} \quad x_1 - 2x_2 + 2x_3 - 2x_4 = 4$$
$$4x_1 - 6x_2 + 9x_3 - 3x_4 = 17$$
$$x_1 \geq 0, \quad x_2 \geq 0, \quad x_3 \geq 0, \quad x_4 \geq 0.$$
$$\text{basis} \quad \mathbf{a_1}, \mathbf{a_2}.$$

# SUPPLEMENTARY EXERCISES

## CHAPTER 1

1. Given the line $3x + 2y = 5$, find a parallel line $ax + by = c$ that is 1 unit higher in the plane. (That is, the $y$-intercept of the new line is 1 unit higher than that of the given line.)

2. Let $(x_1, y_1)$ and $(x_2, y_2)$ be two points in the plane.
   (a) use the Pythagorean Theorem to show that the distance between the points is $d = \sqrt{(x_2 - x_1)^2 + (y_2 - y_1)^2}$.
   (b) Find the distance between $(7, 1)$ and $(4, -2)$.

3. Let $L$ be the line $y = -\frac{1}{2}x + 3$ and $P$ be the point $(-1, 4)$. Let $Q$ be that point on $L$ that is closest to $P$ (so that the line through $P$ and $Q$ is perpendicular to $L$).
   (a) Find the equation of the line through $P$ and $Q$. Then find $Q$.
   (b) Find the distance from $P$ to the line $L$. (The distance from a point to a line is defined to be the distance from the given point to the closest point on the line.)

4. Find the value of $B$ and $k$ such that the system

$$2x + 3y = k$$
$$-x + By = 5$$

   has an infinite number of solutions.

5. Find linear inequalities that correspond to the following closed half–planes.
   (a) The points $(-1, 1)$ and $(1, 4)$ are on the boundary line and $(0, 0)$ lies in the half–plane.
   (b) The points $(0, 0)$ and $(2, -1)$ are on the boundary line and $(1, 1)$ lies in the half–plane.

6. Solve the linear programs by graphical methods.
   (a) Graph the feasibility region and find all corner points.

$$x + y \leq 4$$
$$x - y \leq 2$$
$$y \leq 2$$
$$x \geq 0, \quad y \geq 0$$

   (b) Find the minimum of $z = -2x + y$ on the region.

(c) Find the maximum of $z = 3x - 5y$ on the region.

7. Graph the region
$$2x - y \leq -3$$
$$x + y \leq 4$$
$$x + 2y \leq 5$$
$$x \geq 0, \quad y \geq 0$$

8. Find a value of for $k$ for which the following feasibility region consists of a single point
$$x - y \geq -2$$
$$x + y \leq 6$$
$$x - 5y \leq -6$$
$$2x - y \geq k$$

9. Let $R$ be the region consisting of all points $(x, y)$ that lie either in the rectangle with corners $(-2, 4), (3, 4), (3, -1), (-2, -1)$ or in the rectangle with corners $(2, 3), (2, 5), (6, 5), (6, 3)$. Find the maximum of $z = y - x$ for $(x, y)$ in $R$.

10. The Wonderful Fund invests money in class $A$ bonds that pay 6% and class $B$ bonds that pay 9%. They have 30 million dollars to invest. Further, there is a restriction that twice the investment in class $B$ bonds must be at most 10 millon dollars less than the investment in class $A$ bonds. Set up and solve the linear program to maximize income.

11. The equations $x = 6 + 2t$, $y = 4 - t$, $t$ any number, describe a line in the plane.
    (a) Find the points that correspond to $t = -1, t = 0, t = 1$ and sketch the line.
    (b) Eliminate $t$ and find an equation of the form $Ax + By = C$ for the given line.

12. Let a line be given by $x = 3 - 2t$, $y = 2 + t$, $t$ any number, and a second line be given by $x = -1 + 3s$, $y = 2 + 2s$, $s$ any number. Determine if the lines intersect, and if they do, find the values of $t$ and $s$ that correspond to the point of intersection. Find the point of intersection.

13. Let a line be given by $x = 1 + t$, $y = 3 + 2t$, $t$ any number, and a second line be given by $x = 2 + s$, $y = 2 + 2s$, $s$ any number. Determine if the lines intersect, and if they do, find the $t$ and $s$ that correspond to the point of intersection. Find the point of intersection.

14. Consider the line $y = 3x - 2$. Find values $x_0$, $y_0$, $a$, $b$ such that the line can be described by

$$x = x_0 + at$$
$$y = y_0 + bt, \quad t \quad \text{any number.}$$

Hint: Let $(x_0, y_0)$ be any chosen point on the line, let $a = 1$ and find $b$.

## CHAPTER 2

1. Consider the matrix $\begin{bmatrix} 2 & 3 & 7 \\ 4 & 9 & 1 \end{bmatrix}$. Show that the row operations

   (a)
   $$R_2' = R_2 - 2R_1$$
   $$R_1' = \tfrac{1}{2}R_1$$

   will produce the same matrix as the row operations

   (b)
   $$R_1' = \tfrac{1}{2}R_1$$
   $$R_2' = R_2 - 4R_1$$

In exercises 2 and 3 we count the number of operations used in performing Gaussian or Gauss–Jordan elimination. In making such a count we assume that each step of the algorithm is applied even if the entry is by chance already in the desired form. For example, consider the pivot on $d$ in the matrix

$$\begin{bmatrix} 1 & b & c \\ 0 & d & e \\ 0 & f & g \end{bmatrix} \quad d \neq 0,$$

where the first column is known to be 1, 0, 0 from a previous step. The operation $R_2' = \tfrac{1}{d}R_2$ would require 2 multiplications by $\tfrac{1}{d}$ even if $d = \pm 1$ or $e = 0$ since these tests are not usually made. The operations $R_1' = R_1 - bR_2$ and $R_3' = R_3 - fR_2$ would then require two multiplications and two subtractions each regardless of the actual values $b$, $f$ and $e$.

2. Consider the augmented matrix

$$\begin{bmatrix} 2 & -2 & 4 & | & 2 \\ 4 & -5 & 9 & | & 6 \\ -2 & 4 & -7 & | & -4 \end{bmatrix}.$$

Count the number $A$ of additions (subtractions) and $M$ of multiplications (divisions) required to put the matrix into reduced echelon form if (a) Gaussian elimination and (b) Gauss–Jordan elimination is used.

3. Suppose that a $3 \times 3$ system of equations has a unique solution. In general, how many additions and multiplications must be performed if the solution is found by (a) Gaussian elimination and (b) Gauss–Jordan elimination.

4. The following augmented matrices are in row echelon form. Without any computations, state whether the corresponding linear systems have no, one, or infinitely many solutions.

(a) $\left[\begin{array}{cc|c} 1 & 2 & 3 \\ 0 & 1 & 2 \\ 0 & 0 & 1 \end{array}\right]$
(b) $\left[\begin{array}{cc|c} 1 & 3 & 2 \\ 0 & 1 & -1 \\ 0 & 0 & 0 \end{array}\right]$

(c) $\left[\begin{array}{ccc|c} 1 & -1 & 2 & 3 \\ 0 & 0 & 1 & 2 \\ 0 & 0 & 0 & 0 \end{array}\right]$
(d) $\left[\begin{array}{ccc|c} 1 & 2 & 3 & 4 \\ 0 & 0 & 1 & 2 \\ 0 & 0 & 0 & 1 \end{array}\right]$

(e) $\left[\begin{array}{ccc|c} 1 & -1 & 2 & 7 \\ 0 & 1 & 3 & 5 \\ 0 & 0 & 1 & 1 \\ 0 & 0 & 0 & 0 \end{array}\right]$

5. Consider the two systems

$$ax + by = e \qquad ax + by = g$$
$$cx + dy = f \qquad cx + dy = f.$$

Is it possible for one system to have no solutions and the other to have infinitely many solutions? Give an example where this happens or show that it cannot happen.

6. True or false? Give an example if the statement is false.
   (a) If a matrix is in reduced echelon form and a column is removed, then the resulting matrix is also in row echelon form.
   (b) If a matrix is in reduced echelon form and two columns are interchanged, then the resulting matrix is also in echelon form.

7. Are the following statements true or false? Given an example if false.
   (a) A linear system with more variables than equations must be consistent.
   (b) A linear system with more equations than variables must be inconsistent.
   (c) If a linear system has a unique solution, then the row rank of the coefficient matrix must equal the number of variables.

8. Consider the matrix

$$\left[\begin{array}{ccc|c} 1 & 1 & 2 & -2 \\ 0 & 2 & 3 & -1 \\ 0 & -3 & 5 & 4 \end{array}\right]$$

Explain why the row operations

$$R'_2 = R_2 - 2R_1$$
$$R'_3 = R_3 + 3R_1$$
$$R_1 \leftrightarrow R_2$$

are not in the spirit of Gaussian elimination.

9. Find the values of $b$ for which the homogeneous system of equations has only the trivial solution

$$3x + by = 0$$
$$9x + 2y = 0$$

10. For what value of $k$ will the following system be inconsistent. For those values of $k$ for which the system is consistent, will the solution be unique or not?

$$\begin{bmatrix} 1 & -4 & -3 & | & -2 \\ 1 & 2 & 1 & | & 1 \\ -2 & 2 & k & | & -3 \end{bmatrix}$$

11. Consider the system of equations

$$2x + 3y - 2z = 4$$
$$x - 2y + z = 2$$
$$4x + 13y - 8z = 12$$

We observe that

$$3(2x + 3y - 2z) - 2(x - 2y + z) - (4x + 13y - 8z) = 0 \cdot x + 0 \cdot y + 0 \cdot z.$$

What can be said about the solutions of the system of equations?

12. Sketch the plane
$$10x + 15y + 6z = -30$$

Show the intercepts and display the traces with dashed lines.

13. Consider the simplex table

$$\begin{bmatrix} 1 & 0 & -2 & 0 & | & +5 & 0 & -3 & | & 20 \\ \hline 0 & 0 & b & 1 & | & 3 & 0 & 4 & | & 6 \\ 0 & 0 & c & 0 & | & -2 & 1 & 2 & | & 0 \\ 0 & 1 & d & 0 & | & -2 & 0 & -5 & | & 2 \end{bmatrix}$$

Find values for $b$, $c$, $d$ such that the current basic feasible solution is optimal.

14. Consider the linear program

$$\text{Maximize} \quad 4x_1 - 2x_2$$
$$\text{subject to} \quad 3x_1 - x_2 \leq 9$$
$$2x_1 + x_2 \leq 8$$
$$x_1 \geq 0, \quad x_2 \leq 0.$$

Find a transformation of the variables that will convert this into a linear program with nonnegative variables. Transform the program.

15. Consider the linear program

$$\text{maximize} \quad 5x_1 + 2x_2$$
$$\text{subject to} \quad 4x_1 + 3x_2 \leq 13$$
$$-2x_1 + x_2 \leq 4$$
$$x_1 \geq 0, \quad x_2 \geq 1.$$

Find a transformation of the variables that will convert this into a linear program with nonnegative variables. Transform the program.

16. Consider the linear program

$$\text{maximize} \quad 2x_1 + 3x_2 + x_3$$
$$\text{subject to} \quad x_1 - x_2 + 2x_3 \leq 10$$
$$3x_1 + 2x_2 - x_3 \leq 12$$
$$-x_1 + 3x_2 + 3x_3 \leq 14$$
$$x_1 \geq 0, \quad x_2 \geq 0$$

and $x_3$ unrestricted in value.

Find a transformation of the variables that will convert this into a linear program with nonnegative variables. Transform the program.

17. It is known that the linear program

$$\text{maximize} \quad -15x_1 - 14x_2 + 24x_3$$
$$\text{subject to} \quad 4x_1 - 2x_2 + 2x_3 \leq 2$$
$$16x_1 - 2x_2 + 4x_3 \leq 10$$
$$15x_1 - 5x_2 + 6x_3 \leq 15$$
$$x_1 \geq 0, \quad x_2 \geq 0, \quad x_3 \geq 0$$

has the maximum of $z = 54$ at $x_1 = 0$, $x_2 = 3$, $x_3 = 4$. Show that the linear program

$$
\begin{array}{lrrrrr}
\text{Maximize} & 15x_1 & + 14x_2 & - 24x_3 & \\
\text{subject to} & 4x_1 & - 2x_2 & + 2x_3 & \leq 2 \\
& 16x_1 & - 2x_2 & + 4x_3 & \leq 10 \\
& 15x_1 & - 5x_2 & + 6x_3 & \leq 15
\end{array}
$$

$$x_1 \geq 0, \quad x_2 \geq 0, \quad x_3 \geq 0$$

has the minimum of $z = -54$ at $x_1 = 0$, $x_2 = 3$, $x_3 = 4$.

18. We consider the simplex table of a linear program. Is it ever possible for a variable to become basic on one pivot and nonbasic on the very next pivot? Give an example or show that it cannot happen.

19. We consider the simplex table of a linear program. Is it ever possible for a variable to become nonbasic on a pivot and basic again on the very next pivot? Give an example or show that it cannot happen.

20. Any augmented matrix with the correct number of basic variables is the simplex table for some maximum program. Find the maximum program which has the following augmented matrix as its simplex table.

$$
\left[
\begin{array}{cccc|ccc|c}
1 & 4 & 0 & -2 & 0 & 2 & 0 & 6 \\
\hline
0 & 3 & 0 & 2 & 1 & 5 & 0 & 8 \\
0 & -2 & 1 & 3 & 0 & 2 & 0 & 2 \\
0 & 1 & 0 & 4 & 0 & -3 & 1 & 4
\end{array}
\right]
$$

## CHAPTER 3

1. Find an example of a $2 \times 2$ matrix $A$ with all entries non–zero such that $A^2 = O$.

2. Find all matrices of the form $A = \begin{bmatrix} 1 & 0 \\ a & b \end{bmatrix}$ such that $A^2 = A$.

3. If $A^2 = I$, does it follows that $A = \pm I$? Prove or give a counterexample.

4. Show that $A^2 = I$ if and only if $(A - I)(A + I) = 0$.

5. Let $A = \begin{bmatrix} 1 & b \\ c & 1 \end{bmatrix}$, $B = \begin{bmatrix} 1 & f \\ g & 1 \end{bmatrix}$. Find $b$, $c$, $g$, $f$ all distinct and nonzero such that $AB = BA$.

6. Find a $3 \times 3$ matrix $A$ with no zero entries and no rows the same such that

$$A \begin{bmatrix} 4 & -3 & 2 \\ 1 & 2 & -1 \\ -2 & -15 & 8 \end{bmatrix} = \begin{bmatrix} 0 & 0 & 0 \\ 0 & 0 & 0 \\ 0 & 0 & 0 \end{bmatrix}$$

7. Let $A$ be symmetric (that is, $a_{ij} = a_{ji}$). Show that $A^2$ is symmetric.

8. Find symmetric, $2 \times 2$ matrices $A$ and $B$ such that $AB$ is not symmetric.

9. Let $A = [a_{ij}]$ and $B = [b_{ij}]$ be $n \times n$ matrices. In each case below, find the matrix product involving $A$ and $B$ or their transposes that has the given summation as its $(i, j)$–entry.

   (a) $\sum_{k=1}^{n} b_{kj} a_{ik}$  
   (b) $\sum_{k=1}^{n} b_{ik} a_{kj}$

   (c) $\sum_{k=1}^{n} a_{ki} b_{jk}$  
   (d) $\sum_{k=1}^{n} a_{ik} b_{jk}$

10. Show that $(AB)^t = B^t A^t$.

11. If $A = \begin{bmatrix} 1 & 2 & 3 \\ 2 & 3 & 4 \\ 3 & 4 & 6 \end{bmatrix}$ has the inverse $A^{-1} = \begin{bmatrix} -2 & a & 1 \\ 0 & b & -2 \\ 1 & c & 1 \end{bmatrix}$ find the values of $a$, $b$, $c$.

12. Show that a $2 \times 2$ matrix $A$ is invertible if there is a matrix $B$ such that

$$BA = \begin{bmatrix} 0 & 1 \\ 1 & 0 \end{bmatrix}$$

13. Let $A$ and $B$ be invertible matrices.
   (a) Show by example that $A + B$ need not be invertible.
   (b) Assuming $A + B$ is also invertible show that $A^{-1} + B^{-1}$ has the inverse $A(A + B)^{-1}B$.

14. The inverse of a matrix $A$ is

$$A^{-1} = \begin{bmatrix} 2 & 3 & 4 \\ 0 & -1 & 1 \\ 4 & 7 & 6 \end{bmatrix}$$

   (a) Suppose $B$ is obtained from $A$ by interchanging rows 2 and 3 of $A$. What is $B^{-1}$?
   (b) Suppose $C$ is obtained from $A$ by interchanging columns 1 and 2 of $A$. What is $C^{-1}$? (Note: no calculation is required.)

15. Suppose that $X_1$ and $X_2$ are solutions of the homogeneous system of equations $AX = 0$. Show that $c_1 X_1 + c_2 X_2$ are also solutions for all numbers $c_1, c_2$.

16. Suppose $A$ and $B$ are $3 \times 3$ matrices with $\det(A) = 2$ and $\det(B) = 5$. Find (a) $\det(A^3)$, (b) $\det(3A)$, (c) $\det(AB^{-1})$, (d) $\det(2B^{-1})$ (e) $\det((2B)^{-1})$.

17. Show without expanding that

$$\begin{vmatrix} 1 & a & bc \\ 1 & b & ac \\ 1 & c & ab \end{vmatrix} = \begin{vmatrix} 1 & a & a^2 \\ 1 & b & b^2 \\ 1 & c & c^2 \end{vmatrix}$$

18. Let $A$ be the $n \times n$ matrix

$$\begin{bmatrix} 1-n & 1 & 1 & \cdots & 1 \\ 1 & 1-n & 1 & \cdots & 1 \\ 1 & 1 & 1-n & \cdots & 1 \\ \vdots & \vdots & \vdots & \ddots & \\ 1 & 1 & 1 & & 1-n \end{bmatrix}$$

Show that $\det(A) = 0$. (Use row operations.)

19. If the matrix

$$A = \begin{bmatrix} 1 & y & 0 \\ 3 & -1 & 2 \\ 2 & 0 & 2 \end{bmatrix}$$

has the adjoint matrix

$$adj(A) = \begin{bmatrix} -2 & x & -4 \\ -2 & 2 & -2 \\ 2 & -4 & 5 \end{bmatrix}$$

find (a) $\det(A)$, (b) the value of $x$, (c) the value of $y$.

20. If $A$ is invertible, show that the inverse of the adjoint matrix is the adjoint of the inverse, that is,

$$(adj\, A)^{-1} = adj(A^{-1}).$$

(Hint: Use Theorem 2 on page 187, and then replace $A$ by $A^{-1}$.)

21. Use Cramer's Rule to find the values of $k$ for which the following system has a unique solution

$$kx + 2y = 5$$
$$8x + ky = 9$$

For those values of $k$, express the solution in terms of $k$.

22. Let $A$ and $C$ be square matrices. Show that

$$\det \left[\begin{array}{c|c} A & O \\ \hline B & C \end{array}\right] = \det(A)\det(C)$$

23. Find a productive $2 \times 2$ consumption matrix that has a row sum greater than 1 and a column sum greater than 1.

24. Show that a $2 \times 2$ stochastic matrix with 2 zero entries is never regular.

25. A certain Markov process with States 1, 2, 3 has transition matrix

$$T = \begin{bmatrix} 0 & 0 & 1 \\ 1 & 0 & 0 \\ 0 & 1 & 0 \end{bmatrix}$$

If an object is initially in State 3, then what state is it in after 2 transitions? After 3 transitions? Is $T$ regular?

26. A Markov process has transition matrix

$$T = \begin{bmatrix} \frac{1}{2} & 0 & \frac{1}{4} \\ \frac{1}{2} & \frac{1}{2} & 0 \\ 0 & \frac{1}{2} & \frac{3}{4} \end{bmatrix}$$

Show that $T$ is regular, and find the stable vector.

27. When will a $2 \times 2$ stochastic matrix with a single zero entry be regular?

## CHAPTER 4

1. A line $L$ in $R^3$ contains the points

$$P_1(1, -1, 3) \quad \text{and} \quad P_2(-1, 2, 5).$$

Do the following points line on $L$?
(a) $Q_1(-3, 5, 7)$          (b) $Q_2(3, -4, 2)$

2. Find the vector equation and parametric equations of the line in $R^4$ through the points $(4, 2, 1, 3)$ and $(2, 5, 3, 4)$. Let $(x, y, z, w)$ be an arbitrary point in 4 dimensions.

3. Do the lines $(1, 3, -1, 2) + t(2, -2, -3, 1)$ and
   $(5, -1, -7, 4) + s(-3, 1, -2, -1)$ in $R^4$ intersect? If so, find the point of intersection.

4. Find all values of $k$ so that $\begin{bmatrix} k \\ k+1 \\ k+2 \end{bmatrix}$ is in the span of $\begin{bmatrix} 1 \\ 2 \\ 1 \end{bmatrix}$ and $\begin{bmatrix} 2 \\ 3 \\ 1 \end{bmatrix}$.

5. Let $u$ be a linear combination of $v$ and $w$ and let $v$ and $w$ be linear combinations of $x$ and $y$. Show that $u$ is a linear combination of $x$ and $y$.

6. Let $W_1$ and $W_2$ be subspaces of $R^3$. Let $W$ be the set of vectors that are in both $W_1$ and $W_2$. Show that $W$ is a subspace of $R^3$.

7. Is the set of vectors $(x, y, z)$ in $R^3$ with $x \leq 0$, $y \geq 0$, $z \geq 0$ a subspace of $R^3$?

8. Suppose that $u$ and $v$ are linearly independent vectors. Let $x = u+v$ and $y = u - v$. Are $x$ and $y$ linearly independent?

9. Prove that any 4 vectors in $R^3$ are linearly dependent.

10. Find a basis for $R^3$ that contains the vectors $(1, 2, -3)$ and $(3, -4, 6)$.

11. Find a basis for $R^3$ which is contained in the vectors $(1, 3, -2)$, $(2, 7, -6)$, $(2, 8, -8)$, $(1, 2, 0)$, $(-2, -10, 7)$.

12. Let
$$A = \begin{bmatrix} 2 & 8 & -12 & 2 & -2 \\ 2 & 9 & -8 & 0 & 1 \\ 3 & 12 & -18 & 4 & -5 \end{bmatrix}$$
   (a) Find the rank of $A$. Find the dimension of the null space of $A$.
   (b) Find basis vectors for the null space of $A$.
   (c) Write the 5–th column of $A$ as a linear combination of the first four columns.

13. Show that $u$, $v$, $w$ are linearly dependent if and only if $au$, $bv$, $cw$, where $a$, $b$, $c \neq 0$, are linearly dependent.

14. Let $x_1$, $x_2$, $x_3$ be linearly independent vectors. Show that $x_1$, $x_1 + x_2$, $x_1 + x_2 + x_3$ are also linearly independent.

15. Prove that the vectors $a = (a_1, a_2, a_3)$ and $b = (b_1, b_2, b_3)$ are linearly dependent if and only if
$$a_1 b_2 - a_2 b_1 = 0$$
$$a_1 b_3 - a_3 b_1 = 0$$
$$a_2 b_3 - a_3 b_2 = 0.$$

16 Let the set of vectors $x$, $y$, $z$ be linearly independent, and the set of vectors $x$, $y$, $z$, $w$ be linearly dependent. Show that $w$ can be written as a linear combination of $x$, $y$, $z$.

17. Suppose that $y$ is a linear combination of $x_1$, $x_2$, $x_3$ but not a linear combination of $x_1$, $x_2$. Show that $x_3$ is a linear combination of $y$, $x_1$, $x_2$.

18. Let $A$ be a given matrix with 3 rows and 4 columns, and let $b$ be a given vector in $R^3$. You are given that a basis for the nullspace of $A$ is given by the vectors

$$v_1 = \begin{bmatrix} 1 \\ 0 \\ 2 \\ 0 \end{bmatrix} \qquad v_2 = \begin{bmatrix} 0 \\ 1 \\ 0 \\ 3 \end{bmatrix}$$

(a) What are the rank of $A$ and the nullity of $A$?
(b) If you know that $x_0 = (2, 4, 3, -1)$ is a particular solution of $Ax = b$, then determine whether or not $x = (4, 6, 5, 2)$ is a solution. (Hint: Use the general form of the solution.)

19. Dan's Outlets has two warehouses and three stores. The shipping costs per unit of a certain product are given in the following table.

|       | $S_1$ | $S_2$ | $S_3$ |
|-------|-------|-------|-------|
| $W_1$ | 15    | 17    | 19    |
| $W_2$ | 9     | 16    | 24    |

Store one will sell 350 units per week, store two will sell 400 units per week, and store three will sell 425 units per week of the product. There are 550 units available in warehouse one and 625 units available in warehouse two.

Set up a linear program to determine the amount of the product to be shipped from each warehouse to each store in such a way that the shipping cost is minimized.

Hint: Let $x_{ij}$ be the amount to be shipped from warehouse $i$ to store $j$.

20. Intercity Recycling has storage for 75,000 lbs. of white glass which initially contains 20,000 lbs. of glass. Each month for the next 3 months the recycler can sell up to 50,000 lbs. of glass. In the first month the glass can be sold for 17 cents/lb., in the second month the glass can be sold for 23 cents/lb. and in the third month the glass can be sold for 21 cents/lb. Further, the recycler can buy up to 40,000 lbs. of glass each month at a projected cost of 14 cents/lb. the first month, 18 cents/lb. the second month and 17 cents/lb the third month. He values the left over glass at 15 cents/lb. Set up the linear program to find the amount of glass to be purchased, stored and sold in each month, if maximum income is to be realized.

## CHAPTER 5

1. Let $\mathbf{u}$, $\mathbf{v}$, $\mathbf{w}$ be mutually orthonormal vectors in $R^3$. Let $\mathbf{x}$ be any vector in $R^3$, and prove that

$$\mathbf{x} = (\mathbf{x} \cdot \mathbf{u})\mathbf{u} + (\mathbf{x} \cdot \mathbf{v})\mathbf{v} + (\mathbf{x} \cdot \mathbf{w})\mathbf{w}$$

2. Let $\mathbf{u} = (a, b, c)$. Show that $|\mathbf{u}/\|\mathbf{u}\|| = 1$.

3. Let $k$ be any number. Show that the triangle with vertices $(k, 1 - k, \sqrt{2})$, $(2, k, -2k)$, $(3k - 1, -1, \sqrt{2})$ is a right triangle.

4. Let $\mathbf{x} = (x_1, x_2, x_3)$ and $\mathbf{y} = (y_1, y_2, y_3)$ be two orthogonal unit vectors in $R^3$. Show how to find a vector $\mathbf{z} = (z_1, z_2, z_3)$ such that $\mathbf{x}$, $\mathbf{y}$, $\mathbf{z}$ is an orthonormal set.

5. Let $\mathbf{u}_1$, $\mathbf{u}_2$, $\mathbf{u}_3$ be a set of orthonormal vectors in $R^3$. Let $Q$ be the matrix that has $\mathbf{u}_1$, $\mathbf{u}_2$, $\mathbf{u}_3$ as its columns. Show that $Q^{-1} = Q^t$.

6. Find an orthonormal basis for the null space of

$$A = \begin{bmatrix} 1 & -2 & 3 & 2 \\ 2 & -4 & 5 & 6 \end{bmatrix}$$

7. Let $\mathbf{v}$ be a unit vector. Prove that $|\mathbf{u}| = |\mathbf{u} \cdot \mathbf{v}|$ if and only if $\mathbf{u}$, $\mathbf{v}$ are linearly dependent.

8. Let $\mathbf{v}_1$ be orthogonal to $\mathbf{v}_2$. Show that $|\mathbf{v}_1 + \mathbf{v}_2|^2 = |\mathbf{v}_1|^2 + |\mathbf{v}_2|^2$.

9. Let $\mathbf{v}_1$, $\mathbf{v}_2$ be a basis for a vector space $S$. Show that $\mathbf{u}$ is orthogonal to every vector in $S$ if and only if $\mathbf{u}$ is orthogonal to $\mathbf{v}_1$, $\mathbf{v}_2$.

10. Find a $2 \times 2$ matrix $A$ such that $A\mathbf{x} = \begin{bmatrix} 1 \\ 2 \end{bmatrix}$ has no solution, but $A^T A\mathbf{x} = A^T \begin{bmatrix} 1 \\ 2 \end{bmatrix}$ does have a solution.

11. Prove that $|\mathbf{a} + \mathbf{b}| \le |\mathbf{a}| + |\mathbf{b}|$ (triangle inequality). (Hint: Work with the square:

$$|\mathbf{a} + \mathbf{b}|^2 = (\mathbf{a} + \mathbf{b}) \cdot (\mathbf{a} + \mathbf{b})$$

and use $|\mathbf{a} \cdot \mathbf{b}| \le |\mathbf{a}||\mathbf{b}|$.)

12. Let $A$ be a $3 \times 2$ matrix with rank 2. Show that $A^T A$ is invertible. (Hint: Use the fact that $|\mathbf{a}_1||\mathbf{a}_2| = |\mathbf{a}_1 \cdot \mathbf{a}_2|$ if and only if $\mathbf{a}_1$ and $\mathbf{a}_2$ are linearly dependent.)

13. Find the point on the line spanned by $(1, 2, 3)$ that is closest to $(3, 2, 1)$.

14. Show that the average of the numbers $b_1, b_2, \ldots, b_n$ gives the coordinates of the closest point to $(b_1, b_2, \ldots, b_n)$ on the line spanned by $(1, 1, \ldots, 1)$.

15. Show that the least squares solution of the system

$$x = 4$$
$$x = 5$$
$$x = 6$$
$$x = 7$$

is given by the average of the numbers.

16. Suppose that a collection of data points $(x_1, y_1), \ldots, (x_n, y_n)$ is to be fit with a curve of the form

$$a_4 x^4 + a_3 x^3 + a_2 x^2 + a_1 x + a_0 = y$$

Show that the least squares solution is given by solving a system of 5 equations in 5 unknowns no matter how many data points there are.

17. Let $v_1$, $v_2$, $v_3$ be an orthonormal basis for $R^3$. Let $\mathbf{a} = a_1 v_1 + a_2 v_2 + a_3 v_3$ and $\mathbf{b} = b_1 v_1 + b_2 v_2 + b_3 v_3$. Show that $\mathbf{a} \cdot \mathbf{b} = a_1 b_1 + a_2 b_2 + a_3 b_3$.

## CHAPTER 6

1. Show that $\lambda = 0$ is an eigenvalue of $A$ if and only if $\det(A) = 0$.

2. The matrix

$$A = \begin{bmatrix} 2 & 5 & 3 & -6 \\ -2 & 4 & 0 & 2 \\ -4 & -10 & -6 & 12 \\ 1 & 7 & 3 & -5 \end{bmatrix}$$

has an eigenvector $\mathbf{v} = (1, 0, -2, 1)$. What is the associated eigenvalue?

3. Suppose that $A\mathbf{v} = \lambda_1 \mathbf{u}$ and $A\mathbf{u} = \lambda_2 \mathbf{v}$, where $\mathbf{v} \neq \mathbf{O}$. Show that $\mathbf{v}$ is an eigenvector for $A^2$ with the associated eigenvalue $\lambda = \lambda_1 \lambda_2$.

4. Let $D$ be a diagonal matrix with indices $d_{11}, d_{22}, \ldots, d_{nn}$. Show that $d_{11}, d_{22}, \ldots, d_{nn}$ are the eigenvalues of $D$.

5. Show that $A$ and $A^t$ have the same characteristic polynomial, and therefore the same eigenvalues.

6. Do $A$ and $A^t$ have the same eigenvectors? Prove or give a counterexample.

7. Let $\lambda_1$ and $\lambda_2$ be distinct eigenvalues of $A$ with associated eigenvectors $x_1$ and $x_2$. Give an example for which $c_1 x_1 + c_2 x_2$ is not an eigenvector of $A$.

8. Let $A$ have eigenvector $\mathbf{x}$ and the associated eigenvalue $\lambda \neq 0$. Show that $A^2 \mathbf{x}$ is also an eigenvector. What is the associated eigenvalue?

9. Let $A$ and $B$ be $3 \times 3$ matrices. Further let $x_1$, $x_2$, $x_3$ be linearly independent eigenvectors of both $A$ and $B$ with nonzero eigenvalues such that $A x_i = \lambda_i x_i$ and $B x_i = \lambda_i x_i$ for $i = 1, 2, 3$. Show that $A = B$.

10. For what values of $k$ will

$$A = \begin{bmatrix} 1 & 0 & 0 \\ 0 & k & 1 \\ 0 & 1 & k \end{bmatrix}$$

have repeated eigenvalues?

11. For what values of $k$ will

$$A = \begin{bmatrix} 1 & 1 & 0 \\ 1 & k & 0 \\ 0 & 0 & k \end{bmatrix}$$

have repeated eigenvalues?

12. Let $\lambda$ be an eigenvalue of $A$. Show that $k\lambda$ is an eigenvalue of $kA$.

13. Let $A$ be $n \times n$ and $B$ be $n \times n$. Prove that $\lambda \neq 0$ is an eigenvalue of $AB$ if and only if $\lambda$ is an eigenvalue of $BA$.

14. If $A$ is invertible and $\lambda$ is a eigenvalue of $A$, then show that $\frac{|A|}{\lambda}$ is an eigenvalue of the adjoint matrix $adj(A)$.

15. Suppose that $C$ is an invertible matrix such that

$$C^{-1} A C = \begin{bmatrix} d_1 & 0 & 0 \\ 0 & d_2 & 0 \\ 0 & 0 & d_3 \end{bmatrix}$$

and

$$C^{-1} B C = \begin{pmatrix} \ell_1 & 0 & 0 \\ 0 & \ell_2 & 0 \\ 0 & 0 & \ell_3 \end{pmatrix}$$

Show that $AB = BA$.

16. Determine whether or not the matrix

$$A = \begin{bmatrix} 2 & 1 & 3 \\ -4 & -2 & -4 \\ 0 & 0 & -1 \end{bmatrix}$$

can be diagonalized.

17. Let $A = \begin{bmatrix} a & b \\ c & d \end{bmatrix}$. Show that if $b$ and $c$ are either both positive or both negative, then $A$ is diagonalizable.
    (Hint: Consider the eigenvalues.)

18. Let $A$ be an $n \times n$ matrix with rank $r$. Show that 0 is an eigenvalue of multiplicity at least $n - r$.
    (Hint: Use the fact that the multiplicity of an eigenvalue is always at least as great as the dimension of its associated eigenspace.)

19. Let $A$ be a $3 \times 3$ matrix with all column sums equal to 1. Show that $\lambda = 1$ is an eigenvalue of the matrix.
    (Hint: Look at the transpose matrix.)

20. Let $x_1$, $x_2$ be eigenvectors corresponding to distinct eigenvalues of a real symmetric matrix $A$. Show that $x_1$ is orthogonal to $x_2$.

# CHAPTER 7

1. Show that the elementary matrices are invertible by finding the inverse of each of the following matrices. The constant $c$ is nonzero.

$$R = \begin{bmatrix} 1 & & & & & & & & & \\ & \ddots & & & & & & & O & \\ & & 1 & & & & & & & \\ & & & 0 & \cdots & 1 & & & & \\ & & & & 1 & & & & & \\ & & & \vdots & & \ddots & & \vdots & & \\ & & & & & & 1 & & & \\ & & & 1 & \cdots & 0 & & & & \\ & & & & & & & 1 & & \\ & O & & & & & & & \ddots & \\ & & & & & & & & & 1 \end{bmatrix} \begin{matrix} \\ \\ \\ \text{row } h \\ \\ \\ \\ \text{row } k \\ \\ \\ \end{matrix}$$

with column $h$ and column $k$ marked.

$$S = \begin{bmatrix} 1 & & & & & \\ & \ddots & & & O & \\ & & 1 & & & \\ & & & c & & \\ & & & & 1 & \\ & O & & & & \ddots \\ & & & & & 1 \end{bmatrix} \begin{matrix} \\ \\ \\ \text{row } h \\ \\ \\ \end{matrix} \qquad T = \begin{bmatrix} 1 & & & & & \\ & \ddots & & & O & \\ & & 1 & \cdots & c & \\ & & & \ddots & \vdots & \\ & & & & 1 & \\ & O & & & & \ddots \\ & & & & & 1 \end{bmatrix} \begin{matrix} \\ \\ \text{row } h \\ \\ \\ \\ \end{matrix}$$

Hint: Consider the row operation that each accomplishes through premultiplication. Then find the row operation which reverses the action of the first operation. Then construct the elementary matrix for this row operation.

2. Show that every invertible matrix, $A$, can be written as a product of elementary matrices.

3. Let the pivot column of a dependency table $T$ be given by

$$\begin{bmatrix} t_{1q} \\ \vdots \\ t_{iq} \\ \vdots \\ t_{pq} \\ \vdots \\ t_{nq} \end{bmatrix}$$

with the pivot element $t_{pq}$. Show that the pivot matrix is

$$p$$

$$P = \begin{bmatrix} 1 & 0 & \cdots & -t_{1q}t_{pq}^{-1} & \cdots & 0 \\ 0 & 1 & & \vdots & & \\ & & & -t_{iq}t_{pq}^{-1} & & \vdots \\ \vdots & & & \vdots & & \\ & \vdots & & t_{pq}^{-1} & & \\ & & & \vdots & & 0 \\ 0 & 0 & & -t_{mq}t_{pq}^{-1} & & 1 \end{bmatrix} \quad \text{row } p$$

4. Show that any pivot matrix is invertible by finding a formula for the inverse. Use the pivot matrix of Exercise 3. Hint: First find the new $p$th column of $T$. Then use this column to construct $P^{-1}$.

5. Suppose that the change of basis matrix $B_1$ will take the initial table $T$ into the table for the basis $\mathbf{B_1}$, and the change of basis matrix $B_2$ will take $T$ into the table for the basis $\mathbf{B_2}$. Find the change of basis matrix which will take the table for the basis $\mathbf{B_1}$ into the table for the basis $\mathbf{B_2}$.

# Appendices

# Appendix A

# Theorems and Corollaries

## Chapter 1
## Linear Systems in the Plane

### 1.1 LINES IN THE PLANE

#### THEOREM 1
Suppose that the line $L_1$ has slope $m_1$ and the line $L_2$ has slope $m_2$. Then:

(i) $L_1$ and $L_2$ are parallel if and only if $m_1 = m_2$.

(ii) $L_1$ and $L_2$ are perpendicular if and only if $m_1 m_2 = -1$.

### 1.4 LINEAR PROGRAMMING IN THE PLANE

#### THEOREM 1

Let $z = ax + by$ be a linear function and let $P$ be a polygon in the plane. Then the maximum value and the minimum value of $z$ are attained at corner points of $P$.

## Chapter 2
## Linear Systems in Higher Dimensions

### 2.1 ROW OPERATIONS AND GAUSSIAN ELIMINATION

#### THEOREM 1

If a system of linear equations is derived from another system by applying any of the three elementary operations, then the solution sets of the two systems are identical.

## 2.2 REDUCED ECHELON FORM

### THEOREM 1

The reduced row echelon form associated with a matrix is uniquely determined.

## 2.3 CONSISTENCY AND ROW RANK

### THEOREM 1

A linear system is consistent if and only if the row rank of the coefficient matrix is equal to the row rank of the augmented matrix.

### THEOREM 2

Suppose that a homogeneous system of $m$ equations in $n$ variables has row rank equal to $r$. If $r = n$, then only the zero solution exists. If $r < n$, then there are infinitely many solutions and there are $n - r$ parameters in the representation of the solution set.

### THEOREM 3

If there are more variables than equations in a homogeneous system, then the system has infinitely many solutions.

## 2.4 EUCLIDEAN 3-SPACE

### THEOREM 1

Two planes are either identical or parallel if and only if the $x, y, z$ coefficients of the one plane are common multiples, respectively, of the $x, y, z$ coefficients of the other plane.

## 2.7 SIMPLEX ALGORITHM: ADDITIONAL CONSIDERATIONS

### THEOREM 1

Let the linear program

$$\text{Maximize} \quad z = c_1 x_1 + \cdots + c_n x_n$$

$$\text{subject to} \quad a_{11}x_1 + \cdots + a_{1n}x_n \leqslant b_1$$
$$\vdots \qquad \qquad \vdots \qquad \vdots$$
$$a_{m1}x_1 + \cdots + a_{mn}x_n \leqslant b_m$$

$$x_1 \geqslant 0, \ldots, x_n \geqslant 0$$

have a simplex table with a negative entry in a constraint variable position of the top row, but no positive entry below it. Then the feasibility region is unbounded in at least one coordinate direction and non negative solutions of the constraint system can be found which give arbitrarily large values for $z$.

## Chapter 3
## Matrices and Determinants

### 3.1 MATRIX OPERATIONS

### *THEOREM 1*

If $a$, $b$ are scalars and if $A$, $B$ are $m \times n$ matrices, then we have the following properties:

(i)  $A + B = B + A$

(ii)  $A + (B + C) = (A + B) + C$

(iii)  $a(bA) = (ab)A$

(iv)  $(a + b)A = aA + bA$

(v)  $a(A + B) = aA + aB$

(vi)  $A + O = A$, and $aO = O$.

### *THEOREM 2*

Let $a$, $b$ be numbers and let $A$, $B$, $C$ be matrices. Assume that the matrix dimensions are such that the sums and products in each of the following are defined. Then we have

(i)  $A(BC) = (AB)C$

(ii)  $(A + B)C = AC + BC$

(iii)  $A(B + C) = AB + AC$

(iv)  $OA = O$, $AO = O$

(v)  $(aA)(bB) = abAB$

### 3.2 THE INVERSE OF A MATRIX

### *THEOREM 1*

Let $A$ and $B$ be square matrices. Then:

(i)  If $A$ is invertible, then the inverse $A^{-1}$ is unique. That is, if $B$ is a matrix such that $BA = AB = I$, then $B = A^{-1}$.

(ii)  If $A$ is invertible, then $A^{-1}$ is invertible and the inverse of $A^{-1}$ is $A$. That is, $(A^{-1})^{-1} = A$.

(iii)  If $A$ and $B$ are invertible, then the product $AB$ is invertible and $(AB)^{-1} = B^{-1}A^{-1}$.

### THEOREM 2

Let $A$ and $B$ be $n \times n$ matrices. If $AB = I$, then $BA = I$ and $B = A^{-1}$.

### THEOREM 3

If $A$ is an $n \times n$ matrix, then the following statements are equivalent:

(*i*)   The row rank of $A$ is $n$.

(*ii*)   $A$ is invertible.

(*iii*)   For any vector $B$, the system $AX = B$ has a unique solution.

## 3.3   THE LEONTIEF OPEN MODEL

### THEOREM 1

If a consumption matrix $C$ for an economy is such that either (a) all column sums are less than 1, or (b) all row sums are less than 1, then the economy is productive.

### THEOREM 2

A consumption matrix $C$ is productive if and only if there is some production schedule $X \geqslant O$ such that $CX < X$.

## 3.4   DETERMINANTS

### THEOREM 1

If $A = [a_{ij}]$ is an $n \times n$ matrix where $n \geqslant 2$, then the cofactor expansion across any row or down any column has the value $\det(A)$. That is, we have for any row $i$

$$\det(A) = a_{i1}A_{i1} + a_{i2}A_{i2} + \cdots + a_{in}A_{in} \quad \text{(cofactor expansion across row } i)$$

and for any column $j$

$$\det(A) = a_{1j}A_{1j} + a_{2j}A_{2j} + \cdots + a_{nj}A_{nj} \quad \text{(cofactor expansion down column } j)$$

### COROLLARY

If $A$ has either a row of zeros or a column of zeros, then $\det(A) = 0$.

### COROLLARY

If $A$ is a square matrix, then

$$\det(A^t) = \det(A).$$

## THEOREM 2

The determinant of a triangular matrix is the product of the main diagonal entries. That is, we have

$$\det \begin{bmatrix} a_{11} & & \text{\LARGE $*$} \\ & \ddots & \\ 0 & & a_{nn} \end{bmatrix} = \det \begin{bmatrix} a_{11} & & 0 \\ & \ddots & \\ \text{\LARGE $*$} & & a_{nn} \end{bmatrix} = a_{11} \cdots a_{nn}$$

## THEOREM 3

Let $A$ be a square matrix. Then the value of $\det(A)$ is affected by the elementary row operations as follows.

(i)   If $A_1$ is obtained from $A$ by the interchange of two rows, then $\det(A_1) = -\det(A)$. That is, the sign of the determinant is changed.

(ii)  If $A_2$ is obtained from $A$ by the multiplication of a row of $A$ by a constant $k$, then $\det(A_2) = k \cdot \det(A)$. That is, the determinant is multiplied by the constant.

(iii) If $A_3$ is obtained from $A$ by the addition of a multiple of one row to another row, then $\det(A_3) = \det(A)$. That is, the determinant is unchanged.

## COROLLARY

If the matrix $A$ has two rows that are proportional then $\det(A) = 0$.

## 3.5 APPLICATIONS OF DETERMINANTS

### THEOREM 1  (Cramer's Rule)

If $A$ is an $n \times n$ matrix with $\det(A) \neq 0$, then the linear system

$$AX = B$$

has the unique solution $X = (x_j)$ given by

$$x_j = \det(A_j)/\det(A), \qquad j = 1, 2, \ldots, n.$$

where $A_j$ is the matrix obtained by replacing the $j^{\text{th}}$ column of $A$ by $B$.

### THEOREM 2

If $A$ is a square matrix such that $D = \det(A) \neq 0$, then $A$ is invertible and the inverse is given by

$$A^{-1} = (1/D) \cdot \text{adj}(A).$$

### THEOREM 3

If $A$ and $B$ are $n \times n$ matrices, then

$$\det(AB) = \det(A)\det(B).$$

### THEOREM 4

A square matrix $A$ has an inverse if and only if $\det(A) \neq 0$. Moreover, if $A^{-1}$ exists, then

$$\det(A^{-1}) = 1/\det(A).$$

### THEOREM 5

The following assertions are equivalent for an $n \times n$ matrix $A$.

(i)    $\det(A) \neq 0$.

(ii)   $A^{-1}$ exists.

(iii)  $AX = B$ has a unique solution for any $B$.

(iv)   The row rank of $A$ is $n$.

### COROLLARY

If $A$ is a square matrix, then the homogeneous system $AX = O$ has infinitely many solutions if and only if $\det(A) = 0$.

## 3.6   MARKOV ANALYSIS

### THEOREM 1

If $T$ is a stochastic matrix, then $T^n$ is again stochastic for any positive integer $n$. Also, if $S_0$ is a distribution vector, then $S_n = T^n S_0$ is a distribution vector for any $n$.

### THEOREM 2

A regular Markov chain with transition matrix $T$ will have a unique stable vector $S$. Successive powers of $T$ will approach the matrix whose columns are all equal to the vector $S$. If a fixed decimal place accuracy is prescribed, then $T^{n+1} = T^n$ for some $n$ so that $T^n$ is the stable matrix up to the prescribed accuracy. Furthermore for any initial distribution vector $S_0$ we have $T^n S_0 = S$.

# Chapter 4
# Vector Spaces

## 4.1 INTRODUCTION TO VECTORS

### THEOREM 1

Let **u**, **v**, **w** be vectors in $R^n$, and let $a$, $b$ be scalars. Then:

$$\mathbf{u} + \mathbf{v} = \mathbf{v} + \mathbf{u} \qquad (\mathbf{u} + \mathbf{v}) + \mathbf{w} = \mathbf{u} + (\mathbf{v} + \mathbf{w})$$

$$a(b\mathbf{u}) = (ab)\mathbf{u} \qquad (a + b)\mathbf{u} = a\mathbf{u} + b\mathbf{u}$$

$$a(\mathbf{u} + \mathbf{v}) = a\mathbf{u} + a\mathbf{v}$$

$$\mathbf{u} + \mathbf{0} = \mathbf{u} \qquad\qquad 1 \cdot \mathbf{u} = \mathbf{u}$$

$$a \cdot \mathbf{0} = \mathbf{0} \qquad\qquad 0 \cdot \mathbf{u} = \mathbf{0}$$

Let $-\mathbf{u} = (-1) \cdot \mathbf{u};$ then $\mathbf{u} + (-\mathbf{u}) = \mathbf{0}.$

If $a \cdot \mathbf{u} = \mathbf{0},$ then either $a = 0$ or $\mathbf{u} = \mathbf{0}.$

## 4.2 LINEAR COMBINATIONS

### THEOREM 1

The linear system $A\mathbf{x} = \mathbf{b}$ has a solution if and only if **b** can be written as a linear combination of the column vectors of $A$. Furthermore, the coefficients in the linear combination are the respective solution values.

## 4.3 SPANS OF VECTORS

### THEOREM 1

A nonempty subset $S$ of $R^n$ is a subspace if and only if it is the span of some finite set of vectors $\{\mathbf{u}_1, \ldots, \mathbf{u}_k\}$ in $R^n$.

### THEOREM 2

The linear system $A\mathbf{x} = \mathbf{b}$ is consistent if and only if **b** is in the column space of $A$.

## 4.4 LINEAR DEPENDENCE AND INDEPENDENCE

### THEOREM 1  (Dependence Criterion)

The vectors $\mathbf{u}_1, \mathbf{u}_2, \ldots, \mathbf{u}_k$ in $R^n$ are linearly dependent if and only if there exist scalars $c_1, c_2, \ldots, c_k$, with at least one of the scalars **not** zero, such that

$$c_1\mathbf{u}_1 + c_2\mathbf{u}_2 + \cdots + c_k\mathbf{u}_k = \mathbf{0}$$

**THEOREM 2** (*Independence Criterion*)

The vectors $\mathbf{u}_1, \mathbf{u}_2, \ldots, \mathbf{u}_k$ in $R^n$ are linearly independent if and only if the only scalars that satisfy

$$c_1\mathbf{u}_1 + c_2\mathbf{u}_2 + \cdots + c_k\mathbf{u}_k = 0$$

are $c_1 = 0, c_2 = 0, \ldots, c_k = 0$.

**THEOREM 3**

Let $\mathbf{u}_1, \ldots, \mathbf{u}_k$ be vectors in $R^n$. If $k > n$, then the vectors are linearly dependent.

**THEOREM 4**

Let $U$ be an $n \times n$ matrix. Then the following statements are all equivalent.

(*i*)   The columns of $U$ are linearly independent.

(*ii*)  The matrix $U$ is invertible.

(*iii*) The determinant of $U$ is not zero.  $Det \neq 0$

## 4.5  BASES AND BASIS SELECTION

### THEOREM 1

The column vectors of an $n \times n$ matrix form a basis for $R^n$ if and only if the matrix is invertible.

### THEOREM 2

Let $\{\mathbf{u}_1, \ldots, \mathbf{u}_k\}$ be a basis for the subspace $S$ of $R^n$. Then for any $\mathbf{v}$ in $S$, there are unique scalars $c_1, \ldots, c_k$ such that $\mathbf{v} = c_1\mathbf{u}_1 + \cdots + c_k\mathbf{u}_k$.

## 4.6  DIMENSION AND RANK

### THEOREM 1

Let $S$ be a subspace of $R^n$. Then every basis for $S$ has the same number of vectors.

### THEOREM 2

Let $S$ be a $k$ dimensional subspace of $R^n$. If a set of $k$ vectors in $S$ either spans $S$ or is linearly independent, then it is a basis for $S$.

### THEOREM 3

The row rank and column rank of any matrix are equal.

### THEOREM 4

Let $A$ be a matrix with $n$ columns. Then

$$\text{rank} + \text{nullity} = n.$$

That is, the rank of $A$ plus the nullity of $A$ equals the number of columns of $A$.

### THEOREM 5

The general solution of $A\mathbf{x} = \mathbf{b}$ is found by adding a particular solution of $A\mathbf{x} = \mathbf{b}$ to the general solution of $A\mathbf{x} = \mathbf{0}$.

# Chapter 5
# Orthogonality

## 5.1 SCALAR PRODUCTS AND ORTHOGONALITY

### THEOREM 1

Let $\mathbf{u}$, $\mathbf{v}$, $\mathbf{w}$ be vectors in $R^n$ and let $a$ be a scalar. Then:

(i)    $\mathbf{u} \cdot \mathbf{v} = \mathbf{v} \cdot \mathbf{u}$

(ii)   $\mathbf{u} \cdot (\mathbf{v} + \mathbf{w}) = \mathbf{u} \cdot \mathbf{v} + \mathbf{u} \cdot \mathbf{w}$

(iii)  $a(\mathbf{u} \cdot \mathbf{v}) = (a\mathbf{u}) \cdot \mathbf{v} = \mathbf{u} \cdot (a\mathbf{v})$

(iv)   $\mathbf{0} \cdot \mathbf{u} = 0$

(v)    $\mathbf{u} \cdot \mathbf{u} = |\mathbf{u}|^2.$

### THEOREM 2

If $\mathbf{u}$, $\mathbf{v}$ are vectors in $R^n$, then

(i)    $|\mathbf{u} \cdot \mathbf{v}| \leqslant |\mathbf{u}|\,|\mathbf{v}|$    (Schwarz's inequality)

(ii)   $|\mathbf{u} + \mathbf{v}| \leqslant |\mathbf{u}| + |\mathbf{v}|$    (Triangle inequality)

## 5.2 ORTHONORMAL VECTORS AND PROJECTIONS

### THEOREM 1

If $\mathbf{v}_1, \ldots, \mathbf{v}_k$ are orthonormal vectors whose span is $S$, and if $\mathbf{u}$ is in $S$, then

$$\mathbf{u} = (\mathbf{u} \cdot \mathbf{v}_1)\mathbf{v}_1 + \cdots + (\mathbf{u} \cdot \mathbf{v}_k)\mathbf{v}_k.$$

### THEOREM 2

If the vectors $\mathbf{v}_1, \ldots, \mathbf{v}_k$ are orthonormal, then they are linearly independent.

### THEOREM 3

If $S$ is a subspace of $R^n$ and if the vector $\mathbf{u}$ is not in $S$, then the vector

$$\mathbf{u}' = \mathbf{u} - \text{Proj}_S(\mathbf{u})$$

is orthogonal to every vector in $S$. Furthermore, the magnitude of $\mathbf{u}'$ is the distance from the terminal point of the position vector $\mathbf{u}$ to $S$.

## 5.3 LEAST SQUARES APPROXIMATION

### THEOREM 1

The slope $m$ and intercept $b$ of the least squares line of approximation for the data points $(x_1, y_1), \ldots, (x_n, y_n)$ are given by

$$m = \frac{n\mathbf{x}\cdot\mathbf{y} - (\mathbf{1}\cdot\mathbf{x})(\mathbf{1}\cdot\mathbf{y})}{n\mathbf{x}\cdot\mathbf{x} - (\mathbf{1}\cdot\mathbf{x})^2}$$

$$b = \frac{(\mathbf{x}\cdot\mathbf{x})(\mathbf{1}\cdot\mathbf{y}) - (\mathbf{x}\cdot\mathbf{y})(\mathbf{1}\cdot\mathbf{x})}{n\mathbf{x}\cdot\mathbf{x} - (\mathbf{1}\cdot\mathbf{x})^2}$$

## 5.4 LEAST SQUARES APPROXIMATION AND GENERALIZED INVERSES (OPTIONAL)

### THEOREM 1

The least squares solution $\mathbf{u}$ of the system $A\mathbf{x} = \mathbf{b}$ is the solution of the consistent system

$$(A^t A)\mathbf{x} = A^t \mathbf{b}$$

Also the projection of $\mathbf{b}$ onto the column space of $A$ is the vector $A\mathbf{u}$.

### THEOREM 2

If $A$ has full column rank and if $A^\dagger$ is its generalized inverse, then the least squares solution of $A\mathbf{x} = \mathbf{b}$ is

$$\mathbf{u} = A^\dagger \mathbf{b}$$

Also the projection of $\mathbf{b}$ onto the column space of $A$ is

$$\text{Proj}(\mathbf{b}) = A A^\dagger \mathbf{b}$$

## THEOREM 3

The slope and intercept of the least squares line of approximation $y = mx + b$ for the noncollinear data points $(x_1, y_1), (x_2, y_2), \dots, (x_n, y_n)$ are given by

$$\begin{bmatrix} m \\ b \end{bmatrix} = A^{\dagger}\mathbf{y} = (A^t A)^{-1} A^t \mathbf{y}$$

where

$$A = \begin{bmatrix} x_1 & 1 \\ x_2 & 1 \\ \vdots & \vdots \\ x_n & 1 \end{bmatrix} \quad \text{and} \quad \mathbf{y} = \begin{bmatrix} y_1 \\ y_2 \\ \vdots \\ y_n \end{bmatrix}$$

## THEOREM 4

If the data points $(x_1, y_1), (x_2, y_2), \dots, (x_n, y_n)$ do not all lie on a quadratic curve, then the least squares quadratic approximation to the points is

$$y = ax^2 + bx + c$$

where the coefficients $a$, $b$, $c$ are given by

$$\begin{bmatrix} a \\ b \\ c \end{bmatrix} = A^{\dagger}\mathbf{y} = (A^t A)^{-1} A^t \mathbf{y}$$

where the matrix $A$ and vector $\mathbf{y}$ are

$$A = \begin{bmatrix} x_1^2 & x_1 & 1 \\ x_2^2 & x_2 & 1 \\ \vdots & \vdots & \vdots \\ x_n^2 & x_n & 1 \end{bmatrix}, \quad \mathbf{u} = \begin{bmatrix} a \\ b \\ c \end{bmatrix}, \quad \mathbf{y} = \begin{bmatrix} y_1 \\ y_2 \\ \vdots \\ y_n \end{bmatrix}$$

## THEOREM 5

If the data points $(x_1, y_1), (x_2, y_2), \dots, (x_n, y_n)$ do not all lie on a quadratic curve, then the least squares approximation to the points is

$$y = ax^2 + bx + c$$

where the coefficients $a$, $b$, $c$ are solutions of the system of equations

$$a\Sigma x^4 + b\Sigma x^3 + c\Sigma x^2 = \Sigma x^2 y$$
$$a\Sigma x^3 + b\Sigma x^2 + c\Sigma x = \Sigma xy$$
$$a\Sigma x^2 + b\Sigma x + cn = \Sigma y$$

## Chapter 6
## Eigenvalues and Eigenvectors

### 6.1   EIGENVALUES AND EIGENVECTORS

#### *THEOREM 1*

A number $\lambda$ is an eigenvalue of the square matrix $A$ if and only if it is a root of the equation

$$\det(A - \lambda I) = 0$$

### 6.2   DIAGONALIZATION OF MATRICES

#### *THEOREM 1*

An $n \times n$ matrix $A$ is diagonalizable if and only if $A$ has $n$ linearly independent eigenvectors.

#### *THEOREM 2*

Each $n \times n$ symmetric matrix $A$ has $n$ eigenvectors $\mathbf{v}_1, \ldots, \mathbf{v}_n$ that are orthonormal. The matrix $Q = [\mathbf{v}_1, \ldots, \mathbf{v}_n]$ has the property that $Q^{-1} = Q^t$, and the product $Q^t A Q$ is a diagonal matrix whose diagonal entries are the eigenvalues of $A$.

## Chapter 7
## Linear Transformations

### 7.1  LINEAR TRANSFORMATIONS

#### THEOREM 1

A transformation $T$ from $R^n$ to $R^n$ is linear if and only if for all $u$, $v$ in $R^n$ and constants $c_1$, $c_2$ it is true that

$$T(c_1 u + c_2 v) = c_1 T(u) + c_2 T(v)$$

### 7.2  A MATRIX REPRESENTATION OF A LINEAR TRANSFORMATION

#### THEOREM 1

Let $e_1, e_2, \ldots, e_n$ be the standard basis for $R^n$ and let

$$T(e_j) = a_j = (a_{1j}, a_{2j}, \ldots, a_{nj})$$

for $j = 1, \ldots, n$. Then

$$T(x) = Ax$$

where $A$ is the matrix $A = (a_1, a_2, \ldots, a_n)$ with columns $a_j$, $j = 1, 2, \ldots, n$.

#### THEOREM 2

If $T_1$ and $T_2$ are linear transformations of $R^n$ to $R^n$, then $T_2 \circ T_1$ is a linear transformation of $R^n$ to $R^n$.

#### THEOREM 3

If $A_1$, $A_2$ are the respective matrix representations of the linear transformations $T_1$, $T_2$, then $A_1 A_2$ is the matrix representation of $T_2 \circ T_1$.

#### THEOREM 4

The inverse of a linear transformation is a linear transformation.

#### THEOREM 5

The matrix representation of $T^{-1}$ is the inverse of the matrix representation of $T$.

# Appendix B

# Mathematical Induction

Mathematical induction is a special method of proof that is used to establish statements about the set of natural numbers

$$N = \{1, 2, 3, \ldots, n, \ldots\}$$

For example consider the following sums of consecutive odd numbers.

$$1 = 1^2$$
$$1 + 3 = 4 = 2^2$$
$$1 + 3 + 5 = 9 = 3^2$$
$$1 + 3 + 5 + 7 = 16 = 4^2$$

Each sum is equal to the square of the number of terms in the sum. It is tempting to assert that the pattern continues and claim that for the $n$th odd number $2n - 1$ we would have the formula

$$1 + 3 + 5 + \cdots + (2n - 1) = n^2$$

But now we have infinitely many statements, one for each natural number, and it is not possible to check all the cases directly. Even computers have finite capacity. Given a particular case, say $n = 50$, how do we know that the formula is true for the odd number $2 \cdot 50 - 1 = 99$:

$$\text{Case 50:} \quad 1 + 3 + \cdots + 99 = 50^2$$

And if this case is verified, then we have the next case, and so on.

Now here is the germ of the idea behind mathematical induction: It is possible to use Case 50 to deduce Case 51. Let us *assume* that case 50 is true. If we add the next odd number 101 to both sides of the assumed equation, we get

$$(1 + 3 + \cdots + 99) + 101 = 50^2 + 101$$

If it happens that $50^2 + 101$ is equal to $51^2$, then we would have the formula for Case 51. We note that

$$50^2 + 101 = 50^2 + 2 \cdot 50 + 1 = (50 + 1)^2 = 51^2$$

Thus we have deduced from the assumed truth of Case 50 that

$$\text{Case 51:} \quad 1 + 3 + \cdots + 101 = 51^2$$

We have shown that *if* Case 50 is true, then it follows that Case 51 is true, thus avoiding the need to check it directly.

Here is the crucial observation. We can argue from *any* case to the next. Consider Case $k$ :

$$1 + 3 + \cdots + (2k - 1) = k^2$$

If we add the next odd number, which is $2k + 1$, to both sides of the equation, we get

$$1 + 3 + \cdots + (2k - 1) + (2k + 1) = k^2 + (2k + 1) = (k + 1)^2$$

This is exactly Case $k + 1$. So we have proved that if Case $k$ is true, then Case $k + 1$ must also be true. Most importantly, the argument works for *any* natural number $k$. Therefore, if Case 1 is true, then Case 2 is true; and if Case 2 is true, then Case 3 is true; and so on. We thus have a way to bridge successive cases and go from the initial case to any other case. We conclude that the formula must hold for any natural number.

We will now give a precise statement of the method of mathematical induction. We will use the notation $P(n)$ to stand for a statement about the natural number $n$. For example, in the preceding discussion, we could use $P(n)$ to indicate the formula for the sum of the first $n$ odd numbers. The notation gives us a convenient way to talk about the setting for mathematical induction.

**The Principle of Mathematical Induction.** For each $n$ in $N$, let $P(n)$ be a statement that involves $n$. Suppose it can be shown that:

(1) *Base case*: $P(1)$ is true,
(2) *Bridge*: The assumed truth of $P(k)$ implies the truth of $P(k+1)$ for all $k \geq 1$,

Then $P(n)$ is true for all $n$ in $N$.

If we imagine a row of dominos, condition (2) states that they are placed close enough together so that each domino can knock over the next one in line. That is, *if* one domino is knocked over, then the next one will be knocked over. Condition (1) states that the first domino is actually knocked over. The two combine to assure us that once the first is knocked over, then all will fall.

A *proof by mathematical induction* thus entails that the two conditions, the base case (1) and the bridge (2), are established. Then we can conclude that all the cases are valid. The following examples illustrate the method of proof.

**EXAMPLE 1**   Prove that $1 + 2 + 3 + \cdots + n = \frac{n(n+1)}{2}$ for all $n$ in $N$.

**SOLUTION**   Let $P(n)$ stand for the stated formula. Then $P(1)$ is true because $1 = \frac{1 \cdot 2}{2}$. So the base case is established. To establish the bridge, we *assume* that $P(k)$ is true:

$$1 + 2 + \cdots + k = \frac{k(k+1)}{2}$$

Then we add $k + 1$ to both sides of the equation to get

$$1 + 2 + \cdots + k + (k+1) = \frac{k(k+1)}{2} + k + 1$$
$$= \frac{k(k+1) + 2(k+1)}{2}$$
$$= \frac{(k+1)(k+2)}{2}$$

Thus if $P(k)$ is true, then it follows that $P(k+1)$ is true. Therefore, by mathematical induction, the formula is true for all $n$.

Other formulas for sums can be verified by mathematical induction in a similar way, although the algebra may be a little more complicated. Here is one more example; others are given in the exercises.

**EXAMPLE 2**  Prove that $1^2 + 2^2 + \cdots + n^2 = \frac{n(n+1)(2n+1)}{6}$.

**SOLUTION**  The base case $n = 1$ is true because $1^2 = \frac{1 \cdot 2 \cdot 3}{6}$ . If we assume the formula is true for $k$, then we add $(k+1)^2$ to both sides of

$$1^2 + 2^2 + \cdots + k^2 = \frac{k(k+1)(2k+1)}{6}$$

to get

$$
\begin{aligned}
1^2 + 2^2 + \cdots + k^2 + (k+1)^2 &= \frac{k(k+1)(2k+1)}{6} + (k+1)^2 \\
&= \frac{k(k+1)(2k+1) + 6(k+1)^2}{6} \\
&= \frac{(k+1)[k(2k+1) + 6(k+1)]}{6} \\
&= \frac{(k+1)(2k^2 + 7k + 6)}{6} \\
&= \frac{(k+1)(k+2)(2k+3)}{6}
\end{aligned}
$$

Since this is the given formula for the case $n = k + 1$, we see that if the formula is true for $k$, then it is also true for $k + 1$. Therefore, by mathematical induction, the formula is true for all $n$ in $N$.

The principle of mathematical induction can be used in a wide variety of situations. In the next example, we establish an inequality.

**EXAMPLE 3**  Prove that $2^n > n$ for all $n$ in $N$.

**SOLUTION**  Since $2 > 1$, the inequality it true for $n = 1$. If we assume that $2^k > k$, then we can multiply both sides by 2 to deduce that

$$2^{k+1} = 2 \cdot 2^k = 2^k + 2^k > k + 2^k > k + 1$$

Thus the inequality for $k$ implies the inequality for $k + 1$. Therefore, by mathematical induction, we have $2^n > n$ for all $n$.

**EXAMPLE 4**  Prove that $11^n - 4^n$ is divisible by 7 for all $n$ in $N$.

**SOLUTION** If $n = 1$, then $11 - 4 = 7$, and the assertion is true for this case. If we assume that $11^k - 4^k$ is divisible by 7, then we have $11^k - 4^k = 7m$ for some natural number $m$. The bridge to the case $k + 1$ follows by

$$
\begin{aligned}
11^{k+1} - 4^{k+1} &= 11^{k+1} - 11 \cdot 4^k + 11 \cdot 4^k - 4^{k+1} \\
&= 11(11^k - 4^k) + 4^k(11 - 4) \\
&= 11 \cdot 7m + 4^k \cdot 7 \\
&= 7(11m + 4^k)
\end{aligned}
$$

Thus if the statement is true for $k$, then it follows that it is true for $k + 1$. Therefore, by mathematical induction, the statement is true for all $n$ in $N$.

*Remark.* It is important to realize that it is possible for the bridge (2) to be valid even when the statements are actually false. For example, consider the statement $P(n) : n = n+5$. Condition (2) can be established as follows. If we assume that $P(k)$ is true, then we have $k = k + 5$. By adding 1 to both sides, we get $k + 1 = (k + 1) + 5$. Therefore, if $P(k)$ is assumed to be true, then we can deduce that $P(k + 1)$ would be true. However, mathematical induction cannot be applied here because the base case is false. In fact, $P(n)$ is false for every $n$.

We have used the base case $n = 1$ as the simplest way to introduce the technique of mathematical induction. However, there are many situations in which the case $n = 1$ is false, and yet the statements are true for all values of $n$ starting at some other place. Using the domino imagery, perhaps we are unable to knock over the first domino, but we can reach the third domino and knock it over. Then it follows that all dominos past the third one will get knocked down. We will give examples in which this type of phenomenon arises, and present others as exercises. The formal statement that deals with this situation is as follows.

**The Principle of Mathematical Induction (Version II).** For each natural number $n \geq n_0$, let $P(n)$ be a statement. If:

(1) *Base case.* $P(n_0)$ is true,
(2) *Bridge.* If the assumed truth of $P(k)$ implies the truth of $P(k+1)$ for all $k \geq n_0$,

then $P(n)$ is true for all natural numbers such that $n \geq n_0$.

**EXAMPLE 5** Find all natural numbers $n$ such that $2^n > 2n + 1$.

**SOLUTION**   Let $P(n)$ be the statement that $2^n > 2n + 1$. Then we note that

$$P(1): \quad 2 > 3 \quad \text{False}$$
$$P(2): \quad 4 > 5 \quad \text{False}$$
$$P(3): \quad 8 > 7 \quad \text{True}$$

We now try to establish a bridge. Assume that $2^k > 2k + 1$ for some $k$. Then if we multiply both sides by 2, we get

$$2^{k+1} = 2 \cdot 2^k > 2(2k+1) = 4k + 2 = 2k + (2k+2) > 2k + 3 = 2(k+1) + 1$$

The last inequality is valid because $2k + 2 > 3$ for all $k \geq 1$. Thus the bridge is valid for all $k = 1, 2, 3, \ldots$, even though the statements are false for $k = 1, 2$. Therefore, since we have the base case $n = 3$, for which we know the inequality to be true, we can apply mathematical induction to conclude that $2^n > 2n + 1$ for all natural numbers $n$ such that $n \geq 3$.

**EXAMPLE 6**   Prove that if $x$ is any real number such that $x > 0$, then $(1+x)^n > 1 + nx$ for all $n$ in $N$.

**SOLUTION**   Let $P(n)$ be the statement: $(1 + x)^n > 1 + nx$ for all $x > 0$. Then, $P(1)$ is false, since we have equality instead of inequality in that case. If $n = 2$, then since $x^2 > 0$, we have

$$(1 + x)^2 = 1 + 2x + x^2 > 1 + 2x$$

Thus $P(2)$ is true, and we will use $n = 2$ as our base case.

Now assume that $P(k)$ is true. Then multiplication by the positive quantity $x + 1$ preserves the inequality and gives us

$$(1 + x)^{k+1} = (1 + x)^k (1 + x)$$
$$> (1 + kx)(1 + x)$$
$$= 1 + (k + 1)x + kx^2$$
$$> 1 + (k + 1)x$$

The last step follows from the fact that $kx^2 > 0$. Thus we have shown that $P(k)$ implies $P(k + 1)$. Therefore, by mathematical induction, the inequality holds for all $n \geq 2$.

### EXERCISES.

In Exercises 1 — 15, use mathematical induction to prove that the given statement is true for all $n$ in $N$.

1.  $1 + 4 + 7 + \cdots + (3n - 2) = \dfrac{n(3n - 1)}{2}$.

2.  $1 + 3 + 6 + \cdots + \dfrac{n(n + 1)}{2} = \dfrac{n(n + 1)(n + 2)}{6}$.

3.  $1^3 + 2^3 + 3^3 + \cdots + n^3 = (\dfrac{n(n + 1)}{2})^2$.

4.  $\dfrac{1}{1 \cdot 2} + \dfrac{1}{2 \cdot 3} + \dfrac{1}{3 \cdot 4} + \cdots + \dfrac{1}{n(n + 1)} = \dfrac{n}{n + 1}$.

5.  $\dfrac{1}{1 \cdot 3} + \dfrac{1}{2 \cdot 4} + \dfrac{1}{3 \cdot 5} + \cdots + \dfrac{1}{n(n + 2)} = \dfrac{n(3n + 5)}{4(n + 1)(n + 2)}$.

6.  $1 + \dfrac{1}{2} + \dfrac{1}{4} + \dfrac{1}{8} + \cdots + (\dfrac{1}{2})^{n-1} = 2 - (\dfrac{1}{2})^{n-1}$.

7.  If $x \neq 1$, then $1 + x + x^2 + \cdots + x^n = \dfrac{1 - x^{n+1}}{1 - x}$.

8.  $n^2 + n$ is a multiple of 2.

9.  $n^3 - n$ is a multiple of 3.

10. $2^{2n} - 1$ is a multiple of 3.

11. $3^{2n} - 1$ is a multiple of 8.

12. $n(n + 1)(n + 2)$ is a multiple of 6.

13. $n^3 + (n + 1)^3 + (n + 2)^3$ is a multiple of 9.

14. $5^n - 2^n$ is divisible by 3.

15. $a^n - b^n$ is divisible by $a - b$.

16. Find a formula for $\dfrac{1}{1 \cdot 3} + \dfrac{1}{3 \cdot 5} + \dfrac{1}{5 \cdot 7} + \cdots + \dfrac{1}{(2n - 1)(2n + 1)}$ and prove it using mathematical induction.

17. Find a formula for $(1 - \dfrac{1}{2})(1 - \dfrac{1}{3})(1 - \dfrac{1}{4}) \cdots (1 - \dfrac{1}{n + 1})$ and prove it using mathematical induction.

18. Prove that $4^n + 5^n > (\dfrac{4 + 5}{2})^n$ for all $n$ in $N$.

19. Prove that if $a$, $b$ are positive, then $a^n + b^n > (\frac{a+b}{2})^n$ for all $n$ in $N$.

20. Prove that $n! > 2^n$ for all $n \geq 4$.

21. Find all natural numbers $n$ for which the inequality $n^2 < 2^n$ is true. Prove your assertion.

# Answers to Odd Exercises

## CHAPTER 1

### Section 1.1, p. 9

**1.** (a) Linear     (b) Not linear     (c) Not linear     (d) Linear     (e) Not linear

**3.** (a) Yes    (b) No    (c) Yes    (d) No    (e) No

**5.** $(\frac{5}{4}, 0)$, $(0, -\frac{5}{2})$         **7.** $(\frac{7}{2}, 0)$         **9.** $y = 3x + 5$, $m = 3$, $(0, 5)$

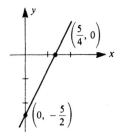 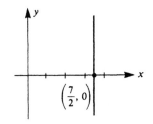 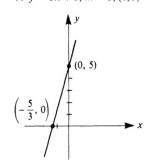

**11.** $y = \frac{4}{5}x - \frac{2}{5}$, $m = \frac{4}{5}$, $(0, -\frac{2}{5})$         **13.** $y = -7x + 2$

                                                       **15.** $y = -\frac{3}{8}x + \frac{7}{3}$

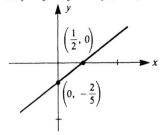

**17.**

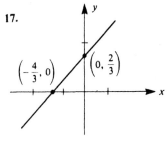

**19.** $y - 3 = 8(x + 5)$

**21.** $y + 3 = \frac{2}{3}(x + 4)$

**23.** $m = \frac{8}{3}$, $y - 9 = \frac{8}{3}(x - 4)$, or $y + 7 = \frac{8}{3}(x + 2)$

**25.** $m = 0$, $y = 6$

**27.** (a) yes, $y - 1 = \frac{1}{2}(x - 5)$      (b) no

**29.** Let $x = 0$, then $y/b = 1$ and $y = b$

     Let $y = 0$, then $x/a = 1$ and $x = a$

**31.** $x/(5/4) + y/(5/2) = 1$

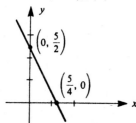

**33.** $x/(-5) + y/6 = 1$
**35.** $x/(1/6) + y/(1/2) = 1$
**37.** $y + 1 = \frac{4}{3}(x - 5)$, $y - 2 = -\frac{3}{4}(x - 6)$

**39.** Each typewriter costs $250 to manufacture.

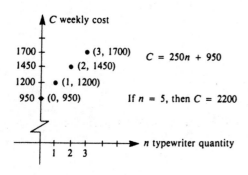

$C = 250n + 950$

If $n = 5$, then $C = 2200$

**41.** Myra is losing 300 people per year.

$$p - 1500 = -300(y - 1962)$$
$$(1967, 0)$$

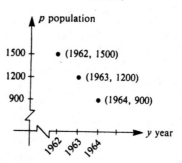

**43.** $y = -7x + 140$, $(7.5, 87.5)$ or $87,500 at 7.5 years.

### Section 1.2, p. 20

**1.** $x = -\frac{5}{19}$, $y = \frac{11}{19}$

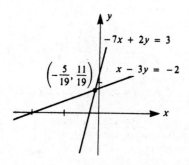

**3.** $x = \frac{74}{21}$, $y = -\frac{82}{21}$

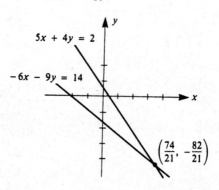

**5.**

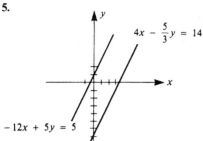

$4x - \frac{5}{3}y = 14$

$-12x + 5y = 5$

**7.**

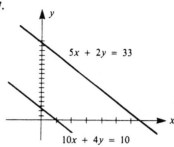

$5x + 2y = 33$

$10x + 4y = 10$

**9.** $(\frac{7}{4}t + \frac{5}{4}, t)$, or $(s, \frac{4}{7}s - \frac{5}{7})$    **11.** $(\frac{1}{6}t + \frac{5}{18}, t)$, or $(s, 6s - \frac{5}{3})$    **13.** No solution    **15.** $(5, 0)$

**17.** $(s, \frac{6}{7}s - \frac{4}{7})$, or $(\frac{7}{6}t + \frac{2}{3}, t)$    **19.** $(\frac{1}{5}t + \frac{3}{5}, t)$, $(s, 5s - 3)$

**21.** $(\frac{3}{5}, 0)$ from $t = 0$ or $s = \frac{3}{5}$ ; $(0, -3)$ from $s = 0$ or $t = -3$    **23.** $(6, 2)$    **25.** $k = -\frac{1}{2}$

**27.** $2x + y = 48$    $(18, 12)$ or 18 5-pound cans Still Day
 $x + 3y = 54$              12 5-pound cans Breezy
 $x \geqslant 0, \quad y \geqslant 0$

**29.** Break-even at $x = 1150$.
 The revenue at break-even is \$9200.

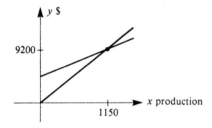

**31.** The break point is 100 of the 5000-piece lots.
 Use machine A for a 750,000-piece run.

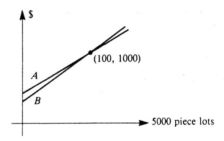

## Section 1.3, p. 30

**1.** $x > \frac{1}{3}$    **3.** $x > \frac{1}{2}$

**5.**

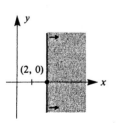

$(2, 0)$

**7.**

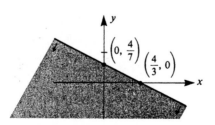

$(0, \frac{4}{7})$  $(\frac{4}{3}, 0)$

**9.**

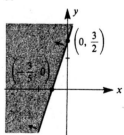

$(0, \frac{3}{2})$

$(-\frac{3}{5}, 0)$

**11.**

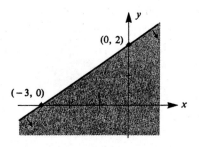

**13.**

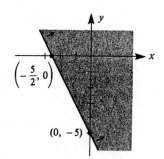

**15.**

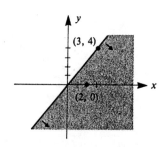

**17.** $\left(-\frac{16}{27}, \frac{95}{27}\right)$

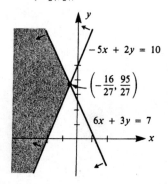

**19.** $\left(\frac{30}{11}, \frac{4}{11}\right)$

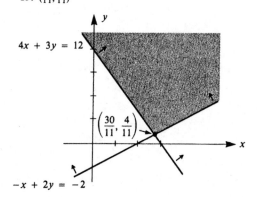

**21.** $\left(-\frac{3}{2}, 0\right), \left(-\frac{5}{2}, 2\right), \left(-\frac{1}{2}, \frac{2}{3}\right)$

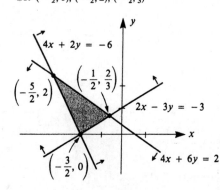

**23.** $\left(\frac{1}{2}, \frac{5}{2}\right), \left(\frac{1}{3}, \frac{10}{3}\right), (1, 2)$

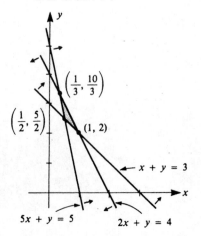

**25.** $(0, 0,), (0, 2), (\frac{3}{4}, \frac{5}{2}), (2, 0)$

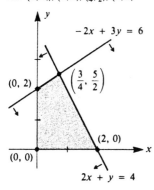

**27.** Let $x$ = pounds of Country Goodness
Let $y$ = pounds of Fast Start
$\quad .8x + .4y \leqslant 1000 \qquad (0, 0), (0, 1400),$
$\quad .2x + .6y \leqslant 840 \qquad (660, 1180), (1250, 0)$
$\quad x \geqslant 0, \quad y \geqslant 0$

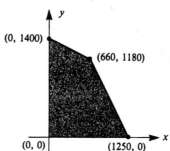

**29.** Let $x$ = number of softballs
Let $y$ = number of hardballs
$\quad 100x + 30y \leqslant 3000 \qquad (0, 0), (0, 90),$
$\quad 12x + \phantom{0}8y \leqslant 720 \qquad (\frac{60}{11}, \frac{900}{11}), (30, 0)$
$\quad x \geqslant \phantom{0}0, \quad y \geqslant 0$

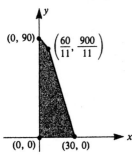

**31.** $-5x + 2y \leqslant 11$
$\quad\phantom{-}x + 6y \leqslant 17$
$\quad -x + 2y \geqslant -1$

## Section 1.4, p. 38

**1.**

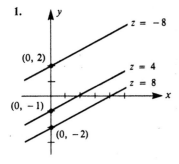

**3.**

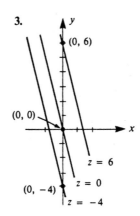

**5.** (a) $10x + 15y = 990$    (b) $10x + 15y = 1500$
$(0, 66), (51, 32), (99, 0)$    $(0, 100), (99, 34), (150, 0)$

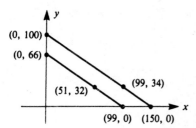

**7.** Maximum of 5 at $(1, -1)$

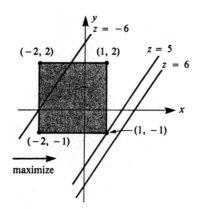

maximize

**9.** Minimum of 14 at $(3, 2)$

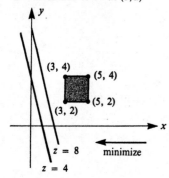

minimize

**11.** (a) $-\frac{13}{6}$ at $(-\frac{1}{2}, \frac{2}{3})$   (b) $-\frac{3}{2}$ at $(-\frac{3}{2}, 0)$
**13.** (a) 9 at $(1, 2)$   (b) 14 at $(\frac{1}{3}, \frac{10}{3})$
**15.** (a) $\frac{31}{2}$ at $(\frac{3}{4}, \frac{5}{2})$   (b) $\frac{63}{4}$ at $(\frac{3}{4}, \frac{5}{2})$
**17.** (a) 80 at $(18, 7)$   (b) $-2$ at $(0, 1)$

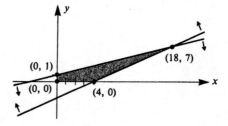

**19.** (a) 8 at $(2, 0)$   (b) $-\frac{181}{13}$ at $(\frac{8}{13}, \frac{63}{13})$

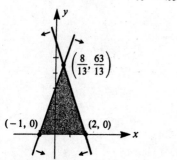

**21.** (a) $-\frac{52}{3}$ at $(\frac{20}{3}, -\frac{4}{3})$   (b) 36 at $(\frac{20}{3}, -\frac{4}{3})$

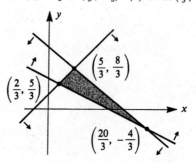

**23.** (a) 15 at $(3,0)$  (b) 9 at $(3,0)$

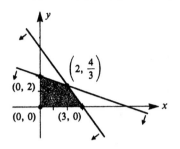

**25.** (a) 19 at $(\frac{9}{5}, \frac{16}{5})$  (b) $-8$ at $(0,2)$

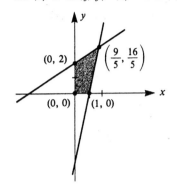

## Section 1.5, p. 49

**1.** Let $x$ = the number of days of operation at North Fork.
Let $y$ = the number of days of operation at East Bend.

Minimize $\quad 50x + 75y$
subject to $\quad 3000x + 1000y \geqslant 30{,}000$
$\qquad\qquad 2000x + 6000y \geqslant 60{,}000$
$\qquad\qquad 0 \leqslant x \leqslant 40, \quad 0 \leqslant y \leqslant 40$
minimum of \$937.50 at $(\frac{15}{2}, \frac{15}{2})$

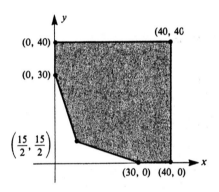

**3.** Let $x$ = the number of days of operation for kiln A.
Let $y$ = the number of days of operation for kiln B.

Minimize $\quad 500x + 400y$
subject to $\quad 2000x + 1000y \geqslant 10{,}000$
$\qquad\qquad 1000x + 1500y \geqslant 9000$
$\qquad\qquad 500x + 2500y \geqslant 7500$
$\qquad\qquad x \geqslant 0, \quad y \geqslant 0$
minimum of \$3100 at $(3,4)$

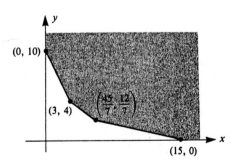

**5.** (a) Minimum of \$937.50 at $(\frac{15}{2}, \frac{15}{2})$  (b) Minimum of \$1375 at $(5, 15)$
**7.** (a) Minimum of \$3100 at $(3,4)$  (b) Minimum of \$3400 at $(2,6)$

**9.** Let $x$ = the number of "A" bumpers.
  Let $y$ = the number of "B" bumpers.

  Maximize     $50x + 60y$
  subject to     $10x + 12y \leqslant 2400$
                    $2x + y \leqslant 305$
                    $x \geqslant 0, \quad y \geqslant 0$
  maximum of \$12,000 at $(0, 200)$, or $(90, 125)$

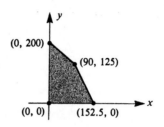

**11.** Let $x$ = the number of packages of Heavenly Chew.
  Let $y$ = the number of packages of Rich-n-Chew

  Maximize     $2x + 1.5y$
  subject to     $x + y \leqslant 425$
                    $2x + y \leqslant 800$
                    $2x + 3y \leqslant 1200$
                    $x \geqslant 0, \quad y \geqslant 0$
  maximum of \$825 at $(375, 50)$

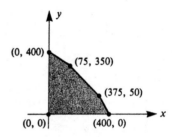

**13.** Let $x$ = the ounces of VIVA.
  Let $y$ = the ounces of Flakey Oats.

  Minimize     $7x + 9y$
  subject to     $5x + 5y \geqslant 10$
                    $x + 3y \geqslant 3$
                    $x \geqslant 0, \quad y \geqslant 0$
  minimum of 15 cents at $(\frac{3}{2}, \frac{1}{2})$

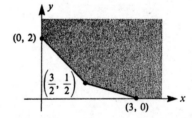

**15.** Let $x$ = the number of servings of fruit salad.
  Let $y$ = the number of servings of vegetable salad.

  Minimize     $10x + 7y$
  subject to     $10x + 30y \geqslant 100$
                    $40x + 20y \geqslant 100$
                    $x \geqslant 0, \quad y \geqslant 0$
  minimum of 31 cents at $(1, 3)$

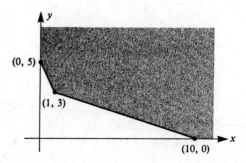

## CHAPTER 2

### Section 2.1, p. 62

**1.** $\begin{bmatrix} 4 & -3 & 1 & 5 \\ 1 & 5 & -2 & -7 \\ -5 & 7 & -6 & 9 \end{bmatrix}$

**3.** $\begin{bmatrix} 5 & -3 & 1 & -1 & 5 \\ 2 & 4 & -5 & 3 & -6 \\ -3 & 3 & -4 & 2 & 1 \end{bmatrix}$

**5.** $\begin{bmatrix} 4 & 2 & 3 & -1 & 10 \\ 8 & 5 & -2 & 4 & -2 \\ 7 & 4 & 5 & 3 & 4 \\ 2 & -1 & 3 & 1 & -5 \end{bmatrix}$

**7.** $\begin{aligned} 4x_1 + 2x_2 - 3x_3 &= 8 \\ x_1 + 5x_2 + 2x_3 &= -6 \\ -6x_1 + x_2 + 7x_3 &= 2 \end{aligned}$

**9.** $\begin{aligned} 5x_1 - x_2 + 4x_3 &= 3 \\ 6x_1 \quad\quad - 4x_3 &= -2 \\ x_1 + 2x_2 + 5x_3 &= 6 \\ 3x_1 + x_2 + 4x_3 &= 2 \end{aligned}$

**11.** $\begin{aligned} 6x_1 + x_2 + 8x_3 + 3x_4 &= -2 \\ -4x_1 + 2x_2 \quad\quad + 4x_4 &= 8 \\ 2x_1 + 7x_2 + 4x_3 + 5x_4 &= 7 \end{aligned}$

**13.** $x_1 = -27, x_2 = 6$    **15.** $x_1 = 22, x_2 = -5, x_3 = 3$
**17.** $x_1 = -1, x_2 = -3, x_3 = 5, x_4 = 2$    **19.** Echelon form

**21.** $\begin{bmatrix} 1 & 2 & 0 & 5 \\ 0 & 0 & 1 & 4 \\ 0 & 0 & 0 & 0 \end{bmatrix}$

**23.** $\begin{bmatrix} 1 & 2 & 4 & -3 \\ 0 & 1 & -2 & -1 \\ 0 & 0 & 1 & -4/3 \end{bmatrix}$

**25.** (a) $\begin{bmatrix} 0 & -18 & -11 & 32 \\ 1 & 5 & 2 & -6 \\ -6 & 1 & 7 & 2 \end{bmatrix}$
(b) $\begin{bmatrix} 4 & 2 & -3 & 8 \\ 31 & 0 & -33 & -16 \\ -6 & 1 & 7 & 2 \end{bmatrix}$

**27.** $\begin{bmatrix} 1 & 2 & 5 & 6 \\ 0 & -12 & -34 & -38 \\ 0 & -11 & -21 & -27 \\ 0 & -5 & -11 & -16 \end{bmatrix}$

**29.** $\begin{bmatrix} 1 & 2 & -4 & 1 \\ 0 & 1 & 2 & -2 \\ 0 & 0 & 1 & -1 \end{bmatrix}$    $\begin{aligned} x_1 &= -3 \\ x_2 &= 0 \\ x_3 &= -1 \end{aligned}$

**31.** $\begin{bmatrix} 1 & 2 & -3 & -1 \\ 0 & 1 & 3 & -5 \\ 0 & 0 & 1 & -1 \end{bmatrix}$    $\begin{aligned} x_1 &= 0 \\ x_2 &= -2 \\ x_3 &= -1 \end{aligned}$

**33.** $\begin{bmatrix} 1 & 2 & -3 & 1 & 2 \\ 0 & 1 & 5/2 & 1/2 & -1/2 \\ 0 & 0 & 1 & 3 & 3 \\ 0 & 0 & 0 & 1 & 2 \end{bmatrix}$    $\begin{aligned} x &= -21 \\ y &= 6 \\ z &= -3 \\ w &= 2 \end{aligned}$

### Section 2.2, p. 70

**1.** $\begin{bmatrix} 1 & 0 & 7 \\ 0 & 1 & -2 \end{bmatrix}$    $\begin{aligned} x_1 &= 7 \\ x_2 &= -2 \end{aligned}$

**3.** $\begin{bmatrix} 1 & 0 & 0 & 45 \\ 0 & 1 & 0 & -9 \\ 0 & 0 & 1 & 2 \end{bmatrix}$    $\begin{aligned} x_1 &= 45 \\ x_2 &= -9 \\ x_3 &= 2 \end{aligned}$

**5.** $\begin{bmatrix} 1 & 0 & 0 & 0 & | & -14 \\ 0 & 1 & 0 & 0 & | & 8 \\ 0 & 0 & 1 & 0 & | & -2 \\ 0 & 0 & 0 & 1 & | & 3 \end{bmatrix}$   $\begin{aligned} x_1 &= -14 \\ x_2 &= 8 \\ x_3 &= -2 \\ x_4 &= 3 \end{aligned}$   **7.** $x = 1, y = 0, z = -1$   **9.** $x_1 = \frac{3}{7}, x_2 = \frac{3}{7}, x_3 = \frac{11}{7}$
**11.** $x = -14, y = -3, z = 2$ and $x = 3, y = 1, z = 1$
**13.** $x_1 = -1, x_2 = 0, x_3 = 1$ and $x_1 = 10, x_2 = 3, x_3 = -2$
**15.** In 1000 pound units (1) $A = 50, H = 190, B = 30$
(2) $A = 50, H = 110, B = 170$

### Section 2.3, p. 82
**7.** 2, 3    **9.** 2, 3    **11.** 3, 4    **13.** $x = 18, y = 6, z = -1$    **15.** Inconsistent    **17.** $k = -1$
**19.** $2a + b - c = 0$

**21.** $\begin{bmatrix} 1 & -2 & 0 & | & -7 \\ 0 & 0 & 1 & | & 5 \end{bmatrix}$    **23.** $\begin{bmatrix} 1 & 0 & 1 & | & 5 \\ 0 & 1 & -2 & | & -3 \end{bmatrix}$

$(-7 + 2t, t, 5)$          $(5 - t, -3 + 2t, t)$
$t = 0, (-7, 0, 5)$        $t = 0, (5, -3, 0)$
$t = 1, (-5, 1, 5)$        $t = 1, (4, -1, 1)$

**25.** $\begin{bmatrix} 1 & 0 & 0 & -61 & | & -87 \\ 0 & 1 & 0 & 8 & | & 12 \\ 0 & 0 & 1 & 21 & | & 31 \end{bmatrix}$    **27.** $\begin{bmatrix} 1 & 0 & -22 & 0 & 5 & | & -20 \\ 0 & 1 & 4 & 0 & -1 & | & 5 \\ 0 & 0 & 0 & 1 & -2 & | & 3 \end{bmatrix}$

$(-87 + 61t, 12 - 8t, 31 - 21t, t)$          $(-20 - 5t + 22s, 5 + t - 4s, s, 3 + 2t, t)$
$t = 1, (-26, 4, 10, 1)$          $s = 1, t = 0, (2, 1, 1, 3, 0)$
$t = 0, (-87, 12, 31, 0)$          $s = 0, t = 1, (-25, 6, 0, 5, 1)$

**29.** Ruff  Fluff  Prowl
$\quad$ 5 $\quad$ 5 $\quad$ 0 $\Big\}$ Batches
$\quad$ 1 $\quad$ 6 $\quad$ 1

**31.** $(7t, -2t, t)$     **33.** $(0, 0, 0)$     **35.** $(-3s + 2t, s, t, 0)$
$\quad$ $2 + 1 = 3$     $\quad$ $3 + 0 = 3$     $\quad$ $2 + 2 = 4$

### Section 2.4, p. 94
**1.**                                    **3.**

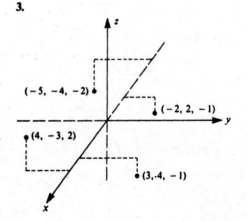

**5.** $x/6 + y/2 + z/3 = 1$

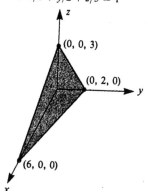

**7.** $x/3 + y/6 + z/2 = 1$

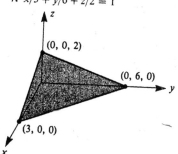

**9.**

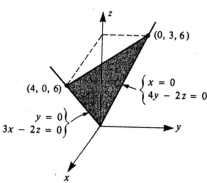

**11.**

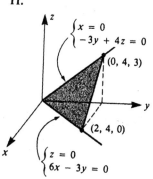

**13.**

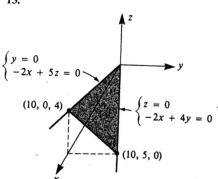

**15.**

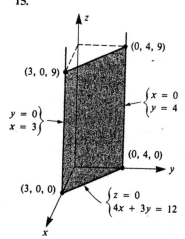

**17.**

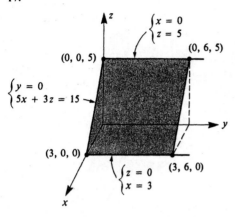

$\begin{cases} x = 0 \\ z = 5 \end{cases}$

(0, 6, 5)

(0, 0, 5)

$\begin{cases} y = 0 \\ 5x + 3z = 15 \end{cases}$

(0, 0, 5)

(3, 0, 0)

(3, 6, 0)

$\begin{cases} z = 0 \\ x = 3 \end{cases}$

**19.**

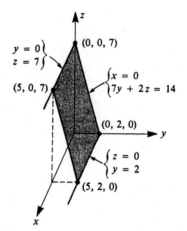

(0, 0, 7)

$\begin{cases} y = 0 \\ z = 7 \end{cases}$

$\begin{cases} x = 0 \\ 7y + 2z = 14 \end{cases}$

(5, 0, 7)

(0, 2, 0)

$\begin{cases} z = 0 \\ y = 2 \end{cases}$

(5, 2, 0)

**21.**

$(0, 4 - 2t, t)$

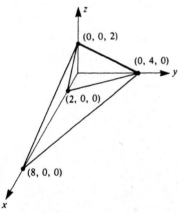

(0, 0, 2)

(0, 4, 0)

(2, 0, 0)

(8, 0, 0)

**23.**

$(14 - \frac{9}{2}t, -2 + t, t)$

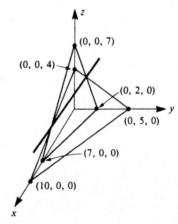

(0, 0, 7)

(0, 0, 4)

(0, 2, 0)

(0, 5, 0)

(7, 0, 0)

(10, 0, 0)

**25.**

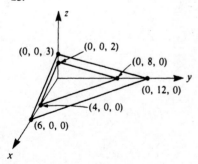

(0, 0, 3)  (0, 0, 2)

(0, 8, 0)

(0, 12, 0)

(4, 0, 0)

(6, 0, 0)

**27.**

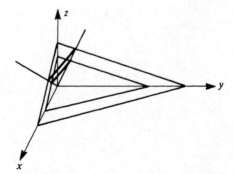

**29.**

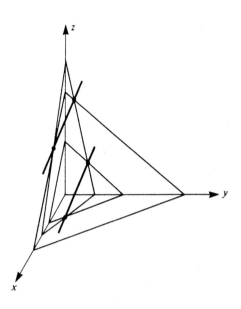

**31.** The system $a_1 x + b_1 y + c_1 z = d_1$
$\qquad\qquad\quad a_2 x + b_2 y + c_2 z = d_2$
has no solution. Thus the augmented matrix reduces to

$$\begin{bmatrix} * & * & * & | & * \\ 0 & 0 & 0 & | & d \neq 0 \end{bmatrix}$$

Thus the assertion is true.

**33.** No two of the planes are parallel.

**35.** $(4 - \frac{4}{3}t, 1, t)$

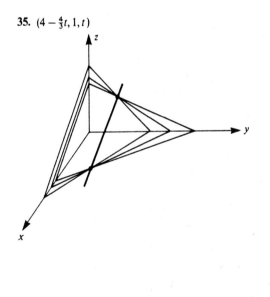

**37.** $(\frac{5}{2}, \frac{19}{21}, \frac{22}{21})$

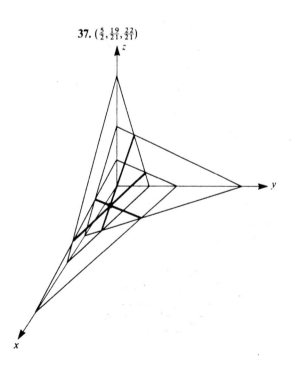

**39.** $-86x + 35y + 3z = 1$

## Section 2.5, p. 101

**1.** $\begin{bmatrix} -2 & 0 & 2 \\ 2 & 1 & -3 \\ -3 & 0 & 4 \end{bmatrix}$ 　**3.** $\left[\begin{array}{ccc|c} 2 & 4 & 0 & -2 \\ -4 & 1 & 0 & 2 \\ -1 & 2 & 1 & -3 \end{array}\right]$ 　**5.** $\begin{bmatrix} 0 & 13 & 0 & 7 \\ -9 & 19 & 0 & 10 \\ 2 & -4 & 1 & -5 \\ 5 & -13 & 0 & 0 \end{bmatrix}$

**7.** $x = -34,\ y = 12,\ z = -1$ 　**9.** $x_1 = -5,\ x_2 = 3,\ x_3 = 5$ 　**11.** $(4, -2, 3, -5)$

**13.** $(2 + 3s - 3t, s, -3 + 2t, t, 4)$ 　**15.** $(15 - 4t, t, -3, -2)$

## Section 2.6, p. 115

**1.** 10 　　**3.** 8 　　**5.** $\begin{aligned} 2x_1 - x_2 + x_3 &= 20 \\ 3x_1 + 4x_2 \quad\ + x_4 &= 5 \\ x_1 \geq 0,\ x_2 \geq 0,\ x_3 \geq 0,\ x_4 &\geq 0 \end{aligned}$

**7.** $\begin{aligned} 6x_1 - 3x_2 + 2x_3 + x_4 \qquad\qquad &= 19 \\ 5x_1 + 2x_2 - 4x_3 \quad\ + x_5 \qquad &= 8 \\ -2x_1 + 3x_2 + 5x_3 \qquad\quad\ + x_6 &= 11 \\ x_1 \geq 0,\ x_2 \geq 0,\ x_3 \geq 0,\ x_4 \geq 0,\ x_5 \geq 0,\ x_6 &\geq 0 \end{aligned}$

**9.** $\left[\begin{array}{ccc|ccc|c} 1 & -2 & -1 & 0 & 0 & & 0 \\ 0 & 1 & 4 & 1 & 0 & & 8 \\ 0 & 3 & 3 & 0 & 1 & & 9 \end{array}\right]$

**11.** $\left[\begin{array}{cccc|ccc|c} 1 & -6 & -3 & -1 & 0 & 0 & 0 & 0 \\ 0 & 4 & 5 & 2 & 1 & 0 & 0 & 11 \\ 0 & 1 & 3 & 1 & 0 & 1 & 0 & 7 \\ 0 & 3 & 1 & 4 & 0 & 0 & 1 & 8 \end{array}\right]$ 　**13.** $\left[\begin{array}{cccc|ccc|c} 1 & -4 & 3 & 0 & 0 & 0 & 0 & 0 \\ 0 & 1 & 0 & -6 & 1 & 0 & 0 & 10 \\ 0 & 3 & -2 & 4 & 0 & 1 & 0 & 8 \\ 0 & 5 & 4 & 0 & 0 & 0 & 1 & 9 \end{array}\right]$

**15.** $\left[\begin{array}{cccc|cc|c} 1 & -4 & -7 & -2 & 0 & 0 & 0 \\ 0 & 3 & 4 & 5 & 1 & 0 & 19 \\ 0 & 2 & 6 & 1 & 0 & 1 & 12 \end{array}\right]$

**17.** Pivot on the 2 in the second column.

$\left[\begin{array}{ccc|ccc} 1 & 0 & 14 & 0 & 3 & 12 \\ 0 & 0 & 1 & 1 & -1/2 & 3 \\ 0 & 1 & 2 & 0 & 1/2 & 2 \end{array}\right]$

The maximum value of $z$ is 12.

**19.** Pivot on the 4 in the fourth column.

$\left[\begin{array}{cccc|ccc} 1 & 13 & -8 & 0 & 0 & 3/2 & 12 \\ 0 & -8 & 10 & 0 & 1 & -1/2 & 6 \\ 0 & 1 & -2 & 1 & 0 & 1/4 & 2 \end{array}\right]$

Not a final table.

**21.** Pivot on the 2 in the fourth column.

$\left[\begin{array}{cccc|cccc} 1 & -2 & 1 & 0 & 0 & 3 & 0 & 12 \\ 0 & 4 & -6 & 0 & 1 & -1/2 & 0 & 8 \\ 0 & -1 & -2 & 1 & 0 & 1/2 & 0 & 2 \\ 0 & -5 & 1 & 0 & 0 & 1/2 & 1 & 5 \end{array}\right]$

Not a final table.

**23.** Pivot on the 2 in the fourth column, third row.

$\left[\begin{array}{cccc|ccc|c} 1 & 2 & 2 & 0 & 0 & 2 & 0 & 16 \\ 0 & -2 & 10 & 0 & 1 & -1 & 0 & 4 \\ 0 & -1 & -3 & 1 & 0 & 1/2 & 0 & 4 \\ 0 & 4 & 6 & 0 & 0 & -1/2 & 1 & 2 \end{array}\right]$

The maximum value of $z$ is 16.

**25.** The basic feasible solution is $x_1 = 1,\ x_4 = 1,\ x_2 = x_3 = 0$ with $z = 12$. The variables $x_1$ and $x_4$ are basic. The variables $x_2$ and $x_3$ are nonbasic. The solution is not optimal.

27. The basic feasible solution is $x_2 = 3$, $x_5 = 7$, $x_1 = x_3 = x_4 = 0$ with $z = 18$. The variables $x_2$ and $x_5$ are basic. The variables $x_1$, $x_3$, $x_4$ are nonbasic. The solution is optimal.

29. The basic feasible solution is $x_2 = 1$, $x_4 = 19$, $x_5 = 2$, $x_1 = x_3 = x_6 = 0$ with $z = 8$. The basic variables are $x_2$, $x_4$, $x_5$. The nonbasic variables are $x_1$, $x_3$, $x_6$. The solution is optimal.

31. $z = 16$ at $(0, 2, 6, 0)$.       33. $z = 52$ at $(0, 7, 4, 0, 0, 6)$       35. $z = 56$ at $(0, 6, 16, 0, 0)$

37. Maximize      $z = 80x_1 + 60x_2 + 50x_3$
    subject to      $3x_1 + 10x_2 + x_3 \leqslant 840$
                    $x_1 + 2x_2 + 3x_3 \leqslant 630$
                    $2x_1 + 3x_2 + x_3 \leqslant 450$
                    $x_1 \geqslant 0, \quad x_2 \geqslant 0, \quad x_3 \geqslant 0$

    The maximum is $z = 19{,}620$ at $(144, 0, 162, 246, 0, 0)$. Make 144 cakes and 162 dozen cookies for an income of \$196.20 with 246 apples left over.

39. Maximize      $z = 18x_1 + 20x_2 + 32x_3$
    subject to      $4x_1 + 8x_2 + 8x_3 \leqslant 88$
                    $18x_1 + 12x_2 + 24x_3 \leqslant 240$
                    $6x_1 + 2x_2 + 4x_3 \leqslant 28$
                    $x_1 \geqslant 0, \quad x_2 \geqslant 0, \quad x_3 \geqslant 0$

    The maximum is $z = 256$ at $(0, 8, 3, 0, 72, 0)$.
    Make 8 chairs and 3 couches for revenue of \$256 with 72 feet of lumber left over.

41. The maximum is $z = 5$ at $(9, 4, 0, 1, 0, 0)$.

## Section 2.7, p. 131

1. The objective function value decreases from 0 to $-2$.
3. The new basic solution is not feasible since $x_1 = -8$.
5. The new basic solution is not feasible since $x_2 = -2$.
7. The objective function value decreases from 0 to $-3$.
   The new basic solution is not feasible since $x_2 = -\frac{3}{2}$.
9. The maximum value is $z = 14$ at $(0, 9, 0, 0, 8)$.
11. The final table is

$$\begin{bmatrix} 1 & -8 & 0 & 3 & 0 & 6 \\ 0 & -2 & 1 & 1/2 & 0 & 1 \\ 0 & -6 & 0 & 2 & 1 & 8 \end{bmatrix}$$

The $x_1$ column shows that the program is unbounded.

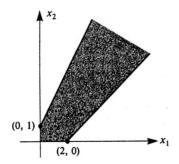

$Z + 4x_1 - 6x_2 = 0$
$6 + 4x_1 - 6(1) = 0$
$4x_1 = 0$
$x_1 = 0$

**13.** The final table is

$$\begin{bmatrix} 1 & -2 & 0 & 0 & 4 & 24 \\ 0 & -3 & 0 & 1 & 2 & 15 \\ 0 & -2 & 1 & 0 & 1/3 & 2 \end{bmatrix}$$

The $x_1$ column shows that the program is unbounded.

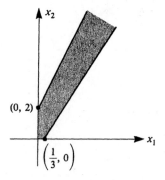

(0, 2)

$\left(\dfrac{1}{3}, 0\right)$

**15.** The final table is

$$\begin{bmatrix} 1 & 0 & -1 & 0 & 0 & 2 & 6 & 16 \\ 0 & 0 & -4 & 0 & 1 & 3 & 5 & 19 \\ 0 & 0 & -1/2 & 1 & 0 & 1/2 & 1 & 3 \\ 0 & 1 & -3 & 0 & 0 & 2 & 5 & 14 \end{bmatrix}$$

The $x_2$ column shows that the program is unbounded. Let $x_2 = 1000$ and the other nonbasic variables $x_5 = x_6 = 0$. Then $z = 1016$ at the point $(3014, 1000, 503, 4019, 0, 0)$.

**17.** Stop. No maximum exists since the $x_2$ column is a potential pivot column but there is no pivot element.

**19.** Paths $O \to C \to B \to A$
$\quad\quad O \to A$

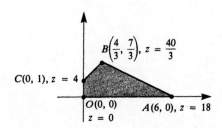

$B\left(\dfrac{4}{3}, \dfrac{7}{3}\right),\ z = \dfrac{40}{3}$

$C(0, 1),\ z = 4$

$O(0, 0)$
$z = 0$

$A(6, 0),\ z = 18$

**21.** Paths $O \to D \to C$
$\quad\quad O \to A \to B \to C$

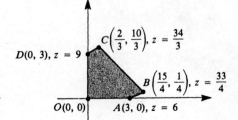

$D(0, 3),\ z = 9$

$C\left(\dfrac{2}{3}, \dfrac{10}{3}\right),\ z = \dfrac{34}{3}$

$B\left(\dfrac{15}{4}, \dfrac{1}{4}\right),\ z = \dfrac{33}{4}$

$O(0, 0)$

$A(3, 0),\ z = 6$

**23.**

Paths $O \rightarrow A \rightarrow B \rightarrow C$
$O \rightarrow A \rightarrow B \rightarrow D \rightarrow C$
$O \rightarrow A \rightarrow D \rightarrow C$
$O \rightarrow B \rightarrow C$
$O \rightarrow B \rightarrow D \rightarrow C$
$O \rightarrow C$

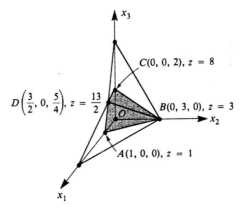

**25.** Maximum $z = 16$ at $(16, 8, 0, 0, 0, 2)$.

**27.** Maximum $z = 12$ at $(8, 34, 40, 0, 0, 0)$.

# CHAPTER 3

## Section 3.1, p. 146

**1.** $a_{12} = -1$, $a_{23} = 2$

**3.** $c_{32} = 3$, $c_{21} = 5$

**5.**
$$A^t = \begin{bmatrix} 5 & -4 \\ -1 & 3 \\ 6 & 2 \end{bmatrix}$$

**7.**
$$C^t = \begin{bmatrix} 1 & 5 & -1 \\ 6 & 2 & 3 \end{bmatrix}$$

**9.**

|  | Saws | Axes | Hatchets |  |
|---|---|---|---|---|
|  | 1500 | 750 | 350 | Downtown |
|  | 1245 | 875 | 200 | Suburban |

or transpose

**11.**

|  | Paul | Jim | Ann |  |
|---|---|---|---|---|
|  | 97 | 59 | 74 | Test 1 |
|  | 93 | 72 | 83 | Test 2 |
|  | 87 | 63 | 95 | Test 3 |
|  | 84 | 85 | 87 | Test 4 |

or transpose

**13.**
$$\begin{bmatrix} 3 & 2 & 1 \\ -7 & 7 & 3 \end{bmatrix}$$

**15.**
$$\begin{bmatrix} 20 & -4 & 24 \\ -16 & 12 & 8 \end{bmatrix}$$

**17.**
$$\begin{bmatrix} -14 \\ -10 \\ -8 \end{bmatrix}, \begin{bmatrix} 4 & 24 \\ 20 & 8 \\ -4 & 12 \end{bmatrix}$$

**19.**
$$\begin{bmatrix} -7 & 4 & -11 \\ 1 & 1 & -1 \end{bmatrix}, \begin{bmatrix} 7 & -4 & 11 \\ -1 & -1 & 1 \end{bmatrix}$$

**21.**
$$\begin{bmatrix} 1 & 5 & -4 \\ -10 & 11 & 4 \end{bmatrix}, \begin{bmatrix} -12 & 5 & -17 \\ 5 & -2 & -3 \end{bmatrix}, \begin{bmatrix} -90 & 18 & -108 \\ 72 & -54 & -36 \end{bmatrix}$$

**23.**
$$\begin{bmatrix} -1 & 8 & -6 \\ 3 & 6 & 4 \end{bmatrix}$$

**25.**
$$\begin{bmatrix} 54 \\ -5 \end{bmatrix}, \begin{bmatrix} -11 & 35 \\ 40 & -41 \end{bmatrix}$$

**27.**
$$\begin{bmatrix} -6 & 46 \\ 9 & -12 \end{bmatrix}, \begin{bmatrix} -4 \\ -11 \end{bmatrix}$$

**29.** $A(CB) = \begin{bmatrix} -126 & 166 & 76 \\ 18 & -21 & -57 \end{bmatrix} = (AC)B$

**31.** $AD + BD = \begin{bmatrix} 35 \\ -2 \end{bmatrix} = (A + B)D$

**33.** $CA + CB = \begin{bmatrix} -39 & 44 & 19 \\ 1 & 24 & 11 \\ -24 & 19 & 8 \end{bmatrix} = C(A + B)$

**35.**
$$\begin{bmatrix} 1500 & 750 & 350 \\ 1245 & 875 & 200 \end{bmatrix} \begin{matrix} w & r & \\ \begin{bmatrix} 5 & 9 \\ 7 & 13 \\ 4 & 7 \end{bmatrix} & \begin{matrix} \text{Saws} \\ \text{Axes} \\ \text{Hatchets} \end{matrix} \end{matrix}$$

**37.** (a) $[1 \ 1 \ 1 \ 1] \begin{bmatrix} 97 & 59 & 74 \\ 93 & 72 & 83 \\ 87 & 63 & 95 \\ 84 & 85 & 87 \end{bmatrix}$   (b) $\begin{bmatrix} 97 & 59 & 74 \\ 93 & 72 & 83 \\ 87 & 63 & 95 \\ 84 & 85 & 87 \end{bmatrix} \begin{bmatrix} 1 \\ 1 \\ 1 \end{bmatrix}$

**39.** $[1 \ 1] \left\{ \begin{bmatrix} 1500 & 750 & 350 \\ 1245 & 875 & 200 \end{bmatrix} \begin{bmatrix} 5 & 9 \\ 7 & 13 \\ 4 & 7 \end{bmatrix} \right\}$   $\left\{ [1 \ 1] \begin{bmatrix} 1500 & 750 & 350 \\ 1245 & 875 & 200 \end{bmatrix} \right\} \begin{bmatrix} 5 & 9 \\ 7 & 13 \\ 4 & 7 \end{bmatrix}$

**41.** (a) $(1/4)[1 \ 1 \ 1 \ 1] \begin{bmatrix} 97 & 59 & 74 \\ 93 & 72 & 83 \\ 87 & 63 & 95 \\ 84 & 85 & 87 \end{bmatrix}$   (b) $(1/3) \begin{bmatrix} 97 & 59 & 74 \\ 93 & 72 & 83 \\ 87 & 63 & 95 \\ 84 & 85 & 87 \end{bmatrix} \begin{bmatrix} 1 \\ 1 \\ 1 \end{bmatrix}$

**43.** $G^2 = \begin{bmatrix} 27 & -16 \\ -8 & 11 \end{bmatrix}$, $G^4 = \begin{bmatrix} 857 & -608 \\ -304 & 249 \end{bmatrix}$   **45.** $x = 1, y = 3$   **47.** $x = 2$
**49.** $x = 4, y = -3$

## Section 3.2, p. 158

**1.** Their product is the identity matrix.   **3.** Their product is the identity matrix.

**5.** $AG = I, BF = I, CH = I$   **7** $AF = I, BD = I$   **9.** $\begin{bmatrix} 3/30 & -3/15 \\ 2/15 & 1/15 \end{bmatrix}$   **11.** $\begin{bmatrix} 2/8 & 2/24 \\ -1/8 & 1/8 \end{bmatrix}$

**13.** No inverse   **15.** $\begin{bmatrix} -7 & 10 & 4 \\ -1 & 2 & 1 \\ 3/2 & -3/2 & -1/2 \end{bmatrix}$   **17.** No inverse   **19.** $\begin{bmatrix} 3/2 & 0 & 1 \\ -4 & 3 & 2 \\ -3 & 2 & 1 \end{bmatrix}$

**21.** $A = \begin{bmatrix} 6 & 4 & -3 \\ -5 & 3 & 2 \end{bmatrix}$, $X = \begin{bmatrix} x_1 \\ x_2 \\ x_3 \end{bmatrix}$, $B = \begin{bmatrix} -7 \\ 4 \end{bmatrix}$

**23.** $A = \begin{bmatrix} 6 & 4 & -3 \\ 3 & -8 & 2 \\ -7 & -3 & 9 \end{bmatrix}$, $X = \begin{bmatrix} x \\ y \\ z \end{bmatrix}$, $B = \begin{bmatrix} 10 \\ 4 \\ -2 \end{bmatrix}$

**25.**
$$A = \begin{bmatrix} 2 & 3 & 7 \\ 4 & 5 & -2 \\ -1 & 2 & 4 \\ -6 & -1 & 3 \end{bmatrix}, \quad X = \begin{bmatrix} x_1 \\ x_2 \\ x_3 \end{bmatrix}, \quad B = \begin{bmatrix} 2 \\ -1 \\ 4 \\ 8 \end{bmatrix}$$

**27.**
$$\begin{aligned} 2x_1 + 4x_2 &= 7 \\ -3x_1 + x_2 &= 4 \end{aligned}$$

**29.**
$$\begin{aligned} 6x_1 + 4x_2 - 2x_3 &= 8 \\ 8x_1 + x_2 + 7x_3 &= -3 \\ 5x_1 + 2x_2 - 2x_3 &= 1 \end{aligned}$$

**31.** $x = \frac{41}{29}, \ y = -\frac{20}{29}$    **33.** $x = \frac{34}{62}, \ y = \frac{38}{62}$

**35.** $x_1 = 15, \ x_2 = 1, \ x_3 = -3$    **37.** $x_1 = -\frac{63}{8}, \ x_2 = -\frac{19}{8}$    **39.** $x_1 = 1, \ x_2 = -\frac{1}{2}, \ x_3 = \frac{9}{2}$

**41.** (a) $x_1 = 25, \ x_2 = -\frac{61}{2}, \ x_3 = -\frac{19}{2}$    (b) $x_1 = 18, \ x_2 = -20, \ x_3 = -\frac{13}{2}$

**43.** $\begin{bmatrix} -1/10 & 2/10 \\ 8/10 & -6/10 \end{bmatrix}$    **45.** $\begin{bmatrix} 6/27 & -3/27 \\ -5/27 & 7/27 \end{bmatrix}$    **47.** $\begin{bmatrix} 0 & 0 & 1/c \\ 0 & 1/b & 0 \\ 1/a & 0 & 0 \end{bmatrix}$    **49.** $k = 1, \ -1$

**51.** $(A^{-1})^t A^t = (AA^{-1})^t = I^t = I.$

## Section 3.3, p. 168

**1.**
$$C = \begin{matrix} & \text{AR} & \text{M} \\ & \begin{bmatrix} .25 & .1 \\ .25 & .2 \end{bmatrix} & \begin{matrix} \text{AR} \\ \text{M} \end{matrix} \end{matrix}, \quad I - C = \begin{bmatrix} .75 & -0.1 \\ -0.25 & .8 \end{bmatrix}$$

$$(I - C)^{-1} = (1/23)\begin{bmatrix} 32 & 4 \\ 10 & 30 \end{bmatrix}, \quad X = \begin{bmatrix} 1040 \\ 900 \end{bmatrix}$$

AR – $1040, M – $900

**3.**
$$C = \begin{matrix} & \text{F} & \text{L} \\ & \begin{bmatrix} .9 & .2 \\ .1 & .6 \end{bmatrix} & \begin{matrix} \text{F} \\ \text{L} \end{matrix} \end{matrix}, \quad I - C = \begin{bmatrix} .1 & -0.2 \\ -0.1 & .4 \end{bmatrix}$$

$$(I - C)^{-1} = \begin{bmatrix} 20 & 10 \\ 5 & 5 \end{bmatrix}, \quad X = \begin{bmatrix} 4000 \\ 1500 \end{bmatrix}$$

F – $4000, L – $1500

**5.**
$$C = \begin{matrix} & \text{E} & \text{L} \\ & \begin{bmatrix} 0 & 1 \\ .4 & .5 \end{bmatrix} & \begin{matrix} \text{E} \\ \text{L} \end{matrix} \end{matrix}, \quad I - C = \begin{bmatrix} 1 & -1 \\ -0.4 & .5 \end{bmatrix}$$

$$(I - C)^{-1} = \begin{bmatrix} 5 & 10 \\ 4 & 10 \end{bmatrix}, \quad X = \begin{bmatrix} 255 \\ 232 \end{bmatrix}(1000)$$

Produce $255,000 in energy, and $232,000 in labor. Use $232,000 in energy and $218,000 in labor internally.

**7.**
$$C = \begin{matrix} & \text{P} & \text{O} \\ & \begin{bmatrix} 0 & 3 \\ .2 & .3 \end{bmatrix} & \begin{matrix} \text{P} \\ \text{O} \end{matrix} \end{matrix}, \quad I - C = \begin{bmatrix} 1 & -3 \\ -0.2 & .7 \end{bmatrix}$$

$$(I - C)^{-1} = \begin{bmatrix} 7 & 30 \\ 2 & 10 \end{bmatrix}, \quad X = \begin{bmatrix} 576 \\ 186 \end{bmatrix}\text{million}$$

576 million dollars plastic and 186 million dollars oil.

**9.**
$$C = \begin{matrix} & \text{c} & \text{h} & \text{f} \\ & \begin{bmatrix} .3 & .1 & .5 \\ .3 & .5 & .1 \\ .1 & 0 & .7 \end{bmatrix} & \begin{matrix} \text{c} \\ \text{h} \\ \text{f} \end{matrix} \end{matrix}, \quad I - C = \begin{bmatrix} .7 & -0.1 & -0.5 \\ -0.3 & .5 & -0.1 \\ -0.1 & 0 & .3 \end{bmatrix}$$

$$(I - C)^{-1} = (1/7)\begin{bmatrix} 15 & 3 & 26 \\ 10 & 16 & 22 \\ 5 & 1 & 32 \end{bmatrix}, \quad X = \begin{bmatrix} 9900 \\ 10,800 \\ 10,300 \end{bmatrix}, \quad X = \begin{bmatrix} 8500 \\ 8000 \\ 7500 \end{bmatrix}$$

1st quarter—$9900 clothing, $10,800 housing, $10,300 food
2nd quarter—$8500 clothing, $8000 housing, $7500 food

**11.** Column sums are less than 1. Profitable.
**13.** Column and row sums are less than 1. Profitable.
**15.** Row sums are less than 1. Not Profitable.
**17.** Column and row sums are less than 1. Profitable.
**19.** We need

$$\begin{bmatrix} .1 & 0 & .2 \\ .3 & 2 & .1 \\ 0 & .2 & .2 \end{bmatrix} \begin{bmatrix} a \\ b \\ c \end{bmatrix} = \begin{bmatrix} .1a + .2c \\ .3a + 2b + .1c \\ .2b + .2c \end{bmatrix} < \begin{bmatrix} a \\ b \\ c \end{bmatrix}$$

where $a$, $b$, and $c$ are nonnegative. From the second position we obtain $.3a + 2b + .1c < b$ which is impossible.

**21.** From the $k$th position of $X > CX$ we obtain the relation

$$x_k > c_{k1}x_1 + \cdots + c_{kk}x_k + \cdots + c_{kn}x_n$$

which is impossible for $c_{kj}, x_j \geqslant 0$, $c_{kk} \geqslant 1$.

## Section 3.4, p. 180

**1.** $-34$     **3.** $-13$     **5.** 140     **7.** $-58$
**9.** $M_{13} = 70$,  $A_{13} = 70$,  $M_{21} = -31$,  $A_{21} = 31$,  $M_{32} = 36$,  $A_{32} = -36$
**11.** $M_{13} = 62$,  $A_{13} = 62$,  $M_{21} = -50$,  $A_{21} = 50$,  $M_{32} = -50$,  $A_{32} = 50$

**13.** (a) $6\begin{vmatrix} 2 & 1 \\ -3 & 8 \end{vmatrix} - 4\begin{vmatrix} 7 & 1 \\ -5 & 8 \end{vmatrix} + 5\begin{vmatrix} 7 & 2 \\ -5 & -3 \end{vmatrix}$   (b) $-4\begin{vmatrix} 7 & 1 \\ -5 & 8 \end{vmatrix} + 2\begin{vmatrix} 6 & 5 \\ -5 & 8 \end{vmatrix} - (-3)\begin{vmatrix} 6 & 5 \\ 7 & 1 \end{vmatrix}$   (c) $-185$

**15.** (a) $5\begin{vmatrix} 3 & 6 & 2 \\ 2 & 1 & 4 \\ 5 & 6 & 3 \end{vmatrix} - \begin{vmatrix} 3 & 6 & 2 \\ 1 & 1 & 4 \\ 3 & 6 & 3 \end{vmatrix} + 2\begin{vmatrix} 3 & 3 & 2 \\ 1 & 2 & 4 \\ 3 & 5 & 3 \end{vmatrix} - 4\begin{vmatrix} 3 & 3 & 6 \\ 1 & 2 & 1 \\ 3 & 5 & 6 \end{vmatrix}$

(b) $-1\begin{vmatrix} 3 & 6 & 2 \\ 1 & 1 & 4 \\ 3 & 6 & 3 \end{vmatrix} + 3\begin{vmatrix} 5 & 2 & 4 \\ 1 & 1 & 4 \\ 3 & 6 & 3 \end{vmatrix} - 2\begin{vmatrix} 5 & 2 & 4 \\ 3 & 6 & 2 \\ 3 & 6 & 3 \end{vmatrix} + 5\begin{vmatrix} 5 & 2 & 4 \\ 3 & 6 & 2 \\ 1 & 1 & 4 \end{vmatrix}$   (c) 120

**17.** 270     **19.** 240     **21.** $-120$     **23.** $-174$     **25.** 100     **27.** $-10$     **29.** 248     **31.** 0
**33.** $-abc$     **35.** $k = \pm6$

## Section 3.5, p. 192

**1.** $x_1 = \frac{9}{14}$,     $x_2 = \frac{17}{14}$     **3.** $x = -\frac{13}{62}, y = \frac{27}{62}$     **5.** Not applicable     **7.** $x_1 = -\frac{43}{84}, x_2 = \frac{50}{84}, x_3 = -\frac{156}{84}$
**9.** $x = -\frac{5}{81}, y = \frac{6}{81}, z = \frac{122}{81}$     **11.** Not applicable     **13.** $\begin{bmatrix} 8 & -2 \\ 3 & 6 \end{bmatrix}$     **15.** $\begin{bmatrix} 22 & 14 & 4 \\ -12 & 31 & 21 \\ 14 & -22 & 18 \end{bmatrix}$

**17.** $(1/50)\begin{bmatrix} 9 & 2 \\ -7 & 4 \end{bmatrix}$     **19.** No inverse     **21.** $(1/156)\begin{bmatrix} 9 & 13 & 25 \\ 18 & -26 & -2 \\ 3 & 39 & -9 \end{bmatrix}$     **23.** No inverse

**25.** $55 \cdot 16 = 880$     **27.** $\det(A) = -38$, $A^{-1}$ exists, $\det(A^{-1}) = -\frac{1}{38}$     **29.** $\det(A) = 0$, no inverse
**31.** $\det(A) = 5$, $A^{-1}$ exists, $\det(A^{-1}) = \frac{1}{5}$     **33.** Determinant nonzero. No nonzero solution.

**35.** Determinant zero. Infinitely many solutions exist.
**37.** Determinant zero. Infinitely many solutions exist.
**39.** Determinant nonzero. No nonzero solution.

### Section 3.6, p. 203

**1.** (a) $A-\frac{21}{40}, B-\frac{19}{40}$ (b) $A-\frac{183}{320}, B-\frac{137}{320}$
**3.** (a) $A-\frac{16}{25}, B-\frac{9}{25}$ (b) $A-\frac{214}{375}, B-\frac{161}{375}$

**5.** $\begin{bmatrix} .65 & .45 \\ .35 & .55 \end{bmatrix}, \begin{bmatrix} .58 \\ .42 \end{bmatrix}, \begin{bmatrix} .566 \\ .434 \end{bmatrix}, \begin{bmatrix} .5625 \\ .4375 \end{bmatrix}, \begin{bmatrix} .5625 & .5625 \\ .4375 & .4375 \end{bmatrix}$

**7.** $\begin{bmatrix} .63 & .59 \\ .37 & .41 \end{bmatrix}, \begin{bmatrix} .6192 \\ .3808 \end{bmatrix}, \begin{bmatrix} .6148 \\ .3852 \end{bmatrix}, \begin{bmatrix} .6146 \\ .3854 \end{bmatrix}, \begin{bmatrix} .6146 & .6146 \\ .3854 & .3854 \end{bmatrix}$

**9.** $\begin{bmatrix} 5/6 & 1/3 \\ 1/6 & 2/3 \end{bmatrix}, \begin{bmatrix} 19/30 \\ 11/30 \end{bmatrix}, \begin{bmatrix} 13/20 \\ 7/20 \end{bmatrix}, \begin{bmatrix} 2/3 \\ 1/3 \end{bmatrix}, \begin{bmatrix} 2/3 & 2/3 \\ 1/3 & 1/3 \end{bmatrix}$

**11.** $\begin{bmatrix} .86 & .12 & .03 \\ .08 & .84 & .14 \\ .06 & .04 & .83 \end{bmatrix}, \begin{bmatrix} .4067 \\ .2682 \\ .3251 \end{bmatrix}, \begin{bmatrix} .3917 \\ .3033 \\ .3050 \end{bmatrix}, \begin{bmatrix} .3830 \\ .3901 \\ .2269 \end{bmatrix}, \begin{bmatrix} .3830 & .3830 & .3830 \\ .3901 & .3901 & .3901 \\ .2269 & .2269 & .2269 \end{bmatrix}$

**13.** yes **15.** no **17.** yes **19.** 6 **21.** 4 **23.** $\det(T-I) = \begin{vmatrix} -0.8 & .9 \\ .8 & -0.9 \end{vmatrix} = 0$

**25.** $\det(T-I) = \begin{vmatrix} -0.9 & .2 & .4 \\ .2 & -0.4 & 0 \\ .7 & .2 & -0.4 \end{vmatrix} = \begin{vmatrix} -0.9 & .2 & .4 \\ .2 & -0.4 & 0 \\ 0 & 0 & 0 \end{vmatrix} = 0$

**27.** Since $t_{11} + t_{21} = 1 = t_{12} + t_{22}$ we have

$\begin{vmatrix} t_{11}-1 & t_{12} \\ t_{21} & t_{22}-1 \end{vmatrix} = \begin{vmatrix} t_{11}-1 & t_{12} \\ 0 & 0 \end{vmatrix} = 0$

# CHAPTER 4

### Section 4.1, p. 218

**1.** $(7, -2), (4, -6), (-15, -3)$ **3.** $(1, 11, -1), (-2, 6, 4), (-6, -24, 9)$
**5.** $(-4, 10, 2, -2), (-6, 8, -10, 4), (3, -18, -21, 12)$
**7.** $\mathbf{d} = (18, 23, 10), \mathbf{e} = (15, 19, 6), \mathbf{t} = \mathbf{d} + \mathbf{e} = (33, 42, 16)$ **9.** $(16, -32)$ **11.** $(64, -48, 8)$
**13.** $\mathbf{u} = (-6, 8)$ **15.** $P_2(3, 3)$

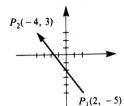

$P_2(-4, 3)$

$P_1(2, -5)$

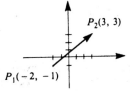

$P_2(3, 3)$

$P_1(-2, -1)$

**17.** $P_1(8, 11)$

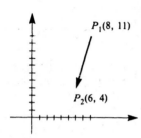

$P_1(8, 11)$

$P_2(6, 4)$

**19.** $\mathbf{u} = (-5, -9)$

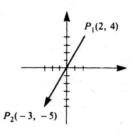

$P_1(2, 4)$

$P_2(-3, -5)$

**21.** $P_2(3, 4)$

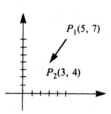

$P_1(5, 7)$

$P_2(3, 4)$

**23.** $P_1(-9, -8)$

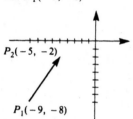

$P_2(-5, -2)$

$P_1(-9, -8)$

**25.** $P_2(1, 6, 3)$

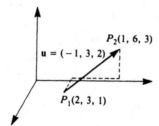

$P_2(1, 6, 3)$

$\mathbf{u} = (-1, 3, 2)$

$P_1(2, 3, 1)$

**27.** $\mathbf{u} = (3, -10, 7)$

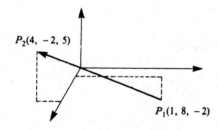

$P_2(4, -2, 5)$

$P_1(1, 8, -2)$

**29.** $P_1(-2, 0, 7)$

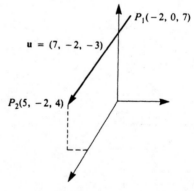

$P_1(-2, 0, 7)$

$\mathbf{u} = (7, -2, -3)$

$P_2(5, -2, 4)$

**31.**

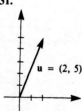

$\mathbf{u} = (2, 5)$

**33.**

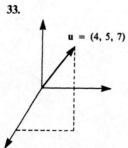

$\mathbf{u} = (4, 5, 7)$

**35.** $\sqrt{45}$   **37.** $\sqrt{41}$   **39.** $\sqrt{31}$

**41.** $\sqrt{65}$   **43.** $\sqrt{98}$   **45.** $\sqrt{19}$

**47.**

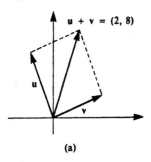

(a)

v

u + v = (2, 8)

(b)

u + v = (-1, -11)

(b)

**49.**

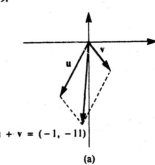

u + v = (-1, -11)

(a)

**51.** (5, 15)

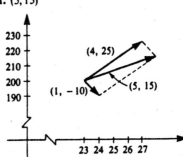

**53.**

u + v + w = (7, 7)

w

v

u

**55.**

u = (8, 2)

u - v = (4, 8)

v = (4, -6)

**57.**

u - v = (8, -8, -3)

v

u

**59.**

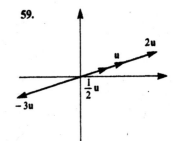

2u

u

½u

-3u

**61.** $(2, -7) + t(5, -3)$ **63.** $(3, 5, -7) + t(-8, 4, 2)$ **65.** $(6, 2, 8, -7, -3) + t(3, 5, -3, 6, 7)$
**67.** $(4, -5) + t(-10, 8)$ **69.** $(5, -5, 2) + t(7, -9, 1)$ **71.** $(4, 1, -3, -2) + t(2, 4, -1, 10)$

**73.** $x = 4 + 3t,\ y = 5 - 2t$ **75.** $x = 3 + 2t,\ y = 2 + 3t,\ z = 1 + 6t$

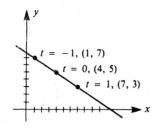

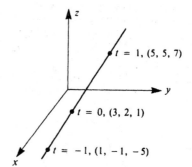

**77.** $(7, 3) + t(5, -3)$

## Section 4.2, p. 228

**1.** $\mathbf{v} = (0, -4)$ **3.** $\mathbf{v} = (16, 30)$ **5.** $\mathbf{v} = (27, -9)$ **7.** $\mathbf{v} = (4, -14, 0)$ **9.** $\mathbf{v} = (28, 6, 5)$
**11.** $\mathbf{v} = 2\mathbf{u}_1 + (\frac{3}{2})\mathbf{u}_2$ **13.** $\mathbf{v} = 3\mathbf{u}_1 + 2\mathbf{u}_2$

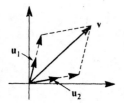

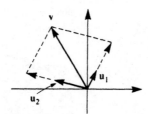

**15.** Yes, $\mathbf{v} = 2\mathbf{u}_1 + \mathbf{u}_2$ **17.** Not possible
**19.** One-day output at Skokie can be replaced by 2-days output at Cicero plus $\frac{1}{3}$-day output at Berwyn.
**21.** $x_1 = 6, x_2 = -2$ **23.** $x_1 = 3, x_2 = -1, x_3 = 2$ **25.** $(13, 4), (2, 8) = 13(2, 4) + 4(-6, -11)$
**27.** $(2, \frac{1}{2}, 1), \mathbf{b} = 2\mathbf{a}_1 + \frac{1}{2}\mathbf{a}_2 + \mathbf{a}_3$ **29.** $(48 - 25t, -14 + 7t, t), t = 0, \mathbf{b} = 48\mathbf{a}_1 - 14\mathbf{a}_2 + 0\mathbf{a}_3$

## Section 4.3, p. 242

**1.** $\mathbf{b} = 4\mathbf{e}_1 + 2\mathbf{e}_2 - 3\mathbf{e}_3$ **3.** $\mathbf{b} = -6\mathbf{e}_1 - 8\mathbf{e}_2 + 2\mathbf{e}_3$
**5.** $\mathbf{v}_1 + \mathbf{v}_2 = 10\mathbf{u}_1 - 3\mathbf{u}_2 - 6\mathbf{u}_3, 3\mathbf{v}_1 = 12\mathbf{u}_1 - 15\mathbf{u}_2 + 3\mathbf{u}_3, 2\mathbf{v}_1 - 4\mathbf{v}_2 = -16\mathbf{u}_1 - 18\mathbf{u}_2 + 30\mathbf{u}_3$
**7.** $\mathbf{v}_1 + \mathbf{v}_2 = -12\mathbf{u}_1 + 5\mathbf{u}_2 - \mathbf{u}_3, 3\mathbf{v}_1 = -24\mathbf{u}_1 + 6\mathbf{u}_2 - 18\mathbf{u}_3, 2\mathbf{v}_1 - 4\mathbf{v}_2 = -8\mathbf{u}_2 - 32\mathbf{u}_3$
**9.** Yes—line through the origin **11.** No—does not contain the origin **13.** No—does not contain the origin
**15.** Yes—plane through the origin **17.** All multiples of $(-5, -2, 1)$ **19.** All multiples of $(2, 1, 0)$

**21.** **0** alone    **23.** All linear combinations of $(-50, 12, 1, 0)$ and $(23, -5, 0, 1)$

**25.** $\mathbf{u}$ — no, $\mathbf{v} = (-7 - 2s)\mathbf{a}_1 + (-2 - s)\mathbf{a}_2 + s\mathbf{a}_3$, any $s$

**27.** $\mathbf{u} = (1 - 3s)\mathbf{a}_1 + (-\frac{5}{2} - s)\mathbf{a}_2 + s\mathbf{a}_3$, any $s$   $\mathbf{v}$ — no

**29.** $4x + y + 3z = 0$    **31.** $-3x - y + z = 0$

**33.** $21x - 9y + z = 0$    **35.** $17x + 9y + z = 0$

$\quad \mathbf{b} = (5x - 2y)\mathbf{a}_1 + (y - 2x)\mathbf{a}_2$    $\quad \mathbf{b} = (-\frac{5}{3}x - y)\mathbf{a}_1 + (-y - 2x)\mathbf{a}_2$

**37.** All $x, y, z$    $\mathbf{b} = (9x - 3y - z)\mathbf{a}_1 + (-2x + y + z)\mathbf{a}_2 + (3x - y)\mathbf{a}_3$

**39.** North End $\mathbf{a}_1 = (92, 6, 2)$, East Side $\mathbf{a}_2 = (70, 20, 10)$

First bottle type, $(74, 22, 4)$ cannot be manufactured.

Second bottle type, $(81, 13, 6) = \frac{1}{2}\mathbf{a}_1 + \frac{1}{2}\mathbf{a}_2$

Bottle type $(a, b, c)$, $[a + b + c = 100]$, can be produced if $4b - 7c = 10$. That is, four times the percentage of brown glass minus seven times the percentage of green glass equals ten.

## Section 4.4, p. 253

**1.** $(4, -3, 11) = -2(1, 0, -4) + 3(2, -1, 1)$

**3.** $(2, 1, 0, -3) = 2(2, 3, 1, -1) + 3(-1, -3, 2, 4) + (1, 4, -8, -5)$

**5.** $\mathbf{u}_1 = -\frac{2}{3}\mathbf{u}_2 - \frac{1}{3}\mathbf{u}_3 + \frac{5}{3}\mathbf{u}_4$

**7.** The vector equation has solutions $(-\frac{1}{2}t, \frac{5}{4}t, t)$   **9.** The vector equation has solutions $(-2t, -3t, t)$

$\quad t = 4: \ -2(1, 4) + 5(2, -4) + 4(-2, 7) = (0, 0)$   $\quad t = 1: \ -2(2, 3, -5) - 3(-4, -1, 3) + (-8, 3, -1) = (0, 0, 0)$

$\quad (1, 4) = \frac{5}{2}(2, -4) + 2(-2, 7)$   $\quad (2, 3, -5) = -\frac{3}{2}(-4, -1, 3) + \frac{1}{2}(-8, 3, -1)$

**11.** The vector equation has solutions $(-3s - 2t, -2s - 3t, s, t)$

$\quad s = 1, t = 1: \ -5(-2, 5, 1, -3) - 5(4, -2, 3, -4) + (2, 11, 9, -17) + (8, 4, 11, -18) = \mathbf{0}$

$\quad (8, 4, 11, -18) = 5(-2, 5, 1, -3) + 5(4, -2, 3, -4) - (2, 11, 9, -17)$

**13, 15, 17, 19, 21.** The vector equation or the homogeneous system has the unique solution **0**.

**23.** Linearly independent.    **25.** $4(2, -2, 3) + (-4, 5, -1) - (4, -3, 11) = (0, 0, 0,)$

**27.** Linearly independent.    **29.** Linearly independent.    **31.** Linearly dependent.

**33.** Three vectors in $R^2$ are linearly dependent.    **35.** Linearly independent.

**37.** Four vectors in $R^3$ are linearly dependent.    **39.** $k = -1$    **41.** $k = -5$

**43.** Three days at plant 1, 6 days at plant 2, 3 days at plant 4.

## Section 4.5, p. 265

**1.** $(8, 3) = 8(1, 0) + 3(0, 1)$    **3.** $(-6, 4) = -6(1, 0) + 4(0, 1)$

**5.** $(4, -2, 8) = 4(1, 0, 0) - 2(0, 1, 0) + 8(0, 0, 1)$    **7.** $(5, -2, 0) = 5(1, 0, 0) - 2(0, 1, 0)$

**9.** $(6, 4, 9, -1) = 6\mathbf{e}_1 + 4\mathbf{e}_2 + 9\mathbf{e}_3 - \mathbf{e}_4$    **11.** $(-\frac{1}{4}, 1, 0), (-\frac{3}{4}, 0, 1)$    **13.** $(-\frac{1}{2}, 1, 0), (\frac{3}{2}, 0, 1)$

**15.** $\begin{bmatrix} 2 & 4 \\ 5 & 3 \end{bmatrix}^{-1} = (-1/14) \begin{bmatrix} 3 & -4 \\ -5 & 2 \end{bmatrix}$,    $\mathbf{b} = -\frac{25}{14}\mathbf{u}_1 + \frac{37}{14}\mathbf{u}_2$

17. $\begin{bmatrix} 1 & -2 \\ 4 & 5 \end{bmatrix}^{-1} = (1/13) \begin{bmatrix} 5 & 2 \\ -4 & 1 \end{bmatrix}$, $\mathbf{b} = (\tfrac{1}{13})(5b_1 + 2b_2)\mathbf{u}_1 + (\tfrac{1}{13})(-4b_1 + b_2)\mathbf{u}_2$

19. $\begin{bmatrix} 2 & 4 & -2 \\ 3 & 8 & -5 \\ -4 & -5 & 0 \end{bmatrix}^{-1} = \begin{bmatrix} 25/4 & -5/2 & 1 \\ -20/4 & 4/2 & -1 \\ -17/4 & 3/2 & -1 \end{bmatrix}$, $\mathbf{b} = 38\mathbf{u}_1 - 31\mathbf{u}_2 - 28\mathbf{u}_3$

21. $(-10, 2) = -2(5, -1)$     23. $(8, -12) = 4(2, -3)$

25. $2(1, 4, -2) + 3(-2, -7, 4) = (-4, -13, 8)$

27. There are only $2 < 3$ vectors.     29. $k = 1$

31. $\begin{array}{c} \\ \mathbf{a}_1 \\ \mathbf{a}_2 \end{array} \begin{array}{ccccc} \mathbf{a}_1 & \mathbf{a}_2 & \mathbf{a}_3 & \mathbf{a}_4 & \mathbf{a}_5 \\ \begin{bmatrix} 1 & 0 & 1 & 1 & -2 \\ 0 & 1 & 2 & 1 & -2 \end{bmatrix} \end{array}$, $\mathbf{a}_5 = -2\mathbf{a}_1 - 2\mathbf{a}_2$

33. $\begin{array}{c} \\ \mathbf{a}_1 \\ \mathbf{a}_3 \\ \mathbf{a}_4 \end{array} \begin{array}{ccccc} \mathbf{a}_1 & \mathbf{a}_2 & \mathbf{a}_3 & \mathbf{a}_4 & \mathbf{a}_5 \\ \begin{bmatrix} 1 & -3 & 0 & 0 & 12 \\ 0 & 0 & 1 & 0 & -10 \\ 0 & 0 & 0 & 1 & -6 \end{bmatrix} \end{array}$, $\mathbf{a}_5 = 12\mathbf{a}_1 - 10\mathbf{a}_3 - 6\mathbf{a}_4$

35. $\begin{array}{c} \\ \mathbf{a}_1 \\ \mathbf{a}_2 \end{array} \begin{array}{ccc} \mathbf{a}_1 & \mathbf{a}_2 & \mathbf{b} \\ \begin{bmatrix} 1 & 0 & | & -1 \\ 0 & 1 & | & -2 \end{bmatrix} \end{array}$, $\mathbf{b} = -\mathbf{a}_1 - 2\mathbf{a}_2$

37. $\begin{array}{c} \\ \mathbf{a}_1 \\ \mathbf{a}_3 \end{array} \begin{array}{cccc} \mathbf{a}_1 & \mathbf{a}_2 & \mathbf{a}_3 & \mathbf{b} \\ \begin{bmatrix} 1 & -2 & 0 & | & 2 \\ 0 & 0 & 1 & | & -3 \end{bmatrix} \end{array}$, $\mathbf{b} = 2\mathbf{a}_1 - 3\mathbf{a}_3$    $(2, 0, -3)$

39. $\begin{array}{c} \\ \mathbf{a}_1 \\ \mathbf{a}_2 \\ \mathbf{e}_3 \end{array} \begin{array}{ccc} \mathbf{a}_1 & \mathbf{a}_2 & \mathbf{b} \\ \begin{bmatrix} 1 & 0 & | & 3 \\ 0 & 1 & | & -1 \\ 0 & 0 & | & 0 \end{bmatrix} \end{array}$, $\mathbf{b} = 3\mathbf{a}_1 - \mathbf{a}_2$    $(3, -1)$

41. $\begin{array}{c} \\ \mathbf{a}_1 \\ \mathbf{a}_2 \end{array} \begin{array}{ccc} \mathbf{a}_1 & \mathbf{a}_2 & \mathbf{a}_3 \\ \begin{bmatrix} 1 & 0 & -7 \\ 0 & 1 & -2 \end{bmatrix} \end{array}$ Basis $\mathbf{a}_1, \mathbf{a}_2$ $\mathbf{a}_3 = -7\mathbf{a}_1 - 2\mathbf{a}_2$

43. $\begin{array}{c} \\ \mathbf{a}_1 \\ \mathbf{a}_3 \end{array} \begin{array}{cccc} \mathbf{a}_1 & \mathbf{a}_2 & \mathbf{a}_3 & \mathbf{a}_4 \\ \begin{bmatrix} 1 & -3 & 0 & 6 \\ 0 & 0 & 1 & -2 \end{bmatrix} \end{array}$ Basis $\mathbf{a}_1, \mathbf{a}_3$ $\mathbf{a}_2 = -3\mathbf{a}_1$ $\mathbf{a}_4 = 6\mathbf{a}_1 - 2\mathbf{a}_3$

45. $\begin{array}{c} \\ \mathbf{a}_1 \\ \mathbf{a}_2 \\ \mathbf{a}_4 \end{array} \begin{array}{ccccc} \mathbf{a}_1 & \mathbf{a}_2 & \mathbf{a}_3 & \mathbf{a}_4 & \mathbf{a}_5 \\ \begin{bmatrix} 1 & 0 & 3 & 0 & -1 \\ 0 & 1 & -2 & 0 & -2 \\ 0 & 0 & 0 & 1 & 2 \end{bmatrix} \end{array}$ Basis $\mathbf{a}_1, \mathbf{a}_2, \mathbf{a}_4$ $\mathbf{a}_3 = 3\mathbf{a}_1 - 2\mathbf{a}_2$ $\mathbf{a}_5 = -\mathbf{a}_1 - 2\mathbf{a}_2 + 2\mathbf{a}_4$

47. Oat squares    $\mathbf{a}_1 = (120, 6, 20)$
Dry milk    $\mathbf{a}_2 = (100, 10, 20)$
Dry potatoes    $\mathbf{a}_3 = (100, 2, 20)$
Noodles    $\mathbf{a}_4 = (110, 4, 20)$
$\mathbf{a}_4 = \tfrac{1}{2}\mathbf{a}_1 + 0\mathbf{a}_2 + \tfrac{1}{2}\mathbf{a}_3$
$\tfrac{1}{2}$ ounce oat squares plus $\tfrac{1}{2}$ ounce dry potatoes yield 1 ounce of synthetic noodles. The cost of synthetic noodles is $\tfrac{1}{2}(7) + \tfrac{1}{2}(5) = 6$ cents per ounce. This is greater than the 3 cents per ounce cost of real noodles.

## Section 4.6, p. 273

1. Yes, since two linearly independent vectors form a basis.
3. No, since the vectors are linearly dependent.
5. $(\frac{5}{2}, 1)$   7. $(-\frac{7}{4}, 0, 1)$, $(\frac{1}{2}, 1, 0)$
9. $\mathbf{v}_1 = \frac{1}{2}\mathbf{u}_2$, $\mathbf{v}_2 = \mathbf{u}_1$, $\mathbf{v}_3 = \mathbf{u}_3 - 2\mathbf{u}_2$
   $\mathbf{u}_1 = \mathbf{v}_2$, $\mathbf{u}_2 = 2\mathbf{v}_1$, $\mathbf{u}_3 = \mathbf{v}_3 + 4\mathbf{v}_1$
11. $\mathbf{w}_1 = 38\mathbf{v}_1 + 13\mathbf{v}_2$, $\mathbf{w}_2 = 6\mathbf{v}_1 + 33\mathbf{v}_2$
13. Refer to Exercises 9–10. Let the matrix $B'$ be obtained from the matrix $B$ by row operations. Then the rows of $B'$ can be written as linear combinations of the rows of $B$ and conversely. Refer to Exercises 11–12. If a set of vectors can each be written in terms of a second set of vectors and each of the vectors in the second set can be written in terms of vectors in a third set, then the vectors in the first set can each be written in terms of the vectors in the third set. Therefore, the rows of $E$ can be written in terms of the rows of $A$, and the rows of $A$ can be written in terms of the rows of $E$.
15. Rank = 2, Nullity = 1. Basis: $(3, -1, 1)$.
17. Rank = 2, Nullity = 2. Basis: $(2, 1, 0, 0)$, $(-4, 0, 2, 1)$.
19. $(2, -2, 1) + t(3, -1, 1)$
21. $(5, 2, -1, -2) + s(2, 1, 0, 0) + t(-4, 0, 2, 1)$

## Section 4.7, p. 299

1. $z = -18$ at $(\frac{5}{2}, \frac{1}{2}, 0, 0)$
3. $z = -20$ at $(0, 7, 0, 2, 0, 0)$
5. $z = -32$ at $(0, 4, 6, 8, 0, 0)$
7. Column bases $\mathbf{a}_2$, $\mathbf{a}_4$, basic variables $x_2$, $x_4$.   9. Column basis $\mathbf{a}_1$, $\mathbf{a}_2$, basic variables $x_1$, $x_2$.
   $\mathbf{b} = 2\mathbf{a}_2 + 3\mathbf{a}_4$, $\mathbf{a}_3 = \frac{1}{4}\mathbf{a}_2 - \frac{1}{2}\mathbf{a}_4$   $\mathbf{b} = 2\mathbf{a}_1 + \frac{9}{2}\mathbf{a}_2$, $\mathbf{a}_3 = 3\mathbf{a}_1 + 5\mathbf{a}_2$
11. Column basis $\mathbf{a}_4$, $\mathbf{a}_2$, $\mathbf{a}_1$, basic variables $x_4$, $x_2$, $x_1$.
   $\mathbf{b} = 13\mathbf{a}_4 + \frac{1}{2}\mathbf{a}_2 + 2\mathbf{a}_1$, $\mathbf{a}_3 = -4\mathbf{a}_4 + 3\mathbf{a}_2 - 14\mathbf{a}_1$
13. $(1, 0) = -\frac{1}{2}(2, 4) - (-2, -2)$,   $(0, 1) = \frac{1}{2}(2, 4) + \frac{1}{2}(-2, -2)$,
   $(4, 9) = \frac{5}{2}(2, 4) + \frac{1}{2}(-2, -2)$
15. $(3, 2) = -(1, 2) - 2(-2, -2)$,   $(-1, 1) = 2(1, 2) + \frac{3}{2}(-2, -2)$
   $(1, 0) = -(1, 2) - (-2, -2)$,   $(0, 1) = (1, 2) + \frac{1}{2}(-2, -2)$
   $(3, 10) = 7(1, 2) + 2(-2, -2)$
17. $(-3, 2, 5) = -4(1, 0, 0) - (2, 1, 4) - 3(-1, -1, -3)$   $(0, 1, 0) = 2(1, 0, 0) - 3(2, 1, 4) - 4(-1, -1, -3)$
   $(0, 0, 1) = -(1, 0, 0) + (2, 1, 4) + (-1, -1, -3)$   $(16, 2, 12) = 8(1, 0, 0) + 6(2, 1, 4) + 4(-1, -1, -3)$
19. $\begin{aligned} 4x_1 - 2x_2 + x_3 &= 7 \\ 3x_1 + 5x_2 \quad\;\; - x_4 &= 4 \\ -6x_1 - 2x_2 \quad\quad &= 4 \end{aligned}$   21. $\begin{aligned} -4x_1 - x_2 - 3x_3 + x_4 &= 2 \\ 6x_1 - 5x_2 - 2x_3 \quad\;\; - x_5 &= 4 \\ -5x_1 + 3x_2 + x_3 \quad\quad\;\; + x_6 &= 2 \\ 3x_1 - 4x_2 - 7x_3 \quad\quad\quad\;\; - x_7 &= 5 \\ 5x_1 + 8x_2 - 2x_3 \quad\quad\quad\quad &= 4 \end{aligned}$

23. Minimize      $z = y_1 + y_2$
    subject to    $2x_1 + 3x_2 - x_3 + y_1 = 4$
                  $-3x_1 - 2x_2 + x_3 \quad\;\; + y_2 = 6$
                  $x_1 \geqslant 0, \quad x_2 \geqslant 0, \quad x_3 \geqslant 0, \quad y_1 \geqslant 0, \quad y_2 \geqslant 0$

|  | $\mathbf{a}_1$ | $\mathbf{a}_2$ | $\mathbf{a}_3$ | $\mathbf{a}_4$ | $\mathbf{a}_5$ | $\mathbf{b}$ |
|---|---|---|---|---|---|---|
| | 1 | $-1$ | 1 | 0 | 0 | 10 |
| $\mathbf{a}_4$ | 0 | 2 | 3 | $-1$ | 1 | 0 | 4 |
| $\mathbf{a}_5$ | 0 | $-3$ | $-2$ | 1 | 0 | 1 | 6 |

**25.** Minimize    $z = y_1 + y_2 + y_3$
subject to

$$6x_1 + 2x_2 - 4x_3 + y_1 \qquad\qquad = 3$$
$$-x_1 - 3x_2 - 5x_3 \qquad + y_2 \qquad = 4$$
$$5x_1 - 4x_2 - x_3 \qquad\qquad + y_3 = 2$$
$$x_1 \geqslant 0, \quad x_2 \geqslant 0, \quad x_3 \geqslant 0, \quad y_1 \geqslant 0, \quad y_2 \geqslant 0, \quad y_3 \geqslant 0$$

$$\begin{array}{c}\\ \mathbf{a_4} \\ \mathbf{a_5} \\ \mathbf{a_6}\end{array}
\begin{array}{c}\begin{array}{cccccccc} & \mathbf{a_1} & \mathbf{a_2} & \mathbf{a_3} & \mathbf{a_4} & \mathbf{a_5} & \mathbf{a_6} & \mathbf{b}\end{array}\\
\left[\begin{array}{c|ccc|ccc|c}
1 & 10 & -5 & -10 & 0 & 0 & 0 & 9 \\
0 & 6 & 2 & -4 & 1 & 0 & 0 & 3 \\
0 & -1 & -3 & -5 & 0 & 1 & 0 & 4 \\
0 & 5 & -4 & -1 & 0 & 0 & 1 & 2
\end{array}\right]\end{array}$$

**27.** $(4, 0, 1)$      **29.** $(0, 2, 7, 0)$      **31.** $(3, 0, 10, 1)$      **33.** None
**35.** One day on each of lines **2, 3, 4.**
**37.** Minimum $z = 84$ at $(17, 0, 0, 33)$
**39.** Minimum $z = -\frac{13}{2}$ at $(5, \frac{1}{2}, 0, 0)$
**41.** The corresponding top row entries are $0 - 1\ 0\ 4\ 11$. $z_2 = 5$, $c_2 = 6$. The equivalent basic process is cheaper. $z_4 = 8$, $c_4 = 4$. The actual process is cheaper.
**43.** Operate line 2 for $\frac{29}{3}$ days at a cost of $\$\frac{5800}{3}$. There will be an overproduction of $\frac{1400}{3}$ cases of cola.

# CHAPTER 5

## Section 5.1, p. 312

**1.** 22      **3.** 11      **5.** $-12$

**7.** $\begin{bmatrix} 2 & -9 \end{bmatrix}\begin{bmatrix} 6 \\ 3 \end{bmatrix}$      **9.** $\begin{bmatrix} 6 & -7 & 3 \end{bmatrix}\begin{bmatrix} 4 \\ 2 \\ -1 \end{bmatrix}$      **11.** 61      **13.** 66      **15.** $\mathbf{u}\cdot\mathbf{v} + \mathbf{u}\cdot\mathbf{w} = -25 = \mathbf{u}\cdot(\mathbf{v} + \mathbf{w})$

**17.** $\mathbf{u}\cdot\mathbf{v} + \mathbf{u}\cdot\mathbf{w} = 27 = \mathbf{u}\cdot(\mathbf{v} + \mathbf{w})$      **19.** Orthogonal      **21.** Not orthogonal      **23.** Orthogonal
**25.** Not orthogonal      **27.** Orthogonal      **29.** $k = 8$      **31.** $(-9, 8, 2)$      **33.** $(-3, 1, 1)$
**35.** $(5, -6, -3)\cdot(x - 2, y + 4, z - 7) = 0$, $5x - 6y - 3z = 13$   or   $5(x - 2) - 6(y + 4) - 3(z - 7) = 0$
**37.** $(2, 8, 9)\cdot(x - 4, y + 4, z - 3) = 0$, $2x + 8y + 9z = 3$   or   $2(x - 4) + 8(y + 4) + 9(z - 3) = 0$
**39.** $4(x - 2) - 3(y - 0) + 5(z - 0) = 0$      **41.** $5(x - 0) + 2(y - 3) - 7(z - 0) = 0$      **43.** $(6, -5, 2)$
**45.** $(5, 6, 6)\cdot(x - 5, y + 1, z - 3) = 0$      **47.** $(2, -7, -11)\cdot(x + 6, y + 9, z + 2) = 0$
$\quad\ 5x + 6y + 6z = 37$      $\qquad\qquad\quad 2x - 7y - 11z = 73$
**49.** $(3, -3, 1)\cdot(x + 1, y - 1, z + 2) = 0$      **51.** $(-12, 4, 1)\cdot(x - 2, y - 4, z - 2) = 0$
$\quad\ 3x - 3y + z = -8$      $\qquad\qquad\quad -12x + 4y + z = -6$
**53.** Unique point $(-\frac{91}{5}, \frac{88}{5}, -\frac{53}{5})$      **55.** 0      **57.** Infinite

## Section 5 2, p. 324

**1.** $\frac{1}{5}(3, 4)$      **3.** $1/\sqrt{21}\,(1, -2, 4)$      **5.** $1/\sqrt{22}\,(-1, -2, 4, 1)$
**7.** The vectors have length 1, and scalar product 0.
**9.** The vectors have length 1, and have scalar product 0.
**11.** The vectors have length 1, and have scalar product 0 in pairs.      **13.** $(7, 3) = 1/\sqrt{5}\,\mathbf{v}_1 + 17/\sqrt{5}\,\mathbf{v}_2$
**15.** $(-3, 1) = -5/\sqrt{5}\,\mathbf{v}_1 - 5/\sqrt{5}\,\mathbf{v}_2$      **17.** $(2, 2, -3) = -1/\sqrt{6}\,\mathbf{v}_1 + 5/\sqrt{11}\,\mathbf{v}_2 + 31/\sqrt{66}\,\mathbf{v}_3$

**19.** $(-2, 4, 3) = 13/\sqrt{6}\,\mathbf{v}_1 + 1/\sqrt{11}\,\mathbf{v}_2 - 7/\sqrt{66}\,\mathbf{v}_3$

**21.** $\text{Proj}_v(\mathbf{u}) = (3, 3)$
$\mathbf{u}' = (-1, 1)$

**23.** $\text{Proj}_v(\mathbf{u}) = (-\frac{9}{2}, \frac{3}{2})$
$\mathbf{u}' = (\frac{1}{2}, \frac{3}{2})$

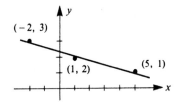

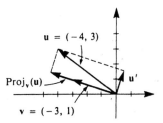

**25.** $\text{Proj}_v(\mathbf{u}) = -\frac{13}{41}(4, 5),$ $\mathbf{u}' = \frac{1}{41}(-235, 188)$

**27.** $\text{Proj}_v(\mathbf{u}) = -\frac{1}{11}(-2, 2, 6),$ $\mathbf{u}' = \frac{1}{11}(9, 57, -16)$

**29.** $\text{Proj}_v(\mathbf{u}) = -\frac{2}{69}(7, 2, -4),$ $\mathbf{u}' = \frac{1}{69}(152, 142, 337)$

**31.** $\text{Proj}_S(\mathbf{u}) = \frac{1}{9}(14, -8, -1),$ $\mathbf{u}' = \frac{13}{9}(1, 2, -2)$

**33.** $\text{Proj}_S(\mathbf{u}) = \frac{1}{9}(-4, 1, -1),$ $\mathbf{u}' = \frac{13}{9}(1, 2, -2)$

**35.** $|\mathbf{u} - \text{Proj}_S(\mathbf{u})| = |(0, 1, 1)| = \sqrt{2}$

**37.** $\frac{1}{5}(4, 3), \frac{1}{5}(-3, 4)$    **39.** $1/\sqrt{6}(1, 1, 2), 1/\sqrt{66}(7, 1, -4), 1/\sqrt{11}(-1, 3, -1)$

**41.** $1/\sqrt{2}(-1, 1, 0), 1/\sqrt{27}(-1, -1, 5)$    **43.** $1/\sqrt{10}(3, 1, 0), 1/\sqrt{65}(-2, 6, 5)$

## Section 5.3, p. 334

**1.** $y = (-\frac{21}{74})x + \frac{176}{74}$

**3.** $y = (-\frac{32}{13})x - \frac{15}{13}$

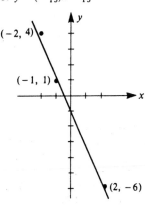

**5.** $y = (-\frac{121}{251})x - \frac{288}{251}$    **7.** $y = (-\frac{30}{37})x - \frac{73}{37}$

**9.** $y = .15x + 1.32$    **11.** $y = .314x - .933$

**13.** $(-1, 4.5), (0, 4.8), (1, 5), y = .25x + 4.77, \$5270$

**15.** $(-1, 1), (0, 1.03), (1, 1.08), y = .04x + 1.037,$ July 15 for $\$1157$

**17.** $(-2, 9.2), (-1, 9.1), (0, 8.9), (1, 8.8), (2, 8.6)$
$y = -0.15x + 8.92,$ 886 sets, $\$451,860$

## Section 5.4, p. 352

**1.** $\begin{bmatrix} 6 & 6 & | & -12 \\ 6 & 24 & | & -6 \end{bmatrix}$    $\mathbf{u} = (-\frac{7}{3}, \frac{1}{3})$
$\text{Proj}_A\mathbf{b} = (3, -4, -1)$

**3.** $\begin{bmatrix} 3 & -3 & | & 3 \\ -3 & 27 & | & 15 \end{bmatrix}$    $\mathbf{u} = (\frac{7}{4}, \frac{3}{4})$
$\text{Proj}_A\mathbf{b} = (\frac{1}{2}, 4, \frac{1}{2})$

**5.** $\frac{1}{3}\begin{bmatrix} 3 & 3 & 0 \\ 1 & 2 & 1 \end{bmatrix}$    **7.** $\frac{1}{35}\begin{bmatrix} -4 & 12 & 7 & 1 \\ 11 & 2 & 7 & 6 \end{bmatrix}$    **9.** $(7, 4)$    **11.** $(\frac{2}{35}, \frac{82}{35})$

**13.** Use .62 units of syrup one to .39 units of syrup two. The blend will be 84.9% corn syrup, 12.5% fructose, 2.5% maple syrup. (*Note:* perform division by $\det(A'A)$ last, or keep 6-decimal-place accuracy.)

**15.** $y = -x + \frac{4}{50}$    **17.** $y = .25x^2 + .11x + .63$    The vertex is $(-0.22, .6179)$

**19.** $y = -0.75x^2 - 0.65x + 1.15$    The vertex is $(-0.4333, 1.291)$    **21.** $y = 9/x + 1/3$

**23.** Let the points be $(-2, 2), (-1, 2.1), (0, 2.3), (1, 2.2), (2, 2.1)$. Then the equation is $y = -0.05x^2 + .03x + 2.24$. The vertex is $(.3, 2.2445)$. Thus sales of 224.45 occur at the price $\$17.50 + \$0.15 = \$17.65$.

# CHAPTER 6

## Section 6.1, p. 364

**1.** $Ax = (12, 8) = 4x$    **3.** $Ax = (3, 3) = 3x$

**5.** $Ax = (-8, -4, -2) = -2x$

**7.** $\lambda^2 - \lambda - 6 = 0, \lambda = 3, -2$    **9.** $\lambda^2 - 4 = 0, \lambda = 2, -2$    **11.** $\lambda^2 - 2\lambda - 9 = 0, \lambda = 1 \pm \sqrt{10}$

**13.** $\lambda^2 - 9\lambda + 26 = 0$, none    **15.** $-\lambda^3 + 2\lambda^2 + \lambda - 2 = 0, \lambda = 2, -1, 1$

**17.** $-\lambda^3 + 2\lambda^2 - \lambda = 0, \lambda = 1, 1, 0$    **19.** $-\lambda^3 + 15\lambda^2 - 22\lambda - 8 = 0, \lambda = 2, (13 \pm \sqrt{185})/2$

**21.** $-\lambda^3 + 2\lambda^2 + 2\lambda + 3 = 0, \lambda = 3$    **23.** $\lambda^2 - 8\lambda + 15 = 0; \lambda = 3, s(1, 1); \lambda = 5, t(1, 2)$

**25.** $\lambda^2 + 10\lambda + 24 = 0; \lambda = -4, s(1, -2); \lambda = -6, t(2, -3)$    **27.** $\lambda^2 - 6\lambda + 9 = 0; \lambda = 3, 3, s(1, -2)$

**29.** $-\lambda^3 + \lambda^2 + 4\lambda - 4 = 0; \lambda = -2, r(1, 0, 2); \lambda = 1, t(2, 3, 4); \lambda = 2, s(5, 4, 6)$

**31.** $-\lambda^3 + 3\lambda^2 - 4 = 0; \lambda = 2, 2, s(1, 1, 0) + t(1, 0, 1); \lambda = -1, r(1, -2, 4)$

**33.** $-\lambda^3 + 5\lambda^2 - 7\lambda + 3 = 0; \lambda = 1, 1, s(1, 0, 1); \lambda = 3, t(3, -1, 2)$

**35.** $-\lambda^3 + 4\lambda^2 - 9\lambda + 10 = 0; \lambda = 2, s(3, 2, 2)$

**37.** The system $\begin{bmatrix} 0 & b \\ 0 & 0 \end{bmatrix} \begin{bmatrix} x_1 \\ x_2 \end{bmatrix} = \begin{bmatrix} 0 \\ 0 \end{bmatrix}$ has the solutions $x_2 = 0, x_1 = t$, any number.

**39.** $\begin{bmatrix} -8 & -9 \\ 12 & -11 \end{bmatrix} + \begin{bmatrix} -6 & 9 \\ -12 & -3 \end{bmatrix} + \begin{bmatrix} 14 & 0 \\ 0 & 14 \end{bmatrix} = \begin{bmatrix} 0 & 0 \\ 0 & 0 \end{bmatrix}$

**41.** $\begin{bmatrix} 15 & -3 & -66 \\ 24 & 96 & 48 \\ -30 & -42 & 60 \end{bmatrix} + \begin{bmatrix} 15 & 57 & 30 \\ -24 & -48 & 24 \\ -6 & -48 & -48 \end{bmatrix} + \begin{bmatrix} -18 & -54 & 36 \\ 0 & -36 & -72 \\ 36 & 90 & 0 \end{bmatrix} - 12I = O$

**43.** $A^2v = A(Av) = A(\lambda v) = \lambda(Av) = \lambda(\lambda v) = \lambda^2 v.$

## Section 6.2, p. 375

**1.** $\begin{bmatrix} 3 & 5 \\ 1 & 2 \end{bmatrix}, \lambda = -3, -4$    **3.** $\begin{bmatrix} -4 & 1 & -2 \\ -2 & 1 & -1 \\ -1 & 2 & -1 \end{bmatrix}, \lambda = -1, 3, 1$

**5.** $\lambda = 2, 2$ has the one-dimensional eigenspace $t(1, 1)$.

**7.** $\lambda = -2, -2$ has the one-dimensional eigenspace $t(1, 0, 1)$.

**9.** $\begin{bmatrix} 4 \\ 3 \end{bmatrix}, \begin{bmatrix} 7 \\ 5 \end{bmatrix}, \begin{bmatrix} 4 & 7 \\ 3 & 5 \end{bmatrix}$    **11.** $\begin{bmatrix} -3 \\ 2 \\ 1 \end{bmatrix}, \begin{bmatrix} -4 \\ 1 \\ 1 \end{bmatrix}, \begin{bmatrix} -2 \\ 2 \\ 1 \end{bmatrix}, \begin{bmatrix} -3 & -4 & -2 \\ 2 & 1 & 2 \\ 1 & 1 & 1 \end{bmatrix}$

**13.** $\begin{bmatrix} 2 & -3 \\ -5 & 8 \end{bmatrix} \begin{bmatrix} -14 & 24 \\ -10 & 17 \end{bmatrix} \begin{bmatrix} 8 & 3 \\ 5 & 2 \end{bmatrix} = \begin{bmatrix} 1 & 0 \\ 0 & 2 \end{bmatrix}$

**15.** $\begin{bmatrix} 2 & 1 & 0 \\ 0 & 1 & 1 \\ -1 & 0 & 1 \end{bmatrix} \begin{bmatrix} 3 & -1 & -3 \\ -4 & 3 & 6 \\ 4 & -1 & -4 \end{bmatrix} \begin{bmatrix} 1 & -1 & 1 \\ -1 & 2 & -2 \\ 1 & -1 & 2 \end{bmatrix} = \begin{bmatrix} 1 & 0 & 0 \\ 0 & 2 & 0 \\ 0 & 0 & -1 \end{bmatrix}$

**17.** $\begin{bmatrix} 23 & -33 \\ 14 & -20 \end{bmatrix}$  **19.** $\begin{bmatrix} -5 & -3 & 3 \\ 0 & -1 & -2 \\ -12 & -9 & 4 \end{bmatrix}$  **21.** $(1/\sqrt{2}) \begin{bmatrix} 1 & 1 \\ 1 & -1 \end{bmatrix}$  **23.** $(1/\sqrt{3}) \begin{bmatrix} \sqrt{2} & 1 \\ -1 & \sqrt{2} \end{bmatrix}$

**25.** $\begin{bmatrix} 1/\sqrt{3} & 1/\sqrt{2} & 1/\sqrt{6} \\ 1/\sqrt{3} & -1/\sqrt{2} & 1/\sqrt{6} \\ 1/\sqrt{3} & 0 & -2/\sqrt{6} \end{bmatrix}$  **27.** $\begin{bmatrix} 1/\sqrt{5} & 4/\sqrt{45} & 2/3 \\ 0 & 5/\sqrt{45} & -2/3 \\ -2/\sqrt{5} & 2/\sqrt{45} & 1/3 \end{bmatrix}$

**29.** The repeated eigenvalue $\lambda = a$, $a$ has a one dimensional eigenspace.

## Section 6.3, p. 386

**1.** $\begin{bmatrix} -1.95 & 0 \\ 0 & 128 \end{bmatrix}$  **3.** $\begin{bmatrix} 1 & 0 & 0 \\ 0 & .478 & 0 \\ 0 & 0 & .321 \end{bmatrix}$

**5.** $\begin{bmatrix} -566 & 945 \\ -378 & 631 \end{bmatrix}$  **7.** $\begin{bmatrix} 64 & 63 & 189 \\ 189 & 190 & 567 \\ -63 & -63 & -188 \end{bmatrix}$

**9.** $T^5 = \begin{bmatrix} .7150 & .71255 \\ .2850 & .28745 \end{bmatrix}$  $T^\infty = \begin{bmatrix} .7143 & .7143 \\ .2857 & .2857 \end{bmatrix}$

$T^8$ approximates $T^\infty$ to four decimal places.
The relative error in $T^8$ is .00016.

**11.** $T^5 = \begin{bmatrix} .3938 & .4715 \\ .6062 & .5285 \end{bmatrix}$  $T^\infty = \begin{bmatrix} .4375 & .4375 \\ .5625 & .5625 \end{bmatrix}$

$T^{19}$ approximates $T^\infty$ to four decimal places.
The relative error in $T^{19}$ is .000078.

**13.** $\begin{matrix} & D & N \\ \begin{bmatrix} .99 & .01 \\ .01 & .99 \end{bmatrix} & \begin{matrix} D \\ N \end{matrix} \end{matrix}$     The probability is .9169 for $n = 9$.

# CHAPTER 7

## Section 7.1, p. 393

1. (a)  $T(4, -2, 1) = (4 + 2, 1 - (-2), 3(4)) = (6, 3, 12)$

   (b)  $T(-3, 3, 2) = (-3 + 4, 2 - 3, 3(-3)) = (1, -1, -9)$

3.  $$T(x, y) = (2x + y, 2x - y)$$
    $$T((x_1 y_2) + (x_2, y_2)) = T(x_1 + x_2, y_1 + y_2)$$
    $$= (2x_1 + 2x_2 + y_1 + y_2, 2x_1 + 2x_2 - y_1 - y_2)$$
    $$= (2x_1 + y_1, 2x_1 - y_1) + (2x_2 + y_2, 2x_2 - y_2)$$
    $$= T(x_1, y_1) + T(x_2, y_2)$$

    $$T(a(x_1, y_1)) = T(ax_1, ay_1) = (2ax_1 + ay_1, 2ax_1 - ay_1)$$
    $$= a(2x_1 + y_1, 2x_1 - y_1) = aT(x_1, y_1)$$

5.  $T(0(0, 0)) = T(0, 0) = (1, -1)$

    $0T(0, 0) = 0 \cdot (1, -1) = (0, 0) \neq (1, -1)$

7.  $T(2, 2) = (4, 2)$

    $2T(1, 1) = 2(1, 1) = (2, 2) \neq (4, 2)$

9.  $T((x_1, y_1) + (x_2, y_2)) = T(x_1 + x_2, y_1 + y_2) = (x_1 + x_2, 0)$
    $$= (x_1, 0) + (x_2, 0) = T(x_1, y_1) + T(x_2, y_2)$$

    $T(c(x, y)) = T(cx, cy) = (cx, 0) = c(x, 0) = cT(x, y)$

11.
    $$T((x_1, y_1) + (x_2, y_2)) = T(x_1 + x_2, y_1 + y_2) = (x_1 + x_2, -y_1 - y_2)$$
    $$= (x_1, -y_1) + (x_2 - y_2) = T(x_1, y_1) + T(x_2, y_2)$$

    $T(c(x, y)) = T(cx, cy) = (cx, -cy) = c(x, -y) = cT(x, y)$

13. (a) $(4,5,3)$　　　　　　　(b) $(4,6,6)$

15. $T[(2,1) + t(3,-2)] = T(2,1) + tT(3,-2) = (3,4) + t(1,-1)$

**Section 7.2, p. 400**

1. $T(1,0) = (4,5),$　　$T(0,1) = (-3,2)$　　$A = \begin{bmatrix} 4 & -3 \\ 5 & 2 \end{bmatrix}$

3. $T(1,0) = (-6,2),$　$T(0,1) = (-3,1)$　$A = \begin{bmatrix} -6 & -3 \\ 2 & 1 \end{bmatrix}$

5. $T(1,0,0) = (1,0,0),\ T(0,1,0) = (0,0,-2),\ T(0,0,1) = (2,1,0)$

$$A = \begin{bmatrix} 1 & 0 & 2 \\ 0 & 0 & 1 \\ 0 & -2 & 0 \end{bmatrix}$$

7. $T(1,0) = (4,-6),$　　$T(0,1) = (3,-5)$

$$\begin{bmatrix} 4 & 3 \\ -6 & -5 \end{bmatrix} \begin{bmatrix} x \\ y \end{bmatrix} = \begin{bmatrix} 4x + 3y \\ -6x - 5y \end{bmatrix} \neq \begin{bmatrix} x + 3 \\ y - 6 \end{bmatrix}$$

9. $T(1,0) = (0,0),$　　$T(0,1) = (0,1)$

$$\begin{bmatrix} 0 & 0 \\ 0 & 1 \end{bmatrix} \begin{bmatrix} x \\ y \end{bmatrix} = \begin{bmatrix} 0 \\ y \end{bmatrix} \neq \begin{bmatrix} xy \\ y \end{bmatrix}$$

11. $T_2 \circ T_1(x,y) = (3x - 2y + 3(2x + y), 3x - 2y - 2(2x + y))$
$$= (9x + y, -x - 4y)$$
$T_1 \circ T_2(x,y) = (3(x + 3y) - 2(x - 2y), 2(x + 3y) + x - 2y)$
$$= (x + 13y, 3x + 4y)$$

13. $\quad T_1(1,0) = (3,2), \quad T_1(0,1) = (-2,1), \quad A_1 = \begin{bmatrix} 3 & -2 \\ 2 & 1 \end{bmatrix}$

$\quad T_2(1,0) = (1,1), \quad T_1(0,1) = (3,-2), \quad A_2 = \begin{bmatrix} 1 & 3 \\ 1 & -2 \end{bmatrix}$

$\quad T_2 \circ T_1 : A_2 A_1 = \begin{bmatrix} 1 & 3 \\ 1 & -2 \end{bmatrix}\begin{bmatrix} 3 & -2 \\ 2 & 1 \end{bmatrix} = \begin{bmatrix} 9 & 1 \\ -1 & -4 \end{bmatrix}$

$\quad T_1 \circ T_2 : A_2 A_1 = \begin{bmatrix} 3 & -2 \\ 2 & 1 \end{bmatrix}\begin{bmatrix} 1 & 3 \\ 1 & -2 \end{bmatrix} = \begin{bmatrix} 1 & 13 \\ 3 & 4 \end{bmatrix}$

15.
$A = \begin{bmatrix} 5 & 7 \\ 3 & 4 \end{bmatrix}, \quad A^{-1} = \begin{bmatrix} -4 & +7 \\ +3 & -5 \end{bmatrix}, \quad T^{-1}(x,y) = (-4x + 7y, 3x - 5y)$

17. $\quad A = \begin{bmatrix} -1 & 2 & 1 \\ 0 & 1 & 3 \\ -1 & 4 & 8 \end{bmatrix}, \quad A^{-1} = \begin{bmatrix} 4 & 12 & -5 \\ 3 & 7 & -3 \\ -1 & -2 & 1 \end{bmatrix}$

$T^{-1}(x,y,z) = (4x + 12y - 5z, 3x + 7y - 3z, -x - 2y + z)$

**Section 7.3, p. 408**

1. $\mathbf{x} = \begin{bmatrix} 4 & -1 \\ 2 & 3 \end{bmatrix}\begin{bmatrix} 5 \\ -1 \end{bmatrix} = \begin{bmatrix} 21 \\ 7 \end{bmatrix}$

3. $\mathbf{x} = \begin{bmatrix} 4 & 12 & -5 \\ 3 & 7 & -3 \\ -1 & -2 & 1 \end{bmatrix}\begin{bmatrix} 1 \\ -3 \\ -4 \end{bmatrix} = \begin{bmatrix} -12 \\ -6 \\ 1 \end{bmatrix}$

5. $\mathbf{x}_B = \begin{bmatrix} -7 & 6 \\ 6 & -5 \end{bmatrix}\begin{bmatrix} 3 \\ 4 \end{bmatrix} = \begin{bmatrix} 3 \\ -2 \end{bmatrix}$

7. $\mathbf{x}_B = \begin{bmatrix} 71 & -19 & -8 \\ -18 & 5 & 2 \\ 8 & -2 & -1 \end{bmatrix}\begin{bmatrix} 1 \\ 2 \\ -3 \end{bmatrix} = \begin{bmatrix} 57 \\ -14 \\ 7 \end{bmatrix}$

9. $\dfrac{1}{14}\begin{bmatrix} 3 & 1 \\ -2 & 4 \end{bmatrix}\begin{bmatrix} 2 & -1 \\ 5 & 3 \end{bmatrix}\begin{bmatrix} 4 & -1 \\ 2 & 3 \end{bmatrix} = \dfrac{1}{14}\begin{bmatrix} 44 & -11 \\ 92 & 26 \end{bmatrix}$

11. $\dfrac{1}{18}\begin{bmatrix} 4 & -2 \\ -3 & 6 \end{bmatrix}\begin{bmatrix} 4 & -1 \\ -2 & 6 \end{bmatrix}\begin{bmatrix} 6 & 2 \\ 3 & 4 \end{bmatrix} = \dfrac{1}{18}\begin{bmatrix} 72 & -24 \\ -27 & 108 \end{bmatrix}$

13. $\begin{bmatrix} -1 & 2 & 1 \\ 0 & 1 & 3 \\ -1 & 4 & 8 \end{bmatrix}\begin{bmatrix} 0 & 0 & 5 \\ 1 & 2 & 4 \\ 0 & 1 & 6 \end{bmatrix}\begin{bmatrix} 4 & 12 & -5 \\ 3 & 7 & -3 \\ -1 & -2 & 1 \end{bmatrix} = \begin{bmatrix} 14 & 41 & -16 \\ -3 & 3 & 2 \\ 5 & 42 & -9 \end{bmatrix}$

15. $\begin{bmatrix} 71 & -19 & -8 \\ -18 & 5 & 2 \\ 8 & -2 & -1 \end{bmatrix}\begin{bmatrix} 1 & -1 & 0 \\ 4 & -5 & 1 \\ 1 & -1 & -2 \end{bmatrix}\begin{bmatrix} 1 & 3 & -2 \\ 2 & 7 & -2 \\ 4 & 10 & -13 \end{bmatrix}$

$= \begin{bmatrix} 39 & 155 & 1 \\ -10 & -41 & -3 \\ 5 & 18 & -4 \end{bmatrix}$

17. $\begin{bmatrix} 1 & 0 & 0 \\ 0 & 2 & 0 \\ 0 & 0 & -1 \end{bmatrix}$

## Section 7.4, p. 418

1. $\begin{bmatrix} 1 & 0 \\ -2 & 1 \end{bmatrix}$       3. $\begin{bmatrix} 1 & -3 \\ 0 & 1/2 \end{bmatrix}$

5. $\begin{bmatrix} 1 & -2 & 0 \\ 0 & 1 & 0 \\ 0 & 3 & 1 \end{bmatrix}$       7. $\begin{bmatrix} 1 & 0 & 3 \\ 0 & 1 & -2 \\ 0 & 0 & 1/2 \end{bmatrix}$

9. $\begin{bmatrix} 5 & 7 \\ 3 & 4 \end{bmatrix}$, $\begin{matrix} \mathbf{a_4} \\ \mathbf{a_2} \end{matrix}\left[\begin{array}{cccc|c} 32 & 0 & 52 & 1 & 17 \\ 19 & 1 & 30 & 0 & 10 \end{array}\right]$

11. 
$$\frac{1}{2}\begin{bmatrix} 1 & 1 & -1 \\ 1 & -1 & 1 \\ -1 & 1 & 1 \end{bmatrix}, \quad \begin{matrix} \mathbf{a}_1 \\ \mathbf{a}_3 \\ \mathbf{a}_5 \end{matrix}\begin{bmatrix} 1 & 6 & 0 & -1 & 0 & 1 \\ 0 & 1 & 1 & 2 & 0 & 4 \\ 0 & 2 & 0 & 2 & 1 & 3 \end{bmatrix}$$

13. $(B^{-1})' = \begin{bmatrix} 1 & 2 & 0 \\ 0 & 1/2 & 0 \\ 0 & -3 & 1 \end{bmatrix}\begin{bmatrix} 1 & -1 & 3 \\ 2 & 4 & -4 \\ -1 & 1 & 2 \end{bmatrix} = \begin{bmatrix} 5 & 7 & -5 \\ 1 & 2 & -2 \\ -7 & -11 & 14 \end{bmatrix}$

15. $B^{-1} = \frac{1}{4}\begin{bmatrix} -1 & 4 \\ -3 & 8 \end{bmatrix}$

| | | 3 | 2 | 3 | 1 | |
|---|---|---|---|---|---|---|
| | | $\mathbf{a}_1$ | $\mathbf{a}_2$ | $\mathbf{a}_3$ | $\mathbf{a}_4$ | b |
| | | 1 | 0 | -20 | -1 | 0 | 84 |
| $c_1 = 3$ | $\mathbf{a}_1$ | 0 | 1 | -7/2 | 1/2 | 0 | 17 |
| $c_4 = 1$ | $\mathbf{a}_4$ | 0 | 0 | -15/2 | 1/2 | 1 | 33 |
| | $z_j$ | 3 | -18 | 2 | 1 | 84 |

# Index

# Supplementary Material by Omar Adawi and Melvin Royer

# Introduction

**TI-83 / 83Plus Instructions**

In this booklet, we will use the following notation:

1. Symbols enclosed in a box refer to keys to be pressed. For example, $\boxed{6}$, $\boxed{\text{MATH}}$, and $\boxed{\text{STO}\Rightarrow}$.

2. If the symbol in the box is *above* rather than *on* the calculator key, the $\boxed{\text{2nd}}$ (for yellow symbols) or $\boxed{\text{ALPHA}}$ (for green symbols) key should first be pressed to access this key. Thus, when you see $\boxed{\text{ANS}}$ in these instructions, you should press $\boxed{\text{2nd}}$ $\boxed{\text{(-)}}$.

3. Symbols enclosed with < > refer to submenu choices to be selected from a menu. For example, <NAMES>, <MATH>, and <EDIT> refer to the submenus in the $\boxed{\text{MATRX}}$ menu. These choices can be selected by using $\boxed{\Rightarrow}$ and $\boxed{\Leftarrow}$ to move the selector box onto the desired choice.

4. Symbols containing a : (colon) between a digit and a keyword refer to commands and names to be selected from a submenu. For example, 2:[B] is a choice from the $\boxed{\text{MATRX}}$ <EDIT> submenu as illustrated below. This selection can be made either by pressing the digit before the desired choice (in this case, $\boxed{2}$), or by using $\boxed{\Downarrow}$ and $\boxed{\Uparrow}$ to move the selector box onto the choice and pressing $\boxed{\text{ENTER}}$. Note that some commands, such as $\boxed{\text{MATRX}}$ <MATH> B:rref(, are preceded by a letter instead of a digit and will require use of the $\boxed{\text{ALPHA}}$ key before pressing the letter of the selection.

```
NAMES MATH EDIT
1:[A]  3×4
2:[B]  2×3
3:[C]
4:[D]
5:[E]
6:[F]
7↓[G]
```

Most of the calculator commands used in this booklet deal with operations on matrices. The TI-83/83Plus has ten storage locations for matrices named [A], [B], . . ., [J].

**Calculator Example Intro.1:  Entering a Matrix**

The following keystrokes illustrate how to enter the matrix

$$\begin{bmatrix} 1 & -2 & 4 \\ 7 & 4 & 2 \end{bmatrix}$$

into location [B].

To choose location:   | MATRX | <EDIT> 2:[B]

To set dimensions:   | 2 | | ENTER | | 3 | | ENTER |

To enter numbers:   | 1 | | ENTER | | (-) | | 2 | | ENTER | | 4 | | ENTER | | 7 |
| ENTER | | 4 | | ENTER | | 2 | | ENTER |

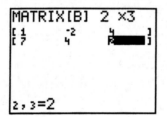

To leave entry screen: | QUIT |

Note: Before leaving the entry screen, the arrow keys can used to move onto any
element and a new value can be entered directly over a value that you wish to change.

**Calculator Example Intro.2:  Referring to a Matrix by Name**

You will often need to access the name of a matrix for use in later commands.  For example, to
display the contents of [A], use the keystrokes

MATRX <NAMES> 1:[A] | ENTER |

# Chapter 1

## Section 1.1

**Exercises:**

1. A PC purchased at a cost of $6000 in 1999 has a scrap value of $1200 at the end of 4 years. Assume that the PC depreciates linearly.

    **a.** Find the linear equation expressing the PC's book value at the end of $x$ years.
    **b.** Determine the value of the PC after $2\frac{1}{2}$ years.
    **c.** Explain the economic significance of the slope of the line.
    **d.** Explain the economic significance of the $y$-intercept of the line.

2. A car is purchased in 2001 and has a book value of $900 in 2006. In 2003 the book value of the car is $2820. Assume that the value depreciates linearly.

    **a.** Find the linear equation expressing the car's book value at the end of $x$ years.
    **b.** Determine the book value of the car in 2002.
    **c.** Explain the economic significance of the slope of the line.
    **d.** Explain the economic significance of the $y$-intercept of the line.

## Section 1.2

**Exercises:**

1. The demand for air conditioners in a city is given by $q = -\frac{p}{8} + 150$, where $q$ is the number of air conditioners that are purchased each year when they are priced at $p$ dollars each. The supply equation is $q = \frac{p}{16} + 48$, where $q$ is the number of air conditioners the manufacturers ship into the city each year when they are priced at $p$ dollars each. Find the equilibrium price and quantity.

2. The demand and supply for a VCR at an electronics store are given in the following table.

| Demand | Supply | Price |
|--------|--------|-------|
| 15     | 45     | $200  |
| 30     | 15     | $170  |

    **a.** Find the linear demand function for the VCR.
    **b.** Find the linear supply function for the VCR.
    **c.** Find the equilibrium quantity and price.

3. Galaxy, Inc. sells new cars and uses a linear revenue function and a linear cost function to analyze their monthly sales. During August, 35 cars were sold which produced $560,000 in revenue at a total operating cost of $488,000. During October, 28 cars were sold at a total operating cost of $404,000.

    **a.** Find the linear revenue function.

    **b.** Find the linear cost function.

    **c.** Find the break-even point.

    **d.** How many cars must be sold in a month to earn a profit of $16,000?

4. The Gamma Corporation manufactures palmtops at its plants in Greenville and Troy. At the Greenville plant, the unit cost is $79 and the fixed cost is $9000. At the Troy plant, the unit cost is $71 and the fixed cost is $9400. The company wants the two plants to produce a combined total of 1000 palmtops, and the total costs at each plant must be the same. How many palmtops should be produced at each plant?

5. The total costs and revenue for an MP3-player at an electronics store are given in the the following table.

| Month | Total Cost | Revenue | Number Sold |
|-------|-----------|---------|-------------|
| June  | $4025     | $5600   | 80          |
| July  | $4550     | $6650   | 95          |

    **a.** Find the linear revenue function for the MP3-player.

    **b.** Find the linear cost function for the MP3-player.

    **c.** Find the break-even point.

    **d.** If 33 MP3-players are sold in a month, will the store incur a profit or a loss?

6. A bookstore sells 200 books in February and receives $7000 in revenue and a profit of $2100. In May, the store sells 180 books and earns a profit of $1640.

    **a.** Find the linear revenue function.

    **b.** Find the linear cost function.

# Section 1.4

**Using EXCEL to Solve a Linear Program**

EXCEL uses the **Solver** add-in to solve linear programs. **Solver** is listed on the **Tools** menu. If **Solver** is not listed, it will need to be installed.

**EXCEL Example 1.4.1:  Solving a maximization linear program (Section 1.4, Example 5, p. 37)**

1. *To label variables.*  In cell A1, type "X".  In cell B1, type "Y".

2. *To define an objective function.*  Choose a cell to be the "Target Cell".  For example, click on cell D1 and type "$= 4 * A2 + 5 * B2$".  The cells A2 and B2 are called the "adjustable cells" and will display the values of $x$ and $y$, respectively.  The press "Enter".  The number "0" will be displayed in cell D1.  This is the current value of the objective function.

3. *To define the constraints.*  Select another cell.  For example, click on cell C4 and type "$= A2 + 2 * B2$".  Then press "Enter".  Click on cell D4 and type "$= 5 * A2 + 4 * B2$".  Then press "Enter".  The number "0" will be displayed in cells C4 and D4.

4. Click on **Solver** on the **Tools** menu.  Click on cell D1.  "$D$1" will appear in the **Set Target Cell** box.  Click on **Max**.  In the **By Changing Cells** box, enter "A2,B2" or click on these cells, using a comma to separate cell names.  Click on **Add** to add the constraints.  The **Add Constraints** box will appear.  Click on cell C4, then <=, then type "6" in the **Constraint** box.  Click **OK**.  Click on cell D4, then <=, then type "20" in the **Constraint** box.  Click **OK**.

5. Click on **Solve**.  The optimum value of $z$ will appear in the "target cell", and the corresponding values of the variables will appear in the "adjustable cells".  For this example, the number "19" will appear in cell D1, and the numbers "2.666667" and "1.666667" will appear in cells A2 and B2, respectively.

|   | A | B | C | D |
|---|---|---|---|---|
| 1 | x | y |   | 19 |
| 2 | 2.666667 | 1.666667 |   |   |
| 3 |   |   |   |   |
| 4 |   |   | 6 | 20 |

# Chapter 2

## Section 2.1

**Calculator Example 2.1.1: Elementary Row Operations**

The following three commands are for executing elementary row operations on the matrix stored in location [A]. The other nine matrix locations can be used in a similar way. Each of these commands is first accessed from the $\boxed{\text{MATRX}}$ <MATH> submenu. After the proper command is selected, the calculator echos the command to the home screen and waits for you to complete it with the instruction you desire. Pressing $\boxed{\text{ENTER}}$ then executes the command.

1. To execute the command $R_2 \leftrightarrow R_1$

   Access the command using:        $\boxed{\text{MATRX}}$ <MATH> C:rowSwap(

   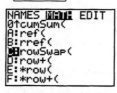

   Complete the command as follows:   rowSwap([A],1,2)

   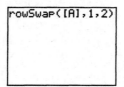

2. To execute the command $R_1' = 2R_1$

   Access the command using:        $\boxed{\text{MATRX}}$ <MATH> E:*row(

   Complete the command as follows:   *row(2,[A],1)

3. To execute the command $R_2' = R_2 + 3R_1$

   Access the command using:        $\boxed{\text{MATRX}}$ <MATH> F:*row+(

   Complete the command as follows:   *row+(3,[A],1,2)

**Calculator Example 2.1.2: Sequence of Row Operations** (Sect 2.1, Example 4, p. 61)

Using the TI-83, perform row operations to put the following matrix in row echelon form.

$$\begin{bmatrix} 1 & -2 & -1 & 3 \\ -1 & 2 & 4 & -1 \\ 3 & -4 & 1 & 5 \end{bmatrix}$$

Store the matrix in location [A].  Enter the following sequence of commands:

$R'_2 = R_2 + R_1$            *row+(1,[A],1,2)

```
*row+(1,[A],1,2)
  [[1  -2 -1  3]
   [0  0   3  2]
   [3  -4  1  5]]
```

$R'_3 = R_3 - 3R_1$          *row+(−3,Ans,1,3)

$R_2 \leftrightarrow R_3$              rowSwap(Ans,2,3)

$R'_2 = \frac{1}{2}R_2$            *row(1/2,Ans,2)

$R'_3 = \frac{1}{3}R_3$            *row(1/3,Ans,3)

```
  [[1  -2 -1  3 ]
   [0  1   2  -2]
   [0  0   3  2 ]]
*row(1/3,Ans,3)
  [[1  -2 -1  3    ...
   [0  1   2  -2   ...
   [0  0   1  .6666...
```

Note the use of the | ANS | key in each command after the first, which tells the calculator to use the result of the previous calculation rather than going back to the original matrix for each operation. This usage is necessary since the | MATRX | <MATH> commands *never* modify the original matrix.

Note:  If fractions are preferred to decimals, the following keystrokes display the matrix using fractions.

| MATH | <MATH>1:⇒Frac | ENTER |

```
  [[1  -2 -1  3     ...
   [0  1   2  -2    ...
   [0  0   1  .6666...
Ans▶Frac
  [[1  -2 -1  3   ]
   [0  1   2  -2  ]
   [0  0   1  2/3]]
■
```

**Exercises**:

In Exercises 1-6, find the augmented matrix of the given system of equations.

1.  $4x_1 - 3x_2 + 2x_3 = 5$
    $2x_1 - x_2 + x_3 = -2$
    $x_1 \qquad - 2x_3 = 3$

2.  $-2x_1 + 5x_2 - x_3 = -12$
    $2x_1 \qquad - 3x_3 = 4$
    $-3x_1 + x_2 - 3x_3 = 8$

3.  $4x_1 + 3x_2 - x_3 + 2x_4 = -8$
    $x_2 + x_3 \qquad = 5$
    $2x_1 + x_2 \qquad = 6$

4.  $-3x_1 + 5x_2 - 6x_3 + x_4 = 2$
    $6x_1 - x_2 + 2x_3 + x_4 = -1$
    $2x_2 \qquad - 3x_4 = 6$

5.  $4x_1 + 3x_2 \qquad = 5$
    $-2x_2 - x_3 = -1$
    $3x_1 \qquad + 2x_3 = 0$
    $2x_1 + x_2 \qquad = 2$

6.  $4x_1 + x_2 - 3x_3 = 0$
    $x_2 + 3x_3 = -2$
    $3x_1 \qquad = 3$
    $x_1 + 2x_2 \qquad = -1$

In Exercises 7-12, find a system of equations for which the given matrix is the augmented matrix of the system.  Use the variable names $x_1$, $x_2$, $x_3$, $x_4$, as needed.

7.  $\begin{bmatrix} 1 & -2 & 3 & 2 \\ 3 & 7 & 0 & 1 \\ 8 & -4 & 4 & 7 \end{bmatrix}$

8.  $\begin{bmatrix} 2 & 0 & 6 & -1 \\ 8 & 5 & 2 & -3 \\ 1 & 0 & 1 & 2 \end{bmatrix}$

9.  $\begin{bmatrix} 3 & 0 & -2 & 1 \\ 0 & 0 & 3 & -1 \\ 2 & 0 & 6 & 4 \\ -7 & -1 & 0 & 2 \end{bmatrix}$

10.  $\begin{bmatrix} 0 & 3 & 8 & 7 \\ -2 & 2 & -1 & 2 \\ -4 & 5 & 0 & -1 \\ 1 & 1 & 3 & 0 \end{bmatrix}$

11.  $\begin{bmatrix} 3 & -2 & 0 & 1 & 3 \\ 1 & -3 & 4 & -1 & 1 \\ 8 & 1 & 1 & 1 & 0 \end{bmatrix}$

12.  $\begin{bmatrix} -1 & 2 & 3 & 4 & 0 \\ 0 & 1 & 0 & 1 & 3 \\ 1 & -3 & 2 & -3 & 1 \end{bmatrix}$

In Exercises 13-18, use back substitution to find the solution to the system of equations that has the given augmented matrix.  Use the variable names $x_1$, $x_2$, $x_3$, $x_4$, as needed.

13.  $\begin{bmatrix} 1 & 2 & -1 \\ 0 & 1 & 1 \end{bmatrix}$

14.  $\begin{bmatrix} 1 & 3 & 2 \\ 0 & 1 & 3 \end{bmatrix}$

15. $\begin{bmatrix} 1 & 2 & 3 & -1 \\ 0 & 1 & 1 & -5 \\ 0 & 0 & 1 & 2 \end{bmatrix}$

16. $\begin{bmatrix} 1 & -1 & 6 & 2 \\ 0 & 1 & -3 & 1 \\ 0 & 0 & 1 & -7 \end{bmatrix}$

17. $\begin{bmatrix} 1 & 2 & -3 & -2 & 0 \\ 0 & 1 & 0 & -1 & 3 \\ 0 & 0 & 1 & 2 & -2 \\ 0 & 0 & 0 & 1 & -4 \end{bmatrix}$

18. $\begin{bmatrix} 1 & -8 & 2 & 3 & 3 \\ 0 & 1 & 4 & 1 & 2 \\ 0 & 0 & 1 & 2 & -1 \\ 0 & 0 & 0 & 1 & -1 \end{bmatrix}$

In Exercises 19-24, perform the row operations in the given sequence on the indicated matrix.

19. For the matrix of Exercise 7,
$$R_2' = R_2 - 3R_1$$
$$R_3' = R_3 - 8R_1$$

20. For the matrix of Exercise 8,
$$R_1 \leftrightarrow R_3$$
$$R_2' = R_2 - 8R_1$$
$$R_3' = R_3 - 2R_1$$

21. For the matrix of Exercise 9,
$$R_1 \leftrightarrow R_3$$
$$R_1' = \tfrac{1}{2}R_1$$
$$R_3' = R_3 - 3R_1$$
$$R_4' = R_4 + 7R_1$$

22. For the matrix of Exercise 10,
$$R_1 \leftrightarrow R_4$$
$$R_2' = R_2 + 2R_1$$
$$R_3' = R_3 + 4R_1$$

23. For the matrix of Exercise 11,
$$R_1' = R_1 + 2R_3$$
$$R_2' = R_2 + 3R_3$$

24. For the matrix of Exercise 12,
$$R_1' = R_1 - 2R_2$$
$$R_3' = R_3 + 3R_2$$

In Exercises 25-30, determine whether or not the matrices are in echelon form.  For those that are not, apply elementary row operations to put them in echelon form.

25. $\begin{bmatrix} 1 & 2 & -4 & 2 \\ 0 & -1 & 2 & 0 \\ 0 & 0 & 1 & -2 \end{bmatrix}$

26. $\begin{bmatrix} 1 & 3 & 2 & 5 \\ 0 & 1 & 2 & -4 \\ 0 & 0 & 0 & 1 \end{bmatrix}$

27. $\begin{bmatrix} 0 & 0 & 1 & 2 \\ 1 & 0 & -3 & -1 \\ 0 & 1 & 9 & -2 \end{bmatrix}$

28. $\begin{bmatrix} 1 & 0 & -1 & -3 \\ 1 & 2 & -1 & 5 \\ 0 & 1 & 0 & -2 \end{bmatrix}$

29. $\begin{bmatrix} 0 & 1 & 9 & -1 \\ 0 & 0 & 0 & 1 \\ 0 & 0 & 0 & 0 \end{bmatrix}$         30. $\begin{bmatrix} 0 & 1 & 8 & -2 \\ 0 & 0 & 0 & 0 \\ 0 & 0 & 1 & 7 \end{bmatrix}$

In Exercises 31-36,

    **a.** use Gaussian elimination to find a row echelon form for the augmented matrix of the given system, and

    **b.** use back substitution to find the solution of the system

31.    $x_1 + 2x_2 - 4x_3 = 1$
        $2x_1 + 5x_2 - 6x_3 = 0$
        $-x_1 + 3x_2 + 6x_3 = -3$

32.    $x_1 - 2x_2 + x_3 = 0$
            $2x_2 - 8x_3 = 8$
       $-4x_1 + 5x_2 + 9x_3 = -9$

33.    $2x_1 + 4x_2 - 6x_3 = -2$
        $3x_1 + 5x_2 - 12x_3 = 2$
      $-5x_1 - 3x_2 + 8x_3 = -2$

34.    $x_1 + x_2 + 2x_3 = 9$
        $2x_1 + 4x_2 - 3x_3 = 1$
        $3x_1 + 6x_2 - 5x_3 = 0$

35.    $x + 2y - 3z + w = 2$
     $-3x - 8y + 4z - 4w = -5$
     $-2x - 4y + 5z - 5w = -7$
       $2x + 4y - 4z - 2w = -10$

36.    $2x + 4y + 3z + 2w = 2$
      $3x + 6y + 5z + 2w = 2$
      $2x + 5y + 2z - 3w = 3$
      $4x + 5y + 14z + 14w = 11$

# Section 2.2

**Calculator Example 2.2.1: Reduced Echelon Form** (Section 2.2, Example 2, pp. 66-67)

Use the TI-83 to put the following matrix in reduced echelon form:

$$\begin{bmatrix} 1 & -2 & 4 & 5 & -3 \\ 0 & 1 & 3 & -1 & 7 \\ 0 & 0 & 0 & 1 & 2 \end{bmatrix}$$

  **1.** Enter the matrix in location [A].

  **2.** Enter the keystrokes $\boxed{\text{MATRX}}$ <MATH> B:rref(

**3.** Complete the command as  rref([A])  and press  ENTER

```
rref([A])
[[1 0 10 0 5]
 [0 1 3  0 9]
 [0 0 0  1 2]]
```

**Exercises:**

In Exercises 1-6 tell whether or not the matrices are in reduced echelon form.  For those that are not, use elementary row operations to put them in reduced echelon form.

1.
$$\begin{bmatrix} 1 & 0 & 3 & 4 \\ 0 & 0 & 1 & 3 \\ 0 & 0 & 0 & 0 \end{bmatrix}$$

2.
$$\begin{bmatrix} 1 & 0 & 6 & -3 \\ 0 & 1 & 4 & -1 \\ 0 & 0 & 0 & 0 \end{bmatrix}$$

3.
$$\begin{bmatrix} 0 & 1 & 0 & 3 \\ 0 & 0 & 1 & -5 \\ 0 & 0 & 0 & 0 \end{bmatrix}$$

4.
$$\begin{bmatrix} 1 & 0 & -6 & 2 \\ 0 & -1 & 2 & 8 \\ 0 & 0 & 1 & 0 \end{bmatrix}$$

5.
$$\begin{bmatrix} 1 & 0 & -3 & 0 & 2 \\ 0 & 1 & 2 & 0 & 2 \\ 0 & 0 & 0 & 1 & -4 \\ 0 & 0 & 0 & 0 & 0 \end{bmatrix}$$

6.
$$\begin{bmatrix} 1 & 0 & 5 & 1 & 0 \\ 0 & 0 & 0 & 0 & 0 \\ 0 & 1 & 0 & 8 & -1 \\ 0 & 0 & 1 & 0 & 0 \end{bmatrix}$$

In Exercises 7-10, solve the given system by using row operations to put the augmented matrix of the system into reduced echelon form.

7.  $\quad x + 2y + 3z = 6$
$\quad\quad 2x - 3y + 2z = 14$
$\quad\quad 3x + y - z = -2$

8.  $\quad x - 2y - z = 3$
$\quad\quad 3x - 6y - 5z = 3$
$\quad\quad 2x - y + z = 0$

9.  $\quad 3x_1 + 2x_2 - x_3 = -15$
$\quad\quad 5x_1 + 3x_2 + 2x_3 = 0$
$\quad\quad 3x_1 + x_2 + 3x_3 = 11$
$\quad\quad 6x_1 + 4x_2 - 2x_3 = -30$

10. $\quad 2x_1 + 2x_2 + 4x_3 = 16$
$\quad\quad x_1 + 2x_2 - x_3 = 6$
$\quad\quad -3x_1 + x_2 - 2x_3 = 0$
$\quad\quad 6x_1 + 3x_2 + 5x_3 = 22$

In Exercises 11-14, solve the given systems of equations simultaneously.

11.   $2x + 2y + z = 9$

$2x - y + 2z = 6$     and     $2x + 2y + z = 8$

$x - y + 2z = 5$           $2x - y + 2z = -4$

                                              $x - y + 2z = 2$

11.
$$2x + 2y + z = 9 \qquad\qquad 2x + 2y + z = 8$$
$$2x - y + 2z = 6 \quad \text{and} \quad 2x - y + 2z = -4$$
$$x - y + 2z = 5 \qquad\qquad x - y + 2z = 2$$

12.
$$2x - 2y + z = 3 \qquad\qquad 2x - 2y + z = -2$$
$$3x + y - z = 7 \quad \text{and} \quad 3x + y - z = 4$$
$$x - 3y + 2z = 0 \qquad\qquad x - 3y + 2z = -1$$

13.
$$2x_1 + 4x_2 - 10x_3 = -2 \qquad\qquad 2x_1 + 4x_2 - 10x_3 = 2$$
$$3x_1 + 9x_2 - 21x_3 = 0 \quad \text{and} \quad 3x_1 + 9x_2 - 21x_3 = 0$$
$$x_1 + 5x_2 - 12x_3 = 1 \qquad\qquad x_1 + 5x_2 - 12x_3 = 6$$

14.
$$2x_1 - 4x_2 + 6x_3 = 10 \qquad\qquad 2x_1 - 4x_2 + 6x_3 = -4$$
$$3x_1 - 5x_2 + 8x_3 = -4 \quad \text{and} \quad 3x_1 - 5x_2 + 8x_3 = 0$$
$$-2x_1 + 6x_2 - 10x_3 = -2 \qquad\qquad -2x_1 + 6x_2 - 10x_3 = 16$$

15. A large pork producer hires a nutritionist to plan a diet which provides hogs with protein, carbohydrates, and fat needed for growth. Suppose the nutritional content of three available feeds are as follows:

|                              | Food A | Food B | Food C |
| ---------------------------- | ------ | ------ | ------ |
| Protein units per pound      | 2      | 3      | 3      |
| Carbohydrate units per pound | 2      | 4      | 3      |
| Fat units per pound          | 1      | 2      | 2      |

For each set of nutrients given below, tell whether it is possible to find a mixture of these feeds which will provide exactly the given amounts. If such a mixture is possible, tell how many pounds of each food it should contain. Use a multisystem to do all three parts simultaneously.

    a.  150 units of protein, 174 units of carbohydrates, and 95 units of fat

    b.  111 units of protein, 131 units of carbohydrates, and 70 units of fat

    c.  73 units of protein, 92 units of carbohydrates, and 52 units of fat

16. A computer manufacturer produces three models of hardware: a "bare-bones" system, a standard desktop system, and a multi-user server. The production times required for each model are shown below:

|  | Bare-bones | Standard | Server |
|---|---|---|---|
| Assembly | 0.5 hour | 1.0 hour | 1.5 hour |
| Testing | 0.6 hour | 0.9 hour | 1.2 hour |
| Packaging | 0.2 hour | 0.3 hour | 0.5 hour |

For each of the total available labor-hours below, tell whether it is possible to find a production schedule so that all three areas operate at full capacity. If such a production schedule exists, tell how many of each type of hardware the manufacturer should produce. Use a multisystem to do all three parts simultaneously.

   a.  120 labor-hours in assembly, 108 labor-hours in testing, 39 labor-hours in packaging
   b.  120 labor-hours in assembly, 108 labor-hours in testing, 50 labor-hours in packaging
   c.  180 labor-hours in assembly, 156 labor-hours in testing, 60 labor-hours in packaging


17.  A company 403(b) plan allows employees to divide their investments among three mutual funds: an aggressive growth fund, a hybrid fund, and an income fund. The aggressive growth fund currently owns 90% stocks, 5% bonds, and 5% cash. The hybrid fund owns 60% stocks, 25% bonds, and 15% cash. The income fund owns 25% stocks, 50% bonds, and 25% cash. Suppose an employee has $6000 to place in her 403(b) this year. For each of the following investment proportions, tell whether it is possible for her to divide the $6000 among the three funds so that the total amount invested in stocks, bonds, and cash are exactly in her desired proportions. If such an investment is possible, tell how much money should be invested in each of the three funds. Use a multisystem to do all three parts simultaneously.

   a.  50% stocks, 32.5% bonds, 17.5% cash
   b.  50% stocks, 35% bonds, 15% cash
   c.  37.5% stocks, 40.5% bonds, 22% cash


18.  Repeat Exercise 17 if the manager of the hybrid fund switches proportions to 60% stocks, 20% bonds, and 20% cash, while the other two funds maintain the same investment proportions.

   a.  50% stocks, 32.5% bonds, 17.5% cash
   b.  50% stocks, 35% bonds, 15% cash
   c.  37.5% stocks, 40.5% bonds, 22% cash


# Section 2.3

**Calculator Example 2.3.1 : A Substitute for Symbolic Manipulation**

Find a relationship between $a$, $b$, and $c$ for which the following system will be consistent

$$x + y + 2z = a$$
$$y + 3z = b$$
$$x + 3y + 8z = c$$

We should do row operations to find the reduced echelon form of the augmented matrix

$$\begin{bmatrix} 1 & 1 & 2 & a \\ 0 & 1 & 3 & b \\ 1 & 3 & 8 & c \end{bmatrix}$$

Matrices with variable entries can be reduced with computer programs such as DERIVE, Mathematica, and Maple, as well as some graphics calculators, such as the TI-89. The TI-83 does not allow variable entries in matrices, but a partial substitute is as follows. The original system is equivalent to:

$$\begin{aligned} x + y + 2z &= 1a + 0b + 0c \\ y + 3z &= 0a + 1b + 0c \\ x + 3y + 8z &= 0a + 0b + 1c \end{aligned}$$

This can be considered as a multisystem with three inputs – those dealing with $a$, with $b$, and with $c$. So on the TI-83, one can instead find the reduced echelon form of the augmented matrix

$$\begin{bmatrix} 1 & 1 & 2 & 1 & 0 & 0 \\ 0 & 1 & 3 & 0 & 1 & 0 \\ 1 & 3 & 8 & 0 & 0 & 1 \end{bmatrix}, \text{ namely } \begin{bmatrix} 1 & 0 & -1 & 0 & -3 & 1 \\ 0 & 1 & 3 & 0 & 1 & 0 \\ 0 & 0 & 0 & 1 & 2 & -1 \end{bmatrix}.$$

The system for the latter matrix is

$$\begin{aligned} x \quad - z &= -3b + c \\ y + 3z &= b \\ 0 &= a + 2b - c \end{aligned}$$

and so $a + 2b - c$ must equal 0 for the system to be consistent.

**Exercises:**

In Exercises 1-8, find a solution to the given system or show that it is inconsistent.

1. $\begin{aligned} x_1 + 3x_2 - 2x_3 &= 5 \\ 4x_1 - x_2 + 3x_3 &= 7 \\ 2x_1 - 7x_2 + 7x_3 &= 4 \end{aligned}$

2. $\begin{aligned} 3x_1 - 2x_2 + 2x_3 &= 10 \\ 2x_1 + x_2 + 3x_3 &= 3 \\ x_1 + x_2 - x_3 &= 5 \end{aligned}$

3. $\begin{aligned} 3x_1 + 2x_2 - x_3 &= -15 \\ 5x_1 + 3x_2 + 2x_3 &= 0 \\ 3x_1 + x_2 + 3x_3 &= 11 \\ -6x_1 - 4x_2 + 2x_3 &= 30 \end{aligned}$

4. $\begin{aligned} 2x_1 - x_2 + 3x_3 + 4x_4 &= 9 \\ x_1 \quad - 2x_3 + 7x_4 &= 11 \\ 3x_1 - 3x_2 + x_3 + 5x_4 &= 8 \\ 2x_1 + x_2 + 4x_3 + 4x_4 &= 10 \end{aligned}$

5.  $x_1 + 2x_2 - x_3 - x_4 = 0$
    $x_1 + 2x_2 \qquad + x_4 = 4$
    $-x_1 - 2x_2 + 2x_3 + 4x_4 = 5$
    $-x_1 - x_2 - x_3 \qquad = 1$

6.  $x_1 + 2x_2 + x_3 = 1$
    $-2x_1 - 4x_2 - x_3 = 0$
    $5x_1 + 10x_2 + 3x_3 = 2$
    $3x_1 + 6x_2 + 3x_3 = 4$

7.  $x_1 + x_2 - x_3 - x_4 = -1$
    $3x_1 - 2x_2 - 4x_3 + 2x_4 = 1$
    $4x_1 - x_2 - 5x_3 + x_4 = 5$

8.  $2x_2 + 2x_3 \qquad = 0$
    $x_1 \qquad\qquad -2x_4 = -3$
    $x_3 + 3x_4 = -4$
    $-2x_1 + 3x_2 + 2x_3 + x_4 = 5$

In Exercises 9-16, find the rank of the coefficient matrix and the augmented coefficient matrix for the system of the indicated exercise.

9.  Exercise 1          10. Exercise 2

11. Exercise 3          12. Exercise 4

13. Exercise 5          14. Exercise 6

15. Exercise 7          16. Exercise 8

In Exercises 17-24, find all values of $k$ for which the system of equations

    a.  has a unique solution
    b.  has no solution
    c.  has infinitely many solutions

17.  $x_1 - 3x_2 = 7$
     $3x_1 - 2x_2 = k$

18.  $2x_1 + 4x_2 = 9$
     $-5x_1 + 2x_2 = k$

19.  $2x_1 + 5x_2 = 8$
     $3x_1 + kx_2 = 6$

20.  $3x_1 - x_2 = -5$
     $kx_1 + 2x_2 = 10$

21.  $kx_1 - 2x_2 = -1$
     $5x_1 - 4x_2 = 4$

22.  $6x_1 - x_2 = 4$
     $2x_1 + kx_2 = 6$

23. $\begin{aligned} x_1 + 4x_2 - 2x_3 &= 13 \\ 3x_1 - x_2 + 4x_3 &= 6 \\ 2x_1 - 5x_2 + 6x_3 &= k \end{aligned}$

24. $\begin{aligned} x_2 + 5x_3 &= 4 \\ x_1 + 4x_2 + 3x_3 &= -2 \\ 2x_1 + 7x_2 + x_3 &= k \end{aligned}$

In Exercises 25-28, find the relationship between $a$, $b$, and $c$ for which the system of equations will be consistent.

25. $\begin{aligned} 3x_1 - x_2 + 2x_3 &= a \\ 2x_1 + 2x_2 + x_3 &= b \\ x_1 - 3x_2 &= c \end{aligned}$

26. $\begin{aligned} x_1 + 2x_2 + 3x_3 &= a \\ 4x_1 + 5x_2 + 6x_3 &= b \\ 7x_1 + 8x_2 &= c \end{aligned}$

27. $\begin{aligned} 2x_1 - 4x_2 - 8x_3 &= a \\ 3x_1 - x_2 + 3x_3 &= b \\ -5x_1 + 3x_2 - x_3 &= c \end{aligned}$

28. $\begin{aligned} x_1 + x_2 + 2x_3 &= a \\ 2x_1 + x_2 - x_3 &= b \\ x_1 - x_3 &= c \end{aligned}$

In Exercises 29-36, put the augmented matrix of the following systems into reduced echelon form and find all solutions. Represent the solutions parametrically.

29. $\begin{aligned} 3x_1 + 4x_2 - x_3 &= 5 \\ 6x_1 + 2x_2 + 2x_3 &= 3 \end{aligned}$

30. $\begin{aligned} -4x_1 + 2x_2 + 5x_3 &= 12 \\ 6x_1 - x_2 + 5z_3 &= -4 \end{aligned}$

31. $\begin{aligned} x_1 + 4x_2 - 3x_3 &= 6 \\ 3x_1 - 2x_2 - x_3 &= 1 \\ 10x_1 - 2x_2 - 6x_3 &= 9 \end{aligned}$

32. $\begin{aligned} 2x_1 - 8x_2 + x_3 &= 1 \\ -9x_1 + 17x_2 - 5x_3 &= -4 \\ -5x_1 + x_2 - 3x_3 &= -2 \end{aligned}$

33. $\begin{aligned} 2x_1 - 4x_2 + x_3 - 2x_4 &= 4 \\ 3x_1 + 5x_2 - 8x_3 + 3x_4 &= -2 \\ -x_1 - 9x_2 + 9x_3 + x_4 &= 0 \end{aligned}$

34. $\begin{aligned} 6x_1 + 4x_2 + 5x_3 - 2x_4 &= 8 \\ 3x_1 - 4x_2 + 4x_3 + x_4 &= -4 \\ -x_1 + x_2 - 4x_3 - 3x_4 &= 11 \end{aligned}$

35. $\begin{aligned} 6x_1 + x_2 - 3x_3 - x_4 + 2x_5 &= 8 \\ x_1 + 3x_2 - 2x_3 + 6x_4 + 4x_5 &= -3 \\ -2x_1 + x_3 + 4x_4 - 2x_5 &= -1 \end{aligned}$

36. $\begin{aligned} -4x_1 + 4x_2 - 5x_3 - 8x_4 + 12x_5 &= 16 \\ 8x_1 + 4x_2 - 4x_4 + x_5 &= -4 \\ -4x_1 + 16x_2 - 15x_3 + 8x_4 &= -2 \end{aligned}$

37. A soft drink company produces three beverages in small vats and sweetens them with mixtures of sugar and corn syrup. Each vat of Fizz requires 2 pounds of sugar and 1.5 pounds of corn syrup, each vat of Jiff contains 1.75 pounds of sugar and 1.5 pounds of corn syrup, and each vat of Squirt contains 2.25 pounds of sugar and 2 pounds of corn syrup. How many vats of each type of soda can be made using exactly 5000 pounds of sugar and 4300 pounds of corn syrup? Assume partially filled vats are allowed.

38. Three foods contain the following numbers of units of vitamins A and C per ounce:

|           | Food A | Food B | Food C |
|-----------|--------|--------|--------|
| Vitamin A | 8      | 5      | 4      |
| Vitamin C | 2      | 5      | 6      |

A diet is to provide exactly 50 units of vitamin A and 70 units of vitamin C. How many ounces of each food could be used to meet the diet requirements? The amounts need not be whole numbers of ounces.

39. Find all possible combinations of pennies, nickels, and dimes so that you have 20 coins total and a cash value of $1.50.

40. Find all possible combinations of pennies, nickels, and dimes so that you have 30 coins total and a cash value of $1.50.

41. A computer manufacturer produces three models of hardware: a "bare-bones" system, a standard desktop system, and a multi-user server. The production times required for each model are shown below:

|           | Bare-bones | Standard  | Server    |
|-----------|------------|-----------|-----------|
| Assembly  | 0.5 hour   | 1.0 hour  | 1.5 hour  |
| Packaging | 0.1 hour   | 0.6 hour  | 1.2 hour  |

Suppose there are 75 labor-hours available in assembly and 54 labor hours available in packaging. Find all possible production schedules. That is, find all possible combinations of the three types of computers which can be manufactured using all the available labor-hours in both areas. Assume partially built machines are not desired.

42. A furniture manufacturer makes end tables, chairs, and hall trees. Each end table has a shipping weight of 30 pounds and a shipping volume of 10 cubic feet; each chair has a shipping weight of 10 pounds and a shipping volume of 10 cubit feet; and each hall tree has a shipping weight of 10 pounds and a shipping volume of 25 cubic feet. A partially loaded shipping truck has 350 pounds and 225 cubic feet remaining in its weight and volume limits. How many pieces of each type of furniture can be loaded to fill both the remaining weight and volume capacity? Assume incomplete items are not desired.

# Section 2.4

**Exercises:**

In Exercises 1-4, plot the given points on a 3-dimensional coordinate system.

1. $(1,3,-2)$, $(-4,2,-1)$, $(1,1,4)$, $(5,0,2)$     2. $(3,6,-3)$, $(0,2,2)$, $(-4,-2,0)$, $(-2,5,-2)$

3. $(3,1,3)$, $(4,-2,1)$, $(-1,-2,-3)$, $(5,0,-2)$     4. $(3,3,3)$, $(-3,6,0)$, $(0,2,-2)$, $(-4,-1,3)$

In Exercises 5-12, write the equation of the plane in intercept form and sketch the first-octant portion of the plane.

5. $3x + 4y + 2z = 12$

6. $8x + 2y + 4z = 8$

7. $3x + 5y + 10z = 30$

8. $4x + y + 6z = 12$

9. $2x + 8z = 16$

10. $4x + 5y = 20$

11. $3x + 4y = 12$

12. $8y + 2z = 16$

In Exercises 13-18, find the points of intersection, if any, of the following planes. Identify the intersection as the empty set, a point, a line, or a plane.

13.   $x + 2y - z = 4$
    $3x + 7y - 2z = 1$
    $-2x + 3y + 3z = -1$

14.   $x + 2y - z = 1$
    $-2x - 3y + 2z = -1$
    $-5x - 8y + 5z = -3$

15.  $3x + y - 2z = 2$
    $x - 2y + z = 3$
    $x + 5y - 4z = -4$

16.   $x - 2y - z = 3$
    $3x - 6y - 5z = 3$
    $2x - y + z = 0$

17.  $3x - 4y - z = 1$
    $2x - 3y + z = 1$
    $x - 2y + 3z = 2$

18.   $3x - y + 2z = 1$
    $-6x + 2y - 4z = -2$
    $9x - 3y + 6z = 3$

In Exercises 19-24, find an equation of the plane that passes through the given points. Write your answer in the form $Ax + By + Cz = D$ where $A$, $B$, $C$, and $D$ are integers with no common factor.

19. $(1,3,-2)$, $(-4,2,-1)$, $(1,1,4)$    20. $(3,6,-3)$, $(0,2,2)$, $(-4,-2,0)$

21. $(3,1,3)$, $(4,-2,1)$, $(-1,-2,-3)$    22. $(3,3,3)$, $(-3,6,0)$, $(0,2,-2)$

23. $(-3,6,0)$, $(0,2,-2)$, $(-4,-1,3)$    24. $(4,-2,1)$, $(-1,-2,-3)$, $(5,0,-2)$

In Exercises 25-28, determine if there is a plane passing through all the given points. If so, find an equation of this plane in the form $Ax + By + Cz = D$ where $A$, $B$, $C$, and $D$ are integers with no common factor.

25. $(1,2,3)$, $(-2,3,-1)$, $(3,1,-4)$, $(4,2,-2)$  26. $(-8,-3,2)$, $(2,-2,-1)$, $(0,2,2)$, $(-2,-1,1)$

27. $(3,1,2)$, $(3,5,-2)$, $(-1,-3,0)$, $(5,5,1)$     28. $(-2,-3,4)$, $(5,1,4)$, $(3,2,-5)$, $(2,5,-1)$

# Section 2.5

**Calculator Example 2.5.1: The PIVOT Program**  (Sect 2.5, Example 2, p. 98)

Pivot in the row 2, column 3 position of the following matrix.

$$\begin{bmatrix} 2 & 1 & -1 & 3 \\ -4 & 6 & -2 & 1 \\ 7 & -5 & 3 & 2 \end{bmatrix}$$

A program which does pivoting on the TI-83 may be distributed by your instructor or (using a TI-83 Graph Link cable and software) can be downloaded from
http://virtual.parkland.cc.il.us/oadawi/pivot.83p.

Store this matrix in [A]. The following keystrokes perform the pivot. Here, # refers to the number of the PIVOT program, which depends on the number of programs stored in the calculator.

| PRGM | <EXEC> #:PIVOT | ENTER |

```
PIVOTING PROGRAM
PRESS ENTER FOR
MATRIX CHOICES.
THE PROGRAM USES
MATRIX [J] TO
STORE RESULTS.
```

1. Press | ENTER |.

2. Press | 1 |

3. At this point, $\Leftarrow$ and $\Rightarrow$ can be used to view the matrix if not all the columns can fit on the screen simultaneously. Press ENTER.

4. Press 2 ENTER to choose the pivot row or 0 to switch rows.

5. Press 3 ENTER to choose the pivot column.

Again, $\Leftarrow$ and $\Rightarrow$ can be used to view the matrix if not all the columns can fit on the screen simultaneously.

6. Press ENTER to repeat steps 4 and 5 as many times as desired.

**Exercises**:

In Exercises 1-6, let $A = \begin{bmatrix} 2 & 5 & -1 & 3 \\ 7 & -4 & -1 & 2 \\ 2 & 12 & -8 & 5 \\ -5 & -1 & 0 & 2 \end{bmatrix}$. Give the matrix resulting from pivoting in $A$ at the

following positions.

1. Row 1, column 3

2. Row 4, column 2

3. Row 2, column 4

4. Row 3, column 4

5. Row 4, column 1

6. Row 1, column 4

In Exercises 7-20, use Gauss-Jordan elimination to solve the given systems of equations.

7.  $\begin{aligned} 2x_1 - x_2 &= 50 \\ -x_1 + 2x_2 - x_3 &= 0 \\ -x_2 - x_3 &= 100 \end{aligned}$

8.  $\begin{aligned} 2x_1 + 4x_2 + 6x_3 &= -12 \\ 2x_1 - 3x_2 - 4x_3 &= 15 \\ 3x_1 + 4x_2 + 5x_3 &= -8 \end{aligned}$

9.  $\begin{aligned} x_1 + x_2 + 2x_3 &= 8 \\ -x_1 - 2x_2 + 3x_3 &= 1 \\ 3x_1 - 7x_2 + 4x_3 &= 10 \end{aligned}$

10.  $\begin{aligned} 2x_1 + 3x_2 - x_3 &= 11 \\ x_1 - x_2 + 2x_3 &= -7 \\ 4x_1 + x_2 - 2x_3 &= 12 \end{aligned}$

11.  $\begin{aligned} 2x_1 + 4x_2 + 3x_3 + 2x_4 &= 2 \\ 3x_1 + 6x_2 + 5x_3 + 2x_4 &= 2 \\ 2x_1 + 5x_2 + 2x_3 - 3x_4 &= 3 \\ 4x_1 + 5x_2 + 14x_3 + 14x_4 &= 11 \end{aligned}$

12.  $\begin{aligned} x_1 + 2x_3 &= 13 \\ x_1 + x_2 + 2x_3 + 2x_4 &= 5 \\ 2x_2 + 2x_3 + 4x_4 &= -13 \\ x_1 + x_2 + 2x_3 + 3x_4 &= 3 \end{aligned}$

13.  $\begin{aligned} 3x_1 - x_2 + 2x_3 &= -4 \\ 2x_1 + x_2 + x_3 &= -1 \\ x_1 + 3x_2 &= 2 \end{aligned}$

14.  $\begin{aligned} 3x_1 + 8x_2 - 5x_3 &= 10 \\ 2x_1 + 4x_2 + x_3 &= 8 \\ 2x_1 + 8x_2 - 12x_3 &= 4 \end{aligned}$

15.  $\begin{aligned} x_1 + 2x_2 + x_3 &= 1 \\ -2x_1 - 4x_2 - x_3 &= 0 \\ 5x_1 + 10x_2 + 3x_3 &= 2 \\ 3x_1 + 6x_2 + 3x_3 &= 4 \end{aligned}$

16.  $\begin{aligned} x_1 + 2x_2 - 2x_3 + 3x_5 &= 7 \\ -3x_1 - 6x_2 - x_3 - 2x_4 - x_5 &= -7 \\ 2x_1 + 4x_2 + x_4 + x_5 &= 6 \end{aligned}$

17.  $\begin{aligned} x_1 - x_2 + 2x_3 &= 2 \\ 2x_1 + 3x_2 - x_3 &= 14 \\ 3x_1 + 2x_2 + x_3 &= 16 \\ x_1 + 4x_2 - 3x_3 &= 12 \end{aligned}$

18.  $\begin{aligned} x_1 + 3x_2 + x_3 + x_4 &= -1 \\ -2x_1 - 6x_2 - x_3 &= 5 \\ x_1 + 3x_2 + 2x_3 + 3x_4 &= 2 \end{aligned}$

19.  $\begin{aligned} x_1 + 2x_2 - 4x_3 - x_4 &= 7 \\ 2x_1 + 5x_2 - 9x_3 - 4x_4 &= 16 \\ x_1 + 5x_2 - 7x_3 - 7x_4 &= 13 \end{aligned}$

20.  $\begin{aligned} x_1 - 2x_2 - x_3 + 3x_4 &= 0 \\ -2x_1 + 4x_2 + 5x_3 - 5x_4 &= 3 \\ 3x_1 - 6x_2 - 6x_3 + 8x_4 &= 2 \end{aligned}$

## Section 2.6

**Exercises:**

In Exercises 1-6, display the initial simplex table for the given linear program.

1. Maximize $z = 5x_1 + 3x_2$
   subject to
   $$6x_1 - 3x_2 \le 4$$
   $$3x_1 + x_2 \le 9$$
   $$x_1 \ge 0, x_2 \ge 0$$

2. Maximize $z = 2x_1 - 4x_2$
   subject to
   $$2x_1 + 3x_2 \le 2$$
   $$-4x_1 + 4x_2 \le 4$$
   $$x_1 \ge 0, x_2 \ge 0$$

3. Maximize $z = 4x_1 + 2x_2 - 5x_3$
   subject to
   $$8x_1 + 3x_2 + x_3 \le 1$$
   $$5x_1 - 12x_2 + 4x_3 \le 6$$
   $$x_1 \ge 0, x_2 \ge 0, x_3 \ge 0$$

4. Maximize $z = 2x_1 - 2x_2 + 10x_3$
   subject to
   $$4x_1 + 6x_2 - 3x_3 \le 15$$
   $$12x_1 + 2x_2 \le 5$$
   $$3x_1 - 4x_2 + 11x_3 \le 8$$
   $$x_1 \ge 0, x_2 \ge 0, x_3 \ge 0$$

5. Maximize $z = -4x_1 + 2x_2 + 3x_3 + x_4$
   subject to
   $$5x_1 - x_2 + 3x_3 - 2x_4 \le 6$$
   $$4x_1 + 3x_2 - x_3 + 12x_4 \le 2$$
   $$16x_1 + 2x_3 \le 10$$
   $$-4x_1 + 10x_2 - x_3 + 4x_4 \le 8$$
   $$x_1 \ge 0, x_2 \ge 0, x_3 \ge 0, x_4 \ge 0$$

6. Maximize $z = 12x_1 + 4x_2 + 2x_3 + x_4$
   subject to
   $$3x_1 - x_2 + 4x_3 + x_4 \le 9$$
   $$3x_1 + 2x_2 + x_4 \le 5$$
   $$6x_1 - 2x_2 + 5x_4 \le 8$$
   $$3x_2 + 4x_3 - x_4 \le 1$$
   $$5x_1 - 3x_2 + x_4 \le 3$$
   $$x_1 \ge 0, x_2 \ge 0, x_3 \ge 0, x_4 \ge 0$$

Note: The simplex algorithm for maximization requires pivoting in a column with a negative number in its top row. The algorithm often finishes in the fewest possible number of pivots if, at each step, the pivot column is chosen by finding the *most* negative number in the top row. In case of a tie for the most negative number, choose either column.

In Exercises 7-14, for each simplex table,

   a.  list *all* valid pivot positions (by row and column number)
   b.  list the pivot position which would be chosen if the above note is followed
   c.  give the simplex table resulting from pivoting at the position chosen in part (b)

7.
$$\begin{bmatrix} 1 & 3 & 0 & -4 & 0 & 10 \\ 0 & -2 & 1 & 2 & 0 & 4 \\ 0 & 2 & 0 & 5 & 1 & 6 \end{bmatrix}$$

8.
$$\begin{bmatrix} 1 & -2 & 0 & 0 & 0 & 15 \\ 0 & 3 & 2 & 1 & 0 & 9 \\ 0 & 1 & 2 & 0 & 1 & 4 \end{bmatrix}$$

9.
$$\left[\begin{array}{cccc|cc|c} 1 & 0 & -4 & 0 & -6 & 2 & 15 \\ \hline 0 & 1 & 2 & 0 & -1 & 3 & 0 \\ \hline 0 & 0 & 6 & 1 & 5 & -3 & 5 \end{array}\right]$$

10.
$$\left[\begin{array}{cccc|cc|c} 1 & -2 & 0 & -4 & 0 & 6 & 40 \\ \hline 0 & 6 & 0 & 1/2 & 1 & -2 & 3 \\ \hline 0 & 12 & 1 & 2 & 0 & 0 & 6 \end{array}\right]$$

11.
$$\left[\begin{array}{cccc|ccc|c} 1 & -3 & 0 & 0 & -6 & 0 & -4 & 20 \\ \hline 0 & 3 & 0 & 0 & -4 & 1 & -5 & 0 \\ \hline 0 & 1/2 & 1 & 0 & 5 & 0 & 10 & 5 \\ \hline 0 & 1 & 0 & 1 & 2/3 & 0 & 4 & 2 \end{array}\right]$$

12.
$$\left[\begin{array}{cccc|ccc|c} 1 & 0 & 0 & -8 & -7 & 0 & -1 & 12 \\ \hline 0 & 1 & 0 & 1/3 & 3 & 1 & 1 & 5 \\ \hline 0 & 0 & 1 & 1 & 0 & 0 & -2 & 7 \\ \hline 0 & 0 & 0 & 1 & 5 & 0 & 2/5 & 2 \end{array}\right]$$

13.
$$\left[\begin{array}{cccc|ccc|c} 1 & -5 & 0 & 0 & -6 & 0 & -2 & 15 \\ \hline 0 & 4 & 1 & 0 & 1/4 & 0 & 1 & 2 \\ \hline 0 & 1 & 0 & 1 & 2 & 0 & 4 & 8 \\ \hline 0 & 9 & 0 & 0 & -4 & 1 & -3 & 0 \end{array}\right]$$

14.
$$\left[\begin{array}{cccc|ccc|c} 1 & 0 & -3 & 4 & -8 & 0 & 0 & 22 \\ \hline 0 & 0 & 1/2 & 3 & -1 & 1 & 0 & 8 \\ \hline 0 & 1 & 1/4 & 0 & 4 & 0 & 0 & 4 \\ \hline 0 & 0 & 1/8 & -3 & 1/4 & 0 & 1 & 2 \end{array}\right]$$

For each simplex table in Exercises 15-20,

    a. give the basic feasible solution.  Use the variable names $x_1$, $x_2$, . . . as needed

    b. give the value of $z$

    c. identify the basic and nonbasic variables

    d. determine if the table gives the optimal value of $z$

15.
$$\left[\begin{array}{ccc|cc|c} 1 & 2 & 0 & -4 & 0 & 10 \\ \hline 0 & 2 & 0 & 2 & 1 & 4 \\ \hline 0 & -5 & 1 & -5 & 0 & 6 \end{array}\right]$$

16.
$$\left[\begin{array}{ccc|cc|c} 1 & 0 & 4 & 2 & 0 & 80 \\ \hline 0 & 1 & -2 & 1 & 0 & 20 \\ \hline 0 & 0 & 1 & -3 & 1 & 5 \end{array}\right]$$

17.
$$\left[\begin{array}{cccc|cc|c} 1 & 3 & 0 & 8 & 0 & 0 & 0 \\ \hline 0 & -2 & 4 & 3 & 0 & 1 & 14 \\ \hline 0 & -3 & -3 & 0 & 1 & 0 & 2 \end{array}\right]$$

18.
$$\left[\begin{array}{cccc|cc|c} 1 & -3 & -4 & 0 & -3 & 0 & 5 \\ \hline 0 & 5 & 2 & 0 & 2 & 1 & 0 \\ \hline 0 & 6 & -3 & 1 & 3 & 0 & 6 \end{array}\right]$$

19.
$$\left[\begin{array}{cccc|ccc|c} 1 & 0 & -3 & 0 & -5 & 0 & 5 & 16 \\ \hline 0 & 0 & 0 & 1 & 6 & 0 & -2 & 10 \\ \hline 0 & 1 & 2 & 0 & 0 & 0 & -4 & 8 \\ \hline 0 & 0 & -2 & 0 & 2 & 1 & 1 & 3 \end{array}\right]$$

20.
$$\left[\begin{array}{cccc|ccc|c} 1 & 0 & -2 & 0 & 0 & 4 & 0 & 5 \\ \hline 0 & 3 & 0 & 0 & 1 & 4 & 0 & 10 \\ \hline 0 & 8 & -5 & 0 & 0 & -7 & 1 & 12 \\ \hline 0 & -2 & 1 & 1 & 0 & 1 & 0 & 4 \end{array}\right]$$

In Exercises 21-30, use the simplex algorithm to solve the given linear program. Your solution should include the maximum value of $z$, the corresponding basic feasible solution, and the corner point (the part of the basic feasible solution corresponding to the original variables).

21. Maximize   $z = 2x_1 + 3x_2$

    subject to   $3x_1 + 5x_2 \leq 6$

                 $2x_1 + 3x_2 \leq 7$

                 $x_1 \geq 0,\ x_2 \geq 0$

22. Maximize   $z = 2x_1 + 3x_2$

    subject to   $x_1\ + x_2 \leq 160$

                 $3x_1 + 2x_2 \leq 240$

                 $x_1 \geq 0,\ x_2 \geq 0$

23. Maximize   $z = 4x_1 + 3x_2 + 2x_3$

    subject to   $3x_1 + 2x_2 + 5x_3 \leq 23$

                 $2x_1\ + x_2\ + x_3 \leq 8$

                 $x_1\ + x_2 + 2x_3 \leq 7$

                 $x_1 \geq 0,\ x_2 \geq 0,\ x_3 \geq 0$

24. Maximize   $z = 7x_1 + 5x_2 + 6x_3$

    subject to   $x_1\ + x_2 - x_3 \leq 3$

                 $x_1 + 2x_2 + x_3 \leq 8$

                 $x_1\ + x_2\ \ \ \ \leq 5$

                 $x_1 \geq 0,\ x_2 \geq 0,\ x_3 \geq 0$

25. Maximize   $z = 8x_1 + 3x_2 + x_3$

    subject to   $x_1 + 6x_2\ + 8x_3 \leq 118$

                 $x_1 + 5x_2 + 10x_3 \leq 220$

                 $x_1 \geq 0,\ x_2 \geq 0,\ x_3 \geq 0$

26. Maximize   $z = 2x_1 + 4x_2 + x_3$ .

    subject to   $x_1\ + x_2 + 2x_3 \leq 200$

                 $10x_1 + 8x_2 + 5x_3 \leq 2000$

                 $2x_1\ + x_2\ \ \ \ \leq\ 250$

                 $x_1 \geq 0,\ x_2 \geq 0,\ x_3 \geq 0$

27. Maximize   $z = 6x_1 + 3x_2 + 2x_3$

    subject to   $8x_1 + 6x_2\ + x_3 \leq 48$

                 $8x_1 + 4x_2 + 3x_3 \leq 40$

                 $4x_1 + 3x_2\ + x_3 \leq 16$

                 $x_1 \geq 0,\ x_2 \geq 0,\ x_3 \geq 0$

28. Maximize   $z = 5x_1 - 8x_2 + 5x_3$

    subject to   $9x_1 - 4x_2 - 2x_3 \leq 10$

                 $- 6x_1 + 2x_2 - 3x_3 \leq 8$

                 $2x_1 + 2x_2 + 3x_3 \leq 16$

                 $x_1 \geq 0,\ x_2 \geq 0,\ x_3 \geq 0$

29. Maximize   $z = 5x_1 + 8x_2 + 2x_3 + 4x_4$

    subject to   $4x_1 + 8x_2 + 3x_3 + 3x_4 \leq 108$

                 $4x_1 + 5x_2\ + x_3 - 3x_4 \leq 275$

                 $3x_1 + 2x_2\ \ \ \ \ \ + 3x_4 \leq\ 90$

                 $3x_2 - 5x_3\ + x_4 \leq 120$

                 $x_1 \geq 0,\ x_2 \geq 0,\ x_3 \geq 0,\ x_4 \geq 0$

30. Maximize   $z = 3x_1 + 12x_2 + 2x_3 + 4x_4$

    subject to   $4x_1 + 3x_2 - 5x_3 + 2x_4 \leq 400$

                 $3x_2 + 3x_3 + 2x_4 \leq 300$

                 $- x_1 + 6x_2 + 3x_3\ + x_4 \leq 300$

                 $x_1 \geq 0,\ x_2 \geq 0,\ x_3 \geq 0,\ x_4 \geq 0$

Note: In accounting, the *contribution margin* for a given product is defined as the sales revenue minus the variable costs associated with the product. For example, if a product sells for $350 and the variable costs per unit for the product are $100, then the contribution margin per unit for the product is $350 − $100 = $250.

31. A computer company assembles two types of desktop computers, A and B. Computer A sells for $1200 and computer B for $1400. The variable costs associated with computers A and B are $500 and $600 respectively. On the assembly line, computer A requires 2 machine-hours, while computer B takes 3 machine-hours. Both computers are tested, and computer A requires 1 hour for testing while computer B requires 1/2 hour for testing. Typically, 480 machine-hours are available daily for assembly and 120 hours are available daily for testing.

    a. How many of each type of computer should be produced to maximize the total contribution margin?

    b. What is the maximum total contribution margin?

32. A luggage manufacturer sells garment bags, totes, and small suitcases. Each garment bag requires $45 in raw materials and requires 10 minutes for leather cutting, 30 minutes for stitching, and 10 minutes for inspection/packaging. Each tote requires $40 dollars in raw materials and requires 10 minutes for cutting, 20 minutes for stitching, and 20 minutes for inspection/packaging. Each suitcase requires $60 in raw materials and requires 10 minutes for cutting, 40 minutes for stitching, and 10 minutes for inspection/packaging. The company has a daily capacity of 1000 machine-minutes on its cutting machines, 2100 machine-minutes in its stitching department, and 1500 machine-minutes in the inspection/packaging area. The company decides to price the garment bags, totes, and suitcases at $48, $45, and $65 respectively.

    a. How many of each type of luggage should it produce per day to maximize its total contribution margin?

    b. What is the maximum total contribution margin?

33. The chair of the Parkland mathematics department is trying to decide how many sections of Linear Algebra, Calculus I, and Statistics he can schedule at 10:00. Each section requires a different classroom, and there are 12 classrooms available at this time. Each Linear Algebra section requires 4 professor-hours, each Calculus I section requires 5 professor-hours, and each Statistics section requires 3 professor-hours. There are 40 professor-hours available for teaching at 10:00. The maximum enrollments for Linear Algebra, Calculus I, and Statistics are 24, 36, and 32 students per section respectively. Only 10 of the classrooms are large enough to hold a Calculus or Statistics section.

    a. How many sections of each course should be scheduled to maximize the total number of seats available in these three classes at 10:00?

    b. How many total seats will be available?

    c. Will any classrooms be unused?

    d. Will any professors be idle?

34. A power company can generate electricity by burning ordinary coal, low sulfur coal, or oil. The cost, emissions, and power generation capability per shipment of each of these energy sources is as follows.

|  | Coal | Low sulfur coal | Oil |
|---|---|---|---|
| Cost (in dollars) | 200 | 350 | 300 |
| Sulfur Dioxide (in tons) | 20 | 9 | 14 |
| Nitrogen Oxide (in tons) | 8 | 6 | 8 |
| Kilowatt hours generated | 800 | 800 | 900 |

Government pollution regulations limit the company to emitting no more than 1560 tons of sulfur dioxide and 960 tons of nitrogen dioxide. The company has $48,000 available to purchase fuel.

    a. How many shipments of each fuel should be used?

    b. How many kilowatt hours can the company generate?

    c. How many tons of sulfur dioxide and nitrogen oxide will be emitted?

35. Suppose a mutual fund manager has $100,000 to invest, and bonds from three companies are available having the following characteristics.

|  | Expected Return | Estimated Default Risk | Duration (years) |
|---|---|---|---|
| Company A | 6% | 1% | 3 |
| Company B | 8% | 3% | 5 |
| Company C | 11% | 6% | 9 |

To control risk, the manager must obey the following prospectus policies:

    i. The total estimated default risk must be at most $5,000. For example, a portfolio with $40,000 invested in A, $40,000 in B, and $20,000 in C would have a total estimated default risk of

$$40000(0.01) + 40000(0.03) + 20000(0.06) = \$2800$$

    ii. The average duration of the fund must be at most 6 years. For example, a portfolio with $40,000 invested in A, $40,000 in B, and $20,000 in C would have an average duration of

$$\frac{40000(3) + 40000(5) + 20000(9)}{100000} = 5 \text{ years}$$

    a. How should the manager divide the money among the three bonds in order to maximize expected return?

    b. What is the maximum expected return?

36. Repeat Exercise 35 assuming the duration of the bond from Company B increases to 6 years.

37. A contractor is planning to develop a subdivision with homes in three styles. Each ranch style house will be built on 0.35 acres of land, will require 2750 hours of labor to build, and will return a profit of $11,000. Each townhouse will be built on 0.25 acres of land, will require 3250 hours of labor to build, and will return a profit of $12,000. Each bi-level house will be built on 0.5 acres of land, will require 3400 hours of labor to build, and will return a profit of $15,000. The contractor does not think that more than 50 bi-level houses can be sold and hence will not build more than this. Suppose 450,000 hours of labor and 50 acres of land are available.

    a.  How many of each type of house should be built to maximize profit?

    b.  What is the maximum profit?

    c.  Will any land be left over?

38. An auto company manufactures cars, pickup trucks, and sports utility vehicles (SUV's). The parts for the body of each vehicle must be stamped out on a press, undercoated, then finish-painted. Suppose the press line can press 35 car bodies per day if just cars are being made (that is, it requires 1/35 of a day to press one car body), 28 truck bodies per day if just trucks are being made, and 24.5 SUV bodies per day if just SUV's are being made. The undercoating line could coat 40 car bodies per day if just cars were being made, 30 trucks per day if just trucks were being made, and 24 SUV's per day if just SUV's were being made. The paint line could paint 30 car bodies per day if just cars were being made, 40 trucks per day if just trucks were being made, and 40 SUV's per day if just SUV's were being made. Assume that the rate at which the vehicles are stamped and painted does not change if a combination of vehicles are made during the day. The profit on a car, truck, and SUV are $350, $450, and $550 respectively.

    a.   How many of each type of vehicle should be made per day to obtain the maximum profit?

    b.  What is the maximum profit per day the company can make?

39. One ounce of each of four foods contains the following.

|                      | Food A | Food B | Food C | Food D |
| -------------------- | ------ | ------ | ------ | ------ |
| Calories             | 90     | 180    | 90     | 140    |
| Cholesterol (grams)  | 3      | 2      | 3      | 6      |
| Sodium (mg)          | 150    | 200    | 75     | 200    |
| Fiber (grams)        | 4      | 6      | 3      | 5      |

A diet (a combination of these four foods) is to be designed containing the largest possible amount of fiber but containing no more than 900 calories, 24 grams of cholesterol, and 900 mg of sodium.

    a.  How many ounces of each food should be eaten?

    b.  How much fiber will the diet provide?

40. Repeat Exercise 39 if food D contains 8 grams of fiber per ounce.

## Section 2.7

**Exercises**:

In Exercises 1-4,

- **a.** use the simplex algorithm to show that there is no upper bound on the objective function value $z$
- **b.** sketch the feasibility region in the plane and draw the lines of constancy $z = 1$ and $z = 5$ to suggest that $z$ can become arbitrarily large

1. Maximize  $z = x_1 + 2x_2$
   subject to  $-3x_1 + x_2 \leq 3$
   $$x_1 - x_2 \leq 2$$
   $$x_1 \geq 0, \, x_2 \geq 0$$

2. Maximize  $z = x_1 + x_2$
   subject to  $x_1 - 2x_2 \leq 2$
   $$-x_1 + x_2 \leq 3$$
   $$x_1 \geq 0, \, x_2 \geq 0$$

3. Maximize  $z = -x_1 + x_2$
   subject to  $4x_1 - 2x_2 \leq 8$
   $$-3x_1 + x_2 \leq 3$$
   $$x_1 \geq 0, \, x_2 \geq 0$$

4. Maximize  $z = -x_1 + 3x_2$
   subject to  $-x_1 + x_2 \leq 2$
   $$-x_1 + 2x_2 \leq 6$$
   $$x_1 \geq 0, \, x_2 \geq 0$$

In Exercises 5-8,

- **a.** use the simplex algorithm to show that there is no upper bound on the objective function value $z$
- **b.** find a specific solution with $z \geq 1000$

5. Maximize  $z = 8x_1 + 6x_2 + 2x_3$
   subject to  $x_1 - 3x_2 + 2x_3 \leq 50$
   $$-2x_1 + 4x_2 + 5x_3 \leq 40$$
   $$x_1 \geq 0, \, x_2 \geq 0, \, x_3 \geq 0$$

6. Maximize  $z = 4x_1 + 5x_2 + x_3$
   subject to  $3x_1 - 8x_2 + x_3 \leq 4$
   $$-6x_1 + 2x_2 + x_3 \leq 16$$
   $$x_1 - 4x_2 - x_3 \leq 10$$
   $$x_1 \geq 0, \, x_2 \geq 0, \, x_3 \geq 0$$

7. Maximize  $z = -3x_1 + 4x_2 + 8x_3$
   subject to  $-3x_1 - 2x_2 + 2x_3 \leq 0$
   $$5x_1 - x_2 + 2x_3 \leq 8$$
   $$2x_1 + x_2 - 4x_3 \leq 5$$
   $$x_1 \geq 0, \, x_2 \geq 0, \, x_3 \geq 0$$

8. Maximize  $z = 2x_1 + 12x_2 - 4x_3$
   subject to  $4x_1 + 3x_2 - 9x_3 \leq 0$
   $$2x_1 + 2x_2 - 4x_3 \leq 6$$
   $$10x_1 - 2x_2 + 3x_3 \leq 8$$
   $$x_1 \geq 0, \, x_2 \geq 0, \, x_3 \geq 0$$

In Exercises 9-14, use the simplex method to attempt to solve the given linear program.  If a solution exists, give the maximum value of $z$, the corresponding basic feasible solution, and the corner point (the part of the basic feasible solution corresponding to the original variables).

9.  Maximize   $z = x_1 + x_2 + 2x_3$

    subject to   $x_1 - 2x_2 + x_3 \leq 9$

              $2x_1 + x_2 + 2x_3 \leq 28$

              $x_1 \geq 0, \, x_2 \geq 0, \, x_3 \geq 0$

10.  Maximize   $z = 13x_1 + 4x_2 - x_3$

    subject to   $6x_1 + x_2 - 4x_3 \leq 18$

              $2x_1 + 12x_2 - 8x_3 \leq 9$

              $x_1 \geq 0, \, x_2 \geq 0, \, x_3 \geq 0$

11.  Maximize   $z = -x_1 + 9x_2 + 3x_3$

    subject to   $3x_1 + 9x_2 + x_3 \leq 420$

              $x_1 + 3x_2 - 6x_3 \leq 0$

                   $x_2 + 3x_3 \leq 350$

              $x_1 \geq 0, \, x_2 \geq 0, \, x_3 \geq 0$

12.  Maximize   $z = 5x_1 + x_2 + x_3$

    subject to   $3x_1 + 6x_2 - x_3 \leq 15$

            $-2x_1 + 8x_2 + x_3 \leq 20$

              $2x_1 - x_2 + 6x_3 \leq 0$

              $x_1 \geq 0, \, x_2 \geq 0, \, x_3 \geq 0$

13.  Maximize   $z = 8x_1 + 4x_2 - x_3$

    subject to   $-6x_1 + 2x_2 - 4x_3 \leq 16$

             $-4x_1 + x_2 + 8x_3 \leq 10$

              $4x_1 - 5x_2 + 12x_3 \leq 8$

              $x_1 \geq 0, \, x_2 \geq 0, \, x_3 \geq 0$

14.  Maximize   $z = 4x_1 + 8x_2 + 3x_3$

    subject to   $2x_1 + 6x_2 + 4x_3 \leq 15$

              $x_1 + 4x_2 + x_3 \leq 6$

              $x_1 + 2x_2 + 3x_3 \leq 18$

              $x_1 \geq 0, \, x_2 \geq 0, \, x_3 \geq 0$

In Exercises 15-18,

    **a.**  sketch the feasibility region for the given linear program, labeling the vertices and the value of the objective function for each vertex

    **b.**  determine all paths that the simplex algorithm could take from the initial vertex (the origin) to the vertex giving the maximal value

    **c.**  perform the simplex algorithm choosing the pivot column to contain the most negative entry in the top row and determine which path in (b) the algorithm followed

15.  Maximize   $z = x_1 + x_2$

    subject to   $2x_1 + x_2 \leq 8$

              $3x_1 + 5x_2 \leq 15$

               $x_1 + 5x_2 \leq 10$

               $x_1 \geq 0, \, x_2 \geq 0$

16.  Maximize   $z = 2x_1 + 5x_2$

    subject to   $5x_1 + 4x_2 \leq 40$

               $x_1 + 3x_2 \leq 9$

               $x_1 + 6x_2 \leq 12$

               $x_1 \geq 0, \, x_2 \geq 0$

17. Maximize $\quad z = x_1 + 2x_2$

   subject to $\qquad\qquad x_2 \leq 4$

   $$x_1 + x_2 \leq 9$$
   $$-2x_1 + 3x_2 \leq 6$$
   $$x_1 - 2x_2 \leq 4$$
   $$x_1 \geq 0,\ x_2 \geq 0$$

18. Maximize $\quad z = x_1 + 12x_2$

   subject to $\quad -x_1 + 3x_2 \leq 9$

   $$-x_1 + x_2 \leq 2$$
   $$x_1 \qquad\ \leq 6$$
   $$x_1 + 2x_2 \leq 12$$
   $$x_1 \geq 0,\ x_2 \geq 0$$

19. A small mutual fund manager is planning to invest in technology stocks, blue chip stocks, and short term bonds. The expected annual returns are 20%, 10%, and 5% on technology stocks, blue chip stocks, and short term bonds, respectively. To control risk, she decides to invest no more than $50,000 in technology stocks, no more in blue chip stocks than in technology stocks and short term bonds put together, and no more in technology stocks and blue chip stocks together than three times the amount in short term bonds.

   a. How much money should she put in each of the three investments to maximize expected return?
   b. Explain the meaning of your answer in (a).

20. An auto company can produce loaded, standard, or economy versions of a sedan and makes a profit of $2000, $1500, and $1000 per car respectively on these versions. The ratio of sales of the versions tends to remain fairly constant, so the company wants to keep the production ratios balanced as well. Management decides to manufacture no more loaded and standard vehicles together than four times the number of economy cars, no more loaded cars than twice the number of standard cars, and no more than 1000 loaded vehicles per quarter.

   a. Find a production schedule which will maximize the company's profit per quarter.
   b. Explain the meaning of your answer in (a).

# Chapter 3

## Section 3.1

**Calculator Example 3.1.1: Matrix Transpose**

Find the transpose of $A = \begin{bmatrix} 1 & 3 \\ -3 & -2 \\ 4 & 2 \end{bmatrix}$

(The coincidence of the matrix name $A$ with the calculator storage location $[A]$ is convenient, but not necessary. $A$ could just as easily be stored in, for example, $[C]$). Enter the keystrokes:

| MATRX | <NAMES> 1:[A] | MATRX | <MATH> 2:$^\mathrm{T}$ | ENTER |

```
[A]
           [[1   3 ]
            [-3  -2]
            [4   2 ]]
[A]ᵀ
           [[1  -3 4]
            [3  -2 2]]
```

**Calculator Example 3.1.2: Matrix Addition and Scalar Multiplication**
(Sect 2.1, Example 1b, p. 139)

Let $A = \begin{bmatrix} -2 & 1 \\ 1 & 0 \end{bmatrix}$ and $B = \begin{bmatrix} 4 & -2 \\ 2 & 3 \end{bmatrix}$. Find $3A - 2B$.

Enter matrices $A$ and $B$ in $[A]$ and $[B]$ respectively. Enter the keystrokes:

| 3 | MATRX | <NAMES> 1:[A] | − | 2 | MATRX | <NAMES> 2:[B] | ENTER |

```
3[A]-2[B]
           [[-14  7 ]
            [-1   -6]]
```

Use of the ☒ key after the 3 and 2 is optional; the calculator treats the above keystrokes correctly as implied multiplication.

**Calculator Example 3.1.3**: **Matrix Multiplication** (Sect 3.1, Example 3, pp. 141-142)

Find the product $AB$ of the matrices $A = \begin{bmatrix} 5 & -1 & 6 & 2 \\ 4 & 3 & -3 & -2 \\ -4 & 6 & 1 & 7 \end{bmatrix}$ and $B = \begin{bmatrix} 2 & -5 \\ -3 & -2 \\ 1 & 4 \\ -5 & 3 \end{bmatrix}$

Enter matrices $A$ and $B$ in $[A]$ and $[B]$ respectively. Enter the following keystrokes:

$\boxed{\text{MATRX}}$ <NAMES> 1:[A] $\boxed{\text{MATRX}}$ <NAMES> 2:[B] $\boxed{\text{ENTER}}$

```
[A] [B]
      [[9     7  ]
       [6    -44 ]
       [-60  33 ]]
```

Use of the $\boxed{\times}$ key after the 1:[A] is optional; the calculator treats the above keystrokes correctly as implied multiplication.

**Calculator Example 3.1.4**: **Matrix Powers** (Sect 3.1, Example 6, pp. 145-146)

Find $A^3$ for the matrix $A = \begin{bmatrix} 0 & 1 \\ 2 & -1 \end{bmatrix}$

Enter the matrix $A$ in $[A]$. Enter the following keystrokes:

$\boxed{\text{MATRX}}$ <NAMES> 1:[A] $\boxed{\wedge}$ $\boxed{3}$ $\boxed{\text{ENTER}}$

```
[A]^3
      [[-2  3 ]
       [6  -5]]
```

**Exercises**:

In Exercises 1-22, $A$, $B$, $C$, $D$, and $E$ refer to the matrices below:

$$A = \begin{bmatrix} 3 & -1 & 6 \\ 2 & 4 & 1 \end{bmatrix} \qquad B = \begin{bmatrix} -3 & 5 \\ 1 & -2 \end{bmatrix} \qquad C = \begin{bmatrix} 6 & 1 & -3 \\ -2 & 5 & 2 \end{bmatrix}$$

$$D = \begin{bmatrix} 5 \\ -2 \\ -3 \end{bmatrix} \qquad E = \begin{bmatrix} 4 & -1 \\ 3 & 0 \\ 1 & 5 \end{bmatrix}$$

Find the indicated entries or matrices if possible, or state that the specified quantity is undefined.

1. $a_{13}$            2. $c_{21}$

3. $A^t$             4. $E^t$

5. $A + C$        6. $C + E^t$

7. $2C$             8. $-3B$

9. $3A^t + 4C$     10. $5C - 2A$

11. $BC$           12. $CB$

13. $A^tB$         14. $EA$

15. $2EB$        16. $-3BA$

17. $EB^3$        18. $B^4C$

19. $(BC^t)^2$      20. $(AE)^2$

21. $(A + C)E$    22. $A(C + E^t)$

23. The daily closing prices per share over one week of three stocks, Windsor, Millworks, and Travelon, were as follows:

|           | Windsor | Millworks | Travelon |
|-----------|---------|-----------|----------|
| Monday    | $67     | $118      | $84      |
| Tuesday   | $63     | $130      | $87      |
| Wednesday | $58     | $122      | $80      |
| Thursday  | $55     | $109      | $83      |
| Friday    | $59     | $108      | $84      |

Two investors, Fred and Barney, have portfolios as follows:  Fred – 80 shares of Windsor, 50 shares of Millworks, and 40 shares of Travelon;  Barney – 70 shares of Windsor, 55 shares of Millworks, and 30 shares of Travelon.

    **a.** Write down a product of two matrices which, when computed, will give the values (in dollars) of each man's portfolio on each day of the week.

    **b.** Compute the product indicated in (a).  Label the row(s) and column(s) with the quantities which they represent.

    **c.** On which day of the week was Fred's portfolio value the highest?

    **d.** On which day of the week was Barney's portfolio value the lowest?

24.  Suppose three sectors of an economy, steel production, railroad services, and coal mining, are mutually interdependent as follows.  For each $1 worth of steel produced, the steel industry purchases $0.10 of its own products, $0.15 of railroad services, and $0.10 worth of coal.  For each $1 worth of railroad services sold, the railroad sector purchases $0.20 worth of steel, $0.10 worth of its own products, and $0.05 worth of coal.  For each $1 worth of coal mined, the mining industry purchases $0.15 worth of steel, $0.30 of railroad services, and $0.10 worth of its own product.  One year, the value of steel, railroad services, and coal sold was $200 million, $150 million, and $125 million.

    **a.** Write down a product of two matrices which, when computed, will give the values (in millions of dollars) of the steel, railroad services, and coal which were used by *these three sectors* this year.

    **b.** Compute the product indicated in (a).  Label the row(s) and column(s) with the quantities which they represent.

25. The scores of three students on four math tests were as follows:

| | Kelly | Cheryl | Maria |
|---|---|---|---|
| Test 1 | 68 | 98 | 85 |
| Test 2 | 79 | 95 | 77 |
| Test 3 | 72 | 89 | 80 |
| Test 4 | 57 | 96 | 92 |

$$\left(1,2,3,4\right)\left(K,C,M\right)$$

$$\left(K,C,M\right)\left(1,2,3,4\right) \quad \left(1,2,3,4\right)$$

    **a.** Write down a product of two matrices which, when computed, will give the average score of each person.

    **b.** Compute the product indicated in (a).  Label the row(s) and column(s) with the quantities which they represent.

    **c.** Write down a product of two matrices which, when computed, will give the average score of these students on each test.

    **d.** Compute the product indicated in (a).  Label the row(s) and column(s) with the quantities which they represent.

26. A furniture company has showrooms in Champaign and Springfield. In Champaign, there are 50 beds, 45 tables, and 25 china cabinets displayed, while in Springfield, there are 32 beds, 37 tables, and 30 china cabinets displayed. The wholesale values of this furniture are $400, $700, and $1100 per bed, table, and china cabinet, respectively. The retail values are $600, $1000, and $1500 per bed, table, and china cabinet respectively.

    a. Write down a product of two matrices which, when computed, will give the wholesale and retail values (in dollars) of the stock in each showroom.

    b. Compute the product indicated in (a). Label the row(s) and column(s) with the quantities which they represent.

27. An appliance manufacturer makes stoves, refrigerators, and dishwashers at plants in California and Wisconsin. Each appliance requires the following number of labor-hours in the assembly, finishing, and packaging areas.

|              | Assembly | Finishing | Packaging |
|--------------|----------|-----------|-----------|
| Stove        | 2        | 1.5       | 0.5       |
| Refrigerator | 3.5      | 1.75      | 0.75      |
| Dishwasher   | 2.75     | 1.5       | 0.4       |

Suppose hourly wages at each plant and in each area are as follows.

|            | Assembly | Finishing | Packaging |
|------------|----------|-----------|-----------|
| California | $18.00   | $21.50    | $13.00    |
| Wisconsin  | $14.00   | $16.00    | $9.50     |

    a. Write down a product of two matrices which, when computed, will give the per unit labor cost (in dollars) to produce each appliance at each plant.

    b. Compute the product indicated in (a). (Give answers to the nearest cent). Label the row(s) and column(s) with the quantities which they represent.

28. Suppose the percentages of the employed population in three countries working in the areas of manufacturing, service, and agriculture are as follows.

|           | Manufacturing | Service | Agriculture |
|-----------|---------------|---------|-------------|
| Country A | 25%           | 30%     | 5%          |
| Country B | 20%           | 15%     | 15%         |
| Country C | 20%           | 25%     | 20%         |

Let $a$, $b$, and $c$ be the total employed populations of countries A, B, and C, respectively. Let $w_1$, $w_2$, and $w_3$ be the total number of people in the three countries working in manufacturing, service, and agriculture, respectively.

**a.** Find a matrix $D$ so that $D \begin{bmatrix} a \\ b \\ c \end{bmatrix} = \begin{bmatrix} w_1 \\ w_2 \\ w_3 \end{bmatrix}$

**b.** If $a = 30$ million, $b = 50$ million, and $c = 15$ million, find $w_1$, $w_2$, and $w_3$ (in millions of people).

29. A fruit cocktail mix from Fantasia Company consists of 35% peaches, 30% pears, 20% pineapple, and 15% grapes, while a mix from Fullsum Company contains 30% peaches, 30% pears, 20% pineapple, and 20% grapes. Suppose in September, the wholesale purchase prices per pound of fruit are $0.89 for peaches, $0.79 for pears, $0.99 for pineapple, and $1.29 for grapes, while in March the purchase prices are $1.29 for peaches, $1.09 for pears, $0.99 for pineapple, and $0.99 for grapes.

   **a.** Write down a product of two matrices which, when computed, will give the cost per pound (in dollars) of the ingredients needed to make Fantasia and Fullsum fruit cocktails in both September and March.

   **b.** Compute the product indicated in (a). (Give answers to the nearest cent). Label the row(s) and column(s) with the quantities which they represent.

   **c.** Suppose the selling price for a 2 pound can of Fantasia is $2.69 and for a 2 pound can of Fullsum is $2.79. If $A$, $B$, and $C$ are the following matrices, write a matrix expression involving these matrices and any other needed quantities which, when computed will give a matrix expressing the profit per can to both Fantasia and Fullsum in both September and March.

$$A = \begin{bmatrix} 0.35 & 0.30 & 0.20 & 0.15 \\ 0.30 & 0.30 & 0.20 & 0.20 \end{bmatrix} \qquad B = \begin{bmatrix} 0.89 & 1.29 \\ 0.79 & 1.09 \\ 0.99 & 0.99 \\ 1.29 & 0.99 \end{bmatrix}$$

$$C = \begin{bmatrix} 2.69 & 2.69 \\ 2.79 & 2.79 \end{bmatrix}$$

   **d.** Evaluate the expression indicated in (c). Label the row(s) and column(s) with the quantities which they represent.

30. A computer manufacturer is making a system box in two configurations. Model #1 consists of a motherboard, three 32MB memory chips, a CPU, and two disk drives. Model #2 consists of a motherboard, four 32 MB memory chips, a CPU, and 3 disk drives. The manufacturer has three suppliers for components, who offer the following wholesale prices. By marketing contract, however, the manufacturer must buy all components from one supplier.

|           | Motherboard | 32 MB Memory | CPU   | Disk Drive |
|-----------|-------------|--------------|-------|------------|
| Supplier A | $320       | $80          | $350  | $130       |
| Supplier B | $375       | $95          | $320  | $110       |
| Supplier C | $295       | $65          | $340  | $125       |

a. Write down a product of two matrices which, when computed, will give the cost per system box (in dollars) of the components needed to build each of the two models using components from each of the three suppliers.

b. Compute the product indicated in (a).  Label the row(s) and column(s) with the quantities which they represent.

c. Suppose the selling price for system #1 is $1700 and the selling price for system #2 is $1900.  If A, B, and C are the following matrices, write an expression involving these matrices and any other needed quantities which, when computed will give a matrix expressing the profits from selling five system #1 units or five system #2 units using components from each supplier.

$$A = \begin{bmatrix} 1 & 3 & 1 & 2 \\ 1 & 4 & 1 & 3 \end{bmatrix} \qquad B = \begin{bmatrix} 320 & 80 & 350 & 130 \\ 375 & 95 & 320 & 110 \\ 295 & 65 & 340 & 125 \end{bmatrix}$$

$$C = \begin{bmatrix} 1700 & 1900 \\ 1700 & 1900 \\ 1700 & 1900 \end{bmatrix}$$

d. Evaluate the expression indicated in (c).  Label the row(s) and column(s) with the quantities which they represent.


# Section 3.2

**Calculator Example 3.2.1: Matrix Inverse** (Sect 3.2, Example 2, p. 153)

Find the inverse of the matrix $A = \begin{bmatrix} 2 & -4 & 6 \\ 3 & -5 & 8 \\ -2 & 6 & -10 \end{bmatrix}$.

Enter the matrix in $[A]$.  Enter the keystrokes:

$\boxed{\text{MATRX}}$ $\boxed{\text{<NAMES> 1:}[A]}$ $\boxed{x^{-1}}$ $\boxed{\text{ENTER}}$

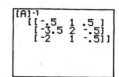

If desired, the keystrokes | MATH | <MATH> 1:⇒Frac can be used to view the matrix entries in fractional form.

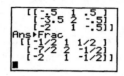

**Exercises**:

In Exercises 1-4, determine whether the two given matrices are inverses.

1. $\begin{bmatrix} 10 & 3 \\ 13 & 4 \end{bmatrix}$, $\begin{bmatrix} 4 & -3 \\ -13 & 10 \end{bmatrix}$

2. $\begin{bmatrix} -12 & 5 \\ -4 & 2 \end{bmatrix}$, $\begin{bmatrix} -1/2 & 5/4 \\ -1 & 3 \end{bmatrix}$

3. $\begin{bmatrix} 1 & 3 & 2 \\ 2 & 4 & 2 \\ 1 & 2 & -1 \end{bmatrix}$, $\begin{bmatrix} -2 & 7/4 & -1/2 \\ 1 & -3/4 & 1/2 \\ 0 & 1/4 & -1/2 \end{bmatrix}$

4. $\begin{bmatrix} 1 & -1 & 1 \\ 0 & 2 & -1 \\ 2 & 3 & 0 \end{bmatrix}$, $\begin{bmatrix} 3 & 3 & -1 \\ -2 & -2 & 1 \\ -4 & -5 & 2 \end{bmatrix}$

In Exercises 5-12, find the inverse of the given matrix or determine that none exists.

5. $\begin{bmatrix} 3 & -7 \\ -2 & 5 \end{bmatrix}$

6. $\begin{bmatrix} 6 & 4 \\ -3 & -2 \end{bmatrix}$

7. $\begin{bmatrix} 4 & 10 \\ -6 & -15 \end{bmatrix}$

8. $\begin{bmatrix} 9 & 7 \\ 7 & 5 \end{bmatrix}$

9. $\begin{bmatrix} -3 & 5 & 6 \\ -1 & 2 & 2 \\ 1 & -1 & -1 \end{bmatrix}$

10. $\begin{bmatrix} -16 & 4 & 3 \\ -2 & 1 & 0 \\ 7 & -2 & -1 \end{bmatrix}$

11. $\begin{bmatrix} 1 & 2 & 0 & 3 \\ 2 & 5 & -1 & 8 \\ 2 & 4 & 1 & 6 \\ 3 & 6 & 1 & 8 \end{bmatrix}$

12. $\begin{bmatrix} -7 & 2 & 3 & -2 \\ 5 & -1 & -2 & 1 \\ 1 & 0 & 0 & 1 \\ -3 & 1 & 1 & -1 \end{bmatrix}$

In Exercises 13-16, determine $A$, $X$, and $B$ if the system is written as $AX = B$.

13.  $3x_1 + 5x_2 = 8$
     $-4x_1 + 3x_2 = -2$

14.  $6x_1 - 4x_2 = 5$
     $7x_1 + x_2 = -3$

15.  $4x_1 \qquad - x_3 = 5$
     $3x_1 - x_2 + 5x_3 = 18$
     $-x_1 + 12x_2 \qquad = -8$

16.  $-8x_1 + 3x_2 - x_3 = -6$
     $9x_1 + 4x_2 - 2x_3 = -15$
     $x_2 - 7x_3 = -4$

In Exercises 17-20, write the given matrix equation as a system of scalar equations.

17. $\begin{bmatrix} 3 & 8 \\ 0 & -4 \end{bmatrix} \begin{bmatrix} x_1 \\ x_2 \end{bmatrix} = \begin{bmatrix} 12 \\ 3 \end{bmatrix}$

18. $\begin{bmatrix} 5 & -2 \\ 4 & 0 \end{bmatrix} \begin{bmatrix} x_1 \\ x_2 \end{bmatrix} = \begin{bmatrix} 0 \\ -9 \end{bmatrix}$

19. $\begin{bmatrix} 3 & 2 & -2 \\ -9 & 0 & 3 \\ 6 & -2 & 8 \end{bmatrix} \begin{bmatrix} x_1 \\ x_2 \\ x_3 \end{bmatrix} = \begin{bmatrix} 4 \\ 2 \\ 3 \end{bmatrix}$

20. $\begin{bmatrix} 8 & 4 & -8 \\ 3 & 8 & 0 \\ -2 & 8 & 7 \end{bmatrix} \begin{bmatrix} x_1 \\ x_2 \\ x_3 \end{bmatrix} = \begin{bmatrix} -3 \\ 5 \\ 0 \end{bmatrix}$

In Exercises 21-26, let $A$ be the coefficient matrix for the matrix equation $AX = B$. Find

   a.  the solution vector $X_1$ for the given constant vector $B_1$
   b.  the solution vector $X_2$ for the given constant vector $B_2$
   c.  the solution vector $X_3$ for the given constant vector $B_3$ (Give an answer in terms of $a$, $b$, and $c$ as needed. Notice that this part is asking you to find a *formula* for the solution)

21. $A = \begin{bmatrix} 1 & 2 \\ 1 & 3 \end{bmatrix}$, $B_1 = \begin{bmatrix} 1 \\ 4 \end{bmatrix}$, $B_2 = \begin{bmatrix} 2 \\ -5 \end{bmatrix}$, $B_3 = \begin{bmatrix} a \\ b \end{bmatrix}$

22. $A = \begin{bmatrix} 3 & -2 \\ -1 & 1 \end{bmatrix}$, $B_1 = \begin{bmatrix} 1 \\ 4 \end{bmatrix}$, $B_2 = \begin{bmatrix} 2 \\ -5 \end{bmatrix}$, $B_3 = \begin{bmatrix} a \\ b \end{bmatrix}$

23. $A = \begin{bmatrix} -40 & 16 & 9 \\ 13 & -5 & -3 \\ 5 & -2 & -1 \end{bmatrix}$, $B_1 = \begin{bmatrix} 1 \\ -3 \\ 2 \end{bmatrix}$, $B_2 = \begin{bmatrix} 2 \\ 1 \\ 8 \end{bmatrix}$, $B_3 = \begin{bmatrix} a \\ b \\ c \end{bmatrix}$

24. $A = \begin{bmatrix} 7 & 6 & -3 \\ 2 & 2 & -1 \\ -6 & -5 & 3 \end{bmatrix}$, $B_1 = \begin{bmatrix} 1 \\ -3 \\ 2 \end{bmatrix}$, $B_2 = \begin{bmatrix} 2 \\ 1 \\ 8 \end{bmatrix}$, $B_3 = \begin{bmatrix} a \\ b \\ c \end{bmatrix}$

25. $A = \begin{bmatrix} 1 & 2 & 2 \\ 2 & -4 & -4 \\ -1 & -2 & -1 \end{bmatrix}$, $B_1 = \begin{bmatrix} 1 \\ -3 \\ 2 \end{bmatrix}$, $B_2 = \begin{bmatrix} 2 \\ 1 \\ 8 \end{bmatrix}$, $B_3 = \begin{bmatrix} a \\ b \\ c \end{bmatrix}$

26. $A = \begin{bmatrix} 1 & 3 & 9 \\ 0 & 1 & 4 \\ 3 & 2 & 3 \end{bmatrix}$, $B_1 = \begin{bmatrix} 1 \\ -3 \\ 2 \end{bmatrix}$, $B_2 = \begin{bmatrix} 2 \\ 1 \\ 8 \end{bmatrix}$, $B_3 = \begin{bmatrix} a \\ b \\ c \end{bmatrix}$

In Exercises 27-32, find the values of $k$ such that the matrix is *not* invertible.

27. $\begin{bmatrix} 4 & k \\ k & 1 \end{bmatrix}$

28. $\begin{bmatrix} k & -8 \\ -2 & k \end{bmatrix}$

29. $\begin{bmatrix} 1 & 5 & -2 \\ 4 & 4 & -2 \\ 4 & 8 & k \end{bmatrix}$

30. $\begin{bmatrix} 8 & 4 & 1 \\ -1 & 6 & 3 \\ 2 & k & 4 \end{bmatrix}$

31. $\begin{bmatrix} 1 & 6 & -1 \\ 4 & k & -130 \\ 3 & 19 & k \end{bmatrix}$

32. $\begin{bmatrix} 1 & 2 & 3 \\ 2 & k & 26 \\ 1 & 3 & k \end{bmatrix}$

In Exercises 33-40, assume $A$, $B$, and $C$ are 4x4 matrices, $D$ and $X$ are 4x1 matrices, and $w$ is a real number.

    a. Determine which matrix or matrices must be invertible for the given system to have a unique solution $X$.

    b. Solve for $X$ assuming the matrix or matrices identified in (a) is/are invertible.

33. $A^2X = D$

34. $AX = BX$

35. $AX = wX + D$

36. $ABX = D$

37. $X - CX = D$

38. $A^2X = w^2X + D$

39. $(A - 3I)X = (2A - wI)X$

40. $AX = 3X + 2D$

41. A financial advisor is constructing a model to help clients decide where to invest. For simplicity, he assumes two options – a blue chip stock mutual fund with an expected annual return of 10%, and a much safer investment grade bond fund with an expected annual return of 6%. The two variables he plans to ask from a client are

     i.  how much the client plans to invest (in dollars), and
    ii.  the smallest expected annual return (in dollars) the client would be satisfied with.

Let $a$ be the planned investment amount and $r$ the chosen annual return.

    a.  Set up and solve (using a matrix inverse) a matrix equation which will give the amount which should be placed in the two investments in terms of $a$ and $r$.
    b.  If a client gives answers $a = \$10,000$ and $r = \$900$, how should the money be placed?
    c.  If a client gives answers $a = \$10,000$ and $r = \$1200$, how should the money be placed?

42. A nutritionist is modeling the dietary needs of cats, and is developing a formula for the daily amounts of two foods a cat should be fed based on its protein and carbohydrate needs. The foods have the following nutritional content per ounce.

|                          | Food A | Food B |
| ------------------------ | ------ | ------ |
| Protein (grams)          | 9      | 7      |
| Carbohydrates (grams)    | 3      | 4      |

Let $p$ be the daily protein requirement and $c$ the daily carbohydrate requirement for a cat.

    a.  Set up and solve (using a matrix inverse) a matrix equation which will give the amounts of each food in terms of $p$ and $c$ which should be fed.
    b.  If a cat needs 60 grams of protein and 30 grams of carbohydrates per day, how many ounces of each food should it be fed?
    c.  If a cat needs 70 grams of protein and 50 grams of carbohydrates per day, how many ounces of each food should it be fed?

# Section 3.3

**Calculator Example 3.3.1:  Computing a Production Vector** (Sect 3.3, Example 1, pp. 162-164)

Compute the production vector $X = (I - C)^{-1}D$ for the consumption matrix

$$C = \begin{bmatrix} 0.2 & 0.1 & 0.3 \\ 0.4 & 0.4 & 0.2 \\ 0.1 & 0 & 0 \end{bmatrix} \text{ and external demand vector } D = \begin{bmatrix} 4200 \\ 8400 \\ 12600 \end{bmatrix}.$$

Enter $C$ in $[C]$ and $D$ in $[D]$.  Enter the keystrokes:

| ( | MATRX | <MATH> 5: identity( | 3 | ) | – | MATRX | <NAMES> 3:[C] | ) | $x^{-1}$ | MATRX |

| <NAMES> 4:[D] | ENTER |

```
(identity(3)-[C]
)⁻¹[D]
          [[14000]
           [28000]
           [14000]]
```

The "identity" command on the TI-83 returns the identity matrix of the size specified – in this case the 3x3 identity matrix.


**Exercises:**

1. Suppose the government and private sectors of an economy interact as follows.  For each $1 of services the government sector produces, it uses $0.15 worth of government services and $0.20 worth of services from the private sector.  For each $1 of services the private sector produces, it uses $0.10 worth of goverment services and $0.20 worth of its own services.

    **a.** Write the consumption matrix, labeling the meaning of the rows and columns.

    **b.** If the government sector produces $20 billion in services and the private sector produces $150 billion, how much of each type of service remains for export?

    **c.** How much must each sector produce to meet an external demand of $10 billion for government services and $120 billion for private sector services?


2. ABC Corporation is divided into consulting and manufacturing divisions.  For each $1 of consulting services generated the consulting division, this division uses $0.30 of its own services and $0.25 of manufacturing services.  For each $1 of products made by the manufacturing division, this division uses $0.15 of consulting services and $0.20 worth of its own services.

    **a.** Write the consumption matrix, labeling the meaning of the rows and columns.

    **b.** If the consulting division produces $15 million in services and the manufacturing division produces $25 million, how much of each type of service remains for sale to the public?

    **c.** How much must each division produce to meet an external demand of $35 million for consulting services and $50 million for manufacturing services?


3. The housing, transportation, and utility sectors of an economy depend on each other as follows. For each $1 of housing products provided, the housing sector uses $0.05 of its own products, $0.20 of transportation services, and $0.15 of utility services.  For each $1 of transporation services provided, the transportation sector uses $0.30 of its own services and $0.15 of utility services.  For each $1 of utility services provided, the utility sector uses $0.05 of housing products, $0.25 of transportation products, and $0.20 of its own services.

    a. Write the consumption matrix, labeling the meaning of the rows and columns.
    b. If the housing, transportation, and utility sectors produce $12 billion, $16 billion, and $6 billion in services respectively, how much of each type of service remains for export?
    c. How much must each sector produce to meet an external demand of $8 billion, $10 billion, and $4 billion for housing, transportation, and utility sectors respectively?

4. Three sectors of an economy, agriculture, manufacturing, and government, interact as follows. Each dollar's worth of agricultural output requires inputs of $0.15 from the agricultural sector, $0.15 from the manufacturing sector, and $0.10 from the government sector. Each dollar's worth of manufacturing output requires inputs of $0.20 from the agricultural sector, $0.35 from the manufacturing sector, and $0.15 from the government sector. Each dollar's worth of government output requires inputs of $0.40 from the agricultural sector, $0.50 from the manufacturing sector, and $0.30 from the goverment sector.

    a. Write the consumption matrix, labeling the meaning of the rows and columns.
    b. If the agricultural, manufacturing, and government sectors produce $45 billion, $100 billion, and $30 billion in services respectively, how much of each type of service remains for external demand?
    c. How much must each sector produce to meet an external demand of $35 billion, $100 billion, and $10 billion for agricultural, manufacturing, and government services respectively?

5. Manchester Corporation has manufacturing plants in Canada, Mexico, and the United States. The plants make loading and packaging equipment used for the company's own manufacturing process as well as for sale. Suppose the dollar value of last year's output was $220 million, $180 million, and $950 million at the Canadian, Mexican, and United States plants, respectively. The value (in millions of dollars) of the company's own products used at each of the plants last year was as follows.

|                |               | Used By |        |               |
|----------------|---------------|---------|--------|---------------|
|                |               | Canada  | Mexico | United States |
|                | Canada        | 20      | 20     | 120           |
| Imported From  | Mexico        | 15      | 25     | 90            |
|                | United States | 40      | 35     | 260           |

    a. Write the consumption matrix, labeling the meaning of the rows and columns.
    b. Assuming last year's consumption matrix remains valid for this year, how much must the plant in each country produce to meet an external demand of $135 million, $80 million, and $650 million for products from the Canadian, Mexican, and United States plants, respectively?

6. Three of the sectors in Leontief's model of the U.S. economy were livestock products, agricultural crops, and agricultural services. Suppose one year the total sector outputs were (in billions) $43, $35, and $3.6 for livestock products, agricultural crops, and agricultural services respectively, and the total value of services used internally by these sectors (in billions of dollars) were as follows.

|  |  | Sector Used By | | |
| --- | --- | --- | --- | --- |
|  |  | Livestock | Ag Crops | Ag Services |
| Sector Produced By | Livestock | 11 | 0.8 | 0.2 |
|  | Ag Crops | 10 | 1.1 | 0.05 |
|  | Ag Services | 1.2 | 1.3 | 0.1 |

    **a.** Write the consumption matrix, labeling the meaning of the rows and columns.

    **b.** Assuming this consumption matrix remains valid, how much must each sector produce to meet an external demand of $10 billion, $8 billion, and $0.5 billion for livestock, agricultural crops, and agricultural services, respectively?

7. Three capitalists are stranded on a desert island and decide to specialize in their production of food. Mr. Dull will raise coconuts, Mr. Dim will raise pineapple, and Mr. Thick will raise mangos. Since they are alone on the island, there is no external demand, but they decide to market to each other rather than to share. Out of each $1 in coconuts raised by Mr. Dull, he will consume $0.35 worth of coconuts, $0.35 worth of pineapple, and $0.30 worth of mangos. Out of each $1 in pineapple raised by Mr. Dim, he will consume $0.20 worth of coconuts, $0.45 worth of pineapple, and $0.35 worth of mangos. Out of each $1 in mangos raised by Mr. Thick, he will consume $0.40 worth of coconuts and $0.60 worth of mangos.

    **a.** Write the consumption matrix, labeling the meaning of the rows and columns.

    **b.** If Mr. Dull raises $2000 in coconuts one year, what dollar value of pineapple and mangos must Mr. Dim and Mr. Thick, respectively, raise to exactly meet demand?

8. Repeat Exercise 7 assuming Mr. Thick learns to like pineapple and decides to eat $0.30 worth of coconut, $0.20 worth of pineapple, and $0.50 worth of mangos per dollar of mangos grown.

9. Suppose a company is divided into sales, manufacturing, research and development, and administration divisions. For each $1 value generated by the sales division, it needs $0.10 of its own products, $0.20 of manufacturing products, $0.05 of research and development services, and $0.10 of administrative services. For each $1 value generated by the manufacturing division, it needs $0.10 of sales services, $0.25 of its own products, $0.15 of research and development services, and $0.10 of administrative services. For each $1 value generated by the research and development division, it needs $0.15 of sales services, $0.15 of manufacturing products, $0.30 of its own services, and $0.15 of administrative services. For each $1 value generated by the administrative division, it needs $0.20 of sales services, $0.20 of manufacturing products, $0.10 of research and development services, and $0.25 of its own services.

    **a.** Write the consumption matrix, labeling the meaning of the rows and columns.

    **b.** If the sales division, manufacturing division, research and development division, and administration division produce $15 million, $25 million, $10 million, and $8 million respectively, is the company self-sustaining in each area or must it purchase external services? If the latter, how much of each service must it purchase?

    **c.** If the sales division, manufacturing division, research and development division, and administration division produce $25 million, $10 million, $10 million, and $3 million respectively, is the company self-sustaining in each area or must it purchase external services? If the latter, how much of each service must it purchase?

    **d.** How much must each division produce to meet an external demand of $35 million, $45 million, $20 million, and $10 million for sales, manufacturing, research and development, and administrative services, respectively?

10. Repeat Exercise 9 assuming administration changes its consumption to $0.15 of sales services, $0.15 of manufacturing products, $0.10 of research and development services, and $0.30 of its own services per dollar produced.

For the consumption matrices in Exercises 11-14,

    **a.** Determine which of the industries, if any, are profitable (call them #1, #2, and #3)

    **b.** Use Theorem 1 to show that the consumption matrix is productive

11.
$$\begin{bmatrix} 0.2 & 0.5 & 0.4 \\ 0.3 & 0.1 & 0.4 \\ 0.3 & 0.1 & 0.1 \end{bmatrix}$$

12.
$$\begin{bmatrix} 0.3 & 0.2 & 0.4 \\ 0.6 & 0.1 & 0.2 \\ 0.2 & 0.1 & 0.5 \end{bmatrix}$$

13.
$$\begin{bmatrix} 0.3 & 0.5 & 0.1 \\ 0.2 & 0.4 & 0.2 \\ 0.4 & 0.2 & 0.2 \end{bmatrix}$$

14.
$$\begin{bmatrix} 0.3 & 0.3 & 0.1 \\ 0.5 & 0.2 & 0.3 \\ 0.1 & 0.4 & 0.3 \end{bmatrix}$$

Determine if the consumption matrices in Exercises 15-18 are productive.

15.
$$\begin{bmatrix} 0.4 & 0.3 & 0.2 \\ 0.3 & 1.1 & 0 \\ 0.2 & 0.2 & 0.4 \end{bmatrix}$$

16.
$$\begin{bmatrix} 0.4 & 0.3 & 0.4 \\ 0.2 & 0.4 & 0.1 \\ 0.5 & 0.3 & 0.2 \end{bmatrix}$$

17.
$$\begin{bmatrix} 0.1 & 0.4 & 0.4 \\ 0.2 & 0.3 & 0.2 \\ 0.2 & 0.5 & 0.4 \end{bmatrix}$$

18.
$$\begin{bmatrix} 0.2 & 0.4 & 0.2 \\ 0.3 & 0.4 & 0.5 \\ 0.4 & 0.1 & 1.8 \end{bmatrix}$$

## Section 3.4

**Calculator Example 3.4.1: Matrix Determinant** (Sect 3.4, Example 1, pp. 172-173)

Find the determinant of $A = \begin{bmatrix} 5 & 3 & -3 \\ -2 & 8 & 1 \\ 1 & -6 & 4 \end{bmatrix}$

Enter the matrix in $[A]$.  Enter the keystrokes:

| MATRX | <MATH> 1:det( | MATRX | <NAMES> 1:[A] | ) | | ENTER |

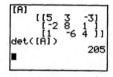

**Exercises**:

In Exercises 1-10, compute the determinant of the given matrix by any method.

1. $\begin{bmatrix} 1 & 3 \\ -2 & 5 \end{bmatrix}$

2. $\begin{bmatrix} 2 & -6 \\ -2 & 3 \end{bmatrix}$

3. $\begin{bmatrix} 6 & 2 & -3 \\ 0 & -2 & 5 \\ 0 & 0 & -5 \end{bmatrix}$

4. $\begin{bmatrix} 2 & 4 & -3 \\ 0 & -5 & 3 \\ 0 & 0 & 7 \end{bmatrix}$

5. $\begin{bmatrix} 2 & -1 & 4 \\ 4 & 0 & 3 \\ -2 & 2 & 0 \end{bmatrix}$

6. $\begin{bmatrix} 3 & -1 & 2 \\ -4 & 2 & 0 \\ 0 & 3 & 8 \end{bmatrix}$

7. $\begin{bmatrix} 5 & -2 & 1 \\ 4 & 3 & -3 \\ 2 & 5 & 0 \end{bmatrix}$

8. $\begin{bmatrix} 3 & 4 & -2 \\ 0 & 2 & 1 \\ -5 & -2 & -1 \end{bmatrix}$

9. $\begin{bmatrix} 1 & 3 & 0 & 2 \\ -3 & 5 & 1 & -4 \\ 6 & 1 & 0 & -1 \\ 0 & 3 & -2 & 1 \end{bmatrix}$    10. $\begin{bmatrix} 4 & -1 & 3 & -2 \\ 0 & 5 & -2 & 0 \\ -2 & -2 & 4 & 1 \\ 3 & 0 & 3 & -1 \end{bmatrix}$

In Exercises 11–16, assume that $A$ is a 3x3 matrix with det $A = 2$ and find the determinant of the matrix resulting from the given sequence of row operations on the matrix $A$.

11. $R_1 \leftrightarrow R_3$
   $R_2' = R_2 - 3R_1$

12. $R_2' = \frac{1}{4}R_2$
    $R_3' = R_3 + 4R_2$

13. $R_2' = 4R_2$
    $R_3' = R_3 - 5R_1$
    $R_2 \leftrightarrow R_3$
    $R_3' = -3R_3$

14. $R_3' = -\frac{1}{6}R_3$
    $R_2' = R_2 + 4R_3$
    $R_1' = R_1 - 2R_3$
    $R_2' = -5R_2$

15. $R_1' = -\frac{1}{3}R_1$
    $R_2' = -\frac{1}{3}R_2$
    $R_3' = -\frac{1}{3}R_3$
    $R_3' = R_3 + 4R_1$
    $R_2 \leftrightarrow R_3$

16. $R_2' = R_2 - 4R_1$
    $R_3' = -6R_3$
    $R_1 \leftrightarrow R_2$
    $R_1' = 4R_1$

In Exercises 17–22, assume $\det \begin{bmatrix} a & b & c \\ d & e & f \\ g & h & i \end{bmatrix} = 6$ and find the determinant of the given matrix.

17. $\begin{bmatrix} a & b & c \\ a & b & c \\ g & h & i \end{bmatrix}$

18. $\begin{bmatrix} a & b & c \\ 3d & 3e & 3f \\ g & h & i \end{bmatrix}$

19. $\begin{bmatrix} a & b & c \\ d-2a & e-2b & f-2c \\ g+a & h+b & i+c \end{bmatrix}$

20. $\begin{bmatrix} a & b & c \\ -3d & -3e & -3f \\ g-3d & h-3e & i-3f \end{bmatrix}$

21. $\begin{bmatrix} -2d & -2e & -2f \\ a+g & b+h & c+i \\ g-2d & h-2e & i-2f \end{bmatrix}$

22. $\begin{bmatrix} -g & -h & -i \\ 2a-3g & 2b-3h & 2c-3i \\ 2d+a & 2e+b & 2f+c \end{bmatrix}$

In Exercises 23-30, find the value(s) of $w$ for which the determinant of the given matrix is 0.

23. $\begin{bmatrix} -w & 2 \\ 5 & -w \end{bmatrix}$

24. $\begin{bmatrix} -w & -2 \\ -3 & -w \end{bmatrix}$

25. $\begin{bmatrix} 1-w & 1 \\ -2 & 4-w \end{bmatrix}$

26. $\begin{bmatrix} 5-w & 1 \\ 4 & 8-w \end{bmatrix}$

27. $\begin{bmatrix} -4-w & 0 & 2 \\ 2 & 4-w & -8 \\ 2 & 0 & -4-w \end{bmatrix}$

28. $\begin{bmatrix} -7-w & 5 & 4 \\ 0 & -3-w & 0 \\ -8 & 9 & 5-w \end{bmatrix}$

29. $\begin{bmatrix} 3-w & -1 & 1 \\ -1 & 3-w & -1 \\ 1 & -1 & 3-w \end{bmatrix}$

30. $\begin{bmatrix} -5-w & 6 & 1 \\ -1 & 2-w & 1 \\ -8 & 6 & 4-w \end{bmatrix}$

## Section 3.5

**Exercises**:

In Exercises 1-8, solve the system with Cramer's Rule if possible.

1. $7x_1 - 2x_2 = 3$
   $3x_1 + x_2 = 5$

2. $5x_1 + 2x_2 = 6$
   $-4x_1 + 2x_2 = 15$

3. $-4x_1 + 2x_2 = 3$
   $6x_1 + 3x_2 = 3$

4. $5x_1 + 4x_2 = 6$
   $2x_1 - 3x_2 = 5$

5.  $x_1 + x_2 + x_3 = 5$
    $x_1 + 2x_2 + 3x_3 = 10$
    $2x_1 + x_2 + x_3 = 6$

6.  $x_1 + 4x_2 - 2x_3 = 2$
    $3x_1 - x_2 + 4x_3 = 3$
    $2x_1 - 5x_2 + 6x_3 = 3$

7.  $3x_1 - 4x_2 - x_3 = 1$
    $2x_1 - 3x_2 + x_3 = 1$
    $x_1 - 2x_2 + 3x_3 = 2$

8.  $x_1 + 2x_2 - x_3 = -1$
    $2x_1 - 3x_2 + 2x_3 = 15$
    $x_2 + 4x_3 = -7$

In Exercises 9-14,

    **a.** Find the values of $s$ for which the given system does *not* have a unique solution

    **b.** Use Cramer's Rule to find the solution to the system (in terms of $s$) which is valid for all values of $s$ except those listed in (a)

9.  $sx_1 + 8x_2 = 5$
    $2x_1 + sx_2 = 4$

10.  $sx_1 + 5x_2 = 5$
     $2x_1 + sx_2 = -3$

11.  $2sx_1 - sx_2 = 5$
     $3x_1 + 2sx_2 = 1$

12.  $4sx_1 - 2sx_2 = 10$
     $3sx_1 + 2x_2 = -2$

13.  $sx_1 + 2x_2 + 2sx_3 = 0$
     $4x_1 + sx_2 = -1$
     $x_2 - sx_3 = 3$

14.  $sx_1 - 9x_2 - 2x_3 = 0$
     $x_1 + sx_3 = 1$
     $sx_2 + 2sx_3 = 1$

In Exercises 15-20,

    **a.** Find the adjoint of the given matrix

    **b.** Find the inverse of the given matrix if it exists

15.  $\begin{bmatrix} 2 & -2 \\ 3 & 4 \end{bmatrix}$

16.  $\begin{bmatrix} 3 & -1 \\ 3 & 5 \end{bmatrix}$

17.  $\begin{bmatrix} 1 & 2 & -3 \\ 1 & -2 & 1 \\ 5 & -2 & -3 \end{bmatrix}$

18.  $\begin{bmatrix} 1 & -2 & 2 \\ 2 & -1 & 3 \\ 0 & 1 & -1 \end{bmatrix}$

19.  $\begin{bmatrix} 1 & 2 & 1 \\ 1 & 1 & 2 \\ 3 & 4 & 8 \end{bmatrix}$

20.  $\begin{bmatrix} 1 & -2 & 1 \\ 2 & -5 & 1 \\ 3 & -7 & 2 \end{bmatrix}$

In Exercises 21-26, use the determinant of the coefficient matrix to decide if the homogeneous system of equations has infinitely many solutions or a unique solution.

21.  $x_1 + x_2 + 3x_3 = 0$
     $3x_1 \quad + 4x_3 = 0$
     $2x_1 - 2x_2 - 2x_3 = 0$

22.  $6x_1 \quad + 2x_3 = 0$
     $30x_1 + 4x_2 + 6x_3 = 0$
     $8x_1 - 2x_2 + 3x_3 = 0$

23.  $x_1 + 6x_2 + 4x_3 = 0$
     $2x_1 + 4x_2 \quad - x_3 = 0$
     $- x_1 + 2x_2 + 5x_3 = 0$

24.  $x_1 + 3x_2 + 2x_3 = 0$
     $2x_1 + 4x_2 + 2x_3 = 0$
     $x_1 + 2x_2 \quad - x_3 = 0$

25.  $x_1 - 2x_2 + 2x_3 = 0$
     $4x_1 + 2x_2 \qquad = 0$
     $4x_1 \qquad + 4x_3 = 0$

26.  $3x_1 - 6x_2 - 3x_3 = 0$
     $4x_1 + 2x_2 - 2x_3 = 0$
     $11x_1 - 2x_2 - 7x_3 = 0$

In Exercises 27-36, assume $A$, $B$, and $C$ are 3x3 matrices with $\det A = 5$, $\det B = -2$, and $\det C = 0$.

27.  Find  $\det(A^2 B)$

28.  Find  $\det(B^2 A^3)$

29.  Find  $\det(A^{-1} B)$

30.  Find  $\det((AB)^{-1})$

31.  Find  $\det(-2A)$

32.  Find  $\det(-5B^{-1})$

33.  Is the matrix  $A^2 B$ invertible?

34.  Is the matrix  $CA^3 B$ invertible?

35.  Is the matrix  $C^2 AB$ invertible?

36.  Is the matrix  $AB^3 A^{-1}$ invertible?

# Section 3.6

**Exercises:**

We use the term "number of transitions of four decimal place stability," for example, to mean the first value of $n$ for which all distribution vectors $S_n$, $S_{n+1}$, $S_{n+2}$, ... from that year on are the same to within four decimal places.

1. Pa Horn and Race are two long-distance phone carriers competing for customers in the city of Talk-A-Lot. Annually, Pa Horn loses 20% of its customers to Race, while Race loses 25% of its customers to Pa Horn. Currently, Pa Horn has 60% of the market.

a. Find the transition matrix, labeling the rows and columns with their meanings.
b. Find the initial distribution vector, labeling the rows with their meanings.
c. Find the distribution vector after the fourth year to four decimal places.
d. Approximate the stable vector to four decimal places.

2. Suppose Federal Express annually picks up 16% of United Parcel Service's business, while in the same time, UPS acquires 12% of Fed-Ex customers. Currently, 3 out of 4 customers use UPS.

a. Find the transition matrix, labeling the rows and columns with their meanings.
b. Find the initial distribution vector, labeling the rows with their meanings.
c. Find the distribution vector after the third year to four decimal places.
d. Approximate the stable vector to four decimal places.

3. Suppose a car rental agency has facilities around New York City at Kennedy Airport, Newark Airport, and a downtown Manhattan location. The agency allows customers to return cars to any of the three locations. It has been found that a car rented at Kennedy will be returned to Kennedy with probability 0.9, to Newark with probability 0.06, and downtown with probability 0.04. A car rented at Newark will be returned to Kennedy with probability 0.25, to Newark with probability 0.7, and downtown with probability 0.05. A car rented downtown will be returned to Kennedy with probability 0.3, to Newark with probability 0.2, and downtown with probability 0.5. Initially, there are 200 cars at Kennedy, and 100 cars each at Newark and downtown.

a. Find the transition matrix, labeling the rows and columns with their meanings.
b. Find the initial distribution vector, labeling the rows with their meanings.
c. Estimate the number of cars at Kennedy after all cars have been rented four times (round to nearest whole number).
d. How many cars will be at Kennedy in the long run (round to nearest whole number).
e. Find the number of rental cycles of four decimal place stability.

4. Mr. Fred Fickle has decided to go by the following dating policy. He will only date women whose last names are Getz, Russell, or Thompson. He will never date two women in a row with the same last name. If he breaks up with a Ms. Getz, he will date a Ms. Russell next with probability 0.5. If he breaks up with a Ms. Russell, he will date a Ms. Thompson next with probability 0.4. If he breaks up with a Ms. Thompson, he will date a Ms. Getz with probability 0.75. His current fiancee is named Jane Russell.

a. Find the transition matrix, labeling the rows and columns with their meanings.
b. Find the initial distribution vector, labeling the rows with their meanings.
c. Find the probability to four decimal places that his third fiancee after Jane will have last name Getz.
d. To four decimal places, in the long run what proportion of his fiancees will have last name Russell?
e. Find the number of fiancees of four decimal place stability.

5.  At meetings of the Federal Reserve Board, the board can elect to leave interest rates unchanged or to raise or lower them.  Suppose a stock market research company discovers that the Fed never lowers rates the next meeting after raising them, nor raises rates the next meeting after lowering them.  20% of the time after raising rates, the Fed has raised them again at the next meeting, while 15% of the time after lowering rates, the Fed has again lowered them at the next meeting.  After a meeting where they left rates unchanged, they have again left them unchanged 3 out of 5 times; otherwise, they have raised and lowered them with equal frequency.  At the last meeting, the Fed did not change the interest rate.

    **a.**  Find the transition matrix, labeling the rows and columns with their meanings.
    **b.**  Find the initial distribution vector, labeling the rows with their meanings.
    **c.**  Find the probability to four decimal places that at the fifth meeting from now, the Fed will lower interest rates.
    **d.**  To four decimal places, in the long run at what proportion of meetings will the Fed leave rates unchanged?
    **e.**  Find the number of meetings of four decimal place stability.

6.  In Illinois, the weather can be classified as hot (above $90°F$), cold (below $0°F$), or just right (between $0°F$ and $90°F$).  Observation clearly shows that the weather is never the same two days in a row.  If it is just right one day, it will be equally likely to be hot or cold the next day.  If it is either hot or cold one day, it will be twice as likely to be just right the next day as to go to the other extreme.  Suppose the forecast for Sunday is a 70% chance it will be just right and a 30% chance it will be hot.

    **a.**  Find the transition matrix, labeling the rows and columns with their meanings.
    **b.**  Find the initial distribution vector, labeling the rows with their meanings.
    **c.**  Find the probability to four decimal places that on the following Friday, it will be cold.
    **d.**  To four decimal places, in the long run what proportion of days will be just right?
    **e.**  Find the day of four decimal place stability.

7.  A molecule of perfume is released into the air in the center of a room.  Suppose the probability that after a collision with another particle the molecule will end up traveling east is three times as large as the probability of traveling west.  The probabilities of ending up traveling north or south after a collision are equal.  Assume the probabilities of ending up traveling east after a collision are 0.6, 0.6, 0.3, and 0.15 if the particle was traveling north, south, east, or west, respectively, before the collision.  After its last collision, the molecule is currently traveling north.

    **a.**  Find the transition matrix, labeling the rows and columns with their meanings.
    **b.**  Find the initial distribution vector, labeling the rows with their meanings.
    **c.**  Find the probability to four decimal places that after six collisions, the particle will be moving north.
    **d.**  Approximate the stable vector to four decimal places.

8. A sociology study of fathers' and sons' incomes defines income categories as shown in the following table. The table also gives the numbers in each category for a group of fathers chosen for the study.

| Category Name | Annual income range (in dollars) | Number of fathers |
| --- | --- | --- |
| High | Over $80,000 | 225 |
| Upper Middle | $40,000 to $80,000 | 525 |
| Lower Middle | $15,000 to $40,000 | 600 |
| Low | Under $15,000 | 150 |

The study shows that of fathers whose income is:

   i.   high, the son's income will be high, upper middle, lower middle, and low with probabilities 0.5, 0.4, 0.08, 0.02 respectively
   ii.  upper middle, the son's income will be high, upper middle, lower middle, and low with probabilities 0.3, 0.5, 0.15, 0.05 respectively
   iii. lower middle, the son's income will be high, upper middle, lower middle, and low with probabilities 0.1, 0.4, 0.4, 0.1 respectively
   iv.  low, the son's income will be high, upper middle, lower middle, and low with probabilities 0.05, 0.15, 0.4, 0.4 respectively

   a. Find the transition matrix, labeling the rows and columns with their meanings.
   b. Find the initial distribution vector, labeling the rows with their meanings.
   c. Find the distribution vector after three generations to four decimal places.
   d. To four decimal places, in the long run what proportion of fathers will be in the lower middle income bracket?

In Exercises 9-12,

   a. find the transition matrix, labeling the rows and columns with their meanings
   b. find the initial distribution vector, labeling the rows with their meanings
   c. find the exact stable vector by solving the system $TS = S$.

9. Barb has a boring linear algebra teacher (unlike yours), so to occupy her time during class, she attempts to predict the color of socks he will wear. The professor has a wardrobe of green plaid socks and of red and purple striped socks. She discovers that the day after wearing his green plaid socks, the professor again wears green plaid 2/3 of the time, while the day after wearing red and purple striped socks, he wears green plaid 1/2 the time. She begins her prediction on St. Patrick's Day, so the professor is wearing green plaid.

10. At many companies, one time per year the employees have the option of adjusting their health care insurance options. Suppose employees may choose between a $200 deductible plan and a $1500 deductible plan. In the past, 85% of the employees with the $200 plan elect to stay with it for another year, while 90% of the employees with the $1500 plan elect to stay with this plan for another year. Currently, 2/3 of the employees have the $200 plan.

11.  Suppose Coca-Cola and Pepsi-Cola currently have 70% and 30% of the soft drink market, respectively.  Attempting to increase its market share, Coke test-markets a new brand, UltraFizz, in several cities.  The following consumer behavior was observed.  From the beginning to end of each month, of those who drank an existing Coca-Cola product, 15% switched to a Pepsi product, and 10% switched to UltraFizz.  Of those who drank a Pepsi product, 10% switched to an existing Coke product, and 5% switched to UltraFizz.  Of those who drank UltraFizz, 20% switched to an existing Coke product, and 20% switched to Pepsi.

12.  Repeat Exercise 11 assuming of those who drank UltraFizz, 5% switched to an existing Coke product, and 5% switched to Pepsi.

In Exercises 13-20, determine if the given transition matrix is regular.

13.  $\begin{bmatrix} 1 & 0.2 \\ 0 & 0.8 \end{bmatrix}$

14.  $\begin{bmatrix} 0 & 0.2 \\ 1 & 0.8 \end{bmatrix}$

15.  $\begin{bmatrix} 0.3 & 1 \\ 0.7 & 0 \end{bmatrix}$

16.  $\begin{bmatrix} 1 & 1 \\ 0 & 0 \end{bmatrix}$

17.  $\begin{bmatrix} 0.4 & 0.4 & 0 \\ 0.3 & 0.1 & 0.6 \\ 0.3 & 0.5 & 0.4 \end{bmatrix}$

18.  $\begin{bmatrix} 0.8 & 0.2 & 1 \\ 0.1 & 0.8 & 0 \\ 0.1 & 0 & 0 \end{bmatrix}$

19.  $\begin{bmatrix} 1 & 0.4 & 0.2 \\ 0 & 0.6 & 0.3 \\ 0 & 0 & 0.5 \end{bmatrix}$

20.  $\begin{bmatrix} 0.4 & 0.4 & 0 \\ 0.5 & 0.3 & 0 \\ 0.1 & 0.3 & 1 \end{bmatrix}$

# Chapter 4

## Section 4.1

**Exercises:**

In Exercises 1-6, find a vector equation and the corresponding parametric equations for the line through $P_0$ and parallel to $\vec{u}$.

1. $P_0(-9,6)$, $\vec{u} = (2,-7)$

2. $P_0(2,-9)$, $\vec{u} = (-4,5)$

3. $P_0(2,-5,8)$, $\vec{u} = (-3,5,-7)$

4. $P_0(-3,4,-9)$, $\vec{u} = (2,-9,7)$

5. $P_0(-3,4,-8,-2)$, $\vec{u} = (5,-4,3,-2)$

6. $P_0(-7,6,5,-7)$, $\vec{u} = (4,-6,2,-8)$

In Exercises 7-12, find a vector equation and the corresponding parametric equations for the line through the given points.

7. $P_1(-3,2)$, $P_2(5,-8)$

8. $P_1(6,-3)$, $P_2(9,-8)$

9. $P_1(-5,3,-2)$, $P_2(-7,-2,4)$

10. $P_1(6,4,-2)$, $P_2(-2,7,-5)$

11. $P_1(6,-2,4,5)$, $P_2(-3,-5,2,3)$

12. $P_1(-4,3,-6,4)$, $P_2(5,-2,3,-7)$

In Exercises 13-14, determine which of the given points lie on the line passing through $P_1$ and $P_2$.

13. $P_1(4,-2,5)$, $P_2(6,-3,7)$

14. $P_1(-2,1,3)$, $P_2(1,-3,10)$

    a. $(8,-4,9)$

    b. $(-2,1,-1)$

    c. $(10,-4,11)$

    a. $(-8,9,-11)$

    b. $(4,-7,18)$

    c. $(7,-11,24)$

In Exercises 15-22, determine if the given set of planes intersect, and if so, find their intersection. Describe your result geometrically.

15. $3x + 4y + 7z = 15$
    $6x + 8y + 14z = 30$

16. $2x - 4y + 6z = 9$
    $4x - 8y + 12z = 20$

17. $5x + 7y - 3z = 9$
    $10x - 4y + 6z = 12$

18. $3x - 2y + 6z = 11$
    $4x + 6y - 3z = 9$

19. $4x + 2y + 6z = 4$
    $6x + 3y + 9z = 6$
    $8x + 4y + 12z = 8$

20. $4x + 3y + 6z = 5$
    $3x + 4y + 3z = 3$
    $8x + 6y + 12z = 6$

21. $x + 2y - z = 12$
    $2x + y + 7z = 3$
    $5x + 7y + 4z = 39$

22. $3x + 2y + 5z = 6$
    $2x + 3y + 5z = 4$
    $4x + 5y + 8z = 7$

## Section 4.2

**Exercises**:

In Exercises 1-4, determine if it is possible to express $\vec{v}$ as a linear combination of $\vec{u}_1$ and $\vec{u}_2$. If it is possible, write $\vec{v}$ explicitly as a linear combination of $\vec{u}_1$ and $\vec{u}_2$.

1. $\vec{v} = (-2, 12, -14)$, $\vec{u}_1 = (-2, 5, -6)$, $\vec{u}_2 = (3, -4, 5)$

2. $\vec{v} = (8, 11, 11)$, $\vec{u}_1 = (4, -3, 1)$, $\vec{u}_2 = (-2, 4, 6)$

3. $\vec{v} = (7, -8, 2)$, $\vec{u}_1 = (5, -4, 8)$, $\vec{u}_2 = (-1, 2, 4)$

4. $\vec{v} = (-7, -12, -8)$, $\vec{u}_1 = (-3, 6, -2)$, $\vec{u}_2 = (8, -3, 7)$

5. The Omega Company produces economy, moderate, and deluxe DVD players at their Joplin, Sapp, and Valero plants. The daily outputs of the three plants are 400 economy, 300 moderate, and 200 deluxe players at Joplin; 350 economy, 250 moderate, and 150 deluxe players at Sapp; and 450 economy, 350 moderate, and 250 deluxe players at Valero. The company would like to cut back on its operating costs by closing the Valero plant. Is there some combination of outputs from the other two plants that will equal the output of the Valero plant?

6. In problem #5, instead of closing the Valero plant, the company decides to close either the Joplin or Sapp plant. Would these closings be feasible? Explain.

In Exercises 7-10, use the given information to find a solution to the system of equations $A\vec{x} = \vec{b}$

7. $\vec{a}_1 = \begin{bmatrix} -3 \\ 4 \end{bmatrix}$, $\vec{a}_2 = \begin{bmatrix} 5 \\ -6 \end{bmatrix}$, $\vec{b} = \begin{bmatrix} -30 \\ 38 \end{bmatrix}$; $5\vec{a}_1 - 3\vec{a}_2 = \vec{b}$

8. $\vec{a}_1 = \begin{bmatrix} 2 \\ -2 \end{bmatrix}$, $\vec{a}_2 = \begin{bmatrix} 9 \\ 3 \end{bmatrix}$, $\vec{b} = \begin{bmatrix} 2 \\ 22 \end{bmatrix}$; $-8\vec{a}_1 + 2\vec{a}_2 = \vec{b}$

9. $A = \begin{bmatrix} 5 & -1 & -3 \\ -4 & 2 & 1 \\ 3 & -2 & 7 \end{bmatrix}$, $\vec{b} = \begin{bmatrix} -8 \\ 14 \\ -28 \end{bmatrix}$; $-2\vec{a}_1 + 4\vec{a}_2 - 2\vec{a}_3 = \vec{b}$

10. $A = \begin{bmatrix} 2 & 4 & 9 \\ -3 & -2 & -1 \\ 6 & 8 & 5 \end{bmatrix}$, $\vec{b} = \begin{bmatrix} 25 \\ -8 \\ 17 \end{bmatrix}$; $3\vec{a}_1 - 2\vec{a}_2 + 3\vec{a}_3 = \vec{b}$

In Exercises 11-14, find a solution of $Ax = \vec{b}$ and use it to determine a linear combination of the columns of $A$ that will equal $\vec{b}$.

11. $A = \begin{bmatrix} 4 & 3 & -4 \\ -2 & 6 & 5 \\ -1 & 2 & 7 \end{bmatrix}$, $\vec{b} = \begin{bmatrix} 40 \\ -5 \\ -29 \end{bmatrix}$

12. $A = \begin{bmatrix} -7 & 2 & 8 \\ 4 & -2 & -6 \\ -3 & 1 & 2 \end{bmatrix}$, $\vec{b} = \begin{bmatrix} 3 \\ -8 \\ -1 \end{bmatrix}$

13. $A = \begin{bmatrix} 6 & 4 & -4 \\ 2 & 3 & -8 \\ -3 & -2 & 2 \end{bmatrix}$, $\vec{b} = \begin{bmatrix} 6 \\ -8 \\ -3 \end{bmatrix}$

14. $A = \begin{bmatrix} 3 & -2 & -2 \\ 5 & 3 & 22 \\ 6 & 4 & 28 \end{bmatrix}$, $\vec{b} = \begin{bmatrix} -22 \\ -5 \\ -4 \end{bmatrix}$

## Section 4.3

**Calculator Example 4.3.1: Describing the Span of a Set of Vectors** (Sect 4.3, Example 7, p. 238)

Describe the span of the vectors $\vec{a}_1 = (1,1,4)$ and $\vec{a}_2 = (1,2,3)$ in $R^3$. The textbook does the following row-reduction using algebra on the variables $x$, $y$, and $z$,

$$\begin{bmatrix} 1 & 1 & x \\ 1 & 2 & y \\ 4 & 3 & z \end{bmatrix} \rightarrow \ldots \rightarrow \begin{bmatrix} 1 & 0 & 2x-y \\ 0 & 1 & y-x \\ 0 & 0 & -5x+y+z \end{bmatrix}$$

and concludes from the bottom row that the span is the plane $-5x + y + z = 0$.

Although the TI-83 cannot do symbolic algebra, the problem can be done by identifying columns of an augmented identity matrix as follows,

$$\begin{matrix} & & x & y & z \\ \begin{bmatrix} 1 & 1 & 1 & 0 & 0 \\ 1 & 2 & 0 & 1 & 0 \\ 4 & 3 & 0 & 0 & 1 \end{bmatrix} \end{matrix} \rightarrow \ldots \rightarrow \begin{matrix} & & x & y & z \\ \begin{bmatrix} 1 & 0 & 2 & -1 & 0 \\ 0 & 1 & -1 & 1 & 0 \\ 0 & 0 & -5 & 1 & 1 \end{bmatrix} \end{matrix}$$

and again concluding the span is $-5x + y + z = 0$.

**Exercises:**

In Exercises 1-2, describe the span of the given vectors as a subspace of $R^3$.

1.  **a.** $\vec{u}_1 = (1,1,1)$
    **b.** $\vec{u}_1 = (1,1,1)$, $\vec{u}_2 = (2,2,2)$
    **c.** $\vec{u}_1 = (1,1,1)$, $\vec{u}_2 = (2,2,2)$, $\vec{u}_3 = (3,3,3)$
    **d.** Compare your answers to parts (a), (b), and (c)

2.  **a.** $\vec{u}_1 = (1,1,1)$
    **b.** $\vec{u}_1 = (1,1,1)$, $\vec{u}_2 = (1,2,1)$
    **c.** $\vec{u}_1 = (1,1,1)$, $\vec{u}_2 = (1,2,1)$, $\vec{u}_3 = (2,3,2)$
    **d.** Compare your answers to parts (a), (b), and (c)

In Exercises 3-10, indicate whether or not the subset of points $P(x,y,z)$ described by the given relations on $x,y,z$ is a subspace of $R^3$.  Briefly explain your answer.

3.  $x = 3t - 4$, $y = t$, $z = t$      4.   $-4x + 2y + 3z = 0$

5.  $x = 5t$, $y = -3t$, $z = 4t$      6.   $5x - 2y + 6z = 8$

7.  $6x - 3y + 2z = 0$      8.   $x = 2$, $y = 3t$, $z = -2t$

9.  $4x + 3y + 4z = 7$      10.   $x = -4t$, $y = 6t$, $z = 4t$

In Exercises 11-18, find the null space of the given matrix $A$.  If the null space is more than the zero vector alone, describe it as the span of a set of vectors.

11. $\begin{bmatrix} 4 & -8 & 16 \\ 8 & -6 & 2 \end{bmatrix}$      12. $\begin{bmatrix} 3 & 4 & -7 \\ -2 & -5 & 14 \end{bmatrix}$

13. $\begin{bmatrix} 3 & 4 & 9 \\ -3 & 6 & 5 \\ 2 & 7 & 11 \end{bmatrix}$      14. $\begin{bmatrix} 2 & -1 & -3 \\ -5 & 3 & 5 \\ -7 & 4 & 8 \end{bmatrix}$

15. $\begin{bmatrix} 3 & 4 & 8 & -34 \\ -2 & 7 & 7 & -10 \\ 1 & -5 & 9 & -62 \end{bmatrix}$      16. $\begin{bmatrix} 4 & -6 & 24 & -32 \\ 5 & 2 & 11 & -2 \\ -3 & 2 & -13 & 14 \end{bmatrix}$

In Exercises 17-20, determine whether or not the given vector is in the column space of matrix $A$. If the vector is in the column space of $A$, write the vector as a linear combination of the columns of $A$.

17. $A = \begin{bmatrix} 3 & 4 & 2 \\ -2 & 5 & -1 \\ 1 & -6 & 5 \end{bmatrix}$     18. $A = \begin{bmatrix} 2 & 3 & 4 \\ -4 & -2 & -3 \\ 7 & 5 & 1 \end{bmatrix}$

   (a) $\vec{u} = (2,-23,40)$         (a) $\vec{u} = (-10,-3,15)$
   (b) $\vec{v} = (-11,-7,24)$         (b) $\vec{v} = (10,-21,18)$

19. $A = \begin{bmatrix} -1 & -4 & 17 \\ 3 & -3 & -6 \\ -7 & 2 & 29 \end{bmatrix}$     20. $A = \begin{bmatrix} 5 & 7 & -1 \\ 2 & -4 & -14 \\ -3 & 3 & 15 \end{bmatrix}$

   (a) $\vec{u} = (-12,6,-24)$         (a) $\vec{u} = (-1,20,-21)$
   (b) $\vec{v} = (8,-9,10)$         (b) $\vec{v} = (4,8,-6)$

In Exercises 21-24, describe the column space of matrix $A$ as a subspace of $R^3$.

21. $\begin{bmatrix} 2 & 5 & -4 \\ 2 & 7 & -8 \\ 3 & 4 & 1 \end{bmatrix}$     22. $\begin{bmatrix} 4 & -2 & 5 \\ -4 & -6 & -5 \\ 12 & 5 & 6 \end{bmatrix}$

23. $\begin{bmatrix} 3 & 2 & 1 \\ 6 & 4 & 2 \\ 9 & 6 & 3 \end{bmatrix}$     24. $\begin{bmatrix} 2 & 6 & 2 \\ 5 & -3 & -3 \\ 5 & 6 & 1 \end{bmatrix}$

In Exercises 25-32, describe the span of the given vectors in terms of the coefficients $x, y, z$ of a general vector $\vec{b} = (x,y,z)$ in the span. Write $\vec{b}$ as a linear combination of the given vectors.

25. $\vec{a}_1 = (3,5,-5)$, $\vec{a}_2 = (1,4,3)$          26. $\vec{a}_1 = (3,3,2)$, $\vec{a}_2 = (-2,5,8)$

27. $\vec{a}_1 = (2,3,2)$, $\vec{a}_2 = (-2,6,1)$          28. $\vec{a}_1 = (2,-1,-1)$, $\vec{a}_2 = (-3,-2,2)$

29. $\vec{a}_1 = (4,-5,2)$, $\vec{a}_2 = (-3,7,5)$, $\vec{a}_3 = (1,-2,-2)$

30. $\vec{a}_1 = (-2,6,4)$, $\vec{a}_2 = (3,-3,1)$, $\vec{a}_3 = (3,-1,2)$

31. $\vec{a}_1 = (2,2,-2)$, $\vec{a}_2 = (4,6,-3)$, $\vec{a}_3 = (4,2,-5)$

32. $\vec{a}_1 = (-2,1,4)$, $\vec{a}_2 = (3,-2,-10)$, $\vec{a}_3 = (-3,1,2)$

# Section 4.4

**Alternate method for Section 4.4, Example 6, p. 251**

Given:  Demand vector per day  $\vec{b} = \begin{bmatrix} 82 \\ 137 \\ 259 \end{bmatrix}$   2-hp motors

1-hp motors

1/2-hp motors

We close down one line and express $\vec{b}$ as a linear combination of the other three lines (as in Section 4.2).

1.  Close Line 1 and find $\vec{b} = c_2\vec{u}_2 + c_3\vec{u}_3 + c_4\vec{u}_4$

$$\begin{array}{cccc} \vec{u}_2 & \vec{u}_3 & \vec{u}_4 & \vec{b} \end{array}$$
$$\begin{bmatrix} 3 & 3 & 2 & 82 \\ 5 & 5 & 3 & 137 \\ 8 & 9 & 7 & 259 \end{bmatrix} \rightarrow \dots \rightarrow \begin{bmatrix} 1 & 0 & 0 & -14 \\ 0 & 1 & 0 & 42 \\ 0 & 0 & 1 & -1 \end{bmatrix}$$

Not feasible:  $\vec{b} = -14\vec{u}_2 + 42\vec{u}_3 - \vec{u}_4$

2.  Close Line 2 and find $\vec{b} = c_1\vec{u}_1 + c_3\vec{u}_3 + c_4\vec{u}_4$

$$\begin{array}{cccc} \vec{u}_1 & \vec{u}_3 & \vec{u}_4 & \vec{b} \end{array}$$
$$\begin{bmatrix} 1 & 3 & 2 & 82 \\ 2 & 5 & 3 & 137 \\ 4 & 9 & 7 & 259 \end{bmatrix} \rightarrow \dots \rightarrow \begin{bmatrix} 1 & 0 & 0 & 7 \\ 0 & 1 & 0 & 21 \\ 0 & 0 & 1 & 6 \end{bmatrix}$$

Feasible, but unbalanced:  $\vec{b} = 7\vec{u}_1 + 21\vec{u}_3 + 6\vec{u}_4$

3.  Close Line 3 and find $\vec{b} = c_1\vec{u}_1 + c_2\vec{u}_2 + c_4\vec{u}_4$

$$\begin{array}{cccc} \vec{u}_1 & \vec{u}_2 & \vec{u}_4 & \vec{b} \end{array}$$
$$\begin{bmatrix} 1 & 3 & 2 & 82 \\ 2 & 5 & 3 & 137 \\ 4 & 8 & 7 & 259 \end{bmatrix} \rightarrow \dots \rightarrow \begin{bmatrix} 1 & 0 & 0 & 14 \\ 0 & 1 & 0 & 14 \\ 0 & 0 & 1 & 13 \end{bmatrix}$$

Feasible, balanced:  $\vec{b} = 14\vec{u}_1 + 14\vec{u}_2 + 13\vec{u}_4$

4.  Close Line 4 and find $\vec{b} = c_1\vec{u}_1 + c_2\vec{u}_2 + c_3\vec{u}_3$

$$\overset{\vec{u}_1 \ \ \vec{u}_2 \ \ \vec{u}_3 \ \ \vec{b}}{\begin{bmatrix} 1 & 3 & 3 & 82 \\ 2 & 5 & 5 & 137 \\ 4 & 8 & 9 & 259 \end{bmatrix}} \rightarrow \ldots \rightarrow \begin{bmatrix} 1 & 0 & 0 & 1 \\ 0 & 1 & 0 & -12 \\ 0 & 0 & 1 & 39 \end{bmatrix}$$

Not feasible: $\vec{b} = \vec{u}_1 - 12\vec{u}_2 + 39\vec{u}_3$

## Exercises

In Exercises 1-8, determine if the given vectors are linearly independent or dependent. If they are linearly dependent, then find a dependency equation.

1. $(8,-4,2),\ (6,0,3),\ (-8,-8,-8)$

2. $(-3,4,-2),\ (5,-3,6),\ (-9,1,-14)$

3. $(2,-4,5),\ (-3,2,1),\ (4,7,8)$

4. $(5,7,8),\ (-2,3,5),\ (4,7,13)$

5. $(1,2,-2),\ (7,2,-3),\ (-11,2,0)$

6. $(9,7,8),\ (-2,3,5),\ (4,3,1)$

7. $(1,-2,3,5),\ (-2,4,7,6),\ (5,8,9,11)$

8. $(-3,4,-2,1),\ (2,3,5,-4),\ (-13,6,-16,11)$

In Exercises 9-12, find value(s) of $k$ such that the given vectors are linearly independent.

9. $(2,3,1),\ (-1,4,2),\ (k,-2,-2)$

10. $(3,-3,5),\ (2,4,8),\ (5,1,k)$

11. $(5,-4,2),\ (k,1,3),\ (6,-2,2k)$

12. $(4,-7,2),\ (6,k,3),\ (k,-6,-2)$

In Exercises 13-14, a company meets its production schedule by operating four plants. Determine if it is possible to close one of the plants and meet the production demands with only three. If it is possible, what are the feasible production schedules? Assume each plant can be operated up to 7 days per week.

13. The Volta Battery Company manufactures AA, A, C, and D batteries in each of four plants. The daily production (in 1000's) for the four plants is given in the following table:

| (1000) | Plant 1 | Plant 2 | Plant 3 | Plant 4 |
|--------|---------|---------|---------|---------|
| AA     | 3       | 4       | 5       | 5       |
| A      | 2       | 3       | 5       | 6       |
| C      | 4       | 5       | 5       | 4       |
| D      | 1       | 2       | 4       | 5       |

The company has contracted to provide 56,000 AA; 53,000 A; 59,000 C; and 40,000 D batteries to a large electronics distributor. This demand is currently met by operating plant 1 for 3 days, plant 2 for 3 days, plant 3 for 4 days, and plant 4 for 3 days.

14. The Optico Camera Company manufactures mini, midi, max, and supermax cameras in each of four plants. The daily production (in 100's) for the four plants is given in the following table:

| (100) | Plant 1 | Plant 2 | Plant 3 | Plant 4 |
|---|---|---|---|---|
| Mini | 2 | 3 | 4 | 7 |
| Midi | 4 | 5 | 4 | 3 |
| Max | 3 | 6 | 5 | 6 |
| Supermax | 4 | 3 | 3 | 2 |

The company has contracted to provide 6700 mini, 6300 midi, 8100 max, and 4700 supermax cameras to a large electronics distributor. This demand is currently met by operating plant 1 for 4 days, plant 2 for 4 days, plant 3 for 3 days, and plant 4 for 5 days.

# Section 4.5

**Exercises**

In Exercises 1-6, find a basis for the given space.

1. $5x - 4y = 0$         2. $2x + 6y = 0$

3. $5x - 3y + 2z = 0$     4. $4x + 5y - 3z = 0$

5. $7x + 2y + 5z = 0$     6. $6x + 4y + 6z = 0$

In Exercises 7-10, determine whether or not the vectors $\vec{u}_1$, $\vec{u}_2$ form a basis for $R^2$. If they do form a basis, express the vector $\vec{b}$ as a linear combination of $\vec{u}_1$, $\vec{u}_2$. If they do not form a basis, express one of them as a scalar multiple of the other.

7. $\vec{u}_1 = (-3, 4)$, $\vec{u}_2 = (5, -2)$, $\vec{b} = (1, 8)$      8. $\vec{u}_1 = (6, -3)$, $\vec{u}_2 = (4, -2)$, $\vec{b} = (3, 5)$

9. $\vec{u}_1 = (-6, 4)$, $\vec{u}_2 = (9, -6)$, $\vec{b} = (5, -7)$      10. $\vec{u}_1 = (7, -4)$, $\vec{u}_2 = (6, 2)$, $\vec{b} = (10, 16)$

In Exercises 11-14, determine whether or not the vectors $\vec{u}_1$, $\vec{u}_2$, $\vec{u}_3$ form a basis for $R^3$. If they do form a basis, express the vector $\vec{b}$ as a linear combination of $\vec{u}_1$, $\vec{u}_2$, $\vec{u}_3$. If they do not form a basis, express one of them as a linear combination of the other two.

11. $\vec{u}_1 = (3,-4,2)$, $\vec{u}_2 = (7,-8,5)$, $\vec{u}_3 = (6,2,1)$, $\vec{b} = (11,4,1)$

12. $\vec{u}_1 = (4,-3,2)$, $\vec{u}_2 = (7,5,-3)$, $\vec{u}_3 = (-2,-19,12)$, $\vec{b} = (5,-6,8)$

13. $\vec{u}_1 = (1,-8,-7)$, $\vec{u}_2 = (4,-3,-5)$, $\vec{u}_3 = (-13,-12,-1)$, $\vec{b} = (12,-8,32)$

14. $\vec{u}_1 = (5,-4,6)$, $\vec{u}_2 = (2,3,5)$, $\vec{u}_3 = (1,7,-3)$, $\vec{b} = (-13,4,2)$

In Exercises 15-20, use dependency tables to select a basis for the column space of a given matrix and write the remaining column vectors as a linear combination of the basic columns.

15. $\begin{bmatrix} 3 & 6 & -6 \\ -5 & -2 & -14 \end{bmatrix}$

16. $\begin{bmatrix} 4 & -3 & 14 \\ 5 & 7 & -4 \end{bmatrix}$

17. $\begin{bmatrix} 7 & 3 & 5 & 30 \\ 5 & -4 & 22 & 46 \end{bmatrix}$

18. $\begin{bmatrix} 4 & 8 & 6 & -6 \\ -2 & -4 & -5 & 9 \end{bmatrix}$

19. $\begin{bmatrix} 2 & 5 & 6 & -1 & 11 \\ -3 & -4 & -2 & 7 & -24 \\ 4 & 6 & 4 & 3 & 8 \end{bmatrix}$

20. $\begin{bmatrix} 3 & 4 & 3 & 5 & -11 \\ -2 & 8 & -34 & 7 & -34 \\ 1 & -3 & 14 & -1 & 7 \end{bmatrix}$

## Section 4.7

**Exercises**:

In Exercises 1-4, use the simplex algorithm to solve the given linear program. Your solution should include the minimum value of $z$, the corresponding basic feasible solution, and the corner point.

1.  Minimize $\quad z = 4x_1 - 3x_2 + 2x_3 - 5x_4$
    subject to $\quad 2x_1 + 3x_2 - 3x_3 + x_4 \le 6$
    $\qquad\qquad\quad x_1 - 4x_2 + 5x_3 - x_4 \le 8$
    $\qquad\qquad\quad x_1 \ge 0, x_2 \ge 0, x_3 \ge 0, x_4 \ge 0$

2.  Minimize $\quad z = -3x_1 + 4x_2 - 5x_3 + 4x_4$
    subject to $\quad x_1 - 4x_2 + 3x_3 + 2x_4 \le 10$
    $\qquad\qquad\quad 3x_1 - 3x_2 + 4x_3 - 2x_4 \le 16$
    $\qquad\qquad\quad x_1 \ge 0, x_2 \ge 0, x_3 \ge 0, x_4 \ge 0$

3. Minimize $\quad z = 5x_1 - 6x_2 - 6x_3$

  subject to $\quad 4x_1 + 3x_2 + 2x_3 \le 150$

$\qquad\qquad 3x_1 + 4x_2 - 3x_3 \le \ 20$

$\qquad\qquad 2x_1 - 2x_2 + 5x_3 \le \ 60$

$\qquad\qquad x_1 \ge 0, x_2 \ge 0, x_3 \ge 0$

4. Minimize $\quad z = -18x_1 - 20x_2 + 4x_3$

  subject to $\quad 4x_1 - 6x_2 + 8x_3 \le 24$

$\qquad\qquad 2x_1 + 4x_2 - 2x_3 \le 40$

$\qquad\qquad -x_1 + 2x_2 \ + x_3 \le 50$

$\qquad\qquad x_1 \ge 0, x_2 \ge 0, x_3 \ge 0$

In Exercises 5-18, use the two-phase method to solve the given linear program.  Your solution should include the optimum value of $z$, the corresponding basic feasible solution, and the corner points.

5. Minimize $\quad z = 2x_1 + x_2 - 3x_3 + 4x_4$

  subject to $\quad 6x_1 \ + x_2 + 3x_3 + 5x_4 = \ 9$

$\qquad\qquad 4x_1 + 2x_2 + 3x_3 \ - x_4 = 10$

$\qquad\qquad x_1 \ge 0, x_2 \ge 0, x_3 \ge 0, x_4 \ge 0$

6. Maximize $\quad z = -3x_1 + 2x_2 - 4x_3 + 5x_4$

  subject to $\quad x_1 - 2x_2 + 3x_3 + 7x_4 = 12$

$\qquad\qquad 3x_1 - 6x_2 + 5x_3 - 4x_4 = \ 7$

$\qquad\qquad x_1 \ge 0, x_2 \ge 0, x_3 \ge 0, x_4 \ge 0$

7. Minimize $\quad z = 8x_1 + 4x_2 + 6x_3$

  subject to $\quad 6x_1 + 4x_2 + 3x_3 \ge 150$

$\qquad\qquad 2x_1 \ + x_2 + 2x_3 \ge \ 50$

$\qquad\qquad x_1 \ge 0, x_2 \ge 0, x_3 \ge 0$

8. Minimize $\quad z = 3x_1 + 6x_2 + 2x_3$

  subject to $\quad 8x_1 + 10x_2 + 5x_3 \ge 120$

$\qquad\qquad 4x_1 \ + 7x_2 + 4x_3 \ge \ 80$

$\qquad\qquad x_1 \ge 0, x_2 \ge 0, x_3 \ge 0$

9. Minimize $\quad z = 5x_1 + 4x_2$

  subject to $\quad 2x_1 + 3x_2 \le 65$

$\qquad\qquad -3x_1 + 4x_2 = 40$

$\qquad\qquad 5x_1 + 6x_2 \ge 25$

$\qquad\qquad x_1 \ge 0, \ x_2 \ge 0$

10. a) Minimize $\quad z = 12x_1 + 6x_2$

   subject to $\quad 5x_1 + 6x_2 \le 20$

$\qquad\qquad 3x_1 + 2x_2 = 10$

$\qquad\qquad 4x_1 + 3x_2 \ge 12$

$\qquad\qquad x_1 \ge 0, \ x_2 \ge 0$

  b) Maximize the objective function in part (a)

11. Maximize $\quad z = 7x_1 + 6x_2 + 5x_3$

   subject to $\quad 3x_1 + 4x_2 + 7x_3 \le 84$

$\qquad\qquad 2x_1 + 3x_2 + 4x_3 = 50$

$\qquad\qquad 6x_1 + 2x_2 + 7x_3 \ge 44$

$\qquad\qquad x_1 \ge 0, x_2 \ge 0, x_3 \ge 0$

12. Minimize the objective function in Exercise 11

13. Maximize    $z = 6x_1 + 2x_2 + 5x_3$

    subject to    $4x_1 \ + 8x_2 + 10x_3 \leq 540$

                $2x_1 \ - 3x_2 \ + 2x_3 = \ \ 80$

                $4x_1 + 12x_2 \ + 6x_3 > 400$

                $x_1 \geq 0, x_2 \geq 0, x_3 \geq 0$

14. Minimize the objective function in Exercise 13.

15. Minimize    $z = 8x_1 + 5x_2 + 4x_3$

    subject to    $2x_1 + 4x_2 + 6x_3 \leq 48$

                $4x_1 + 6x_2 + 2x_3 = 20$

                $3x_1 + 6x_2 + 4x_3 \geq 32$

                $x_1 \geq 0, x_2 \geq 0, x_3 \geq 0$

16. Maximize    $z = 8x_1 + 5x_2 + 4x_3$

    subject to    $2x_1 + 6x_2 + 4x_3 \leq 25$

                $3x_1 + 4x_2 + 2x_3 = 24$

                $2x_1 + 4x_2 + 6x_3 \geq 30$

                $x_1 \geq 0, x_2 \geq 0, x_3 \geq 0$

17. Maximize    $z = 10x_1 + 12x_2 + 9x_3$

    subject to    $3x_1 + 5x_2 + 4x_3 \leq 56$

                $2x_1 + 5x_2 + 3x_3 = 48$

                $5x_1 + 4x_2 + 5x_3 \geq 60$

                $x_1 \geq 0, x_2 \geq 0, x_3 \geq 0$

18. Minimize the objective function in Exercise 17.

19. A hospital dietician is planning a meal consisting of three foods whose major ingredients per ounce of food are given in the following chart:

|         | Units of protein | Units of carbohydrates | Units of calcium | Calories |
|---------|------------------|------------------------|------------------|----------|
| Food A  | 8                | 2                      | 3                | 90       |
| Food B  | 10               | 1                      | 5                | 100      |
| Food C  | 12               | 2                      | 2                | 110      |

Assuming that a balanced meal contains at least 48 units of protein, 8 units of carbohydrates, and 10 units of calcium, how many ounces of each food should the dietician use in order to minimize the total number of calories per meal?

20. The Whole Grain Cereal Company has four lines that produce "Cornies" and "Oaties" cereals. The capacities of the lines are given in the table below in hundreds of cartons per day. The company has a daily demand for at least 5000 cartons of Cornies and 4000 cartons of Oaties. If the cost per day is $600 for line 1, $300 for line 2, $400 for line 3, and $200 for line 4, find a production schedule that will meet or exceed the Cornies and Oaties cereal requirements at minimum cost.

Line

|         | 1  | 2 | 3 | 4 |
|---------|----|---|---|---|
| Cornies | 10 | 5 | 7 | 1 |
| Oaties  | 8  | 5 | 6 | 2 |

21. Jorge's Electronics Outlet is planning to restock its supply of VCR's, TV's, and cassette players. Xenon is offering a package of 20 VCR's, 40 TV's, and 25 cassette players for $6,000. Radon is offering a package of 15 VCR's, 30 TV's, and 20 cassette players for $4,000. Neptune is offering a package of 12 VCR's, 35 TV's, and 20 cassette players for $3,500. If Jorge's Electronics Outlet needs at least 150 VCR's, 250 TV's, and 120 cassette players, how many of each package should the store order to minimize the total cost? What is the minimum cost?

22. Repeat Exercise 21 if Neptune's package consists of 15 VCR's, 35 TV's, and 20 cassette players for $3,500.

In Exercises 23 - 26, rework the given problem from the text using the two-phase method.

23. Exercise 3, Section 1.5, p. 49

24. Exercise 4, Section 1.5, p. 49

25. Exercise 15, Section 1.5, p. 50

26. Exercise 16, Section 1.5, p. 51

# Chapter 5

## Section 5.4

**EXCEL Example 5.4.1:  Least Squares Regression Line** (Section 5.4, Example 5, p. 344)

EXCEL uses the **LINEST** function to calculate the least squares regression line that best fits a set of data.

1.  *To find the slope of the least squares regression line.*  Use the function
    **INDEX(LINEST(Known-y's,Known-x's),1)**.  **Known–y's** are the y-coordinates of the data points.  **Known-x's** are the x-coordinates of the data points.  These may be entered as arrays.  If the data has been entered into an EXCEL worksheet, then the cells corresponding to these coordinates may be typed beginning with the first cell, followed by a colon, then the last cell for each set of coordinates.  For this example, click on a cell and type

    **=INDEX(LINEST({5,4,3,1},{1,3,4,6}),1)**

    Then press "Enter".  The number "–0.80769" will be displayed in the selected cell.

2.  *To find the y-intercept of the least squares regression line.*  Use the function
    **INDEX(LINEST(Known-y's,Known-x's),2)**.  For this example, click on a cell and type

    **=INDEX(LINEST({5,4,3,1},{1,3,4,6}),2)**

    Then press "Enter".  The number "6.076923" will be displayed in the selected cell.

**Calculator Example 5.4.1:  Least Squares Regression Line** (Section 5.4, Example 5, p. 344)

1.  *Entering Lists of Data*:

    ┌──────┐
    │ STAT │ <EDIT>
    └──────┘

    For this example, enter the x-coordinates $\{1,3,4,6\}$ in L1 and y-coordinates $\{5,4,3,1\}$ in L2.

    ┌───────┐
    │ QUIT  │
    └───────┘

**2.** *Finding the Least Squares Regression Line*:

$\boxed{\text{STAT}}$ <CALC> 4: LinReg(ax+b) $\boxed{\text{L1}}$ $\boxed{,}$ $\boxed{\text{L2}}$ $\boxed{,}$ $\boxed{\text{VARS}}$ <Y-VARS> 1:Function 1:$Y_1$
$\boxed{\text{ENTER}}$

**3.** *Plotting Data and Regression Line*:

$\boxed{\text{STAT PLOT}}$ 1:Plot 1

Complete entry screen and draw graph as follows.

   $\boxed{\text{ZOOM}}$ 9:ZoomStat

**Exercises**:

In Exercises 1-4, use matrices to find the least squares regression line for the given data points.

1. $(0,4)$, $(-2,5)$, $(1,3)$, $(3,2)$         2. $(-2,-10)$, $(1,-7)$, $(3,-5)$, $(10,1)$

3. $(-4,-2)$, $(-3,-1)$, $(1,8)$, $(3,10)$    4. $(-2,16)$, $(1,7)$, $(4,-3)$, $(5,-6)$

In Exercises 5-8, use matrices to find the least squares quadratic polynomial of the form $y = ax^2 + bx + c$, $a \neq 0$, for the given data points.

5. $(-3,1)$, $(-1,0)$, $(1,7)$, $(3,19)$         6. $(-1,8)$, $(0,4)$, $(2,7)$, $(4,23)$

7. $(-2,20)$, $(1,4)$, $(2,-1)$, $(3,-10)$      8. $(-4,-3)$, $(-2,-6)$, $(2,4)$, $(3,8)$

9. The number of calculators sold per week at a store related to the selling price is tabulated below:

| Price | $80 | $75 | $82 | $79 | $83 |
|---|---|---|---|---|---|
| Number of Calculators | 50 | 55 | 49 | 51 | 47 |

    a. Use matrices to find the least squares regression line that relates the selling price to the number of calculators sold per week (i.e. find the weekly demand function for calculators at the store).

    b. What does the slope of the line represent?

    c. What does the $y$-intercept of the line represent?

    d. Use your result from part (a) to estimate how many calculators the store would sell in a week at a price of $77.

    e. Can the result from (a) be used to estimate how many calculators the store would sell in a week at a price of $135? Briefly explain why or why not.

10. The number of expresso makers sold per week at a store related to the selling price is tabulated below.

| Price | $90 | $85 | $95 | $92 | $86 |
|---|---|---|---|---|---|
| Number sold per week | 30 | 34 | 26 | 28 | 33 |

    a. Use matrices to find the least squares regression line that relates the selling price to the number of calculators sold per week (i.e. find the weekly demand function for calculators at the store).

    b. Use your result from (a) to estimate how many expresso makers the store would sell a week at a price of $88.

    c. Can the result from (a) be used to estimate how many expresso makers the store would sell in a week at a price of $129? Briefly explain why or why not.

11. The total annual U.S. book sales are listed in the table below:

| Year | 1992 | 1994 | 1995 | 1996 |
|---|---|---|---|---|
| Sales (Billions of dollars) | 21 | 24 | 25 | 26 |

(Source: Book Industry Trends, 1995)

    a. Use matrices to find the least squares regression line that relates the year to the total annual U.S. book sales.

    b. What does the slope of the line represent?

    c. What does the $y$-intercept of the line represent?

    d. Use your result from part (a) to estimate the total U.S. book sales in 1993.

12. The total annual U.S. health-care expenditures are listed in the table below:

| Year | 1985 | 1986 | 1988 | 1989 | 1990 |
|---|---|---|---|---|---|
| Expenditure (Billions of dollars) | 422.6 | 454.8 | 546.0 | 602.8 | 666.2 |

(Source: 1992 World Almanac)

    **a.** Use matrices to find the least squares regression line that relates the year to annual U.S. health-care expenditures.

    **b.** What does the slope of the line represent?

    **c.** What does the $y$-intercept of the line represent?

    **d.** Use your result from part (a) to estimate the U.S. health-care expenditure in 1987.


13. The weekly costs of operating a telemarketing company related to the number of telephone operators are given in the table below:

| Number of Operators | 1 | 2 | 3 | 5 | 6 |
|---|---|---|---|---|---|
| Weekly Costs | $2290 | $2570 | $2800 | $3400 | $3670 |

    **a.** Use matrices to find the least squares regression line that relates the weekly cost to the number of operators.

    **b.** What does the slope of the line represent?

    **c.** What does the $y$-intercept of the line represent?

    **d.** Use your result from part (a) to estimate the weekly cost if 4 telephone operators are working.

14. The average annual costs of tuition and fees at private four-year colleges are listed in the table below:

| Year | 1985 | 1987 | 1989 | 1991 | 1993 |
|---|---|---|---|---|---|
| Tuition and Fees | $6121 | $7116 | $8446 | $10,017 | $11,025 |

(Source: The College Board)

    **a.** Use matrices to find the least squares regression line that relates the year to the average annual cost of tuition and fees.

    **b.** What does the slope of the line represent?

    **c.** What does the $y$-intercept of the line represent?

    **d.** Use your result from part (a) to estimate the cost of tuition and fees in 1990.

Use EXCEL or a graphics calculator to solve Exercises 15-17.

15. The annual world production of vegetables (including melons) is listed in the table below:

| Year | 1990 | 1991 | 1992 | 1994 | 1995 | 1996 | 1997 |
|------|------|------|------|------|------|------|------|
| Production (millions of metric tons) | 461.4 | 462.4 | 478.6 | 532.9 | 559.9 | 589.1 | 595.6 |

(Source: U.S. Department of Agriculture)

a. Use matrices to find the least squares regression line that relates the year to the annual world production of vegetables.
b. Use your result from part (a) to estimate the world production of vegetables in 1993.

16. The annual median sales price of existing one-family homes in the United States is listed in the table below:

| Year | 1986 | 1987 | 1988 | 1989 | 1991 | 1992 | 1993 |
|------|------|------|------|------|------|------|------|
| Sales Price (thousands of dollars) | 80.3 | 85.6 | 89.3 | 93.1 | 100.3 | 103.7 | 106.8 |

(Source: National Association of Realtors)

a. Use matrices to find the least squares regression line that relates the year to the annual median sales price of one-family homes in the U.S.
b. Use your result from part (a) to estimate the median sales price of one-family homes in 1990.

17. The total annual number of people in the United States labor force is listed in the table below:

| Year | 1987 | 1988 | 1989 | 1990 | 1991 | 1993 | 1994 | 1995 | 1996 | 1997 |
|------|------|------|------|------|------|------|------|------|------|------|
| People (millions) | 120 | 122 | 124 | 126 | 126 | 129 | 131 | 132 | 134 | 136 |

(Source: U.S. Bureau of Labor Statistics)

a. Use matrices to find the least squares regression line that relates the year to the total annual number of people in the U.S. labor force.
b. Use your result from part (a) to estimate the total number of people in the U.S. labor force in 1992.

# Chapter 6

## Section 6.1

**Calculator Example 6.1.1: Finding Eigenvalues & Eigenvectors** (Section 6.1, Example 7, p. 363)

Although some graphing calculators have built-in functions for finding eigenvalues and eigenvectors, the TI-83 does not. Some of the steps in calculating eigenvalues and eigenvectors by hand, however, can be replaced with TI-83 functions. In particular, the calculator program CHPOLY, which can be downloaded at http://virtual.parkland.cc.il.us/oadawi/chpoly.83p, will easily find the characteristic polynomial of a square matrix.

Use the TI-83 to help find the eigenvalues and eigenvectors of the matrix $\begin{bmatrix} 3 & -2 & -2 \\ -2 & 3 & 2 \\ 3 & -3 & -2 \end{bmatrix}$.

1.  Enter the matrix in location $[A]$

2.  Enter the following sequence of keystrokes. Here, # refers to the number of the CHPOLY program, which depends on the number of programs stored in the calculator.

    $\boxed{\text{PRGM}}$ <EXEC> #:CHPOLY $\boxed{\text{ENTER}}$

3.  Press $\boxed{0}$ $\boxed{\text{ENTER}}$ to choose location $[A]$.

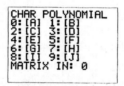

4.  The output {1 −4 5 −2} is to be interpreted as $\lambda^3 - 4\lambda^2 + 5\lambda - 2$. In another problem, if the output list did not completely appear on the screen, the $\boxed{\Leftarrow}$ and $\boxed{\Rightarrow}$ keys could be used to scroll to the undisplayed coefficients. Press $\boxed{\text{ENTER}}$ to terminate the program.

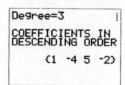

**5.** If desired, the calculator can further be used to graph the polynomial and numerically search for real zeros. Press $\boxed{\text{Y=}}$ and enter the polynomial function $X^3 - 4X^2 + 5X - 2$.

After experimenting with the window settings, one might settle on Xmin=−1, Xmax=3, Ymin=−1, Ymax=1, which results in the following graph:

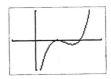

**6.** The roots can be approximated by using the TRACE feature and zooming in on the zeros. The TI-83 zero function gives much more accuracy in case the eigenvalues are not easily recognized as integers. Enter the keystrokes $\boxed{\text{CALC}}$ 2:zero and use the $\boxed{\Leftarrow}$ and $\boxed{\Rightarrow}$ keys to move the cursor to points to the left, right, and on the desired intercept as prompted, pressing $\boxed{\text{ENTER}}$ each time when the cursor is at the desired position. Once $\lambda_1 = 1$ has been identified as an eigenvalue, long division can be used to compute the quotient

$$\frac{\lambda^3 - 4\lambda^2 + 5\lambda - 2}{\lambda - 1} = \lambda^2 - 3\lambda + 2 = (\lambda - 1)(\lambda - 2)$$

and identify the other eigenvalues as 1 and 2.

**7.** Finally, the calculator can be used to row-reduce the matrix $A - \lambda I$ when finding the eigenvectors for each eigenvalue. Enter the keystrokes

$\boxed{\text{MATRX}}$ <MATH> B:rref(

and complete the command with the following keystrokes (here, the "1" is entered to specify $A - 1I$ and the "3" tells the calculator desired identity matrix is 3x3).

$\boxed{\text{MATRX}}$ <NAMES> 1:A − $\boxed{1}$ $\boxed{\text{MATRX}}$ <MATH> 5:identity( $\boxed{3}$ $\boxed{)}$ $\boxed{)}$ $\boxed{\text{ENTER}}$

```
rref([A]-1identi
ty(3))
        [[1 -1 -1]
         [0  0  0 ]
         [0  0  0 ]]
```

**Exercises:**

In Exercises 1-8,

    **a.** by computing $A\vec{x}$, determine if the given vector $\vec{x}$ is an eigenvector of the given matrix $A$

    **b.** if the answer to (a) is yes, find the corresponding eigenvalue

1. $\begin{bmatrix} 2 & -2 \\ 5 & -6 \end{bmatrix}$, $(4,2)$

2. $\begin{bmatrix} -2 & 7 \\ -3 & 12 \end{bmatrix}$, $(-2,-1)$

3. $\begin{bmatrix} 7 & 2 \\ -4 & 1 \end{bmatrix}$, $(1,-2)$

4. $\begin{bmatrix} 7 & 2 \\ 2 & 4 \end{bmatrix}$, $(2,1)$

5. $\begin{bmatrix} 2 & 0 & 1 \\ 4 & -2 & 1 \\ 2 & -2 & 3 \end{bmatrix}$, $(2,0,-4)$

6. $\begin{bmatrix} -2 & 0 & 1 \\ -6 & -2 & 0 \\ 19 & 5 & -4 \end{bmatrix}$, $(1,1,-6)$

7. $\begin{bmatrix} 5 & 6 & 2 \\ 0 & -1 & -8 \\ 1 & 0 & -2 \end{bmatrix}$, $(-6,8,3)$

8. $\begin{bmatrix} 1 & -3 & 1 \\ 0 & 2 & 5 \\ 1 & -1 & 4 \end{bmatrix}$, $(2,2,4)$

In Exercises 9-28, for the given matrix $A$,

    **a.** compute the characteristic equation
    **b.** find the real eigenvalues
    **c.** find the eigenspace for each real eigenvalue

9. $\begin{bmatrix} 1 & -1 \\ 2 & 4 \end{bmatrix}$

10. $\begin{bmatrix} 4 & -5 \\ 2 & -3 \end{bmatrix}$

11. $\begin{bmatrix} 3 & 5 \\ -5 & -3 \end{bmatrix}$

12. $\begin{bmatrix} 6 & -3 \\ -2 & 1 \end{bmatrix}$

13. $\begin{bmatrix} 7 & 4 \\ -3 & -1 \end{bmatrix}$

14. $\begin{bmatrix} 10 & -9 \\ 4 & -2 \end{bmatrix}$

15. $\begin{bmatrix} 2 & 3 \\ 3 & -6 \end{bmatrix}$

16. $\begin{bmatrix} 5 & 3 \\ -4 & 4 \end{bmatrix}$

17. $\begin{bmatrix} 1 & 2 & -2 \\ -2 & 5 & -2 \\ -6 & 6 & -3 \end{bmatrix}$

18. $\begin{bmatrix} 1 & -1 & -1 \\ 1 & 3 & 1 \\ -3 & 1 & -1 \end{bmatrix}$

19. $\begin{bmatrix} 2 & -2 & 0 \\ 2 & -2 & -1 \\ -2 & 2 & 3 \end{bmatrix}$

20. $\begin{bmatrix} 1 & 3 & 3 \\ -3 & -5 & -3 \\ 3 & 3 & 1 \end{bmatrix}$

21. $\begin{bmatrix} 7 & 4 & 16 \\ 2 & 5 & 8 \\ -2 & -2 & -5 \end{bmatrix}$

22. $\begin{bmatrix} -2 & 4 & -1 \\ -3 & 5 & -1 \\ -1 & 1 & 1 \end{bmatrix}$

23. $\begin{bmatrix} 0 & 3 & 0 \\ -3 & 0 & 4 \\ 0 & -4 & 0 \end{bmatrix}$

24. $\begin{bmatrix} 1 & 1 & -1 \\ -2 & 4 & -1 \\ -4 & 4 & 1 \end{bmatrix}$

25. $\begin{bmatrix} 26 & 0 & 24 & -16 \\ 26 & 0 & 20 & -12 \\ -37 & 1 & -32 & 22 \\ -1 & 1 & 2 & 0 \end{bmatrix}$

26. $\begin{bmatrix} -8 & 2 & 1 & -1 \\ 0 & -4 & 2 & -2 \\ 0 & 6 & -5 & -3 \\ 0 & -2 & -1 & -7 \end{bmatrix}$

27. $\begin{bmatrix} 1 & 45 & 26 & 17 \\ -2 & 20 & 8 & 6 \\ 6 & -30 & -9 & -13 \\ -6 & 30 & 14 & 18 \end{bmatrix}$

28. $\begin{bmatrix} -2 & -44 & -46 & -34 \\ -10 & 4 & -6 & 26 \\ -25 & -46 & -1 & 9 \\ -5 & 2 & -17 & -15 \end{bmatrix}$

29. Show that if $\lambda$ is an eigenvalue of a matrix $A$, then $\lambda^3$ is an eigenvalue of $A^3$.

30. Show that if $\lambda$ is a nonzero eigenvalue of an invertible matrix $A$, then $\frac{1}{\lambda^2}$ is an eigenvalue of $(A^{-1})^2$.

## Section 6.2

**Exercises**:

In Exercises 1-10, for the given matrix $A$,

    **a.** if possible, find a matrix $P$ and a diagonal matrix $D$ so that $P^{-1}AP = D$

    **b.** if an answer exists for part (a), check the answer by direct computation

1. $\begin{bmatrix} 1 & -1 \\ 2 & 4 \end{bmatrix}$

2. $\begin{bmatrix} 4 & -5 \\ 2 & -3 \end{bmatrix}$

3. $\begin{bmatrix} 3 & 5 \\ -5 & -3 \end{bmatrix}$

4. $\begin{bmatrix} 6 & -3 \\ -2 & 1 \end{bmatrix}$

5. $\begin{bmatrix} 7 & 4 \\ -3 & -1 \end{bmatrix}$

6. $\begin{bmatrix} 10 & -9 \\ 4 & -2 \end{bmatrix}$

7. $\begin{bmatrix} 2 & 3 \\ 3 & -6 \end{bmatrix}$

8. $\begin{bmatrix} 5 & 3 \\ -4 & 4 \end{bmatrix}$

9. $\begin{bmatrix} 1 & 2 & -2 \\ -2 & 5 & -2 \\ -6 & 6 & -3 \end{bmatrix}$

10. $\begin{bmatrix} 1 & -1 & -1 \\ 1 & 3 & 1 \\ -3 & 1 & -1 \end{bmatrix}$

In Exercises 11-16, find a matrix with the given eigenvalues and associated eigenvectors.

11. $\lambda = 2$, $(-2, 1)$; $\lambda = -3$, $(5, 1)$

12. $\lambda = 0$, $(2, -1)$; $\lambda = 4$, $(7, -1)$

13. $\lambda = 3$, $(2, 1, -1)$, $(3, -1, 0)$; $\lambda = -2$, $(1, 1, 1)$

14. $\lambda = -1$, $(2, 0, 1)$; $\lambda = 4$, $(-1, 2, 1)$; $\lambda = 2$, $(3, 2, 1)$

15. $\lambda = 2$, $(1, 1, 1, -1)$, $(2, 0, 0, -1)$; $\lambda = -1$, $(-2, 3, 0, 1)$, $(-3, 1, 5, 0)$

16. $\lambda = 4$, $(-2, 3, 0, 1)$, $(0, 0, 1, -1)$, $(-2, 1, 1, 0)$; $\lambda = -1$, $(1, 4, 0, -1)$

# Section 6.3

The following examples, which extend the idea of a transition matrix to more general cases than that of Markov Chains, illustrate that the size of the eigenvalue of largest magnitude is of critical importance in determining the behavior of a system.

**Example 1:** The administrators of a state wildlife preserve want to maintain a stable number of foxes and rabbits in the preserve. By controlling the amount of natural vegetation, the administrators have some control over the average number, $r$, of rabbits killed and eaten monthly per fox. Define the following:

$$\vec{x}_0 = \begin{bmatrix} F_0 \\ R_0 \end{bmatrix} = \begin{bmatrix} \text{initial number of foxes (in thousands)} \\ \text{initial number of rabbits (in thousands)} \end{bmatrix}$$

$$\vec{x}_k = \begin{bmatrix} F_k \\ R_k \end{bmatrix} = \begin{bmatrix} \text{number of foxes in } k \text{ months (in thousands)} \\ \text{number of rabbits in } k \text{ months (in thousands)} \end{bmatrix}$$

From past observations, ecologists estimate that

$$F_{k+1} = 0.3F_k + 0.5R_k$$
$$R_{k+1} = -rF_k + 1.5R_k$$

In matrix form, this system can be written as

$$\vec{x}_{k+1} = A\vec{x}_k \text{ where } A = \begin{bmatrix} 0.3 & 0.5 \\ -r & 1.5 \end{bmatrix}$$

Notice that $a_{21}$ is negative, reflecting the fact that more foxes result in more rabbits being eaten. Also note that $\vec{x}_k$ is *not* a distribution vector, nor is $A$ a stochastic matrix. Suppose the current populations of foxes and rabbits are 2 thousand and 10 thousand respectively.

  a.  What will happen to the fox and rabbit populations in the long run if $r = 0.64$?
  b.  What will happen to the fox and rabbit populations in the long run if $r = 0.715$?
  c.  For which value(s) of $r$, if any, will the populations neither approach extinction nor become unbounded in the long run?

**Solution:**

  a.  A routine computation shows that the matrix $A = \begin{bmatrix} 0.3 & 0.5 \\ -0.64 & 1.5 \end{bmatrix}$ has eigenvalues and

  associated eigenvectors $\lambda_1 = 1.1$, $\vec{v}_1 = \begin{bmatrix} 5 \\ 8 \end{bmatrix}$, and $\lambda_2 = 0.7$, $\vec{v}_2 = \begin{bmatrix} 5 \\ 4 \end{bmatrix}$. Hence

$$\vec{x}_k = A^k \vec{x}_0$$

$$= PD^k P^{-1} \vec{x}_0$$

$$= \begin{bmatrix} 5 & 5 \\ 8 & 4 \end{bmatrix} \begin{bmatrix} 1.1 & 0 \\ 0 & 0.7 \end{bmatrix}^k \begin{bmatrix} 5 & 5 \\ 8 & 4 \end{bmatrix}^{-1} \begin{bmatrix} 2 \\ 10 \end{bmatrix}$$

$$= \begin{bmatrix} \frac{21}{2}(1.1)^k - \frac{17}{2}(0.7)^k \\ \frac{84}{5}(1.1)^k - \frac{34}{5}(0.7)^k \end{bmatrix}$$

In the long run (as $k$ gets large), the quantity $(0.7)^k$ approaches 0 but the quantity $(1.1)^k$ increases without bound. In other words, both the fox and the rabbit populations will get arbitrarily large. From the point of view of the preserve administrators, this is undesirable.

  b.  The matrix $A = \begin{bmatrix} 0.3 & 0.5 \\ -0.715 & 1.5 \end{bmatrix}$ has eigenvalues and associated eigenvectors

$\lambda_1 = 0.95$, $\vec{v}_1 = \begin{bmatrix} 10 \\ 13 \end{bmatrix}$, and $\lambda_2 = 0.85$, $\vec{v}_2 = \begin{bmatrix} 10 \\ 11 \end{bmatrix}$. Hence,

$$\vec{x}_k = \begin{bmatrix} 10 & 10 \\ 13 & 11 \end{bmatrix} \begin{bmatrix} 0.95 & 0 \\ 0 & 0.85 \end{bmatrix}^k \begin{bmatrix} 10 & 10 \\ 13 & 11 \end{bmatrix}^{-1} \begin{bmatrix} 2 \\ 10 \end{bmatrix}$$

$$= \begin{bmatrix} 39(0.95)^k - 37(0.85)^k \\ \frac{507}{10}(0.95)^k - \frac{407}{10}(0.85)^k \end{bmatrix}$$

In the long run, both quantities $(0.95)^k$ and $(0.85)^k$ will go to zero. In other words, both the foxes and the rabbits will approach extinction. This is also undesirable for the preserve administrators.

c.  Note that if the matrix $A$ has an eigenvalue greater than 1, the populations will grow without bound, while if both eigenvalues are between 0 and 1, the populations decline to 0. We must choose $r$ so that the matrix has an eigenvalue exactly equal to 1. Now

$$\det(A - \lambda I) = \det \begin{bmatrix} 0.3 - \lambda & 0.5 \\ -r & 1.5 - \lambda \end{bmatrix} = \lambda^2 - 1.8\lambda + 0.45 + 0.5r$$

Recall that the quadratic formula $x = \dfrac{-b \pm \sqrt{b^2 - 4ac}}{2a}$ gives the solutions of the equation

$ax^2 + bx + c = 0$. Applying the formula to $\lambda^2 - 1.8\lambda + 0.45 + 0.5r = 0$ gives

$$\lambda = \frac{-(-1.8) \pm \sqrt{(-1.8)^2 - 4(1)(0.45 + 0.5r)}}{2(1)} = \frac{1.8 \pm \sqrt{1.44 - 2r}}{2}$$

The root using the "+" sign gives the larger eigenvalue $\lambda_1$, so set $\dfrac{1.8 + \sqrt{1.44 - 2r}}{2} = 1$.

Solving for $r$ gives $r = 0.7$. The smaller eigenvalue then becomes

$$\lambda_2 = \frac{1.8 - \sqrt{1.44 - 2(0.7)}}{2} = 0.8,\ \text{which will result in a term that goes to 0 in the}$$

expression for $\vec{x}_k$. So the administrators should control the vegetation so that foxes eat an average of only 0.7 rabbits per month.

To verify that this kill rate does give satisfactory results, note that the matrix

$A = \begin{bmatrix} 0.3 & 0.5 \\ -0.7 & 1.5 \end{bmatrix}$ has eigenvectors $\vec{v}_1 = \begin{bmatrix} 5 \\ 7 \end{bmatrix}$ and $\vec{v}_2 = \begin{bmatrix} 1 \\ 1 \end{bmatrix}$ associated with

the eigenvalues $\lambda_1 = 1$ and $\lambda_2 = 0.8$.

Therefore,

$$\vec{x}_k = \begin{bmatrix} 5 & 1 \\ 7 & 1 \end{bmatrix} \begin{bmatrix} 1 & 0 \\ 0 & 0.8 \end{bmatrix}^k \begin{bmatrix} 5 & 1 \\ 7 & 1 \end{bmatrix}^{-1} \begin{bmatrix} 2 \\ 10 \end{bmatrix} = \begin{bmatrix} 20 - 18(0.8)^k \\ 28 - 18(0.8)^k \end{bmatrix}$$

So in the long run, the fox population will stabilize at 20 thousand and the rabbit population at 28 thousand.

In summary, we note the general situation regarding the eigenvalue $\lambda_1$ with the largest magnitude:

If $0 \le \lambda_1 < 1$, then the populations approach extinction.
If $\lambda_1 = 1$, then the populations approach a stable nonzero state.
If $1 < \lambda_1$, then the populations grow without bound.

**Example 2**: Suppose manufacturing and agriculture are two sectors of an economy. To produce $1 in manufactured goods requires $0.30 in manufactured products and $0.20 in agricultural products. To produce $1 in agricultural goods requires $r in manufactured products and $0.25 in agricultural products. Suppose there is an external demand of $40 billion in manufactured products and $35 billion in agricultural products.

    a. If $r = 1.25$, find (if possible) the production vector necessary to meet external demand.
    b. If $r = 2.75$, find (if possible) the production vector necessary to meet external demand.
    c. How efficiently must the agricultural sector use manufactured products to meet the external demand? That is, the value of $r$ must be below what value for a production vector to exist?

**Solution**:

    a. The consumption matrix is $C = \begin{bmatrix} 0.3 & 1.25 \\ 0.2 & 0.25 \end{bmatrix}$ and so from the discussion in Section 3.3,

$$(I - C)^{-1} = \left( \begin{bmatrix} 1 & 0 \\ 0 & 1 \end{bmatrix} - \begin{bmatrix} 0.3 & 1.25 \\ 0.2 & 0.25 \end{bmatrix} \right)^{-1} \approx \begin{bmatrix} 2.7273 & 4.5455 \\ 0.72727 & 2.5455 \end{bmatrix}$$

$$X = (I - C)^{-1}D \approx \begin{bmatrix} 2.7273 & 4.5455 \\ 0.72727 & 2.5455 \end{bmatrix} \begin{bmatrix} 40 \\ 35 \end{bmatrix} = \begin{bmatrix} 268.18 \\ 118.18 \end{bmatrix}$$

The manufacturing sector should produce $268.18 billion and the agricultural sector $118.18 billion. Note that the economy is productive even though the agricultural sector is not profitable. For later discussion, we note that the eigenvalues of $C$ are $\lambda_1 \approx 0.776$ and $\lambda_2 \approx -0.226$.

b. Using $C = \begin{bmatrix} 0.3 & 2.75 \\ 0.2 & 0.25 \end{bmatrix}$,

$$(I - C)^{-1} = \left( \begin{bmatrix} 1 & 0 \\ 0 & 1 \end{bmatrix} - \begin{bmatrix} 0.3 & 2.75 \\ 0.2 & 0.25 \end{bmatrix} \right)^{-1} = \begin{bmatrix} -30.0 & -110.0 \\ -8.0 & -28.0 \end{bmatrix}$$

Since the entries of the demand vector $D$ are positive, the production vector $X = (I - C)^{-1}D$ will have negative entries. The economic interpretation of this fact is that the economy is no longer productive. It cannot meet this external demand since agriculture is consuming too much of the production internally. For later discussion, we note that the eigenvalues of $C$ are $\lambda_1 \approx 1.017$ and $\lambda_2 \approx -0.467$.

c. We want to find the value of $r$ below which $(I - C)^{-1}$ will have all positive entries. It turns out that a positive matrix $C$ has the property that $(I - C)^{-1}$ is positive if the largest eigenvalue of $C$ is less than 1. (Note that if $C$ has an eigenvalue exactly equal to 1, then $C\vec{x} = \vec{x}$ for some eigenvector $\vec{x}$ and $I - C$ is not invertible.)

$$\det(C - \lambda I) = \det \begin{bmatrix} 0.3 - \lambda & r \\ 0.2 & 0.25 - \lambda \end{bmatrix} = \lambda^2 - 0.55\lambda + 0.075 - 0.2r$$

Using the quadratic equation to solve $\lambda^2 - 0.55\lambda + 0.075 - 0.2r = 0$ gives

$\lambda = \dfrac{0.55 \pm \sqrt{0.0025 + 0.8r}}{2}$. Setting the larger eigenvalue obtained by choosing the "+"

sign equal to 1 gives $\dfrac{0.55 + \sqrt{0.0025 + 0.8r}}{2} = 1$. The solution of this equation is

$r = 2.625$. As long as agriculture uses less than $2.625 of manufactured goods to produce $1 in agricultural products, the economy remains productive.

In summary, we note the general situation for a positive matrix $C$ regarding the eigenvalue $\lambda_1$ with the largest magnitude:

If $\lambda_1 < 1$, then $(I - C)^{-1}$ is positive (the economy is productive)
If $\lambda_1 = 1$, then $(I - C)^{-1}$ does not exist (the economy is not productive)
If $1 < \lambda_1$, then $(I - C)^{-1}$ is not positive (the economy is not productive)

**Example 3**: Consider the difference equation $a_{k+1} = -a_k + 6a_{k-1}$ with the initial conditions $a_{-1} = 2$ and $a_0 = 0$.

a. Calculate $a_k$ for $k = 5$
b. Find an expression for $a_k$ which is valid for $k \geq 1$.

**Solution:**

a. Repeatedly using the difference equation,

$$
\begin{aligned}
a_1 &= a_0 + 6a_{-1} = -0 + 6(2) &= 12 \\
a_2 &= -a_1 + 6a_0 = -12 + 6(0) &= -12 \\
a_3 &= -a_2 + 6a_1 = -(-12) + 6(12) &= 84 \\
a_4 &= -a_3 + 6a_2 = -84 + 6(-12) &= -156 \\
a_5 &= -a_4 + 6a_3 = -(-156) + 6(84) &= 660
\end{aligned}
$$

b. This second order difference equation can be transformed into a system of first order of equations as follows. Let $b_k = a_{k-1}$. Then

$$
\begin{aligned}
a_{k+1} &= -a_k + 6a_{k-1} \\
b_{k+1} &= a_k
\end{aligned}
$$

or as a system

$$
\vec{x}_{k+1} = A\vec{x}_k \quad \text{where } \vec{x}_k = \begin{bmatrix} a_k \\ b_k \end{bmatrix} \text{ and } A = \begin{bmatrix} -1 & 6 \\ 1 & 0 \end{bmatrix}
$$

The initial conditions can be expressed as

$$
\vec{x}_0 = \begin{bmatrix} a_0 \\ b_0 \end{bmatrix} = \begin{bmatrix} a_0 \\ a_{-1} \end{bmatrix} = \begin{bmatrix} 0 \\ 2 \end{bmatrix}
$$

The matrix $A$ has eigenvalue and associated eigenvector pairs $\lambda_1 = 2$, $\vec{v}_1 = \begin{bmatrix} 2 \\ 1 \end{bmatrix}$ and

$\lambda_2 = -3$, $\vec{v}_2 = \begin{bmatrix} -3 \\ 1 \end{bmatrix}$. So

$$
\vec{x}_k = A^k \vec{x}_0
$$

$$
= \begin{bmatrix} 2 & -3 \\ 1 & 1 \end{bmatrix} \begin{bmatrix} 2 & 0 \\ 0 & -3 \end{bmatrix}^k \begin{bmatrix} 2 & -3 \\ 1 & 1 \end{bmatrix}^{-1} \begin{bmatrix} 0 \\ 2 \end{bmatrix}
$$

$$
= \begin{bmatrix} \frac{12}{5}(2)^k - \frac{12}{5}(-3)^k \\ \frac{6}{5}(2)^k + \frac{4}{5}(-3)^k \end{bmatrix}
$$

Hence, $a_k = \frac{12}{5}(2)^k - \frac{12}{5}(-3)^k$

**Example 4:** Suppose the agricultural sector of an economy is very competitive and that each season, farmers have the option of taking land out of production in favor of collecting a government subsidy. Because crop prices are inversely related to the number of acres in production, farmers try to act "against the crowd," taking land out of production when they think others are putting land into production and vice versa. Suppose the relationship can be modeled as follows. Each year, the number of acres in production decreases by an amount proportional to the increase in production acreage from last year to the current year. Mathematically, let $a_k$ be the number of acres in production $k$ years from now. Then the economy works according to the difference equation

$$a_{k+1} = a_k - r(a_k - a_{k-1})$$

The expression $a_k - a_{k-1}$ is the change in acreage last season and $r$ is a positive constant of proportionality. The model suggests that farmers are trying to move their own land in the opposite direction of the latest trend which they observed. Suppose 1.5 million acres are in production this year and 1.2 million acres were in production last year.

a. If $r = 0.5$, calculate the number of acres (in millions) in production for the next 5 years.
b. If $r = 1.5$, calculate the number of acres (in millions) in production for the next 5 years.
c. For which values of $r$ will the number of acres in production stabilize in the long run?

**Solution:**

a. Using $a_{k+1} = a_k - 0.5(a_k - a_{k-1}) = 0.5a_k + 0.5a_{k-1}$,

$$
\begin{aligned}
a_1 &= 0.5a_0 + 0.5a_{-1} = 0.5(1.5) + 0.5(1.2) &&= 1.35 \\
a_2 &= 0.5a_1 + 0.5a_0 = 0.5(1.35) + 0.5(1.5) &&= 1.425 \\
a_3 &= 0.5a_2 + 0.5a_1 = 0.5(1.425) + 0.5(1.35) &&= 1.3875 \\
a_4 &= 0.5a_3 + 0.5a_2 = 0.5(1.3875) + 0.5(1.425) &&= 1.40625 \\
a_5 &= 0.5a_4 + 0.5a_3 = 0.5(1.40625) + 0.5(1.3875) &&= 1.396875
\end{aligned}
$$

Plotting acreage as a function of time shows the following graph.

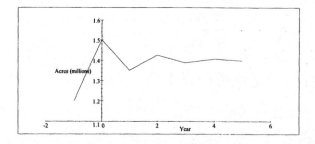

Note that the acreage is oscillating, but the amplitude of the oscillations is decreasing with each year. In part (c), a formula will be obtained showing the acreage approaches 1.4 million acres in the long run.

b. Using $a_{k+1} = a_k - 1.5(a_k - a_{k-1}) = -0.5a_k + 1.5a_{k-1}$,

$$a_1 = -0.5a_0 + 1.5a_{-1} = -0.5(1.5) + 1.5(1.2) \qquad = 1.05$$
$$a_2 = -0.5a_1 + 1.5a_0 \ = -0.5(1.05) + 1.5(1.5) \qquad = 1.725$$
$$a_3 = -0.5a_2 + 1.5a_1 \ = -0.5(1.725) + 1.5(1.05) \qquad = 0.7125$$
$$a_4 = -0.5a_3 + 1.5a_2 \ = -0.5(0.7125) + 1.5(1.725) \qquad = 2.23125$$
$$a_5 = -0.5a_4 + 1.5a_3 \ = -0.5(2.23125) + 1.5(0.7125) = -0.046875$$

Plotting acreage as a function of time shows the following graph.

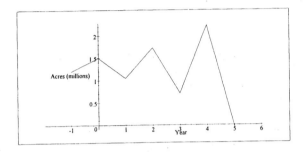

Note that the acreage is oscillating, and the amplitude of the oscillations increases with each year.  Since $a_5$ is a meaningless negative number, the model is no longer valid after 5 years.

c.  The difference equation can be simplified as $a_{k+1} = (1-r)a_k + ra_{k-1}$. Let $b_k = a_{k-1}$.
    Then

$$a_{k+1} = (1-r)a_k + ra_{k-1} = (1-r)a_k + rb_k$$
$$b_{k+1} = a_k$$

or as a system

$$\vec{x}_{k+1} = A\vec{x}_k \ \text{ where } \vec{x}_k = \begin{bmatrix} a_k \\ b_k \end{bmatrix} \text{ and } A = \begin{bmatrix} 1-r & r \\ 1 & 0 \end{bmatrix}$$

The initial conditions can be expressed as

$$\vec{x}_0 = \begin{bmatrix} a_0 \\ b_0 \end{bmatrix} = \begin{bmatrix} a_0 \\ a_{-1} \end{bmatrix} = \begin{bmatrix} 1.5 \\ 1.2 \end{bmatrix}$$

Then

$$\det(A - \lambda I) = \det \begin{bmatrix} 1-r-\lambda & r \\ 1 & -\lambda \end{bmatrix} = \lambda^2 + (r-1)\lambda - r = (\lambda - 1)(\lambda + r)$$

The eigenvectors corresponding to $\lambda_1 = 1$ and $\lambda_2 = -r$ are $v_1 = \begin{bmatrix} 1 \\ 1 \end{bmatrix}$ and $v_2 = \begin{bmatrix} -r \\ 1 \end{bmatrix}$. Therefore,

$$\vec{x}_k = A^k \vec{x}_0$$

$$= \begin{bmatrix} 1 & -r \\ 1 & 1 \end{bmatrix} \begin{bmatrix} 1 & 0 \\ 0 & -r \end{bmatrix}^k \begin{bmatrix} 1 & -r \\ 1 & 1 \end{bmatrix}^{-1} \begin{bmatrix} 1.5 \\ 1.2 \end{bmatrix}$$

$$= \frac{1}{1+r} \begin{bmatrix} 1.5 + r[0.3(-r)^k + 1.2] \\ 1.5 + r[-0.3(-r)^k + 1.2] \end{bmatrix}$$

If $0 < r < 1$, then $a_k$ approaches $\dfrac{1.5 + 1.2r}{1 + r}$ in the long run.

If $r = 1$, then $a_k = \frac{1}{2}[2.7 + 0.3(-1)^k]$, which oscillates back and forth between 1.5 and 1.2

If $r > 1$, then $a_k$ oscillates with increasing magnitude until it becomes negative, at which time the model is no longer valid. The farmers are overreacting to the past changes in acreage.

Note that since $r = -\lambda_2$, the magnitude of the eigenvalues again determines the overall long term behavior of the system.

**Exercises:**

In Exercises 1-6, the given matrix $A$ is the matrix from the given exercise in Section 6.2. Find an expression for $A^n$.

1. $\begin{bmatrix} 1 & -1 \\ 2 & 4 \end{bmatrix}$ (Exercise 1)

2. $\begin{bmatrix} 4 & -5 \\ 2 & -3 \end{bmatrix}$ (Exercise 2)

3. $\begin{bmatrix} 7 & 4 \\ -3 & -1 \end{bmatrix}$ (Exercise 5)

4. $\begin{bmatrix} 6 & -3 \\ -2 & 1 \end{bmatrix}$ (Exercise 4)

5. $\begin{bmatrix} 1 & 2 & -2 \\ -2 & 5 & -2 \\ -6 & 6 & -3 \end{bmatrix}$ (Exercise 9)

6. $\begin{bmatrix} 1 & -1 & -1 \\ 1 & 3 & 1 \\ -3 & 1 & -1 \end{bmatrix}$ (Exercise 10)

In Exercise 7-12, for the given transition matrix $T$.

    a. find an expression for $T^n$
    b. use the eigenvalue method to find the stable distribution vector $\vec{s}$ for which $T\vec{s} = \vec{s}$
    c. find the smallest integer $k$ so that $T^k$ approximates the limiting matrix $T^\infty$ to four decimal places
    d. find the relative error in $T^k$ for the value of $k$ found in part (c)

7. $\begin{bmatrix} 0.4 & 0.3 \\ 0.6 & 0.7 \end{bmatrix}$          8. $\begin{bmatrix} 0.8 & 0.7 \\ 0.2 & 0.3 \end{bmatrix}$

9. $\begin{bmatrix} 0.9 & 0.2 \\ 0.1 & 0.8 \end{bmatrix}$        10. $\begin{bmatrix} 0.8 & 0.5 \\ 0.2 & 0.5 \end{bmatrix}$

11. $\begin{bmatrix} 0.5 & 0.2 & 0.4 \\ 0.4 & 0.4 & 0.4 \\ 0.1 & 0.4 & 0.2 \end{bmatrix}$      12. $\begin{bmatrix} 0.7 & 0.5 & 0.1 \\ 0.2 & 0.4 & 0.3 \\ 0.1 & 0.1 & 0.6 \end{bmatrix}$

13. Suppose that a lake contains both bass and sunfish, with the bass population preying on young sunfish. The number of bass, $B_k$, and sunfish, $S_k$, in $k$ months is given by the system

$$B_{k+1} = 0.4B_k + 0.3S_k$$
$$S_{k+1} = -rB_k + 1.2S_k$$

where the positive constant $r$ is a capture rate of sunfish by the bass. For which values of $r$ will the populations neither approach extinction nor become unbounded in the long run?

14. Repeat Exercise 13 if the sunfish population grows according to the equation $S_{k+1} = -rB_k + S_k$.

15. Suppose the populations of hare (the prey species), $H_k$, and lynx (the predator species), $L_k$, in thousands, $k$ years from now are governed by the following equations

$$H_{k+1} = rH_k - L_k$$
$$L_{k+1} = 0.375H_k + 0.25L_k$$

where the positive constant $r$ represents the reproduction rate of the hare. Initially, there are 5 thousand hares and 1.5 thousand lynx in a wilderness area.

    a. What will happen to the populations in the long run if $r = 1.475$?
    b. For which value(s) of $r$, if any, will the populations neither approach extinction nor become unbounded in the long run?

16. Repeat Exercise 15 if the lynx population grows according to the equation $L_{k+1} = 0.1875H_k + 0.25L_k$.

17. Suppose coal mining and steel production are two sectors of an economy. To produce $1 in coal requires $0.20 of coal and $0.15 of steel. To produce $1 in steel requires $r in coal and $0.30 in steel. How efficiently must the steel sector use coal for the economy to be productive? That is, the value of $r$ must be below what value for a production vector to exist for any external demand?

18. Repeat Exercise 17 if $0.25 of steel is required to produce $1 in steel.

19. Suppose computing and statistical services are two divisions of a company. To produce $1 in computing services requires $0.35 in computing services and $0.05 in statistical services. To produce $1 in statistical services requires $0.25 in computing services and $r in statistical services. How efficiently must the statistical service division use its own services for the company to be productive? That is, the value of $r$ must be below what value for a production vector to exist for any external demand?

20. Repeat Exercise 19 if $0.35 in computing services are required to produce $1 in statistical services.

In Exercises 21 - 24, find an expression for $a_k$ which is valid for $k \geq 1$.

21. $a_{k+1} = -3a_k + 4a_{k-1}$, $a_0 = -2$, $a_{-1} = 1$

22. $a_{k+1} = 8a_k + 9a_{k-1}$, $a_0 = 1$, $a_{-1} = -2$

23. $a_{k+1} = 8a_k - 7a_{k-1}$, $a_0 = -3$, $a_{-1} = 0$

24. $a_{k+1} = -7a_k - 10a_{k-1}$, $a_0 = 2$, $a_{-1} = -3$

# Answers to Odd Exercises

## Chapter 1

### Section 1.1

1. **(a)** $y = -1200x + 6000$  **(b)** \$3000  **(c)** The value decreases by \$1200 each year
   **(d)** The initial value is \$6000

### Section 1.2

1. \$544, 82 air conditioners

3. **(a)** $R(x) = 16,000x$  **(b)** $C(x) = 68,000 + 12,000x$  **(c)** 17 cars  **(d)** 21 cars

5. **(a)** $R(x) = 70x$  **(b)** $C(x) = 1225 + 35x$  **(c)** 35 players  **(d)** a loss

## Chapter 2

### Section 2.1

1. $\begin{bmatrix} 4 & -3 & 2 & 5 \\ 2 & -1 & 1 & -2 \\ 1 & 0 & -2 & 3 \end{bmatrix}$    3. $\begin{bmatrix} 4 & 3 & -1 & 2 & -8 \\ 0 & 1 & 1 & 0 & 5 \\ 2 & 1 & 0 & 0 & 6 \end{bmatrix}$    5. $\begin{bmatrix} 4 & 3 & 0 & 5 \\ 0 & -2 & -1 & -1 \\ 3 & 0 & 2 & 0 \\ 2 & 1 & 0 & 2 \end{bmatrix}$

7. $\begin{aligned} x_1 - 2x_2 + 3x_3 &= 2 \\ 3x_1 + 7x_2 &= 1 \\ 8x_1 - 4x_2 + 4x_3 &= 7 \end{aligned}$   9. $\begin{aligned} 3x_1 \quad - 2x_3 &= 1 \\ 3x_3 &= -1 \\ 2x_1 \quad + 6x_3 &= 4 \\ -7x_1 - x_2 \quad &= 2 \end{aligned}$   11. $\begin{aligned} 3x_1 - 2x_2 \quad + x_4 &= 3 \\ x_1 - 3x_2 + 4x_3 - x_4 &= 1 \\ 8x_1 + x_2 + x_3 + x_4 &= 0 \end{aligned}$

13. $x_1 = -3, x_2 = 1$   15. $x_1 = 7, x_2 = -7, x_3 = 2$   17. $x_1 = 12, x_2 = -1, x_3 = 6, x_4 = -4$

19. $\begin{bmatrix} 1 & -2 & 3 & 2 \\ 0 & 13 & -9 & -5 \\ 0 & 12 & -20 & -9 \end{bmatrix}$   21. $\begin{bmatrix} 1 & 0 & 3 & 2 \\ 0 & 0 & 3 & -1 \\ 0 & 0 & -11 & -5 \\ 0 & -1 & 21 & 16 \end{bmatrix}$   23. $\begin{bmatrix} 19 & 0 & 2 & 3 & 3 \\ 25 & 0 & 7 & 2 & 1 \\ 8 & 1 & 1 & 1 & 0 \end{bmatrix}$

**25. No,**
$$\begin{bmatrix} 1 & 2 & -4 & 2 \\ 0 & 1 & -2 & 0 \\ 0 & 0 & 1 & -2 \end{bmatrix}$$
**27. No,**
$$\begin{bmatrix} 1 & 0 & -3 & -1 \\ 0 & 1 & 9 & -2 \\ 0 & 0 & 1 & 2 \end{bmatrix}$$
**29. Yes**

**31. (a)**
$$\begin{bmatrix} 1 & 5/2 & -3 & 0 \\ 0 & 1 & 6/11 & -6/11 \\ 0 & 0 & 1 & -1 \end{bmatrix}$$

**33. (a)**
$$\left[\begin{array}{ccc|ccc|c} 1 & 3/5 & -8/5 & 2/5 & 1 & 3/5 & -8/5 \\ 0 & 1 & -9/4 & 1/4 & 0 & 1 & -9/4 \\ 0 & 0 & 1 & -1 & 0 & 0 & 1 \end{array}\begin{array}{c} 2/5 \\ 1/4 \\ -1 \end{array}\right]$$

**(b)** $x_1 = -3$, $x_2 = 0$, $x_3 = -1$

**(b)** $x_1 = 0$, $x_2 = -2$, $x_3 = -1$

**35. (a)**
$$\left[\begin{array}{cccc|c} 1 & 8/3 & -4/3 & 4/3 & 5/3 \\ 0 & 1 & 7/4 & -7/4 & -11/4 \\ 0 & 0 & 1 & -7 & -17 \\ 0 & 0 & 0 & 1 & 2 \end{array}\right]$$

**(b)** $x_1 = -21$, $x_2 = 6$, $x_3 = -3$, $x_4 = 2$

## Section 2.2

**1.**
$$\begin{bmatrix} 1 & 0 & 0 & -5 \\ 0 & 0 & 1 & 3 \\ 0 & 0 & 0 & 0 \end{bmatrix}$$
**3.** Reduced echelon form  **5.** Reduced echelon form

**7.** $x = 1$, $y = -2$, $z = 3$  **9.** $x_1 = -4$, $x_2 = 2$, $x_3 = 7$

**11.** $x = 1$, $y = 2$, $z = 3$; $x = -6$, $y = 32/5$, $z = 36/5$

**13.** $x_1 = -2$, $x_2 = 3$, $x_3 = 1$; $x_1 = -5$, $x_2 = -17$, $x_3 = -8$

**15. (a)** 15 lbs A, 24 lbs B, 16 lbs C  **(b)** 12 lbs A, 20 lbs B, 9 lbs C  **(c)** Not possible

**17. (a)** $1500 stocks, $1500 bonds, $3000 cash  **(b)** Not possible  **(c)** Not possible

## Section 2.3

**1.** Inconsistent  **3.** $x_1 = -4$, $x_2 = 2$, $x_3 = 7$  **5.** $x_1 = -9$, $x_2 = 6$, $x_3 = 2$, $x_4 = 1$

**7.** Inconsistent  **9.** rank coefficient matrix = 2, rank augmented matrix = 3

**11.** rank coefficient matrix = 3, rank augmented matrix = 3

**13.** rank coefficient matrix = 4, rank augmented matrix = 4

**15.** rank coefficient matrix = 2, rank augmented matrix = 3

**17.** (a) All real $k$  (b) None  (c) None  **19.** (a) $k \neq \dfrac{15}{2}$  (b) $k = \dfrac{15}{2}$  (c) None

**21.** (a) $k \neq \dfrac{5}{2}$  (b) $k = \dfrac{5}{2}$  (c) None  **23.** (a) None  (b) $k \neq -7$  (c) $k = -7$

**25.** All $a, b, c$  **27.** $2a + 7b + 5c = 0$

**29.** $x_1 = \dfrac{1}{9} - \dfrac{5}{9}t,\ x_2 = \dfrac{7}{6} + \dfrac{2}{3}t,\ x_3 = t$   **31.** $x_1 = \dfrac{8}{7} + \dfrac{5}{7}t,\ x_2 = \dfrac{17}{14} + \dfrac{4}{7}t,\ x_3 = t$

**33.** $x_1 = \dfrac{7}{11} + \dfrac{27}{22}t,\ x_2 = -\dfrac{2}{11} + \dfrac{19}{22}t,\ x_3 = t,\ x_4 = -1$

**35.** $x_1 = \dfrac{20}{3} - \dfrac{19}{3}s + 4t,\ x_2 = 5 - 11s + 4t,\ x_3 = \dfrac{37}{3} - \dfrac{50}{3}s + 10t,\ x_4 = s,\ x_5 = t$

**37.** $-\dfrac{200}{3} + \dfrac{1}{3}t$ vats Fizz, $\dfrac{8800}{3} - \dfrac{5}{3}t$ vats Jiff, $t$ vats Squirt, $200 \leq t \leq 1760$

**39.**

|         | #1 | #2 |
|---------|----|----|
| Pennies | 0  | 5  |
| Nickels | 10 | 1  |
| Dimes   | 10 | 14 |

**41.**

|            | #1 | #2 | #3 | #4 |
|------------|----|----|----|----|
| Bare Bones | 0  | 6  | 12 | 18 |
| Standard   | 30 | 21 | 12 | 3  |
| Server     | 30 | 34 | 38 | 42 |

## Section 2.4

**5.** $\dfrac{x}{4} + \dfrac{y}{3} + \dfrac{z}{6} = 1$

**7.** $\dfrac{x}{10} + \dfrac{y}{6} + \dfrac{z}{3} = 1$

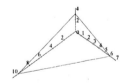

**9.** $\dfrac{x}{8} + \dfrac{z}{2} = 1$

**11.** $\dfrac{x}{4} + \dfrac{y}{3} = 1$

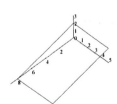

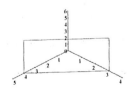

**13.** $x = -16$, $y = 3$, $z = -14$, Point   **15.** $x = 1 + \frac{3}{7}t$, $y = -1 + \frac{5}{7}t$, $z = t$, Line

**17.** No solution, Empty Set   **19.** $-2x + 15y + 5z = 33$   **21.** $12x + 14y - 15z = 5$

**23.** $-26x - 7y - 25z = 36$   **25.** No   **27.** $3x - 2y - 2z = 3$

## Section 2.5

**1.**
$$\begin{bmatrix} -2 & -5 & 1 & -3 \\ 5 & -9 & 0 & -1 \\ -14 & -28 & 0 & -19 \\ -5 & -1 & 0 & 2 \end{bmatrix}$$
**3.**
$$\begin{bmatrix} -17/2 & 11 & 1/2 & 0 \\ 7/2 & -2 & -1/2 & 1 \\ -31/2 & 22 & -11/2 & 0 \\ -12 & 3 & 1 & 0 \end{bmatrix}$$
**5.**
$$\begin{bmatrix} 0 & 23/5 & -1 & 19/5 \\ 0 & -27/5 & -1 & 24/5 \\ 0 & 58/5 & -8 & 29/5 \\ 1 & 1/5 & 0 & -2/5 \end{bmatrix}$$

**7.** $x_1 = 10$, $x_2 = -30$, $x_3 = -70$   **9.** $x_1 = 3$, $x_2 = 1$, $x_3 = 2$

**11.** $x_1 = -66$, $x_2 = 27$, $x_3 = 6$, $x_4 = 4$   **13.** $x_1 = -1 - \frac{3}{5}t$, $x_2 = 1 + \frac{1}{5}t$, $x_3 = t$

**15.** Inconsistent   **17.** $x_1 = 4 - t$, $x_2 = 2 + t$, $x_3 = t$

**19.** $x_1 = 3 + 2s - 3t$, $x_2 = 2 + s + 2t$, $x_3 = s$, $x_4 = t$

## Section 2.6

**1.**
$$\left[\begin{array}{ccc|ccc} 1 & -5 & -3 & 0 & 0 & 0 \\ 0 & 6 & -3 & 1 & 0 & 4 \\ 0 & 3 & 1 & 0 & 1 & 9 \end{array}\right]$$
**3.**
$$\left[\begin{array}{cccc|ccc} 1 & -4 & -2 & 5 & 0 & 0 & 0 \\ 0 & 8 & 3 & 1 & 1 & 0 & 1 \\ 0 & 5 & -12 & 4 & 0 & 1 & 6 \end{array}\right]$$

**5.**
$$\left[\begin{array}{ccccc|ccccc} 1 & 4 & -2 & -3 & -1 & 0 & 0 & 0 & 0 & 0 \\ 0 & 5 & -1 & 3 & -2 & 1 & 0 & 0 & 0 & 6 \\ 0 & 4 & 3 & -1 & 12 & 0 & 1 & 0 & 0 & 2 \\ 0 & 16 & 0 & 2 & 0 & 0 & 0 & 1 & 0 & 10 \\ 0 & -4 & 10 & -1 & 4 & 0 & 0 & 0 & 1 & 8 \end{array}\right]$$

**7. (a)** R3, C4   **(b)** R3, C4   **(c)**
$$\left[\begin{array}{cccc|c} 1 & 23/5 & 0 & 0 & 4/5 & 74/5 \\ 0 & -14/5 & 1 & 0 & -2/5 & 8/5 \\ 0 & 2/5 & 0 & 1 & 1/5 & 6/5 \end{array}\right]$$

**9. (a)** R2, C3; R3, C5   **(b)** R3, C5   **(c)**
$$\left[\begin{array}{ccccc|c} 1 & 0 & 16/5 & 6/5 & 0 & -8/5 & 21 \\ 0 & 1 & 16/5 & 1/5 & 0 & 12/5 & 1 \\ 0 & 0 & 6/5 & 1/5 & 1 & -3/5 & 1 \end{array}\right]$$

**11.** **(a)** R2, C2; R3, C5; R3, C7; R4, C7   **(b)** R3, C5

**(c)**
$$\left[\begin{array}{ccccccc|c} 1 & -12/5 & 6/5 & 0 & 0 & 0 & 8 & 26 \\ 0 & 17/5 & 4/5 & 0 & 0 & 1 & 3 & 4 \\ 0 & 1/10 & 1/5 & 0 & 1 & 0 & 2 & 1 \\ 0 & 14/15 & -2/15 & 1 & 0 & 0 & 8/3 & 4/3 \end{array}\right]$$

**13.** **(a)** R4, C2; R3, C5; R2, C7; R3, C7   **(b)** R3, C5   **(c)**
$$\left[\begin{array}{cccccc|c} 1 & -2 & 0 & 3 & 0 & 0 & 10 & 39 \\ 0 & 31/8 & 1 & -1/8 & 0 & 0 & 1/2 & 1 \\ 0 & 1/2 & 0 & 1/2 & 1 & 0 & 2 & 4 \\ 0 & 11 & 0 & 2 & 0 & 1 & 5 & 16 \end{array}\right]$$

**15.** **(a)** $x_1 = 0$, $x_2 = 6$, $x_3 = 0$, $x_4 = 4$   **(b)** $z = 10$   **(c)** $x_2$, $x_4$ basic; $x_1$, $x_3$ nonbasic   **(d)** No

**17.** **(a)** $x_1 = 0$, $x_2 = 0$, $x_3 = 0$, $x_4 = 2$, $x_5 = 14$   **(b)** $z = 0$   **(c)** $x_4$, $x_5$ basic; $x_1$, $x_2$, $x_3$ nonbasic   **(d)** Yes

**19.** **(a)** $x_1 = 8$, $x_2 = 0$, $x_3 = 10$, $x_4 = 0$, $x_5 = 3$, $x_6 = 0$   **(b)** $z = 16$   **(c)** $x_1$, $x_3$, $x_5$ basic; $x_2$, $x_4$, $x_6$ nonbasic   **(d)** No

**21.** $z = 4$, BFS: $(2,0,0,3)$, CP: $(2,0)$   **23.** $z = 22$, BFS: $(1,6,0,8,0,0)$, CP: $(1,6,0)$

**25.** $z = 944$, BFS: $(118,0,0,0,102)$, CP: $(118,0,0)$

**27.** $z = 28$, BFS: $(2,0,8,24,0,0)$, CP: $(2,0,8)$

**29.** $z = 138$, BFS: $(18,0,0,12,0,239,0,108)$, CP: $(18,0,0,12)$

**31.** **(a)** 60 of A, 120 of B   **(b)** \$138,000

**33.** **(a)** 2 Linear Algebra, 1 Calculus, 9 Statistics   **(b)** 372 seats   **(c)** No   **(d)** No

**35.** **(a)** \$0 in A, \$75,000 in B, \$25,000 in C   **(b)** \$8750

**37.** **(a)** 25 ranch, 65 townhouses, 50 bi-level   **(b)** \$1,805,000   **(c)** No

**39.** **(a)** 1 ounce of A, 1.5 ounces of B, 6 ounces of C, 0 ounces of D   **(b)** 31 grams

## Section 2.7

**1. (a)** Pivoting at R2, C3 produces all negatives in column 2

**(b)**

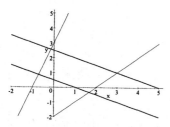

**3. (a)** Pivoting at R3, C3 produces all negatives in column 2

**(b)**

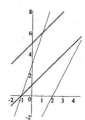

**5. (a)** Pivoting at R2, C2 produces all negatives in column 3

**7. (a)** Pivoting at R2, C4, then at R3, C3 produces all negatives in column 5

**9.** $z = 28$, BFS: $(0, 2, 13, 0, 0)$, CP: $(0, 2, 13)$

**11.** $z = 630$, BFS: $(0, 35, 105, 0, 525, 0)$, CP: $(0, 35, 105)$

**13.** No maximum value

**15. (a)**

| $(x_1, x_2)$ | $z = x_1 + x_2$ |
|---|---|
| $(0, 0)$ | 0 |
| $(0, 2)$ | 2 |
| $(5/2, 3/2)$ | 4 |
| $(25/7, 6/7)$ | 31/7 |
| $(4, 0)$ | 4 |

**(b)** $(0, 0) \to (0, 2) \to (5/2, 3/2) \to (25/7, 6/7)$,
$(0, 0) \to (4, 0) \to (25/7, 6/7)$

**(c)** $(0, 0) \to (4, 0) \to (25/7, 6/7)$ if pivot is $R2, C2$
$(0, 0) \to (0, 2) \to (5/2, 3/2) \to (25/7, 6/7)$ if pivot is $R4, C3$

**17. (a)**

| $(x_1, x_2)$ | $z = x_1 + 2x_2$ |
|---|---|
| $(0, 0)$ | 0 |
| $(0, 2)$ | 4 |
| $(3, 4)$ | 11 |
| $(5, 4)$ | 13 |
| $(22/3, 5/3)$ | 32/3 |
| $(4, 0)$ | 4 |

**(b)** $(0, 0) \to (0, 2) \to (3, 4) \to (5, 4)$
$(0, 0) \to (4, 0) \to (22/3, 5/3) \to (5, 4)$

**(c)** $(0, 0) \to (0, 2) \to (3, 4) \to (5, 4)$

**19. (a)** No maximum on expected return  **(b)** There is no upper bound put on the amount invested in blue chip stocks and short term bonds.

# Chapter 3

**Section 3.1**

**1.** 6    **3.** $\begin{bmatrix} 3 & 2 \\ -1 & 4 \\ 6 & 1 \end{bmatrix}$    **5.** $\begin{bmatrix} 9 & 0 & 3 \\ 0 & 9 & 3 \end{bmatrix}$    **7.** $\begin{bmatrix} 12 & 2 & -6 \\ -4 & 10 & 4 \end{bmatrix}$    **9.** Undefined

**11.** $\begin{bmatrix} -28 & 22 & 19 \\ 10 & -9 & -7 \end{bmatrix}$    **13.** $\begin{bmatrix} -7 & 11 \\ 7 & -13 \\ -17 & 28 \end{bmatrix}$    **15.** $\begin{bmatrix} -26 & 44 \\ -18 & 30 \\ 4 & -10 \end{bmatrix}$    **17.** $\begin{bmatrix} -292 & 523 \\ -201 & 360 \\ 53 & -95 \end{bmatrix}$

**19.** Undefined    **21.** $\begin{bmatrix} 39 & 6 \\ 30 & 15 \end{bmatrix}$

**23. (a)** $\begin{bmatrix} 67 & 118 & 84 \\ 63 & 130 & 87 \\ 58 & 122 & 80 \\ 55 & 109 & 83 \\ 59 & 108 & 84 \end{bmatrix}$ $\begin{bmatrix} 80 & 70 \\ 50 & 55 \\ 40 & 30 \end{bmatrix}$    **(b)**

|        | Fred | Barney |           |
|--------|-------|--------|-----------|
|        | 14620 | 13700  | Monday    |
|        | 15020 | 14170  | Tuesday   |
|        | 13940 | 13170  | Wednesday |
|        | 13170 | 12335  | Thursday  |
|        | 13480 | 12590  | Friday    |

**(c)** Tuesday  **(d)** Thursday

**25. (a)** $\begin{bmatrix} 1/4 & 1/4 & 1/4 & 1/4 \end{bmatrix}$ $\begin{bmatrix} 68 & 98 & 85 \\ 79 & 95 & 77 \\ 72 & 89 & 80 \\ 57 & 96 & 92 \end{bmatrix}$    **(b)**

|  | Kelly | Cheryl | Maria |
|--|-------|--------|-------|
|  | 69    | 94.5   | 83.5  |

**(c)** $\begin{bmatrix} 68 & 98 & 85 \\ 79 & 95 & 77 \\ 72 & 89 & 80 \\ 57 & 96 & 92 \end{bmatrix}$ $\begin{bmatrix} 1/3 \\ 1/3 \\ 1/3 \end{bmatrix}$    **(d)**

| | |
|--|--|
| 83 2/3 | Test 1 |
| 83 2/3 | Test 2 |
| 80 1/3 | Test 3 |
| 81 2/3 | Test 4 |

**27. (a)**
$$\begin{bmatrix} 2 & 1.5 & 0.5 \\ 3.5 & 1.75 & 0.75 \\ 2.75 & 1.5 & 0.4 \end{bmatrix} \begin{bmatrix} 18 & 14 \\ 21.5 & 16 \\ 13 & 9.5 \end{bmatrix}$$

**(b)**
$$\begin{array}{cc} \text{Calif} & \text{Wisc} \\ \begin{bmatrix} 74.75 & 56.75 \\ 110.38 & 84.13 \\ 86.95 & 66.30 \end{bmatrix} & \begin{array}{l} \text{Stove} \\ \text{Refrigerator} \\ \text{Dishwasher} \end{array} \end{array}$$

**29. (a)**
$$\begin{bmatrix} 0.35 & 0.3 & 0.2 & 0.15 \\ 0.3 & 0.3 & 0.2 & 0.2 \end{bmatrix} \begin{bmatrix} 0.89 & 1.29 \\ 0.79 & 1.29 \\ 0.99 & 1.09 \\ 1.29 & 0.99 \end{bmatrix}$$

**(b)**
$$\begin{array}{cc} \text{Sept} & \text{March} \\ \begin{bmatrix} 0.94 & 1.21 \\ 0.96 & 1.19 \end{bmatrix} & \begin{array}{l} \text{Fantasia} \\ \text{Fullsum} \end{array} \end{array}$$

**(c)**
$$\begin{bmatrix} 2.69 & 2.69 \\ 2.79 & 2.79 \end{bmatrix} - 2 \begin{bmatrix} 0.35 & 0.3 & 0.2 & 0.15 \\ 0.3 & 0.3 & 0.2 & 0.15 \end{bmatrix} \begin{bmatrix} 0.89 & 1.29 \\ 0.79 & 1.09 \\ 0.99 & 0.99 \\ 1.29 & 0.99 \end{bmatrix}$$

**(d)**
$$\begin{array}{cc} \text{Sept} & \text{March} \\ \begin{bmatrix} 0.81 & 0.28 \\ 0.87 & 0.41 \end{bmatrix} & \begin{array}{l} \text{Fantasia} \\ \text{Fullsum} \end{array} \end{array}$$

## Section 3.2

**1.** Yes  **3.** Yes  **5.** $\begin{bmatrix} 5 & 7 \\ 2 & 3 \end{bmatrix}$  **7.** No inverse  **9.** $\begin{bmatrix} 0 & 1 & 2 \\ -1 & 3 & 0 \\ 1 & -2 & 1 \end{bmatrix}$

**11.** $\begin{bmatrix} 10 & -2 & -1 & -1 \\ -6 & 1 & -1 & 2 \\ -2 & 0 & 1 & 0 \\ 1 & 0 & 1 & -1 \end{bmatrix}$  **13.** $A = \begin{bmatrix} 3 & 5 \\ -4 & 3 \end{bmatrix}$, $X = \begin{bmatrix} x_1 \\ x_2 \end{bmatrix}$, $B = \begin{bmatrix} 8 \\ -2 \end{bmatrix}$

**15.** $A = \begin{bmatrix} 4 & 0 & -1 \\ 3 & -1 & 5 \\ -1 & 12 & 0 \end{bmatrix}$, $X = \begin{bmatrix} x_1 \\ x_2 \\ x_3 \end{bmatrix}$, $B = \begin{bmatrix} 5 \\ 18 \\ -8 \end{bmatrix}$  **17.** $\begin{aligned} 3x_1 + 8x_2 &= 12 \\ -4x_2 &= 3 \end{aligned}$

**19.** $\begin{aligned} 3x_1 + 2x_2 - 2x_3 &= 4 \\ -9x_1 + 3x_3 &= 2 \\ 6x_1 - 2x_2 + 8x_3 &= 3 \end{aligned}$  **21.** $X_1 = \begin{bmatrix} -5 \\ 3 \end{bmatrix}$, $X_2 = \begin{bmatrix} 16 \\ -7 \end{bmatrix}$, $X_3 = \begin{bmatrix} 3a - 2b \\ -a + b \end{bmatrix}$

**23.** $X_1 = \begin{bmatrix} 1 \\ -7 \\ 17 \end{bmatrix}, X_2 = \begin{bmatrix} 28 \\ 33 \\ 66 \end{bmatrix}, X_3 = \begin{bmatrix} a + 2b + 3c \\ 2a + 5b + 3c \\ a \quad + 8c \end{bmatrix}$

**25.** $X_1 = \begin{bmatrix} -1/4 \\ -19/8 \\ 3 \end{bmatrix}, X_2 = \begin{bmatrix} 5/4 \\ -77/8 \\ 10 \end{bmatrix}, X_3 = \begin{bmatrix} a/2 + b/4 \\ -3a/4 - b/8 - c \\ a \quad + c \end{bmatrix}$

**27.** $k = 2, -2$  **29.** $k = -\dfrac{7}{2}$  **31.** $k = 3, 18$  **33.** (a) $A^2$ (b) $(A^2)^{-1}D$

**35.** (a) $A - wI$ (b) $(A - wI)^{-1}D$  **37.** (a) $I - C$ (b) $(I - C)^{-1}D$  **39.** (a) $A - (w - 3)I$ (b) $O$

**41.** (a) $\begin{bmatrix} 1 & 1 \\ 0.1 & 0.06 \end{bmatrix} \begin{bmatrix} x_1 \\ x_2 \end{bmatrix} = \begin{bmatrix} a \\ r \end{bmatrix}$  Put $x_1 = -1.5a + 25r$ into blue chips,

$x_2 = 2.5a - 25r$ into bonds  (b) $7500 in blue chips, $2500 in bonds  (c) Not possible

## Section 3.3

**1.** (a)
$$\begin{matrix} G & P \\ \begin{bmatrix} 0.15 & 0.10 \\ 0.20 & 0.20 \end{bmatrix} & \begin{matrix} G \\ P \end{matrix} \end{matrix}$$
(b) $2 billion government, $116 billion private sector

(c) $30.30 billion government, $157.6 billion private sector

**3.** (a)
$$\begin{matrix} H & T & U \\ \begin{bmatrix} 0.05 & 0 & 0.05 \\ 0.20 & 0.30 & 0.25 \\ 0.15 & 0.15 & 0.20 \end{bmatrix} & & \begin{matrix} H \\ T \\ U \end{matrix} \end{matrix}$$

(b) $11.1 billion housing, $7.3 billion transportation, $0.6 billion utility
(c) $8.98 billion housing, $20.62 billion transportation, $10.55 billion utility

**5.** (a)
$$\begin{matrix} C & M & U \\ \begin{bmatrix} 0.091 & 0.111 & 0.126 \\ 0.068 & 0.139 & 0.095 \\ 0.182 & 0.194 & 0.274 \end{bmatrix} & & \begin{matrix} C \\ M \\ U \end{matrix} \end{matrix}$$

(b) $320.8 million in Canada, $232.8 million in Mexico, $1038 million in U.S.

**7. (a)**

|  | Di | Du | Th |  |
|---|---|---|---|---|
|  | 0.35 | 0.20 | 0.40 | Di |
|  | 0.35 | 0.45 | 0 | Du |
|  | 0.30 | 0.35 | 0.60 | Th |

**(b)** $1273 in pineapple, $2614 in mangos

**9. (a)**

|  | S | M | R | A |  |
|---|---|---|---|---|---|
|  | 0.10 | 0.10 | 0.15 | 0.20 | S |
|  | 0.20 | 0.25 | 0.15 | 0.20 | M |
|  | 0.05 | 0.15 | 0.30 | 0.10 | R |
|  | 0.10 | 0.10 | 0.15 | 0.25 | A |

**(b)** Self-sustaining

**(c)** Must purchase $2.75 million in outside administrative services
**(d)** $72.16 million sales, $105.15 million manufacturing, $63.35 million research, $49.65 million administration

**11. (a)** #1, #2, #3  **(b)** Column sums are less than 1     **13. (a)** #1, #3  **(b)** Row sums are less than 1

**15.** No    **17.** Yes

## Section 3.4

**1.** 11   **3.** 60   **5.** 26   **7.** 101   **9.** –318   **11.** –2   **13.** 24   **15.** 2/27   **17.** 0

**19.** 6   **21.** 12   **23.** $\sqrt{10}, -\sqrt{10}$   **25.** 2, 3   **27.** 4, –2, –6   **29.** 2, 5

## Section 3.5

**1.** $x_1 = 1, x_2 = 2$    **3.** $x_1 = -1/8, x_2 = 5/4$    **5.** $x_1 = 1, x_2 = 3, x_3 = 1$

**7.** Not applicable    **9. (a)** 4, –4  **(b)** $x_1 = \dfrac{5s - 32}{(s - 4)(s + 4)}, x_2 = \dfrac{4s - 10}{(s - 4)(s + 4)}$

**11. (a)** 0, –3/4   **(b)** $x_1 = \dfrac{11}{4s + 3}, x_2 = \dfrac{2s - 15}{s(4s + 3)}$

**13. (a)** 4, –4, 0   **(b)** $x_1 = \dfrac{6s + 4}{(s - 4)(s + 4)}, x_2 = \dfrac{-s - 24}{(s - 4)(s + 4)}, x_3 = \dfrac{-3s^2 - s + 24}{s(s - 4)(s + 4)}$

**15. (a)** $\begin{bmatrix} 4 & 2 \\ -3 & 2 \end{bmatrix}$  **(b)** $\begin{bmatrix} 2/7 & 1/7 \\ -3/14 & 1/7 \end{bmatrix}$  **17. (a)** $\begin{bmatrix} 8 & 12 & -4 \\ 8 & 12 & -4 \\ 8 & 12 & -4 \end{bmatrix}$  **(b)** Not invertible

**19.** **(a)** $\begin{bmatrix} 0 & -12 & 3 \\ -2 & 5 & -1 \\ 1 & 2 & -1 \end{bmatrix}$ **(b)** $\begin{bmatrix} 0 & 4 & -1 \\ 2/3 & -5/3 & 1/3 \\ -1/3 & -2/3 & 1/3 \end{bmatrix}$   **21.** Unique solution

**23.** Infinitely many **25.** Unique solution   **27.** $-50$   **29.** $-2/5$   **31.** $-40$   **33.** Yes   **35.** No

**Section 3.6**

**1.** **(a)** $\begin{array}{cc} \phantom{0}P & \phantom{0}R \\ \begin{bmatrix} 0.80 & 0.25 \\ 0.20 & 0.75 \end{bmatrix} & \begin{array}{c} P \\ R \end{array} \end{array}$ **(b)** $\begin{bmatrix} 0.6 \\ 0.4 \end{bmatrix} \begin{array}{c} P \\ R \end{array}$ **(c)** $\begin{bmatrix} 0.5596 \\ 0.4404 \end{bmatrix}$ **(d)** $\begin{bmatrix} 0.5556 \\ 0.4444 \end{bmatrix}$

**3.** **(a)** $\begin{array}{ccc} K & N & D \\ \begin{bmatrix} 0.90 & 0.25 & 0.30 \\ 0.06 & 0.70 & 0.20 \\ 0.04 & 0.05 & 0.50 \end{bmatrix} & & \begin{array}{c} K \\ N \\ D \end{array} \end{array}$ **(b)** $\begin{bmatrix} 0.50 \\ 0.25 \\ 0.25 \end{bmatrix} \begin{array}{c} K \\ N \\ D \end{array}$ **(c)** 277 cars **(d)** 290 cars **(e)** 20

**5.** **(a)** $\begin{array}{ccc} U & R & L \\ \begin{bmatrix} 0.60 & 0.80 & 0.85 \\ 0.20 & 0.20 & 0 \\ 0.20 & 0 & 0.15 \end{bmatrix} & & \begin{array}{c} U \\ R \\ L \end{array} \end{array}$ **(b)** $\begin{bmatrix} 1 \\ 0 \\ 0 \end{bmatrix} \begin{array}{c} U \\ R \\ L \end{array}$ **(c)** 0.1585 **(d)** 0.6733 **(e)** 6

**7.** **(a)** $\begin{array}{cccc} N & S & E & W \\ \begin{bmatrix} 0.10 & 0.10 & 0.30 & 0.40 \\ 0.10 & 0.10 & 0.30 & 0.40 \\ 0.60 & 0.60 & 0.30 & 0.15 \\ 0.20 & 0.20 & 0.10 & 0.05 \end{bmatrix} & & & \begin{array}{c} N \\ S \\ E \\ W \end{array} \end{array}$ **(b)** $\begin{bmatrix} 1 \\ 0 \\ 0 \\ 0 \end{bmatrix} \begin{array}{c} N \\ S \\ E \\ W \end{array}$ **(c)** 0.2264 **(d)** $\begin{bmatrix} 0.2241 \\ 0.2241 \\ 0.4138 \\ 0.1379 \end{bmatrix}$

**9.** **(a)** $\begin{array}{cc} G & RP \\ \begin{bmatrix} 2/3 & 1/2 \\ 1/3 & 1/2 \end{bmatrix} & \begin{array}{c} G \\ RP \end{array} \end{array}$ **(b)** $\begin{bmatrix} 1 \\ 0 \end{bmatrix} \begin{array}{c} G \\ RP \end{array}$ **(c)** $\begin{bmatrix} 3/5 \\ 2/5 \end{bmatrix} \begin{array}{c} G \\ RP \end{array}$

|  | C | P | U |  |
|---|---|---|---|---|
| **11. (a)** | 0.75 | 0.1 | 0.2 | C |
|  | 0.15 | 0.85 | 0.2 | P |
|  | 0.1 | 0.05 | 0.6 | U |

**(b)**

$$\begin{bmatrix} 0.7 \\ 0.3 \\ 0 \end{bmatrix} \begin{matrix} C \\ P \\ U \end{matrix}$$

**(c)**

$$\begin{bmatrix} 20/61 \\ 32/61 \\ 9/61 \end{bmatrix}$$

**13.** No  **15.** Yes  **17.** Yes  **19.** No

# Chapter 4

### Section 4.1

**1.** $(x,y) = (-9,6) + t(2,-7)$; $x = -9 + 2t$, $y = 6 - 7t$

**3.** $(x,y,z) = (2,-5,8) + t(-3,5,-7)$; $x = 2 - 3t$, $y = -5 + 5t$, $z = 8 - 7t$

**5.** $(x,y,z,w) = (-3,4,-8,-2) + t(5,-4,3,-2)$; $x = -3 + 5t$, $y = 4 - 4t$, $z = -8 + 3t$, $w = -2 - 2t$

**7.** $(x,y) = (-3,2) + t(8,-10)$; $x = -3 + 8t$, $y = 2 - 10t$

**9.** $(x,y,z) = (-5,3,-2) + t(-2,-5,6)$; $x = -5 - 2t$, $y = 3 - 5t$, $z = -2 + 6t$

**11.** $(x,y,z,w) = (6,-2,4,5) + t(-9,-3,-2,-2)$; $x = 6 - 9t$, $y = -2 - 3t$, $z = 4 - 2t$, $w = 5 - 2t$

**13.** (a) and (b) lie on the line    **15.** Two coincident planes; $3x + 4y + 7z = 15$

**17.** Two planes intersecting in a line; $x = 4/3 - t/3$, $y = 1/3 + 2t/3$, $z = t$

**19.** Three coincident planes; $2x + y + 3z = 2$

**21.** Three planes intersecting in a line; $x = -2 - 5t$, $y = 7 + 3t$, $z = t$

### Section 4.2

**1.** Yes, $\vec{v} = 4\vec{u}_1 + 2\vec{u}_2$    **3.** Not possible

**5.** Not feasible    **7.** $x_1 = 5$, $x_2 = -3$    **9.** $x_1 = -2$, $x_2 = 4$, $x_3 = -2$

**11.** $(2,4,-5)$; $\vec{b} = 2\vec{a}_1 + 4\vec{a}_2 - 5\vec{a}_3$

**13.** $(5 - 2t, -6 + 4t, t)$; $t = 0$, $\vec{b} = 5\vec{a}_1 - 6\vec{a}_2 + 0\vec{a}_3$

## Section 4.3

1. (d) In (a), (b), and (c), the span is the line through the origin in $R^3$; $x = t$, $y = t$, $z = t$

3. No - line not through origin    5. Yes - line through origin    7. Yes - plane through origin

9. No - plane not through origin    11. All multiples of $(2, 3, 1)$    13. $\vec{0}$ alone

15. All multiples of $(2, -3, 5, 1)$

17. (a) $\vec{u} = 2\vec{a}_1 - 3\vec{a}_2 + 4\vec{a}_3$  (b) $\vec{v} = -3\vec{a}_1 - 2\vec{a}_2 + 3\vec{a}_3$

19. (a) $\vec{u} = (4 + 5t)\vec{a}_1 + (2 + 3t)\vec{a}_2 + t\vec{a}_3$, any $t$    (b) Not possible for $\vec{v}$

21. A plane through the origin in $R^3$; $13x - 7y - 4z = 0$

23. A line through the origin in $R^3$; $x = t$, $y = 2t$, $z = 3t$

25. Plane through origin, $5x - 2y + z = 0$, $\vec{b} = \frac{1}{7}(4x - y)\vec{a}_1 - \frac{1}{7}(5x - 3y)\vec{a}_2$

27. Plane through origin, $3x + 2y - 6z = 0$, $\vec{b} = \frac{1}{9}(3x + y)\vec{a}_1 - \frac{1}{18}(3x - 2y)\vec{a}_2$

29. All $x, y, z$; $\vec{b} = \frac{1}{13}(4x + y + z)\vec{a}_1 + \frac{1}{13}(14x + 10y - 3z)\vec{a}_2 + (3x + 2y - z)\vec{a}_3$

31. Plane through origin, $3x - y + 2z = 0$, $\vec{b} = (\frac{3}{2}x - y - 4t)\vec{a}_1 + (\frac{-x}{2} + \frac{y}{2} + t)\vec{a}_2 + t\vec{a}_3$, any $t$

## Section 4.4

1. $-2(8, -4, 2) + 4(6, 0, 3) + (-8, -8, -8) = (0, 0, 0)$    3. Linearly independent

5. $3(1, 2, -2) - 2(7, 2, -3) - (-11, 2, 0) = (0, 0, 0)$    7. Linearly independent    9. $k \neq 6$

11. $k \neq -3$, $k \neq \frac{9}{4}$

13. Close plant 3 and operate plant 1 for 1 day, plant 2 for 7 days, and plant 4 for 5 days; or close plant 2 and operate plant 1 for 4.5 days, plant 3 for 7 days, and plant 4 for 1.5 days.

## Section 4.5

1. $\{(4, 5)\}$    3. $\{(3, 5, 0), (-2, 0, 5)\}$    5. $\{(-2, 7, 0), (-5, 0, 7)\}$    7. $\vec{b} = 3\vec{u}_1 + 2\vec{u}_2$

9. $\vec{u}_1 = -\frac{2}{3}\vec{u}_2$    11. $\vec{b} = 2\vec{u}_1 - \vec{u}_2 + 2\vec{u}_3$    13. $\vec{u}_3 = 3\vec{u}_1 - 4\vec{u}_2$

$\vec{a}_1 \ \vec{a}_2 \ \vec{a}_3$

**15.** $\begin{array}{c} \vec{a}_1 \\ \vec{a}_2 \end{array} \begin{bmatrix} 1 & 0 & 4 \\ 0 & 1 & -3 \end{bmatrix}$     Basis: $\{\vec{a}_1, \vec{a}_2\}$; $\vec{a}_3 = 4\vec{a}_1 - 3\vec{a}_2$

$\vec{a}_1 \ \vec{a}_2 \ \vec{a}_3 \ \vec{a}_4$

**17.** $\begin{array}{c} \vec{a}_1 \\ \vec{a}_2 \end{array} \begin{bmatrix} 1 & 0 & 2 & 6 \\ 0 & 1 & -3 & -4 \end{bmatrix}$     Basis: $\{\vec{a}_1, \vec{a}_2\}$; $\begin{array}{l} \vec{a}_3 = 2\vec{a}_1 - 3\vec{a}_2 \\ \vec{a}_4 = 6\vec{a}_1 - 4\vec{a}_2 \end{array}$

$\vec{a}_1 \ \vec{a}_2 \ \vec{a}_3 \ \vec{a}_4 \ \vec{a}_5$

**19.** $\begin{array}{c} \vec{a}_1 \\ \vec{a}_2 \\ \vec{a}_4 \end{array} \begin{bmatrix} 1 & 0 & -2 & 0 & 2 \\ 0 & 1 & 2 & 0 & 1 \\ 0 & 0 & 0 & 1 & -2 \end{bmatrix}$     Basis: $\{\vec{a}_1, \vec{a}_2, \vec{a}_4\}$; $\begin{array}{l} \vec{a}_3 = -2\vec{a}_1 + 2\vec{a}_2, \\ \vec{a}_5 = 2\vec{a}_1 + \vec{a}_2 - 2\vec{a}_4 \end{array}$

## Section 4.7

**1.** $z = -121$, BFS: $(0,0,7,27,0,0)$, CP: $(0,0,7,27)$

**3.** $z = -240$, BFS: $(0,20,20,50,0,0)$, CP: $(0,20,20)$

**5.** $z = -7$, BFS: $(0,1,8/3,0)$, CP: $(0,1,8/3,0)$

**7.** $z = 180$, BFS: $(0,30,10,0,0)$, CP: $(0,30,10)$

**9.** $z = 40$, BFS: $(0,10,35,35)$, CP: $(0,10)$

**11.** $z = 175$, BFS: $(25,0,0,9,106)$, CP: $(25,0,0)$

**13.** $z = 3770/7$, BFS: $(565/7, 190/7, 0, 0, 1740/7)$, CP: $(565/7, 190/7, 0)$

**15.** $z = 92/3$, BFS: $(0,4/3,6,20/3,0)$, CP: $(0,4/3,6)$

**17.** $z = 784/5$, BFS: $(8,32/5,0,0,28/5)$, CP: $(8,32/5,0)$

**19.** 2/5 oz of Food A, 2/5 oz of Food B, 17/5 oz of Food C

**21.** 0 packages from Xenon, 10 packages from Radon, 0 packages from Neptune. Minimum cost of $40,000.

# Chapter 5

## Section 5.4

**1.** $y = -\dfrac{8}{13}x + \dfrac{99}{26}$     **3.** $y = \dfrac{241}{131}x + \dfrac{672}{131}$     **5.** $y = \dfrac{13}{16}x^2 + \dfrac{61}{20}x + \dfrac{43}{16}$

**7.** $y = -0.412x^2 - 5.492x + 10.594$

**9. (a)** $q = -0.943p + 125.675$   **(b)** the decrease in number sold per dollar of selling price   **(c)** the demand when the price is \$0   **(d)** $\approx 53$ calculators   **(e)** No, the demand is nonnegative.

**11. (a)** Letting $x = 0$ represent 1992, $y = \frac{44}{35}x + \frac{741}{35}$   **(b)** the increase in the amount of book sales per year   **(c)** the approximate amount of book sales in 1992   **(d)** Letting $x = 1$ represent 1993,   $\approx \$22$ billion

**13. (a)** $y = 277.209x + 2003.488$   **(b)** the weekly cost per operator   **(c)** the fixed cost of operating the company   **(d)** $\approx \$3112$

**15. (a)** Letting $x = 0$ represent 1990, $y = 21.863x + 447.618$
   **(b)** Letting $x = 3$ represent 1993,   $\approx 513.2$ million metric tons

**17. (a)** Letting $x = 0$ represent 1987, $y = 1.5x + 120.5$
   **(b)** Letting $x = 5$ represent 1992,   $\approx 128$ million

# Chapter 6

**Section 6.1**

**1.** No   **3.** Yes, $\lambda = 3$   **5.** No   **7.** Yes, $\lambda = -4$

**9. (a)** $\lambda^2 - 5\lambda + 6 = 0$   **(b)** 2, 3   **(c)** $\lambda = 2$, $t(-1,1)$; $\lambda = 3$, $t(1,-2)$

**11. (a)** $\lambda^2 + 16 = 0$   **(b)** None

**13. (a)** $\lambda^2 - 6\lambda + 5 = 0$   **(b)** 5, 1   **(c)** $\lambda = 5$, $t(-2,1)$; $\lambda = 1$, $t(2,-3)$

**15. (a)** $\lambda^2 + 4\lambda - 21 = 0$   **(b)** $-7$, 3   **(c)** $\lambda = -7$, $t(1,-3)$; $\lambda = 3$, $t(3,1)$

**17. (a)** $\lambda^3 - 3\lambda^2 - 9\lambda + 27 = 0$   **(b)** 3, $-3$   **(c)** $\lambda = 3$, $s(-1,0,1) + t(1,1,0)$; $\lambda = -3$, $t(1,1,3)$

**19. (a)** $\lambda^3 - 3\lambda^2 + 2\lambda = 0$   **(b)** 1, 2, 0   **(c)** $\lambda = 1$, $t(2,1,1)$; $\lambda = 2$, $t(1,0,2)$; $\lambda = 0$, $t(1,1,0)$

**21. (a)** $\lambda^3 - 7\lambda^2 + 15\lambda - 9 = 0$   **(b)** 3, 1   **(c)** $\lambda = 3$, $s(-1,1,0) + t(-4,0,1)$; $\lambda = 1$, $t(-2,-1,1)$

**23. (a)** $\lambda^3 + 25\lambda = 0$   **(b)** 0   **(c)** $\lambda = 0$, $t(4,0,3)$

**25. (a)** $\lambda^4 + 6\lambda^3 - 12\lambda^2 - 56\lambda + 96 = 0$   **(b)** $-6$, $-4$, 2
   **(c)** $\lambda = -6$, $t(-2,0,2,-1)$; $\lambda = -4$, $t(-4,2,3,-3)$; $\lambda = 2$, $s(2,8,0,3) + t(0,2,2,3)$

**27. (a)** $\lambda^4 - 30\lambda^3 + 325\lambda^2 - 1500\lambda + 2500 = 0$   **(b)** 5, 10
   **(c)** $\lambda = 5$, $s(-3,2,0,-6) + t(-2,0,1,-2)$; $\lambda = 10$, $s(-1,0,-1,1) + t(5,1,0,0)$

**29.** Let $\vec{x}$ be an eigenvector of $A$ corresponding to eigenvalue $\lambda$. Then
   $A^3\vec{x} = A^2(A\vec{x}) = A^2(\lambda\vec{x}) = \lambda A(A\vec{x}) = \lambda A(\lambda\vec{x}) = \lambda^2(A\vec{x}) = \lambda^2(\lambda\vec{x}) = \lambda^3\vec{x}$

## Section 6.2

Answers to Exercises 1-10 are not unique.

1. $P = \begin{bmatrix} -1 & 1 \\ 1 & -2 \end{bmatrix}$, $D = \begin{bmatrix} 2 & 0 \\ 0 & 3 \end{bmatrix}$    3. Not possible

5. $P = \begin{bmatrix} -2 & 2 \\ 1 & -3 \end{bmatrix}$, $D = \begin{bmatrix} 5 & 0 \\ 0 & 1 \end{bmatrix}$    7. $P = \begin{bmatrix} 1 & 3 \\ -3 & 1 \end{bmatrix}$, $D = \begin{bmatrix} -7 & 0 \\ 0 & 3 \end{bmatrix}$

9. $P = \begin{bmatrix} 1 & -1 & 1 \\ 1 & 0 & 1 \\ 0 & 1 & 3 \end{bmatrix}$, $D = \begin{bmatrix} 3 & 0 & 0 \\ 0 & 3 & 0 \\ 0 & 0 & -3 \end{bmatrix}$    11. $\begin{bmatrix} -11/7 & -50/7 \\ -5/7 & 4/7 \end{bmatrix}$

13. $\begin{bmatrix} 22/9 & -5/3 & -25/9 \\ -5/9 & 4/3 & -25/9 \\ -5/9 & -5/3 & 2/9 \end{bmatrix}$    15. $\begin{bmatrix} 21/2 & 2 & 13/2 & 17 \\ -15/2 & -1 & -9/2 & -15 \\ -15/2 & 0 & -11/2 & -15 \\ -2 & -1 & -1 & -2 \end{bmatrix}$

## Section 6.3

1. $\begin{bmatrix} 2(2)^n - (3)^n & (2)^n - (3)^n \\ -2(2)^n + 2(3)^n & -(2)^n + 2(3)^n \end{bmatrix}$    3. $\begin{bmatrix} \frac{3}{2}(5)^n - \frac{1}{2} & (5)^n - 1 \\ -\frac{3}{4}(5)^n + \frac{3}{4} & -\frac{1}{2}(5)^n + \frac{3}{2} \end{bmatrix}$

5. $\begin{bmatrix} \frac{2}{3}(3)^n + \frac{1}{3}(-3)^n & \frac{1}{3}(3)^n - \frac{1}{3}(-3)^n & -\frac{1}{3}(3)^n + \frac{1}{3}(-3)^n \\ -\frac{1}{3}(3)^n + \frac{1}{3}(-3)^n & \frac{4}{3}(3)^n - \frac{1}{3}(-3)^n & -\frac{1}{3}(3)^n + \frac{1}{3}(-3)^n \\ -(3)^n + (-3)^n & (3)^n - (-3)^n & (-3)^n \end{bmatrix}$

7. (a) $\begin{bmatrix} \frac{1}{3} + \frac{2}{3}(0.1)^n & \frac{1}{3} - \frac{1}{3}(0.1)^n \\ \frac{2}{3} - \frac{2}{3}(0.1)^n & \frac{2}{3} + \frac{1}{3}(0.1)^n \end{bmatrix}$ (b) $\begin{bmatrix} \frac{1}{3} \\ \frac{2}{3} \end{bmatrix}$ (c) 5 (d) $2 \times 10^{-5}$

9. (a) $\begin{bmatrix} \frac{2}{3} + \frac{1}{3}(0.7)^n & \frac{2}{3} - \frac{2}{3}(0.7)^n \\ \frac{1}{3} - \frac{1}{3}(0.7)^n & \frac{1}{3} + \frac{2}{3}(0.7)^n \end{bmatrix}$ (b) $\begin{bmatrix} \frac{2}{3} \\ \frac{1}{3} \end{bmatrix}$ (c) 27 (d) $1.31 \times 10^{-4}$

**11. (a)** $\begin{bmatrix} \frac{16}{45} + \frac{13}{9}(0.1)^n & \frac{16}{45} - \frac{14}{9}(0.1)^n & \frac{16}{45} + \frac{4}{9}(0.1)^n \\ \frac{2}{5} & \frac{2}{5} & \frac{2}{5} \\ \frac{11}{45} - \frac{13}{9}(0.1)^n & \frac{11}{45} + \frac{14}{9}(0.1)^n & \frac{11}{45} - \frac{4}{9}(0.1)^n \end{bmatrix}$ **(b)** $\begin{bmatrix} \frac{16}{45} \\ \frac{2}{5} \\ \frac{11}{45} \end{bmatrix}$ **(c)** 5

**(d)** $6.36 \times 10^{-5}$

**13.** 0.4    **15. (a)** Both will approach extinction **(b)** 1.5    **17.** $\frac{56}{15}$    **19.** $\frac{51}{52}$    **21.** $-\frac{12}{5}(-4)^k + \frac{2}{5}$

**23.** $-\frac{7}{2}(7)^k + \frac{1}{2}$